HAESE & HARRIS PUBLICATIONS

Specialists in mathematics

CW00538732

Mathematics

for the international student

Mathematics HL (Options)

Including coverage on CD of the
Geometry option for **Further Mathematics SL**

Peter Blythe

Peter Joseph

Paul Urban

David Martin

Robert Haese

Michael Haese

International
Baccalaureate
Diploma
Programme

MATHEMATICS FOR THE INTERNATIONAL STUDENT
International Baccalaureate Mathematics HL (Options)

Peter Blythe   B.Sc.
Peter Joseph   M.A.(Hons.), Grad.Cert.Ed.
Paul Urban   B.Sc.(Hons.), B.Ec.
David Martin   B.A., B.Sc., M.A., M.Ed.Admin.
Robert Haese   B.Sc.
Michael Haese   B.Sc.(Hons.), Ph.D.

Haese & Harris Publications
3 Frank Collopy Court, Adelaide Airport, SA 5950, AUSTRALIA
Telephone: +61 8 8355 9444, Fax: + 61 8 8355 9471
Email: info@haeseandharris.com.au
Web: www.haeseandharris.com.au

National Library of Australia Card Number & ISBN 1 876543 33 7

© Haese & Harris Publications 2005

Published by Raksar Nominees Pty Ltd
3 Frank Collopy Court, Adelaide Airport, SA 5950, AUSTRALIA

First Edition   2005   *Reprinted*   2006 (twice)

Cartoon artwork by John Martin. Artwork by Piotr Poturaj and David Purton.
Cover design by Piotr Poturaj.
Computer software by David Purton.

Typeset in Australia by Susan Haese and Charlotte Sabel (Raksar Nominees).

Typeset in Times Roman $10\frac{1}{2}/11\frac{1}{2}$

The textbook and its accompanying CD have been developed independently of the International Baccalaureate Organization (IBO). The textbook and CD are in no way connected with, or endorsed by, the IBO.

Acknowledgements: The publishers acknowledge the cooperation of many teachers in the preparation of this book. A full list appears on page 4.

While every attempt has been made to trace and acknowledge copyright, the authors and publishers apologise for any accidental infringement where copyright has proved untraceable. They would be pleased to come to a suitable agreement with the rightful owner.

Disclaimer: All the internet addresses (URL's) given in this book were valid at the time of printing. While the authors and publisher regret any inconvenience that changes of address may cause readers, no responsibility for any such changes can be accepted by either the authors or the publisher.

FOREWORD

Mathematics for the International Student: Mathematics HL (Options) has been written as a companion book to the **Mathematics HL (Core)** textbook. Together, they aim to provide students and teachers with appropriate coverage of the two-year Mathematics HL Course (first examinations 2006), which is one of the courses of study in the International Baccalaureate Diploma Programme.

It is not our intention to define the course. Teachers are encouraged to use other resources. We have developed the book independently of the International Baccalaureate Organization (IBO) in consultation with many experienced teachers of IB Mathematics. The text is not endorsed by the IBO.

On the accompanying CD, we offer coverage of the Euclidean Geometry Option for students undertaking the IB Diploma course **Further Mathematics SL**. This Option (with answers) can be printed from the CD.

The interactive features of the CD allow immediate access to our own specially designed geometry packages, graphing packages and more. Teachers are provided with a quick and easy way to demonstrate concepts, and students can discover for themselves and re-visit when necessary.

Instructions appropriate to each graphics calculator problem are on the CD and can be printed for students. These instructions are written for Texas Instruments and Casio calculators.

In this changing world of mathematics education, we believe that the contextual approach shown in this book, with associated use of technology, will enhance the students understanding, knowledge and appreciation of mathematics and its universal application.

We welcome your feedback   Email: info@haeseandharris.com.au
                                             Web: www.haeseandharris.com.au

PJB   PJ   PMU
DCM   RCH   PMH

ACKNOWLEDGEMENTS

The authors and publishers would like to thank all those teachers who have read the proofs of this book and offered advice and encouragement.

Special thanks to Mark Willis for permission to include some of his questions in HL Topic 8 'Statistics and probability'. Others who offered to read and comment on the proofs include: Mark William Bannar-Martin, Nick Vonthethoff, Hans-Jørn Grann Bentzen, Isaac Youssef, Sarah Locke, Ian Fitton, Paola San Martini, Nigel Wheeler, Jeanne-Mari Neefs, Winnie Auyeungrusk, Martin McMulkin, Janet Huntley, Stephanie DeGuzman, Simon Meredith, Rupert de Smidt, Colin Jeavons, Dave Loveland, Jan Dijkstra, Clare Byrne, Peter Duggan, Jill Robinson, Sophia Anastasiadou, Carol A. Murphy, Janet Wareham, Robert Hall, Susan Palombi, Gail A. Chmura, Chuck Hoag, Ulla Dellien, Richard Alexander, Monty Winningham, Martin Breen, Leo Boissy, Peter Morris, Ian Hilditch, Susan Sinclair, Ray Chaudhuri, Graham Cramp. To anyone we may have missed, we offer our apologies.

The publishers wish to make it clear that acknowledging these individuals does not imply any endorsement of this book by any of them, and all responsibility for the content rests with the authors and publishers.

TABLE OF CONTENTS

FURTHER MATHEMATICS SL TOPIC 1

GEOMETRY

Available only by clicking on the icon alongside.
This chapter plus answers is fully printable.

HL TOPIC 8

(Further mathematics SL Topic 2)

HL TOPIC 9

(Further mathematics SL Topic 3)

HL TOPIC 10

(Further mathematics SL Topic 4)

HL TOPIC 11

(Further mathematics SL Topic 5)

SYMBOLS AND NOTATION

$E(X)$ the expected value of X, which is μ

$Var(X)$ the variance of X, which is σ_X^2

$Z = \dfrac{X - \mu}{\sigma}$ the standardised variable

$P(.......)$ the probability of .... occurring

$\sim$ is distributed as

$\approx$ is approximately equal to

$\overline{x}$ the sample mean

s_n^2 the sample variance

s_{n-1}^2 the unbiassed estimate of σ^2

μ_X the mean of random variable X

σ_X the standard deviation of random variable X

$DU(n)$ the discrete uniform distribution

$B(n, p)$ the binomial distribution

$B(1, p)$ the Bernoulli distribution

$Hyp(n, M, N)$ the hypergeometric distribution

$Geo(p)$ the geometric distribution

$NB(r, p)$ the negative binomial distribution

$Po(m)$ the Poisson distribution

$U(a, b)$ the continuous uniform distribution

$Exp(\lambda)$ the exponential distribution

$N(\mu, \sigma^2)$ the normal distribution

$\widehat{p}$ the random variable of sample proportions

$\overline{X}$ the random variable of sample means

T the random variable of the t-distribution

ν the number of degrees of freedom

H_0 the null hypothesis

H_1 the alternative hypothesis

χ_{calc}^2 the chi-squared statistic

$\{ .... \}$ the set of all elements ....

$\in$ is an element of

$\notin$ is not an element of

$\{x \mid .... \}$ the set of all x such that ......

$\mathbb{N}$ the set of all natural numbers

$\mathbb{Z}$ the set of integers

$\mathbb{Q}$ the set of rational numbers

$\mathbb{R}$ the set of real numbers

$\mathbb{C}$ the set of all complex numbers

$\mathbb{Z}^+$ the set of positive integers

$\mathbb{P}$ the set of all prime numbers

$\mathbb{U}$ the universal set

$\emptyset$ or $\{\ \}$ the empty (null) set

$\subseteq$ is a subset of

$\subset$ is a proper subset of

$P(A)$ the power of set A

$A \cap B$ the intersection of sets A and B

$A \cup B$ the union of sets A and B

$\Rightarrow$ implies that

$\not\Rightarrow$ does not imply that

A' the complement of the set A

$n(A)$ the number of elements in the set A

$A \setminus B$ the difference of sets A and B

$A \Delta B$ the symmetric difference of sets A and B

$A \times B$ the Cartesian product of sets A and B

R a relation of ordered pairs

xRy x is related to y

$x \equiv y (\bmod n)$ x is equivalent to y, modulo n

$\mathbb{Z}_n$ the set of residue classes, modulo n

$\times_n$ multiplication, modulo n

$2\mathbb{Z}$ the set of even integers

$f : A \to B$ f is a function under which each element of set A has an image in set B

$f : x \mapsto y$ f is a function under which x is mapped to y

$f(x)$ the image of x under the function f

f^{-1} the inverse function of the function f

$f \circ g$ or $f(g(x))$	the composite function of f and g
$\lvert x \rvert$	the modulus or absolute value of x
$[a, b]$	the closed interval, $a \leqslant x \leqslant b$
$]a, b[$	the open interval $a < x < b$
u_n	the nth term of a sequence or series
$\{u_n\}$	the sequence with nth term u_n
S_n	the sum of the first n terms of a sequence
S_∞	the sum to infinity of a series
$\displaystyle\sum_{i=1}^{n} u_i$	$u_1 + u_2 + u_3 + \ldots + u_n$
$\displaystyle\prod_{i=1}^{n} u_i$	$u_1 \times u_2 \times u_3 \times \ldots \times u_n$
$\displaystyle\lim_{x \to a} f(x)$	the limit of $f(x)$ as x tends to a
$\displaystyle\lim_{x \to a+} f(x)$	the limit of $f(x)$ as x tends to a from the positive side of a
$\max\{a, b\}$	the maximum value of a or b
$\displaystyle\sum_{n=0}^{\infty} c_n x^n$	the power series whose terms have form $c_n x^n$
$a \mid b$	a divides b, *or* a is a factor of b
$a \nmid b$	a does not divide b, *or* a is a not a factor of b
$\gcd(a, b)$	the greatest common divisor of a and b
$\operatorname{lcm}(a, b)$	the least common multiple of a and b
$\cong$	is isomorphic to
$\overline{G}$	is the complement of G
$\mathbf{A}$	matrix $\mathbf{A}$
$\mathbf{A}^n$	matrix $\mathbf{A}$ to the power of n
$\mathbf{A}(G)$	the adjacency matrix of G
$A(x, y)$	the point A in the plane with Cartesian coordinates x and y
$[AB]$	the line segment with end points A and B
AB	the length of $[AB]$
(AB)	the line containing points A and B
$\widehat{A}$	the angle at A
$\widehat{CAB}$ or $\angle CAB$	the angle between $[CA]$ and $[AB]$
$\triangle ABC$	the triangle whose vertices are A, B and C
	or the area of triangle ABC
$\parallel$	is parallel to
$\nparallel$	is not parallel to
$\perp$	is perpendicular to
$AB.CD$	length AB $\times$ length CD
PT^2	$PT \times PT$
Power M_C	the power of point M relative to circle C
$\overrightarrow{AB}$	the vector from A to B

HL Topic 8

(Further Mathematics SL Topic 2)

Before beginning any work on this option, it is recommended that a careful revision of the core requirements for statistics and probability is made.

This is identified by "**Topic 6 – Core: Statistics and Probability**" as expressed in the syllabus guide on pages 26–29 of IBO document on the Diploma Programme Mathematics HL for the first examination 2006.

Throughout this booklet, there will be many references to the core requirements, taken from "Mathematics for the International Student Mathematics HL (Core)" Paul Urban et al, published by Haese and Harris, especially chapters 18, 19, and 30. This will be referred to as "from the text".

Statistics and probability

Contents:

A   Expectation algebra

B   Cumulative distribution functions (for discrete and continuous variables)

C   Distribution of the sample mean and the Central Limit Theorem

D   Confidence intervals for means and proportions

E   Significance and hypothesis testing and errors

F   The Chi-squared distribution, the "goodness of fit" test, the test for the independence of two variables.

EXPECTATION ALGEBRA

E(X), THE EXPECTED VALUE OF X

Recall that if a random variable X has mean μ then μ is known as the **expected value** of X, or simply $E(X)$.

$$\mu = E(X) = \begin{cases} \sum xP(x), & \text{for discrete } X \\ \int xf(x)\ dx, & \text{for continuous } X \end{cases}$$

From section **30E.1** of the text (*Investigation 1*) we noticed that

$$E(aX + b) = aE(X) + b$$

Proof: (discrete case only)
$$\begin{aligned} E(aX + b) &= \sum (ax + b)P(x) \\ &= \sum [axP(x) + bP(x)] \\ &= a\sum xP(x) + b\sum P(x) \\ &= aE(X) + b(1) \qquad \{\text{as } \sum P(x) = 1\} \\ &= aE(X) + b \end{aligned}$$

Var(X), THE VARIANCE OF X

A random variable X, has **variance** σ^2, also known as $\text{Var}(X)$

where
$$\sigma^2 = \mathbf{Var}(X) = E((X - \mu)^2)$$

Notice that for **discrete** X
- $\mathbf{Var}(X) = \sum (x - \mu)^2 p(x)$
- $\mathbf{Var}(X) = \sum x^2 p(x) - \mu^2$
- $\mathbf{Var}(X) = E(X^2) - \{E(X)\}^2$

Again, from *Investigation 1* of **Section 30E.1**, $\mathbf{Var}(aX + b) = a^2\,\mathbf{Var}(X)$

Proof: (discrete case only)
$$\begin{aligned} \text{Var}(aX + b) &= E((aX + b)^2) - \{E(aX + b)\}^2 \\ &= E(a^2 X^2 + 2abX + b^2) - \{aE(X) + b\}^2 \\ &= a^2\,E(X^2) + 2ab\,E(X) + b^2 - a^2\{E(X)\}^2 - 2ab\,E(X) - b^2 \\ &= a^2 E(X^2) - a^2\{E(X)\}^2 \\ &= a^2[E(X^2) - \{E(X)\}^2] \\ &= a^2\text{Var}\,(X) \end{aligned}$$

THE STANDARDISED VARIABLE, Z

If a random variable X is normally distributed with mean μ and variance σ^2 we write $X \sim N(\mu, \sigma2)$, where $\sim$ reads *is distributed as*.

The standardised variable Z is defined as $Z = \dfrac{X - \mu}{\sigma}$ and has mean 0 and variance 1.

Proof: The mean of Z is

$$\begin{aligned} \mathrm{E}(Z) &= \mathrm{E}\left(\tfrac{1}{\sigma}X - \tfrac{\mu}{\sigma}\right) \\ &= \tfrac{1}{\sigma}\mathrm{E}(X) - \tfrac{\mu}{\sigma} \\ &= \tfrac{1}{\sigma}\mu - \tfrac{\mu}{\sigma} \\ &= 0 \end{aligned}$$

and

$$\begin{aligned} \mathrm{Var}(Z) &= \mathrm{Var}\left(\tfrac{1}{\sigma}X - \tfrac{\mu}{\sigma}\right) \\ &= \left(\tfrac{1}{\sigma}\right)^2 \mathrm{Var}(X) \\ &= \tfrac{1}{\sigma^2} \times \sigma^2 \\ &= 1 \end{aligned}$$

This now gives us a formal basis on which we can standardise a normal variable, as described in the Core text.

Example 1

Suppose the scores in a Mathematics exam are distributed normally with unknown mean μ and standard deviation of 25.5. If only the top 10% of students receive an A, and the cut-off score for an A is any mark greater than 85%, find the mean, μ, of this distribution.

$$P(X > 85) = 0.1 \qquad \{\text{as} \quad 10\% = 0.1\}$$
$$\therefore \quad P(X \leqslant 85) = 0.9$$
$$\therefore \quad P\left(\frac{X - \mu}{25.5} \leqslant \frac{85 - \mu}{25.5}\right) = 0.9$$
$$\therefore \quad P\left(Z \leqslant \frac{85 - \mu}{25.5}\right) = 0.9$$
$$\therefore \quad \frac{85 - \mu}{25.5} = \text{invNorm}\,(0.9)$$
$$\therefore \quad \mu = 85 - 25.5 \times \text{invNorm}(0.9)$$
$$\therefore \quad \mu \approx 52.3$$

For **two independent random variables** X_1 and X_2 (not necessarily from the same population)

- $\mathbf{E}(a_1 X_1 \pm a_2 X_2) = a_1 \mathbf{E}(X_1) \pm a_2 \mathbf{E}(X_2)$
- $\mathbf{Var}(a_1 X_1 \pm a_2 X_2) = a_1{}^2 \mathbf{Var}(X_1) + a_2{}^2 \mathbf{Var}(X_2)$

The proof of these results is beyond the scope of this course.

The generalisation of the above is:

For n independent random variables; $X_1, X_2, X_3, X_4, \ldots\ldots X_n$

- $\mathbf{E}(a_1 X_1 \pm a_2 X_2 \pm \ldots \pm a_n X_n) = a_1 \mathbf{E}(X_1) \pm a_2 \mathbf{E}(X_2) \pm \ldots \pm a_n \mathbf{E}(X_n)$
- $\mathbf{Var}(a_1 X_1 \pm a_2 X_2 \pm \ldots \pm a_n X_n) = a_1{}^2 \mathbf{Var}(X_1) + a_2{}^2 \mathbf{Var}(X_2) + \ldots + a_n{}^2 \mathbf{Var}(X_n)$

Note: These generalised results can be proved using the Principle of Mathematical Induction assuming that the case $n = 2$ is true.

Proof: (by the Principle of Mathematical Induction)

(Firstly for the mean)

(1)   When $n = 2$, the result is true (assumed).

(2)   If P_k is true, then

$\mathrm{E}(a_1 X_1 \pm a_2 X_2 \pm ...... \pm a_k X_k) = a_1 \mathrm{E}(X_1) \pm a_2 \mathrm{E}(X_2) \pm ...... \pm a_k \mathrm{E}(X_k)......(*)$

$\therefore \quad \mathrm{E}(a_1 X_1 \pm a_2 X_2 \pm ...... \pm a_k X_k \pm a_{k+1} X_{k+1})$

$\quad = \mathrm{E}([a_1 X_1 \pm a_2 X_2 \pm ...... \pm a_k X_k] \pm a_{k+1} X_{k+1})$

$\quad = \mathrm{E}([a_1 X_1 \pm a_2 X_2 \pm ...... \pm a_k X_k]) \pm \mathrm{E}(a_{k+1} X_{k+1}) \quad \{\text{case } n = 2\}$

$\quad = a_1 \mathrm{E}(X_1) \pm a_2 \mathrm{E}(X_2) \pm ...... \pm a_k \mathrm{E}(X_k) \pm a_{k+1} \mathrm{E}(X_{k+1}) \quad \{\text{using } (*)\}$

Thus P_{k+1} is true whenever P_k is true and $P(2)$ is true.

$\Rightarrow P_n$ is true for all $n \in \mathbb{Z}^+, \; n \geqslant 2$.

(For the variance)

(1)   When $n = 2$, the result is true (given).

(2)   If P_k is true, then

$\mathrm{Var}(a_1 X_1 \pm a_2 X_2 \pm ...... \pm a_k X_k)$

$= a_1^2 \mathrm{Var}(X_1) + a_2^2 \mathrm{Var}(X_2) + ... + a_k^2 \mathrm{Var}(X_k) ...... (*)$

Now $\mathrm{Var}(a_1 X_1 \pm a_2 X_2 \pm ...... \pm a_k X_k \pm a_{k+1} X_{k+1})$

$\quad = \mathrm{Var}([a_1 X_1 \pm a_2 X_2 \pm ...... \pm a_k X_k] \pm a_{k+1} X_{k+1}) \quad \{\text{case } n = 2\}$

$\quad = \mathrm{Var}[a_1 X_1 \pm a_2 X_2 \pm ...... \pm a_k X_k] + \mathrm{Var}(a_{k+1} X_{k+1})$

$\quad = a_1^2 \mathrm{Var}(X_1) + a_2^2 \mathrm{Var}(X_2) + ... + a_k^2 \mathrm{Var}(X_k) + a_{k+1}^2 \mathrm{Var}(X_{k+1}) \quad \{\text{using } *\}$

Thus P_{k+1} is true whenever P_k is true and P_2 is true.

$\therefore \quad P_n$ is true   {Principle of Math. Induction}

Note: Any linear combination of independent normal random variables is itself a normal random variable.

For example,   if X_1, X_2 and X_3 are independent normal random variables (RV)

then $2X_1 + 3X_2 - 4X_3$ is a normal random variable.

$\mathrm{E}(2X_1 + 3X_2 - 4X_3) = 2\mathrm{E}(X_1) + 3\mathrm{E}(X_2) - 4\mathrm{E}(X_3)$ and

$\mathrm{Var}(2X_1 + 3X_2 - 4X_3) = 4\mathrm{Var}(X_1) + 9\mathrm{Var}(X_2) + 16\mathrm{Var}(X_3)$

Example 2

The weights of male employees in a bank are normally distributed with a mean $\mu = 71.5$ kg and standard deviation $\sigma = 7.3$ kg. The bank has an elevator with a maximum recommended load of 444 kg for safety reasons. Six male employees enter the elevator. Calculate the probability p that their combined weight exceeds the maximum recommended load.

We are concerned with the sum of their weights

and consider $Y = X_1 + X_2 + X_3 + X_4 + X_5 + X_6$ {independent RV's}

Now $\mathrm{E}(Y) = \mathrm{E}(X_1) + \mathrm{E}(X_2) + ...+ \mathrm{E}(X_6)$

$\qquad = 71.5 + 71.5 + ... + 71.5$

$\qquad = 6 \times 71.5 = 429$ kg

and $\text{Var}(Y)$

$$= \text{Var}(X_1) + \text{Var}(X_2) + \ldots + \text{Var}(X_6)$$
$$= 7.3^2 + 7.3^2 + \ldots + 7.3^2$$
$$= 6 \times 7.3^2$$
$$= 319.74$$

$\therefore$ Y is normally distributed with mean 429 kg and variance 319.74 kg^2
i.e., $Y \sim \text{N}(429, 319.74)$ $\sigma^2 = 319.74$

Now $\text{P}(Y > 444) = \text{normalcdf}(444, \text{E}99, 429, \sqrt{319.74})$
$$\approx 0.201$$

So, there is a 20.1% chance that their combined weight will exceed 444 kg.

Example 3

For **Example 2**, do a suitable calculation to recommend the maximum number of males to use the elevator, given that there should be no more than a 0.1% chance of the total weight exceeding 444 kg.

From **Example 2**, six men is too many as there is a 20.1% chance of overload.
Now we try $n = 5$ $\text{E}(Y)$ $\text{Var}(Y)$
$$\qquad\qquad = 5 \times 71.5 \qquad = 5 \times 7.3^2$$
$$\qquad\qquad = 357.5 \text{ kg} \qquad \approx 266.45 \text{ kg}^2$$

Now $Y \sim \text{N}(357.5, 266.45)$ i.e., $\sigma^2 = 266.45$

and $\text{P}(Y > 444) = \text{normalcdf}(444, \text{E}99, 357.5, \sqrt{266.45})$
$$\approx 5.83 \times 10^{-8}$$

So, for $n = 5$ there is much less than a 0.1% chance of the total weight exceeding 444 kg. Hence, we should recommend for safety reasons that a maximum of 5 men use the elevator at the same time.

Example 4

Given three independent samples $X_1 = 2X$, $X_2 = 4 - 3X$,   and $X_3 = 4X + 1$, taken from a random distribution X with mean 11 and standard deviation 2, find the mean and standard deviation of the random variable $(X_1 + X_2 + X_3)$.

mean	variance
$= \text{E}(X_1 + X_2 + X_3)$	$= \text{Var}(X_1 + X_2 + X_3)$
$= \text{E}(X_1) + \text{E}(X_2) + \text{E}(X_3)$	$= \text{Var}(X_1) + \text{Var}(X_2) + \text{Var}(X_3)$
$= 2\text{E}(X) + 4 - 3\text{E}(X) + 4\text{E}(X) + 1$	$= 4\text{Var}(X) + 9\text{Var}(X) + 16\text{Var}(X)$
$= 3\text{E}(X) + 5$	$= 29\text{Var}(X)$
$= 3(11) + 5$	$= 29 \times 2^2$
$= 38$	$= 116$

$\therefore$ mean is 38 and standard deviation is $\sqrt{116} \approx 10.8$.

Example 5

A cereal manufacturer produces packets of cereal in two sizes, small (S) and economy (E). The amount in each packet is distributed normally and independently as follows:

	Mean (g)	Variance (g^2)
Small	315	4
Economy	950	25

a A packet of each size is selected at random. Find the probability that the economy packet contains less than three times the amount of the small packet.

b One economy and three small packets are selected at random.
Find the probability that the amount in the economy packet is less than the total amount in the three small packets.

$S \sim \text{N}(315, 4)$ and $E \sim \text{N}(950, 25)$.

a To find the probability that the economy packet contains less than three times the amount in a small packet we need to calculate $\text{P}(e < 3s)$
i.e., $\text{P}(e - 3s < 0)$

Now $\text{E}(E - 3S)$ and $\text{Var}(E - 3S)$
$\qquad = \text{E}(E) - 3\,\text{E}(S)$ $= \text{Var}(E) + 9\,\text{Var}(S)$
$\qquad = 950 - 3 \times (315)$ $= 25 + 9 \times 4$
$\qquad = 5$ $= 61$

$\qquad \therefore\ E - 3S \sim \text{N}(5, 61)$

and $\text{P}(e - 3s < 0) \approx 0.261$ {calculator}

b This time we need to calculate $\text{P}(e < s_1 + s_2 + s_3)$
i.e., $\text{P}(e - (s_1 + s_2 + s_3) < 0)$

Now $\text{E}(E - (S_1 + S_2 + S_3))$
$\qquad = \text{E}(E) - 3\,\text{E}(S)$
$\qquad = 950 - 3 \times 315$
$\qquad = 5$

and $\text{Var}(E - (S_1 + S_2 + S_3))$
$\qquad = \text{Var}(E) + \text{Var}(S_1) + \text{Var}(S_2) + \text{Var}(S_3)$
$\qquad = 25 + 12$
$\qquad = 37$

$\therefore\ E - (S_1 + S_2 + S_3) \sim \text{N}(5, 37)$

and $\text{P}(e - (s_1 + s_2 + s_3)) \approx 0.206$ {calculator}

UNBIASED ESTIMATORS OF MEAN μ AND VARIANCE σ^2 FOR A POPULATION

Often μ and σ for a population are unknown and we may wish to use a representative sample to estimate μ and σ. We observed in section **18F** of the text that:

- $\overline{x}$, the sample mean, gives us an **unbiased** estimate of μ

- $s_{n-1}^2 = \dfrac{n}{n-1} s_n^2$, where s_n^2 is the sample's variance and n is the sample size, gives us an **unbiased** estimate of the population's variance σ^2.

Note: $\overline{x}$ is an **unbiased** estimate of μ if $E(\overline{X}) = \mu$.

Proof: (that $\overline{x}$ is an unbiased estimate of μ)

$$E(\overline{X}) = E\left(\frac{X_1 + X_2 + X_3 + ... + X_n}{n}\right)$$

$$= E\left(\tfrac{1}{n}(X_1 + X_2 + X_3 + ... + X_n)\right)$$

$$= \tfrac{1}{n} E(X_1 + X_2 + X_3 + ... + X_n) \qquad \{\text{assuming independence}\}$$

$$= \tfrac{1}{n}(\mu + \mu + \mu + ... + \mu) \qquad \{n \text{ of them}\}$$

$$= \tfrac{1}{n} \times n\mu$$

$$= \mu \qquad \therefore \quad \overline{x} \text{ is an unbiased estimate of } \mu.$$

Notice also that $\text{Var}(\overline{X}) = \left(\tfrac{1}{n}X_1 + \tfrac{1}{n}X_2 + ... + \tfrac{1}{n}X_n\right)$

$$= \tfrac{1}{n^2}\text{Var}(X_1) + \tfrac{1}{n^2}\text{Var}(X_2) + ... + \tfrac{1}{n^2}\text{Var}(X_n)$$

$$= \tfrac{1}{n^2}(\sigma^2 + \sigma^2 + ... + \sigma^2) \qquad \{n \text{ of them}\}$$

$$= \tfrac{1}{n^2} \times n\sigma^2$$

$$\therefore \quad \text{Var}(\overline{X}) = \frac{\sigma^2}{n}$$

Note: s_{n-1}^2 is an unbiased estimate of σ^2.

To prove this we need to show that $E(s_{n-1}^2) = \sigma^2$.

Proof: $s_n^2 = \dfrac{1}{n}\sum_{i=1}^{n}(X_i - \overline{X})^2 = \dfrac{1}{n}\left[\sum_{i=1}^{n} X_i^2 - n\overline{X}^2\right] = \dfrac{1}{n}\sum_{i=1}^{n} X_i^2 - \overline{X}^2$

$$\therefore \quad E(s_n^2) = \frac{1}{n} E\left(\sum_{i=1}^{n} X_i^2\right) - E(\overline{X}^2) \qquad \{\text{assuming independence}\}$$

$$= \frac{1}{n}\sum_{i=1}^{n} E(X_i^2) - E(\overline{X})^2$$

$$= \frac{1}{n}\left[\sum_{i=1}^{n}\left(\text{Var}(X_i) + \{E(X_i)\}^2\right)\right] - \left[\text{Var}(\overline{X}) + \{E(\overline{X})\}^2\right]$$

$$\{\text{using} \quad \text{Var}(Y) = E(Y^2) - \{E(Y)\}^2\}$$

$$= \frac{1}{n}\left[\sum_{i=1}^{n}(\sigma^2 + \mu^2)\right] - \left[\frac{\sigma^2}{n} + \mu^2\right]$$

$$= \frac{1}{n}\left(n\sigma^2 + n\mu^2\right) - \frac{\sigma^2}{n} - \mu^2$$

$$= \sigma^2 + \mu^2 - \frac{\sigma^2}{n} - \mu^2$$

$$= \sigma^2\left(1 - \frac{1}{n}\right) \quad \text{or} \quad \sigma^2\left(\frac{n-1}{n}\right)$$

But $s_{n-1}^2 = \dfrac{n}{n-1}\,s_n^2$ and so $\mathrm{E}\!\left(s_{n-1}^2\right) = \dfrac{n}{n-1}\,\mathrm{E}(s_n^2) = \sigma^2$

i.e., s_{n-1}^2 is an unbiased estimate of σ^2.

The following example may be useful for designing a portfolio item.

Example 6

In a gambling game you bet on the outcomes of two spinners. These outcomes are called X and Y and the probability distributions for each spinner are tabled below:

x	-3	-2	3	5
$\mathrm{P}(X = x)$	0.25	0.25	0.25	0.25

y	-3	2	5
$\mathrm{P}(Y = y)$	0.5	0.3	0.2

a Briefly explain why these are *well-defined* probability distributions.

b Find the mean and standard deviation of each random variable.

c Suppose it costs \$1 to get a spinner spun and you receive the dollar value of the outcome. For example, if the result is 3 you win \$3 but if the result is -3 you need to pay an extra \$3. In which game are you likely to achieve a better result? On average, do you expect to win, lose or break even? Use **b** to justify your answer.

d Comment on the differences in standard deviation.

e The players get bored with these two simple games and ask if they can play a \$1 game using the *sum* of the scores obtained on each of the spinners. Complete a table like the one given below to show the probability distribution of $X + Y$. A grid may help you do this.

$X + Y$	-6	-5	....	10
$\mathrm{P}(X + y)$		0.125		

Note: If you score a 10, you receive \$10 after paying out \$1. Effectively you win \$9.

f Calculate the mean and standard deviation of U if $U = X + Y$.

g Are you likely to win, lose or draw in the new game? Use **f** to justify your answer.

a As $\sum P(x) = 1$ in each distribution, each is a well-defined probability distribution.

b $E(X) = \sum xP(x)$
$$= -3(0.25) - 2(0.25) + 3(0.25) + 5(0.25)$$
$\therefore \quad \mu_x = 0.75$

$Var(X) = E(X^2) - \{E(X)\}^2$
$$= 9(0.25) + 4(0.25) + 9(0.25) + 25(0.25) - 0.75^2$$
$$= 47 \times 0.25 - 0.75^2$$
$$= 11.1875 \quad \text{and so} \quad \sigma_X \approx 3.34$$

$E(Y) = \sum yP(y)$
$$= -3(0.5) + 2(0.3) + 5(0.2)$$
$\therefore \quad \mu_Y = 0.1$

$Var(Y) = E(Y^2) - \{E(Y)\}^2$
$$= 9(0.5) + 4(0.3) + 25(0.2) - 0.1^2$$
$$= 10.69 \quad \text{and so} \quad \sigma_Y \approx 3.27$$

c   With X, the expected win is \$0.75 per game. However, it costs \$1 to play so overall there is an expected loss of \$0.25 per game.

With Y, \$0.10 $-$ \$1 $= -$\$0.90, so there is an expected loss of \$0.90 per game.

d   As $\sigma_X > \sigma_Y$ we expect a greater variation in the results of game X.

e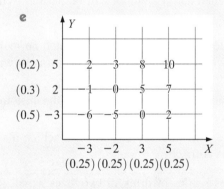

$P(-6) = 0.25 \times 0.5 = 0.125$
$P(-5) = 0.25 \times 0.5 = 0.125$
$P(-1) = 0.25 \times 0.3 = 0.075$
$P(0) = 0.25 \times 0.5 + 0.25 \times 0.3 = 0.200$
$P(2) = 0.25 \times 0.5 + 0.25 \times 0.2 = 0.175$
$P(3) = 0.25 \times 0.2 = 0.050$
$P(5) = 0.25 \times 0.3 = 0.075$
$P(7) = 0.25 \times 0.3 = 0.075$
$P(8) = 0.25 \times 0.2 = 0.050$
$P(10) = 0.25 \times 0.2 = 0.050$

$X + Y$	-6	-5	-1	0	2	3	5	7	8	10	$\sum$
$P(X+Y)$	0.125	0.125	0.075	0.200	0.175	0.050	0.075	0.075	0.050	0.050	1.000

f   If $U = X + Y$
$E(U) = -6(0.125) - 5(0.125) - 1(0.075) + 0 + 2(0.175) + 3(0.050) + 5(0.075)$
$$+ 7(0.075) + 8(0.050) + 10(0.050)$$
$\therefore \quad \mu_U = 0.85$

$Var(U) = 36(0.125) + 25(0.125) + 1(0.075) + 4(0.175) + 9(0.050) + 25(0.075)$
$$+ 49(0.075) + 64(0.050) + 100(0.050) - (0.85)^2$$
$$= 21.8775$$
$\therefore \quad \sigma_U = \sqrt{21.8775} \approx 4.68$

g   With the new game the expected loss is \$0.15 per game.   {\$0.85 $-$ \$1}

EXERCISE 8A

1 Given two independent random variables X and Y whose means and standard deviations are given in the table:

	mean	*s.d.*
X	3.8	0.323
Y	5.7	1.02

   a find the mean and standard deviation of $3X - 2Y$

   b find the $P(3X - 2Y > 3)$,   given that X and Y are distributed normally. You need to know that any linear combination of independent normal random variables is also normal.

2 X and Y are independent normal random variables with $X \sim N(-10, 1)$ and $Y \sim (25, 25)$. Find:

   a the mean and standard deviation of the random variable $U = 3X + 2Y$.

   b $P(U < 0)$.

3 The marks in an IB Mathematics HL exam are distributed normally with mean μ and standard deviation σ. If the cut off score for a 7 is a mark of 80%, and 10% of students get a 7, and the cut off score for a 6 is a mark of 65% and 30% of students get a 6 or 7, find the mean and standard deviation of the marks in this exam.

4 In a lift, the maximum recommended load is 440 kg. The weights of men are distributed normally with mean 61 kg and standard deviation of 11 kg. The weights of children are also normally distributed with mean 48 kg and standard deviation of 4 kg.

   Find the probability that the lift containing 4 men and 3 children will be unsafe. What assumption have you made in your calculation?

5 A coffee machine dispenses white coffee made up of black coffee distributed normally with mean 120 mL and standard deviation 7 mL, and milk distributed normally with mean 28 mL and standard deviation 4.5 mL.

   Each cup is marked to a level of 135.5 mL, and if this is not attained then the customer will receive a cup of white coffee free of charge.

   Determine whether or not the proprietor should adjust the settings on her machine if she wishes to give away no more than 1% in "free coffees".

6 A drinks manufacturer independently produces bottles of drink in two sizes, small (S) and large (L). The amount in each bottle is distributed normally as follows:

   $S \sim N(280 \text{ mL}, 4 \text{ mL}^2)$ and $L \sim N(575 \text{ mL}, 16 \text{ mL}^2)$

   a When a bottle of each size is selected at random, find the probability that the large bottle contains less than two times the amount in the small bottle.

   b One large and two small bottles are selected at random. Find the probability that the amount in the large bottle is less than the total amount in the two small bottles.

7 Chocolate bars are produced independently in two sizes, small (S) and large (L). The amount in each bar is distributed normally as follows:

   $S \sim N(21, 5)$ and $L \sim N(90, 15)$

   a One of each type of bar is selected at random. Find the probability that the large bar contains more than five times the amount in the small bar.

   b One large and five small bars are selected at random. Find the probability that the amount in the large bar is more than the total amount in the five small bars.

B CUMULATIVE DISTRIBUTION FUNCTIONS

We will examine **cumulative distribution functions (cdf)** for both **discrete random variables (drv)** and **continuous random variables (crv).**

Definition: The **cumulative distribution function (cdf)** of a random variable X is the probability that X takes a value less than or equal to x,

i.e., $F(x) = P(X \leqslant x)$.

Recall that a random variable is
- **discrete** if you can *count* the outcomes
- **continuous** if you can *measure* the outcomes.

Example 7

Classify the following as a discrete or continuous random variable:
a   the outcomes when you roll an unbiased die
b   the heights of students studying the final year of high school
c   the outcomes from the two spinners in **Example 6**.

a   discrete as you can count them
b   continuous as you measure them
c   discrete as you can count them

DISCRETE RANDOM VARIABLES

A discrete random variable X has a **probability mass function** given by $p_x = P(X = x)$ where x is one of the possible outcomes.

A probability mass function of a discrete random variable must be **well-defined,**

i.e., $\displaystyle\sum_{i=1}^{n} p_i = 1$ and $0 \leqslant p_i \leqslant 1$ for $i = 1, 2, 3, \ldots, n.$

The **cumulative distribution function (cdf)** of a **discrete** random variable X is the probability that X takes a value less than or equal to x,

i.e., $\displaystyle F(x) = P(X \leqslant x) = \sum_{y \leqslant x} P(X = y)$

For example, consider
- tossing one coin, where X is the number of 'heads' resulting

  $X = 0$ or 1 and $F(0) = P(X \leqslant 0) = P(X = 0) = \frac{1}{2}$

  $F(1) = P(X \leqslant 1) = P(X = 0 \text{ or } 1) = 1$

- tossing two coins, where X is the number of 'heads' resulting

  $X = 0, 1$ or 2 and $F(0) = P(X \leqslant 0) = P(X = 0) = \frac{1}{4}$

  $F(1) = P(X \leqslant 1) = P(X = 0 \text{ or } 1) = \frac{3}{4}$

  $F(2) = P(X \leqslant 2) = P(X = 0, 1 \text{ or } 2) = 1$

TYPES OF DISCRETE RANDOM VARIABLES

DISCRETE UNIFORM

For a **discrete uniform** random variable, the probability mass function takes the same value for all outcomes x.

For example,   when rolling a fair (unbiased) die the sample space is $\{1, 2, 3, 4, 5, 6\}$ and $p_x = \frac{1}{6}$ for all x.

The name 'uniform' comes from the fact that p_x values do not change as x changes.

If we are interested in getting a result smaller than 5, we are concerned with the cdf and in this case $P(X < 5) = P(X \leqslant 4) = F(4) = 4 \times \frac{1}{6} = \frac{2}{3}$

If X is a discrete uniform random variable with n distinct outcomes, 1, 2, 3, 4, ..., n, we write $X \sim \mathrm{DU}(n)$.

Note: The outcomes do not have to be 1, 2, 3, 4, ..., n.

This is illustrated in **Example 6** where the random variable X had four possible outcomes -3, -2, 3 and 5.

BINOMIAL

The binomial distribution was observed in **Section 30F** of the Core HL text.

For the **binomial distribution**, the probability mass function is

$P(X = x) = \binom{n}{x} p^x (1-p)^{n-x}$ where n is the number of independent trials,

x is the number of successes in n trials,

p is the probability of success in one trial.

The cdf is $F(x) = P(X \leqslant x) = \sum_{r=0}^{x} \binom{n}{r} p^r (1-p)^{n-r}$.

We write $X \sim \mathrm{B}(n, p)$ to indicate that X is distributed binomially. Note that a binomial distribution occurs in *sampling with replacement.*

BERNOULLI

A **Bernoulli distribution** is a binomial distribution where only one trial is conducted, i.e., $n = 1$.

$$P(X = x) = p^x (1-p)^{1-x}, \quad \text{where} \quad x = 0 \text{ or } 1$$

The cdf is $F(x) = P(X \leqslant x) = \sum_{r=0}^{x} p^r (1-p)^{1-r}$,   where $x = 0$ or 1.

Hence, a binomial distribution consists of n independent Bernoulli trials.

Note: If $x = 0$, $F(0) = P(x \leqslant 0) = p^0 (1-p)^1 = 1 - p$

If $x = 1$, $F(1) = P(x \leqslant 1) = P(X = 0 \text{ or } X = 1) \; = 1 - p + p^1 (1-p)^0$

$= 1 - p + p$

$= 1$

Discuss what this means.

We write $X \sim \mathrm{B}(1, p)$ to indicate that X is Bernoulli distributed.

EXERCISE 8B.1

Uniform, Binomial, Bernoulli Distribution Refer to Core Text **Exercise 19H**, pages 515-516.

1 The discrete random variable X is such that $P(X = x) = k$,   for $X = 5, 10, 15, 20$, 25, 30.   Find:

     a   the probability distribution of x **b** μ, the expected value of X

     c $P(X < \mu)$ **d** σ, the standard deviation of X.

2 Given the random variable X such that $X \sim B(7, p)$ and $P(X = 4) = 0.097\,24$, find $P(X = 2)$ where $p < 0.5$.

3 In parts of the USA the probability that it will rain on any given day in August is 0.35. Calculate the probability that in a given week in August in that part of the USA, it will rain on:

     a   exactly 3 days   **b**   at least 3 days

     c   at most 3 days   **d**   exactly 3 days in succession.

State any assumptions made in your calculations.

4 A box contains a very large number of red and blue pens. The probability that a pen is blue is 0.8. How many pens would you need to select to be more than 90% certain of picking at least one red pen? State any assumptions made in your calculations.

5 A satellite relies on solar cells for its operation and will be powered provided at least one of its cells is working. Solar cells operate independently of each other, and the probability that an individual cell operates within one year is 0.3.

     a   For a satellite with 15 solar cells, find the probability that all 15 cells fail within one year.

     b   For a satellite with 15 solar cells, find the probability that the satellite is still operating at the end of one year.

     c   For the satellite with n solar cells, find the probability that it is still operating at the end of one year. Hence, find the smallest number of cells required so that the probability of the satellite still operating at the end of one year is at least 0.98.

6 Seventy percent (70%) of the mail to ETECH Couriers is addressed to the Accounts Department.

     a   In a batch of 20 letters, what is the probability that there will be at least 11 letters to the Accounts Department?

     b   On average 70 letters arrive each day. What is the mean and standard deviation of the number of letters to the Accounts Department?

7 The table shown gives information about the destination and type of parcels handled by ETECH Couriers.

     a   What is the probability that a parcel is being sent interstate given that it is priority paid?

Destination		Priority	Standard
Local	40%	70%	30%
Country	20%	45%	55%
Interstate	25%	70%	30%
International	15%	40%	60%

     (**Hint:**   Use **Bayes theorem**: refer HL Core text, page 528)

     b   If two standard parcels are selected, what is the probability that only one will be leaving the state (i.e., Interstate or International)?

Note: The table on **page 31** can be used in the following question.

8   At a school fete fundraiser, an unbiased spinning wheel has numbers 1 to 50 inclusive.

  a   What is the mean expected score obtained on this wheel during the day?

  b   What is the standard deviation of the scores obtained during the day?

  c   What is the probability of getting a multiple of 7 in one spin of the wheel?

  If the wheel is spun 500 times during the day:

  d   What is the likelihood of getting a multiple of 7 more than 15% of the time?

  Given that 20 people play each time the wheel is spun, and when a multiple of 7 comes up $5 is paid to players, but when it does not the players must pay $1:

  e   How much would the wheel be expected to make or lose for the school if it was spun 500 times?

  f   What are the chances the school would lose if the wheel was spun 500 times?

HYPERGEOMETRIC

If we are *sampling without replacement* then we have a **hypergeometric distribution**.

Finding the probability mass function involves the use of combinations to count possible outcomes. Probability questions of this nature were in the Core HL text.

Example 8

A class of IB students contains 10 females and 9 males. A student committee of three is to be randomly chosen. If X is the number of females on the committee, find: a $P(X = 0)$ b $P(X = 1)$ c $P(X = 2)$ d $P(X = 3)$

The total number of unrestricted committees $= \binom{19}{3}$ or C_3^{19}

{as there are 19 students to choose from and we want any 3 of them}

a   The number of committees consisting of 0 females and 3 males is $\binom{10}{0}\binom{9}{3}$ $\therefore$ $P(X = 0) = \dfrac{\binom{10}{0}\binom{9}{3}}{\binom{19}{3}}$

b   Likewise, $P(X = 1) = \dfrac{\binom{10}{1}\binom{9}{2}}{\binom{19}{3}}$

c $P(X = 2) = \dfrac{\binom{10}{2}\binom{9}{1}}{\binom{19}{3}}$ d $P(X = 3) = \dfrac{\binom{10}{3}\binom{9}{0}}{\binom{19}{3}}$

From **Example 8**, notice that we can write all four possible results in the form

$$P(X = x) = \frac{\binom{10}{x}\binom{9}{3-x}}{\binom{19}{3}} \quad \text{where} \quad x = 0, 1, 2 \text{ or } 3.$$

This is the probability mass function for this example.

In general:

If we have a population of size N consisting of two types with size M and $N - M$ respectively, and we take a sample of size n *without replacement*, then for the random variable X consisting of how many of M we want to include in the sample, the **hypergeometric distribution** has probability mass function

$$P(X = x) = \frac{\binom{M}{x} \binom{N-M}{n-x}}{\binom{N}{n}} \quad \text{where} \quad x = 0, 1, 2, 3, \ldots, \text{Min}\,(n, M)$$

$$\text{The cdf is} \quad F(x) = P(X \leqslant x) = \sum_{r=0}^{x} \frac{\binom{M}{x} \binom{N-M}{n-x}}{\binom{N}{n}} \quad \text{for} \quad x \leqslant n, M.$$

We write $X \sim \text{Hyp}(n, M, N)$ to show that X is hypergeometrically distributed.

GEOMETRIC

Consider the following:

A sports magazine gives away photographs of famous football players. 15 photographs are randomly placed in every 100 magazines.

Consider X, the number of magazines you purchase before you get a photograph.

$P(X = 1) = $ P(the first magazine contains a photo) $= 0.15$
$P(X = 2) = $ P(the second magazine contains a photo) $= 0.85 \times 0.15$
$P(X = 3) = $ P(the third magazine contains a photo) $= (0.85)^2 \times 0.15$

So, $P(X = 4) = (0.85)^3 \times 0.15$, $P(X = 5) = (0.85)^4 \times 0.15$,   etc.

This is an example of a geometric distribution.

> If X is the number of trials needed to get a successful outcome, then X is a **geometric discrete** random variable and has probability mass function
>
> $$P(X = x) = p(1 - p)^{x-1} \quad \text{where} \quad x = 1, 2, 3, 4, \ldots$$
>
> The cdf is $F(x) = P(X \leqslant x) = \displaystyle\sum_{r=1}^{x} p(1 - p)^{r-1}$ for $r = 1, 2, 3, 4, \ldots$

We write $X \sim \text{Geo}(p)$ to show that X is a geometric discrete random variable.

Example 9

In a spinning wheel game with numbers 1 to 50 on the wheel, you win if you get a multiple of 7. Assuming the game is fair, find the probability that you win:

a   after exactly four games   **b**   if you need at most four games
c   after no more than three games   **d**   after more than three games.

If X is the number of games played until you win

then $X \sim \text{Geo}(p)$ where $p = \frac{7}{50} = 0.14$ and $1 - p = 0.86$

a $P(X = 4)$
$= p(1 - p)^3$
$= 0.14 \times (0.86)^3$
≈ 0.0890

b   P(need at most four games)
$= P(X \leqslant 4)$
$= p + p(1 - p) + p(1 - p)^2 + p(1 - p)^3$
$= p\left[1 + (1 - p) + (1 - p)^2 + (1 - p)^3\right]$
$= 0.14\left[1 + 0.86 + 0.86^2 + 0.86^3\right]$
≈ 0.453

Note: $P(X \leqslant 4)$ = P(win in one of the first four games)
$$= 1 - \text{P(does not win in first four games)}$$
$$= 1 - (1 - p)^4$$
$$= 1 - (0.86)^4 \quad \text{which} \approx 0.453$$

gives us an alternative method of calculation.

c   P(wins after no more than three games)
$$= P(X \leqslant 3)$$
$$= 1 - \text{P(does not win in one of the first three games)}$$
$$= 1 - (1 - p)^3$$
$$= 1 - 0.86^3$$
$$\approx 0.364$$

d   P(wins after more than 3 games) $= P(X > 3)$
$$= 1 - P(X \leqslant 3)$$
$$\approx 1 - 0.364 \qquad \{\text{from } \mathbf{c}\}$$
$$\approx 0.636$$

Note: •   In **Example 9** we observed that if $X \sim \text{Geo}(p)$ then

$$P(X \leqslant x) = \sum_{r=1}^{x} p(1-p)^{r-1} = 1 - (1-p)^x.$$

Can you prove this result algebraically?

Hint: $P(X \leqslant x) = \displaystyle\sum_{r=1}^{x} p(1-p)^{r-1} = p \sum_{r=1}^{x} (1-p)^{r-1}$

and $\displaystyle\sum_{r=1}^{x} (1-p)^{r-1}$ is a geometric series.

•   The **modal score** (the score with the highest probability of occurring) for a geometric random variable is always $x = 1$.   Can you explain why?

Example 10

Show that if $X \sim \text{Geo}(p)$ then $\displaystyle\sum_{i=1}^{\infty} P(X = i) = 1$.

$\displaystyle\sum_{i=1}^{\infty} P(X = i)$ $= P(X = 1) + P(X = 2) + P(X = 3) + \ldots\ldots$
$$= p(1-p)^0 + p(1-p)^1 + p(1-p)^2 + \ldots\ldots$$
$$= p\left[1 + (1-p) + (1-p)^2 + (1-p)^3 + \ldots\ldots\right]$$
$$= p\left(\frac{1}{1-(1-p)}\right) \qquad \begin{array}{l}\text{as we have an infinite GS with } u_1 = 1 \\ \text{and } r = 1-p \text{ where } 0 < r < 1\end{array}$$
$$= p\left(\frac{1}{p}\right)$$
$$= 1$$

NEGATIVE BINOMIAL (PASCAL'S DISTRIBUTION)

If X is the number of Bernoulli trials required for r successes then X has a **negative binomial** distribution.

Note: If $r = 1$, the negative binomial distribution reduces to the geometric distribution.

Example 11

In grand slam tennis, the player who wins a match is the first player to win 3 sets. Suppose that P(Federer beats Safin in one set) $= 0.72$.   Find the probability that when Federer plays Safin in the grand slam event:

a   Federer wins the match in three sets

b   Federer wins the match in four sets

c   Federer wins the match in five sets

d   Safin wins the match.

Let X be the number of sets played until Federer wins.

a $P(X = 3)$
$= (0.72)^3$
≈ 0.373

b $P(X = 4)$
$= P(SFFF \text{ or } FSFF \text{ or } FFSF)$
$= 3 \times 0.72^3 \times 0.28^1 \approx 0.314$

c $P(X = 5)$
$= P(SSFFF \text{ or } SFSFF \text{ or } SFFSF \text{ or } FSSFF \text{ or } FSFSF \text{ or } FFSSF)$
$= 6 \times 0.72^3 \times 0.28^2$
≈ 0.176

d $P(\text{Safin wins the match})$
$= 1 - P(\text{Federer wins the match})$
$= 1 - \left[0.72^3 + 3 \times 0.72^3 \times 0.28 + 6 \times 0.72^3 \times 0.28^2 \right]$
≈ 0.138

Examining **b** from the above **Example 11**, we notice that

$$P(X = 4) = P(\text{Federer wins 2 of the first 3 and wins the 4th}) = \underbrace{\binom{3}{2} (0.72)^2 (0.28)^1}_{\text{binomial}} \times 0.72$$

Generalising,

$$P(X = x) = P(r - 1 \text{ successes in } x - 1 \text{ independent trials and success in the last trial})$$
$$= \binom{x-1}{r-1} p^{r-1}(1-p)^{x-r} \times p$$
$$= \binom{x-1}{r-1} p^{r}(1-p)^{x-r}$$

So: In repeated independent Bernoulli trials, where p is the probability of success in one of them, let X denote the number of trials needed to gain r successes.

X has a **negative binomial distribution** with probability mass function

$$P(X = x) = \binom{x-1}{r-1} p^{r}(1-p)^{x-r}, \quad r \geqslant 1, \quad x \geqslant r.$$

The cdf is $F(x) = \text{P}(X \leqslant x) = \sum\limits_{y=r}^{x} \binom{y-1}{r-1} p^r (1-p)^{y-r}$ where $1 \leqslant r \leqslant y \leqslant x$.

Note: We write $X \sim \text{NB}(r,\, p)$ for X being a Negative Binomial random variable, where x is the number of independent Bernoulli trials needed to achieve r successes and p is the probability of getting a success in one trial.

EXERCISE 8B.2

Geometric and Negative Binomial distributions. The **table** on **page 31** can be used in the following questions, where appropriate.

1 X is a discrete random variable where $X \sim \text{Geo}(0.25)$. Calculate:

    a $\text{P}(X = 4)$ **b** $\text{P}(X > 3)$ **c** $\text{P}(X \leqslant 2)$ **d** $\text{E}(X)$

    Comment on your answer to part **d**.

2 Given that $X \sim \text{Geo}(0.33)$, find:

    a the mode of X **b** the mean of X **c** the standard deviation of X.

3 In a game of ten-pin bowling, Xu has a 29% chance of getting a strike with every bowl he attempts. (A strike is obtained by knocking down all ten pins).

    a Find the probability of Xu getting a strike after exactly 4 bowls.

    b Find (nearest integer) the average number of bowls required for Xu to get a strike.

    c Find the probability that Xu will take 7 bowls to secure 3 strikes.

    d What is the average number of bowls Xu will take to get 3 strikes?

4 $X \sim \text{Geo}(p)$ and the probability that the first success is obtained on the 3rd attempt is $0.023\,987$. If $p > 0.5$,   find $p(X \geqslant 3)$.

5 A dart player has a 5% chance of getting a bullseye with any dart thrown at the board. What is the expected number of throws for this dart player to get a bullseye?

6 In any game of squash Paul has a 65% chance of beating Eva. To win a match in squash, a player must win three games.

    a Find the probability that Eva beats Paul by 3 games to 1.

    b Find the probability that Eva beats Paul in a match of squash. State the nature of the distribution used in this example.

7 At a luxury ski resort in Switzerland, the probability that snow will fall on any given day in the snow season is 0.15.

    a If the snow season begins on November 1st, find the probability that the first snow will fall on November 15.

    b Given that no snow fell during November, a tourist decides to wait no longer to book a holiday. The tourist decides to book for the earliest date for which the probability that snow will have fallen on or before that date is greater than 0.85. Find the exact date of the booking.

8 In a board game for four players, each player must roll two fair dice in turn to get a difference of "no more than 3" before they can begin to play.

    a Find the probability of getting a difference of "no more than 3" when rolling two unbiased dice.

b Find the probability that player 1 is the first to begin playing on his second roll, given that player 1 rolls the dice first.

c On average how many rolls of the dice will it take each player to begin playing?

d Find the average number of rolls of the dice it will take all 4 players to begin playing, giving your answer to the nearest integer.

POISSON

The **Poisson distribution** was observed in **Section 30H** of the Core text.

It has probability mass function $P(X = x) = \dfrac{m^x e^{-m}}{x!}$ where $x = 0, 1, 2, 3, 4, \ldots\ldots$

and m is the mean and variance of the Poisson random variable

i.e., $E(X) = \text{Var}(X) = m$ and the cdf is $F(x) = P(X \leqslant x) = \displaystyle\sum_{r=0}^{x} \dfrac{m^x e^{-m}}{x!}.$

Note:

- For the Poisson distribution, the mean always equals the variance.
- We write $X \sim P_0(m)$ to indicate that X is the random variable for the Poisson distribution, with mean and variance m.
- The conditions for a distribution to be Poisson are:

  1 The average number of occurrences (μ) is constant for each interval (i.e., it should be equally likely that the event occurs in one specific interval as in any other).

  2 The probability of more than one occurrence in a given interval is very small (i.e., the typical number of occurrences in a given interval should be much less than is theoretically possible (say about 10%)).

  3 The number of occurrences in disjoint intervals are independent of each other.

Example 12

Let X be the number of patients that arrive at a hospital emergency room. Patients arrive at random and the average number of patients per hour is constant.

a Explain why X is a random variable of a Poisson distribution.

b Suppose we know that $3\,\text{Var}(X) = [E(X)]^2 - 4$.

  i Find the mean of X.   **ii** Find $P(X \leqslant 4)$.

c If Y is another random variable with a Poisson distribution, independent of X such that $\text{Var}(Y) = 3$,   show that $X + Y$ is also a Poisson variable and hence find $P(X + Y < 5)$.

d Let U be the random variable defined by $U = X - Y$.

  i Find the mean and variance of U.   **ii** Comment on the distribution of U.

---

a X is a Poisson random variable as the average number of patients arriving at random per hour is constant (assuming it is also constant per any time period).

b **i** Since $E(X) = \text{Var}(X) = m,$ then $3m = m^2 - 4$

$$\therefore \quad m^2 - 3m - 4 = 0$$
$$\therefore \quad (m-4)(m+1) = 0$$
$$\therefore \quad m = 4 \text{ or } -1$$

But $m > 0,$ so $m = 4$

ii $P(X \leqslant 4) = \text{poissoncdf}(4, 4) \approx 0.629$

c

$E(X + Y)$
$= E(X) + E(Y)$
$= 4 + 3 \quad \{E(Y) = \text{Var}(Y) = 3\}$
$= 7$

$\text{Var}(X + Y)$
$= \text{Var}(X) + \text{Var}(Y)$
$= 4 + 3$
$= 7$

Since the mean and variance of $X + Y$ are equal, $X + Y$ is also Poisson and $X + Y \sim P_0(7)$

$$P(X + Y < 5) = P(X + Y \leqslant 4)$$
$$= \text{poissoncdf}(7, 4)$$
$$\approx 0.173$$

d **i**

$E(U)$
$= E(X - Y)$
$= E(X) - E(Y)$
$= 4 - 3$
$= 1$

$\text{Var}(U)$
$= \text{Var}(X - Y)$
$= \text{Var}(X) + \text{Var}(Y)$
$= 4 + 3$
$= 7$

ii As $E(U) \neq \text{Var}(U)$ then $X - Y$ cannot be Poisson.

EXERCISE 8B.3

Hypergeometric and Poisson distributions. (Core Text **Exercise 30H** pages 747-8.)
The **table** on **page 31** can be used in the following questions, where appropriate.

1 X is a discrete random variable such that $X \sim \text{Hyp}(5, 5, 12)$.   Find:

  a $P(X = 3)$ **b** $P(X = 5)$ **c** $P(X \leqslant 2)$ **d** $E(X)$ **e** $\text{Var}(X)$

2 X is a discrete random variable such that $X \sim P_o(\mu)$ and
    $P(X = 2) = P(X = 0) + 2P(X = 1).$

  a Find the value of μ.   **b** Hence, evaluate $P(1 \leqslant X \leqslant 5)$.

3 A box containing two dozen batteries is known to have five defective batteries included in it. If four batteries are randomly selected from the box, find the probability that:
  a exactly two of the batteries will be defective
  b none of the batteries is defective.

4 It is known that chains used in industry have faults at the average rate of 1 per every kilometre of chain. In a particular manufacturing process they regularly use chains of length 50 metres. Find the probability that there will be:
  a no faults in the 50 metre length of chain
  b at most two faults in the 50 metre length of chain.

It is considered 'safe' if there is at least a 99.5% chance there will be no more than 1 fault in 50 m of chain.   **c** Is this chain 'safe'?

5 A large aeroplane has 250 passenger seats. The airline has found from years of business that on average 3.75% of travellers who have bought tickets do not arrive for any given flight. The airline sells 255 tickets for this large aeroplane on a particular flight. Let X be the number of ticket holders who do not arrive for the flight.

    a State the distribution of X.

    b Calculate the probability that more than 250 ticket holders will arrive for the flight.

    c Calculate the probability that there will be empty seats on this flight.

    d Calculate the:

        i mean   **ii** variance of X.

        iii Hence use a suitable approximation for X to calculate the probability that more than 250 ticket holders will arrive for the flight.

        iv Use a suitable approximation for X to calculate the probability there will be empty seats on this flight.

    e Use your answers to determine whether the approximation was a good one.

6 The cook at a school needs to buy five dozen eggs for a school camp. The eggs are sold by the dozen. Being experienced the cook checks for rotten eggs. He selects two eggs simultaneously from the dozen pack and if they are not rotten he purchases the dozen eggs.

    Given that there is one rotten egg on average in each carton of one dozen eggs, find:

    a the probability he will accept a given carton of 1 dozen eggs

    b the probability that he will purchase the first five cartons he inspects

    c on average, how many cartons the cook will inspect if he is to purchase exactly five cartons of eggs (answer to nearest integer).

7 A receptionist in a High School receives on average five internal calls per 20 minutes and ten external calls per half hour.

    a Calculate the probability that the receptionist will receive exactly three calls in five minutes.

    b How many calls will the receptionist receive on average every five minutes (answer to nearest integer)?

    c Find the probability that the receptionist receives more than five calls in:

        i 5 minutes   **ii** 7 minutes.

8 One percent of all of a certain type of tennis ball produced is faulty. Tennis balls are sold in cartons of eight. Let X be a random variable which gives the number of faulty tennis balls in each carton.

    a State the distribution of X and give its probability mass function, with correct domain.

    Organisers of a local tennis tournament purchase these balls. They sample 2 balls from each carton and if they are both not faulty, they purchase the carton.

    b Find the proportion of all cartons that would be rejected by the purchasers. How many of 1000 cartons would the buyers expect to reject?

        Hint: • Draw a probability distribution table for X.

                • Calculate a probability distribution for rejecting a carton for each of the values of X.

THE MEAN AND VARIANCE OF DISCRETE RANDOM VARIABLES

Recall that to calculate the mean and variance of a discrete random variable we use:

- the **mean** $\qquad \mathrm{E}(X) = \mu = \sum x_i p_i$

- the **variance** $\qquad \mathrm{Var}(X) = \sigma^2 = \sum (x_i - \mu)^2 p_i$

$$\text{i.e.,} \quad \mathrm{Var}(X) = \mathrm{E}(X^2) - \{\mathrm{E}(X)\}^2 \quad \text{or} \quad \sum x_i^2 p_i - \mu^2$$

Using these basic results we can establish the mean and variance of the special discrete distributions we discussed earlier.

Example 13

Given that $\quad 1^2 + 2^2 + 3^2 + \ldots\ldots + n^2 = \dfrac{n(n+1)(2n+1)}{6} \quad$ for all n in Z^+,

and that $\quad X \sim \mathrm{DU}(n) \quad$ show that $\quad \mathrm{E}(X) = \dfrac{n+1}{2} \quad$ and $\quad \mathrm{Var}(X) = \dfrac{n^2-1}{12}$.

$\mathrm{E}(X) = \sum x_i p_i$

$\qquad = 1\left(\frac{1}{n}\right) + 2\left(\frac{1}{n}\right) + 3\left(\frac{1}{n}\right) + \ldots\ldots + n\left(\frac{1}{n}\right)$

$\qquad = \frac{1}{n}(1 + 2 + 3 + 4 + \ldots\ldots + n) \quad$ where $\quad 1 + 2 + 3 + \ldots\ldots + n$ is an
$\qquad\qquad\qquad\qquad\qquad\qquad\qquad\qquad\quad$ arithmetic series with $u_1 = 1$ and $d = 1$

$\qquad = \frac{1}{n}\left[\frac{n}{2}(2u_1 + (n-1)d)\right]$

$\qquad = \frac{1}{2}[2 + (n-1)]$

$\qquad = \dfrac{n+1}{2}$

$\mathrm{Var}(X) = \sum x_i^2 p_i - \mu^2$

$\qquad = 1^2\left(\frac{1}{n}\right) + 2^2\left(\frac{1}{n}\right) + 3^2\left(\frac{1}{n}\right) + \ldots\ldots + n^2\left(\frac{1}{n}\right) - \left(\dfrac{n+1}{2}\right)^2$

$\qquad = \frac{1}{n}\left(1^2 + 2^2 + 3^2 + \ldots\ldots + n^2\right) - \dfrac{(n+1)^2}{4}$

$\qquad = \frac{1}{n}\left[\dfrac{n(n+1)(2n+1)}{6}\right] - \dfrac{(n+1)^2}{4}$

$\qquad = \dfrac{(n+1)(2n+1)}{6} - \dfrac{(n+1)^2}{4}$

$\qquad = (n+1)\left[\dfrac{2n+1}{6} - \dfrac{n+1}{4}\right]$

$\qquad = (n+1)\left[\dfrac{4n+2}{12} - \dfrac{3n+3}{12}\right]$

$\qquad = (n+1)\left[\dfrac{n-1}{12}\right]$

$\qquad = \dfrac{n^2-1}{12}$

Reminder:

For the uniform distribution in **Example 13** the sample space $U = \{1, 2, 3, 4, \ldots, n\}$.

However, the n distinct outcomes of a uniform distribution do not have to equal the set U.

The **Mathematics HL information booklet** available for tests and examinations contains the table shown below:

DISCRETE DISTRIBUTIONS

Distribution	Notation	Probability mass function	Mean	Variance
Bernoulli	$X \sim \mathrm{B}(1,\, p)$	$p^x(1-p)^{1-x}$ $x = 0,\, 1$	p	$p(1-p)$
Binomial	$X \sim \mathrm{B}(n,\, p)$	$\binom{n}{x} p^x (1-p)^x$ for $x = 0,\, 1,\, \ldots,\, n$	np	$np(1-p)$
Hyper-geometric	$X \sim \mathrm{Hyp}(n,\, M,\, N)$	$\dfrac{\binom{M}{x}\binom{N-M}{n-x}}{\binom{N}{n}}$ for $x = 0,\, 1,\, \ldots,\, n$	np where $p = \dfrac{M}{N}$	$np(1-p)\left(\dfrac{N-n}{N-1}\right)$
Poisson	$X \sim \mathrm{P}_0(m)$	$\dfrac{m^x e^{-m}}{x!}$ for $x = 0,\, 1,\, \ldots$	m	m
Geometric	$X \sim \mathrm{Geo}(p)$	pq^{x-1} for $x = 1,\, 2,\, \ldots$	$\dfrac{1}{p}$	$\dfrac{q}{p^2}$
Negative binomial (Pascal's)	$X \sim \mathrm{NB}(r,\, p)$	$\binom{x-1}{r-1} p^r q^{x-r}$ for $x = r,\, r+1,\, \ldots$	$\dfrac{r}{p}$	$\dfrac{rq}{p^2}$
Discrete uniform	$X \sim \mathrm{DU}(n)$	$\dfrac{1}{n}$ for $x = 1,\, \ldots,\, n$	$\dfrac{n+1}{2}$	$\dfrac{n^2-1}{12}$

While each of these values for the mean and variance can be found using the rules for calculating mean and variance given above, the formal treatment of proofs of means and variances are excluded from the syllabus.

However, just as in **Example 12**, it is possible to derive these values. In the case of the Binomial distribution, using the result that

$$r \binom{n}{r} = n \binom{n-1}{r-1}$$

is most useful in attempting to establish the required result.

Proving the results formally may be useful as part of a portfolio piece of work.

Example 14

Prove that $x \binom{n}{x} = n \binom{n-1}{x-1}$.

Hence prove that for a Binomial random variable, the mean is equal to np.

Proof: $\text{LHS} = x \binom{n}{x}$ $\qquad\qquad$ $\text{RHS} = n \binom{n-1}{x-1}$

$$= x \times \frac{n!}{(n-x)!\, x!} \qquad\qquad = n \times \frac{(n-1)!}{(n-x)!(x-1)!}$$

$$= \frac{n!}{(n-x)!(x-1)!} \qquad\qquad = \frac{n!}{(n-x)!(x-1)!}$$

$\therefore$ $\text{LHS} = \text{RHS}$ as required

Now if $X \sim B(n,\,p)$,

$$P(x) = \binom{n}{x} p^x q^{n-x} \quad \text{where} \quad q = 1 - p$$

$$\therefore \quad \mu = \sum_{x=0}^{n} x\, P(x)$$

$$= \sum_{x=0}^{n} x \binom{n}{x} p^x q^{n-x} \qquad \{\text{as } P(x) = \binom{n}{x} p^x q^{n-x}\}$$

$$= \sum_{x=1}^{n} x \binom{n}{x} p^x q^{n-x} \qquad \{\text{as when } x = 0, \text{ the term is } 0\}$$

$$= \sum_{x=1}^{n} n \binom{n-1}{x-1} p^x q^{n-x} \qquad \{\text{using the above result}\}$$

$$= np \sum_{x=1}^{n} \binom{n-1}{x-1} p^{x-1} q^{n-x}$$

$$= np \sum_{r=0}^{n-1} \binom{n-1}{r} p^r q^{n-(r+1)} \qquad \{\text{replacing } x-1 \text{ by } r\}$$

$$= np \sum_{r=0}^{n-1} \binom{n-1}{r} p^r q^{(n-1)-r}$$

$$= np(p+q)^{n-1}$$

$$= np \times 1$$

$$= np$$

Example 15

Sheep are transported by road to the city on big trucks taking 500 sheep at a time. On average, on arrival 0.8% of the sheep have to be removed because of illness.
a   Describe the nature of the random variable X, which indicates the number of ill sheep on arrival.
b   State the mean and variance of this random variable.
c   Find the probability that on a truck with 500 sheep, exactly three are ill on arrival.
d   Find the probability that on a truck with 500 sheep, at least four are ill on arrival.
e   By inspection of your answer to b, comment as to what type of random variable X may approximate.
f   Repeat c and d above with the approximation from e and hence verify the validity of the approximation.

a X is a binomial random variable and $X \sim B(500, 0.008)$

b $\mu = np = 500 \times 0.008 = 4$ $\sigma^2 = npq = 4 \times 0.992 \approx 3.97$

c $P(X = 3) = \binom{500}{3}(0.008)^3(0.992)^{497}$ d   P(at least 4 are ill)
      or binompdf(500, 0.008, 3) $= P(X \geqslant 4)$
      ≈ 0.196 $= 1 - P(X \leqslant 3)$
                                                              $= 1 - $ binomcdf(500, 0.008, 3)
                                                              ≈ 0.567

e $\mu \approx \sigma^2$ from b, which suggests we may approximate X as Poisson
      i.e., X is approximately distributed as $P_0(4)$.

f $P(X = 3)$ $P(X \geqslant 4)$ These results are
      = poissonpdf(4, 3) $= 1 - P(X \leqslant 3)$ excellent approximations
      ≈ 0.195 ✓   = 1$-$ poissoncdf(4, 3)   to c and d.
                                ≈ 0.567 ✓

Note: The results in f verify that:

"When n is large $(n > 50)$ and p is small $(p < 0.1)$ the binomial distribution can be approximated using a Poisson distribution with the same mean".

EXERCISE 8B.4

Where appropriate in the following exercises, clearly state the type of discrete distribution used as well as answering the question.

1   On average an office confectionary dispenser breaks down six times during the working week (Monday to Saturday with each day including the same number of working hours). Which of the following is most likely to occur?
   A   The machine breaks down three times a week.
   B   The machine breaks down once on Saturday.
   C   The machine breaks down less than seventeen times in 4 weeks.

2   A spinning wheel has the numbers 1 to 50 inclusive on it. Assuming that the wheel is unbiased, find the mean and standard deviation of all the possible scores when the wheel is spun.

3   In a World Series contest between the Redsox and the Yankees, the first team to win four games is declared world champion. Recent evidence suggests that the Redsox have a 53% chance of beating the Yankees in any game. Find the probability that:

   a   the Yankees will beat the Redsox in exactly five games
   b   the Yankees will beat the Redsox in exactly seven games
   c   the Redsox will be declared world champions.
   d   How many games on average would it take the Redsox to win four games against the Yankees. Comment on your result!

4   During the busiest period on the internet, you have a 62% chance of getting through to an important website. If you do not get through, you simply keep trying until you do make contact. Let X be the number of times you have to try, to get through.

   a   Stating any necessary assumptions, identify the nature of the random variable X.
   b   Find $P(X \geqslant 3)$.
   c   Find the mean and standard deviation of the random variable X.

5   In a hand of poker from a well shuffled pack, you are dealt five cards at random.

   a   Describe the distribution of X, where X is the number of aces you are dealt in a hand of poker.
   b   Find the probability of being dealt exactly two aces in a hand of poker.
   c   During the poker evening, you are dealt a total of 30 hands from a well shuffled pack.
      i   Describe the distribution of Y, where Y is the number of times you have been dealt 2 aces in a hand of poker.
      ii   Find $P(Y \geqslant 5)$.
      iii   How many times would you expect to have been dealt two aces during the night?
      iv   How many aces would you expect to be dealt in a hand of poker?

6   It costs you $15 to enter a game where you have to randomly select a marble from ten differently marked marbles in a barrel. The marbles are marked 10 cents, 20 cents, 30 cents, 40 cents, 50 cents, 60 cents, 70 cents, $15, $30 and $100, and you receive the marked amount in return for playing the game.

   a   Define a random variable X which is the outcome of selecting a marble from the barrel.
   b   Find $E(X)$ and $Var(X)$.
   c   Briefly explain why you cannot use the rules given for $DU(n)$ to find the answers to **b** above.
   d   The people who run the game expect to make a profit but want to encourage people to play by not charging too much.
      i   Find to the nearest 10 cents the smallest amount they need to charge to still expect to make a profit.
      ii   Find the expected return to the organisers if they charge $16 a game and a total of 1000 games are played in one day.

7 A person raising funds for cancer research telephones people at random asking for a donation, knowing he has a 1 in 8 chance of being successful.

    a Describe the random variable X that indicates the number of calls made before a success is obtained.

    b State one assumption made in your answer to **a** above.

    c Find the average number of calls required for success, and the standard deviation of the number of calls for success.

    d Find the probability that it takes less than five calls to obtain success.

8 The probability that I dial a wrong number is 0.005 when I make a telephone call. In a typical week I will make 75 telephone calls.

    a Describe the distribution of the random variable T that indicates the number of times I dial a wrong number in a week.

    b In a given week, find the probability that:

        i I dial no wrong numbers   i.e., $P(T = 0)$

        ii I dial more than two wrong numbers.

        iii Find $E(T)$ and $Var(T)$.   Comment on your results!

    c Now assuming T is a Poisson distribution with the same mean as found above, again find the probability in a given week that:

        i I dial no wrong numbers

        ii I dial more than two wrong numbers. What does this result verify?

CONTINUOUS RANDOM VARIABLES

A **continuous random variable** X has a **probability density function (pdf)** given by $f(x)$ where

    • $f(x) \geqslant 0$ for all $x \in$ the domain of f

    • $\displaystyle\int_a^b f(x)\, dx = 1$ if the domain is $[a, b]$

Note: • x can take any real value on the domain of f

         •   the domain of f could be $]-\infty, \infty[$

Refer to **Section 30I** of the Core text to revise the definition of a pdf and the methods used to find the *mode, median, mean, variance* and *standard deviation* of a continuous random variable X.

THE CUMULATIVE DISTRIBUTION FUNCTION (cdf)

As probabilities are calculated by finding an appropriate area under a pdf, we define

    the **cumulative distribution function (cdf)** as

    $F(X) = P(X \leqslant x) = \int_a^x f(t)\, dt$

    where $f(x)$ is the probability density function (pdf) with domain $[a, b]$.

Note: Sometimes this area can be found using simple methods, for example, the area of a rectangle or triangle.

Example 16

The continuous random variable X has pdf $f(x) = kx$, $0 \leqslant x \leqslant 6$.

Find:
a k
b   the tenth percentile of the random variable X.

a
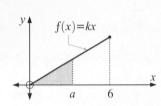

as $\int_0^6 f(x)\,dx = 1$

$\int_0^6 kx\,dx = 1$

$\therefore \quad k\left[\dfrac{x^2}{2}\right]_0^6 = 1$

$\therefore \quad k(18 - 0) = 1$

$\therefore \quad k = \frac{1}{18}$

b   We need to find a such that $P(X < a) = 0.10$

$\therefore \quad \frac{1}{2} \times a \times \dfrac{a}{18} = 0.1$

$\therefore \quad a^2 = 3.6$

$\therefore \quad a \approx 1.90 \quad \{\text{as } a > 0\}$

i.e.,   the 10th percentile ≈ 1.90

Note: We could have used the area of a triangle formula instead of integrating.

THE MEAN AND VARIANCE OF A CONTINUOUS RANDOM VARIABLE

Recall that (Core Section **30I**) the method for calculating the mean and variance of a continuous random variable is:

- $E(X) = \mu = \int x\,f(x)\,dx$ for the **mean**
- $\text{Var}(X) = \sigma^2 = \int (x - \mu)^2\,f(x)\,dx$
  or $\text{Var}(X) = E(X - \mu)^2$ or $E(X^2) - \mu^2$ or $\int x^2\,f(x)\,dx - \mu^2$

TYPES OF CONTINUOUS RANDOM VARIABLES

CONTINUOUS UNIFORM

We write $X \sim U(a, b)$ to indicate that X is a **continuous uniform** random variable with a pdf given by $f(x) = \dfrac{1}{b - a}$, $a \leqslant x \leqslant b$

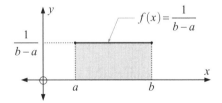

This pdf is a horizontal line segment above the x-axis on $[a, b]$.

So, in general, a continuous uniform random variable has a pdf given by $f(x) = k$ where k is a positive constant.

Example 17

Prove that the pdf of a continuous uniform random variable X defined on the interval $[a, b]$ is given by $f(x) = \dfrac{1}{b-a}, \quad a \leqslant x \leqslant b.$

As X is a continuous uniform random variable, it has a pdf given by $f(x) = k$, where k is constant on the interval $[a, b]$.

For a pdf, $\int_a^b k \, dx = 1$ $\qquad \therefore \quad [kx]_a^b = 1$

$\qquad\qquad\qquad\qquad\qquad \therefore \quad kb - ka = 1$

$\qquad\qquad\qquad\qquad\qquad \therefore \quad k(b-a) = 1$

$$k = \frac{1}{b-a}$$

So, $f(x) = \dfrac{1}{b-a}$ on $[a, b]$.

Example 18

If X is a continuous uniform random variable,   i.e., $X \sim \text{U}(a, b)$,   show that:

a $\mu = \dfrac{a+b}{2}$ b   variance $(\sigma^2) = \dfrac{(b-a)^2}{12}$

As $X \sim \text{U}(a, b)$,   its pdf is $f(x) = \dfrac{1}{b-a}, \quad a \leqslant x \leqslant b.$

a $\mu = \text{E}(x)$

$\quad = \displaystyle\int_a^b \frac{x}{b-a} \, dx$

$\quad = \dfrac{1}{b-a} \left[\dfrac{x^2}{2} \right]_a^b$

$\quad = \dfrac{\dfrac{b^2}{2} - \dfrac{a^2}{2}}{b-a}$

$\quad = \dfrac{b^2 - a^2}{2(b-a)}$

$\quad = \dfrac{(b+a)(b-a)^{\,1}}{2(b-a)_{\,1}}$

$\quad = \dfrac{a+b}{2}$

b $\sigma^2 = \text{Var}(X) = \text{E}(X^2) - \mu^2$

$\quad = \displaystyle\int_a^b \frac{x^2}{b-a} \, dx - \left(\frac{a+b}{2} \right)^2$

$\quad = \dfrac{1}{b-a} \left[\dfrac{x^3}{3} \right]_a^b - \left(\dfrac{a+b}{2} \right)^2$

$\quad = \dfrac{\dfrac{b^3}{3} - \dfrac{a^3}{3}}{b-a} - \left(\dfrac{a+b}{2} \right)^2$

$\quad = \dfrac{b^3 - a^3}{3(b-a)} - \left(\dfrac{a+b}{2} \right)^2$

$\quad = \dfrac{(b-a)(b^2 + ab + a^2)}{3(b-a)_{\,1}} - \dfrac{a^2 + 2ab + b^2}{4}$

$\quad = \dfrac{4b^2 + 4ab + 4a^2}{12} - \dfrac{3a^2 + 6ab + 3b^2}{12}$

$\quad = \dfrac{b^2 - 2ab + a^2}{12}$

$\quad = \dfrac{(a-b)^2}{12}$

Example 19

The error in seconds made by an amateur timekeeper at an athletics meeting may be modelled by the random variable X, with probability density function

$$f(x) = \begin{cases} 0.5 & -0.5 \leqslant x \leqslant 1.5 \\ 0 & \text{otherwise} \end{cases}$$ Find the probability that:

a   an error is positive   **b**   the magnitude of an error exceeds 0.5 seconds

c   the magnitude of an error is less than 1.2 seconds

$f(x) = 0.5$ on $-0.5 \leqslant x \leqslant 1.5$

a $P(X > 0)$

$= P(0 < X < 1.5)$

$= \dfrac{1.5}{2}$

$= 0.75$

b $P(\text{magnitude} > 0.5)$

$= P(|X| > 0.5)$

$= P(X > 0.5 \quad \text{or} \quad X < -0.5)$

$= P(X > 0.5)$

$= \frac{1}{2}$

$= 0.5$

c $P(\text{magnitude} < 1.2) \ = P(|X| < 1.2)$

$= P(-1.2 < X < 1.2)$

$= P(-0.5 < X < 1.2)$

$= \dfrac{1.2 - (-0.5)}{2}$

$= 0.85$

Note: These values are given by areas of rectangles.

EXPONENTIAL

We write $X \sim \text{Exp}(\lambda)$ to indicate that X is a **continuous exponential** random variable with pdf given by $f(x) = \lambda e^{-\lambda x}$ for $x \geqslant 0$.

Note: • λ must be positive since $f(x) > 0$ for all x and $e^{-\lambda x} > 0$ for all x.

• $f(x)$ is decreasing for all $x \geqslant 0$ as $f'(x) = \lambda e^{-\lambda x}(-\lambda) = -\lambda^2 e^{-\lambda x}$
where λ^2 and $e^{-\lambda x}$ are positive for all $x \geqslant 0$,   i.e., $f'(x)$ is negative for all x.

• $\displaystyle \int_0^\infty \lambda e^{-\lambda t}\, dt$ must equal 1   {as $f(x)$ is a pdf}

$\therefore \quad \displaystyle \lim_{x \to \infty} \int_0^x \lambda e^{-\lambda t}\, dt = 1$

• The mean $\mu = E(X) = \dfrac{1}{\lambda}$ and $\text{Var}(X) = \dfrac{1}{\lambda^2}$.

• A typical continuous exponential pdf is shown alongside.

Notice that $f(x) \to 0$ (from above) as $x \to \infty$.

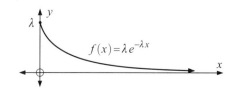

The proofs of these results for the mean and variance are not required for exam purposes and will be given in the Mathematics HL Information Booklet.

Example 20

The continuous random variable X has probability density function $f(x) = 2e^{-2x}$, $x \geqslant 0$.

a   Show that $f(x)$ is a well-defined pdf.

b   Find $E(X)$.

c   Find Var(X).

d   Find the median and modal values of X.

a $f(x)$ is a well-defined pdf if $\int_0^\infty f(x)\,dx = 1$

Now $\int_0^\infty f(x)\,dx = \int_0^\infty 2e^{-2x}\,dx$

$$= \left[\frac{2e^{-2x}}{-2}\right]_0^\infty$$

$$= \left[-e^{-2x}\right]_0^\infty$$

$$= -e^{-\infty} - (-1)$$

$$= 1 - 0$$

$$= 1$$

As X is a continuous exponential random variable

b $E(X) = \dfrac{1}{\lambda} = \frac{1}{2}$ **c**   Var$(X) = \dfrac{1}{\lambda^2} = \frac{1}{4}$

d   If the median is m, we need to find m such that

$$\int_0^m 2e^{-2x}\,dx = 0.5 \quad \therefore \quad \left[\left(\tfrac{1}{-2}\right) 2e^{-2x}\right]_0^m = 0.5$$

$$\therefore \quad \left[-e^{-2x}\right]_0^m = 0.5$$

$$\therefore \quad -e^{-2m} - (-1) = 0.5$$

$$\therefore \quad e^{-2m} = 0.5$$

$$\therefore \quad e^{2m} = 2 \quad \{\text{reciprocals}\}$$

$$\therefore \quad 2m = \ln 2$$

$$\therefore \quad m = \tfrac{1}{2}\ln 2 \approx 0.347$$

The mode occurs at the maximum value of $f(x)$,

$\therefore$ mode $= 0$.

It is interesting to note that the **cdf of a continuous exponential** random variable,

$F(x) = P(X \leqslant x) = \int_0^x \lambda e^{-\lambda t}\,dt$ is a function which increases at a decreasing rate.

Hence, most of the area under the graph occurs for relatively small values of x.

Example 21

Find the 80th percentile of the random variable X with pdf $f(x) = \lambda e^{-\lambda x}$, $x \geqslant 0$,   giving your answer in terms of λ. If $\lambda > 4$, find possible values for the 80th percentile. Comment on your answer.

We want to find a such that $\int_0^a \lambda e^{-\lambda t}\, dt = 0.80$

$$\therefore \quad \lambda \int_0^a e^{-\lambda t}\, dt = 0.8$$

$$\therefore \quad \lambda \left[\frac{e^{-\lambda t}}{-\lambda} \right]_0^a = 0.8$$

$$\therefore \quad -\left[e^{-\lambda a} - e^0 \right] = 0.8$$

$$\therefore \quad e^{-\lambda a} - 1 = -0.8$$

$$\therefore \quad e^{-\lambda a} = 0.2$$

and reciprocating gives $e^{\lambda a} = 5$

$$\therefore \quad \lambda a = \ln 5 \quad \text{and so} \quad a = \frac{\ln 5}{\lambda}$$

$\therefore$ 80th percentile is $\dfrac{\ln 5}{\lambda}$

If $\lambda > 4$, $\dfrac{1}{\lambda} < \dfrac{1}{4}$ $\therefore$ 80th percentile $< \dfrac{\ln 5}{4} \approx 0.402$

i.e.,   for $\lambda > 4$,   80% of the scores are less than 0.402

i.e.,   most of the area lies in $[0,\,0.402]$ which is a very small interval compared with $[\,0,\,\infty\,[$.

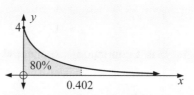

Notice that if we are given the cdf of a continuous random variable then we can find its pdf using the Fundamental theorem of calculus. In particular:

If the cdf is $F(x) = \int_a^x f(t)\,dt$ then its pdf is given by $f(x) = F'(x)$.

Example 22

Given a random variable with cdf $F(x) = \int_0^x \lambda e^{-\lambda t}\, dt$,   find its pdf.

$$f(x) = F'(x) = \frac{d}{dx} \int_0^x \lambda e^{-\lambda t}\, dt, \quad x \geqslant 0$$

$$= \frac{d}{dx} \left[\frac{\lambda e^{-\lambda t}}{-\lambda} \right]_0^x$$

$$= \frac{d}{dx} \left[-e^{-\lambda t} \right]_0^x$$

$$= \frac{d}{dx} \left(-e^{-\lambda x} - (-1) \right)$$

$$= -e^{-\lambda x}(-\lambda) + 0$$

$$\therefore \quad f(x) = \lambda e^{-\lambda x}, \quad x \geqslant 0$$

NORMAL

We write $X \sim N(\mu, \sigma^2)$ to indicate that X is a **continuous normal** random variable with pdf given by

$$f(x) = \frac{1}{\sigma\sqrt{2\pi}}e^{-\frac{1}{2}\left(\frac{x-\mu}{\sigma}\right)^2} \quad \text{for} \quad]-\infty, \infty[.$$

Note: • The mean of the normal distribution is μ and the variance is σ^2.

• In section **30J** of the Core text, the properties of the normal distribution are discussed.   Recall that the normal curve is bell-shaped with the percentages within its portions as shown:

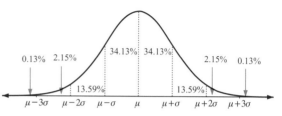

• $Z = \dfrac{X - \mu}{\sigma}$ is the standard normal random variable and $Z \sim N(0, 1)$

This transformation is useful when determining an unknown mean or standard deviation. Also conversion to Z-scores is very important for the understanding of the theory behind **confidence intervals** and **hypothesis testing** which are dealt with later in this topic.

Example 23

Given a random variable $X \sim N(\mu, \sigma^2)$, find its mean and standard deviation given that area $A = 0.11506$ and area $B = 0.13566$

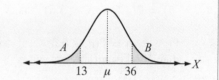

$$P(X < 13) = 0.11506 \quad \text{and} \quad P(X > 36) = 0.13566$$

$$\therefore \ P\left(\frac{X - \mu}{\sigma} < \frac{13 - \mu}{\sigma}\right) = 0.11506 \qquad \therefore \ P(X < 36) = 0.86434$$

$$\therefore \ P\left(Z < \frac{13 - \mu}{\sigma}\right) = 0.11506 \qquad \therefore \ P\left(Z < \frac{36 - \mu}{\sigma}\right) = 0.86434$$

$$\therefore \ \frac{13 - \mu}{\sigma} = \text{invNorm}(0.11506) \qquad \therefore \ \frac{36 - \mu}{\sigma} = \text{invNorm}(0.86434)$$

$$\therefore \ \mu - 1.2\sigma = 13 \ ..... \ (1) \qquad \therefore \ \mu + 1.1\sigma = 36 \ ..... \ (2)$$

$$\text{Equating} \ \ \sigma\text{s}, \quad \frac{\mu - 13}{1.2} = \frac{36 - \mu}{1.1}$$

which when solved gives $\mu = 25$

and in (1) $25 - 1.2\sigma = 13$

$$\therefore \quad 1.2\sigma = 12$$

$$\therefore \quad \sigma = 10$$

The Mathematics HL Information Booklet available for teachers and students during the course and in the examinations from 2006 contains the following table.

CONTINUOUS DISTRIBUTIONS

Distribution	Notation	Probability density function	Mean	Variance
Uniform	$X \sim \text{U}(a, b)$	$\dfrac{1}{b-a}, \quad a \leqslant x \leqslant b$	$\dfrac{a+b}{2}$	$\dfrac{(b-a)^2}{12}$
Exponential	$X \sim \text{Exp}(\lambda)$	$\lambda e^{-\lambda x}, \quad x \geqslant 0$	$\dfrac{1}{\lambda}$	$\dfrac{1}{\lambda^2}$
Normal	$X \sim \text{N}(\mu, \sigma^2)$	$\dfrac{1}{\sigma\sqrt{2\pi}} e^{-\frac{1}{2}\left(\frac{x-\mu}{\sigma}\right)^2}$	μ	σ^2

FINDING $P(X = a)$ FOR A CONTINUOUS RANDOM VARIABLE

Generally we are asked to find probabilities over some interval like [0, 30] when the random variable X is continuous. How then do we find $P(X = 5)$, say?

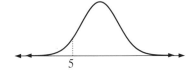

The probability is 0, if we consider areas.

If $P(X = 5)$ needs to be found where X has been rounded to the nearest integer, then $P(X = 5) = P(4.5 \leqslant X < 5.5)$ as X is continuous.

So, $P(X = a) = P(a - 0.5 \leqslant X < a + 0.5)$ if we are interested in the probability that X takes an integer value.

Example 24

Given a random variable $X \sim \text{N}(7.2, 28)$, find $P(X = 10)$.

$$\begin{aligned}
P(X = 10) &= P(9.5 \leqslant X < 10.5) \\
&= \text{normalcdf}(9.5, 10.5, 7.2, \sqrt{28}) \\
&\approx 0.0655
\end{aligned}$$

THE NORMAL APPROXIMATION TO THE BINOMIAL DISTRIBUTION

If $X \sim \text{B}(n, p)$, then for large n,

$X \sim \text{N}(np, npq)$ approximately, where $q = 1 - p$.

What does large n mean?

A useful rule to follow is: If $np > 5$ and $nq > 5$ then we can be reasonable confident that the binomial distribution is approximately normal. The teaching notes of the syllabus use the common but more conservative rule for the application of this approximation: $np \geqslant 10$ and $n(1 - p) \geqslant 10$.

This can be observed by drawing histograms for binomial distributions for different values of n and p. When n and p satisfy the above, the histogram begins to approximate a bell-shaped curve, like the pdf of a normal distribution. The greater the values of np and nq, the better the approximation becomes.

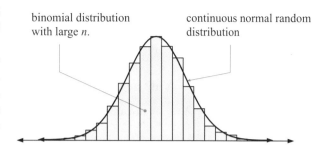

binomial distribution with large n.

continuous normal random distribution

Example 25

Consider the random variable $X \sim B(15, 0.4)$.   Find

a $E(X)$ and $Var(X)$

b   **i** $P(X \leqslant 7)$ **ii** $P(3 \leqslant X \leqslant 12)$.

c   By approximating X with a normal distribution, find
       i $P(X \leqslant 7)$ **ii** $P(3 \leqslant X \leqslant 12)$.
       Compare your answers with **b**.

d   Now using the normal approximation, find
       i $P(X < 7.5)$ **ii** $P(2.5 \leqslant X < 12.5)$.
       Again, compare your answers with **b**.   Which is the better approximation?
       Can you explain why?

---

a $E(X) = \mu = np$ $Var(X) = \sigma^2 = npq$

   $\therefore$ $E(X) = 15 \times 0.4$ $\therefore$ $Var(X) = 6 \times 0.6$

            $= 6$ $= 3.6$

b   **i** $P(X \leqslant 7)$ **ii** $P(3 \leqslant x \leqslant 12)$
         $= \text{binomcdf}(15, 0.4, 7)$ $= P(X \leqslant 12) - P(X \leqslant 2)$
         ≈ 0.787 $= \text{binomcdf}(15, 0.4, 12)$
                                                          $- \text{binomcdf}(15, 0.4, 2)$
                                                      ≈ 0.973

c   Using a normal approximation, X is approximately distributed as $N(6, 3.6)$

   i $P(X \leqslant 7)$ **ii** $P(3 \leqslant X \leqslant 12)$
         $= \text{normalcdf}(-E99, 7, 6, \sqrt{3.6})$ $= \text{normalcdf}(3, 12, 6, \sqrt{3.6})$
         ≈ 0.701 ≈ 0.942

   These answers are not really close to those in **b** and this is not surprising as $np = 6$ and $n(1 - p) = 9$ which under the conditions $np \geqslant 10$ and $n(1 - p) \geqslant 10$ are not large enough.

d   Using a normal approximation,

   i $P(X < 7.5)$ **ii** $P(2.5 \leqslant X < 12.5)$
         $= \text{normalcdf}(-E99, 7.5, 6, \sqrt{3.6})$ $= \text{normalcdf}(2.5, 12.5, 6, \sqrt{3.6})$
         ≈ 0.785 ≈ 0.967

   These results are very close to the actual values.
   We say there has been a **correction for continuity** and this is sensible because the binomial distribution is *discrete* and the normal distribution is *continuous*.

Note: • If we want to find $P(X = 7)$ for a discrete distribution, we can use the continuous normal distribution since:

$$P(X = 7) \approx P(6.5 \leqslant X < 7.5)$$
$$\uparrow \qquad\qquad\qquad \uparrow$$
$$X \text{ discrete} \qquad X \text{ continuous}$$

• Also, $X \leqslant 7$ means $X < 7.5$ and $X \geqslant 7$ means $X \geqslant 6.5$.
$$\uparrow \qquad\qquad \uparrow \qquad\qquad\qquad \uparrow \qquad\qquad \uparrow$$
$$X \text{ discrete} \qquad X \text{ continuous} \qquad X \text{ discrete} \qquad X \text{ continuous}$$

EXERCISE 8B.5

Where appropriate in the following exercise, clearly state the type of discrete or continuous distribution used as well as answering the question.

1 The continuous random variable T has a probability density function given by

$$f(t) = \begin{cases} \frac{1}{2\pi} & -\pi \leqslant t \leqslant \pi \\ 0 & \text{otherwise} \end{cases}.$$

Find the mean and standard deviation of T.

2 The Australian football Grand Final is held annually on the last Saturday in September. With approximately 100 000 in attendance each year, ticket sales are heavily in demand upon release. Let X be the random variable which gives the time (in hours) taken for a successful purchase of a Grand Final ticket after their release.

   a Give reasons why X could best be modelled by a continuous exponential random variable.

   b If the median value of X is 10 hours, find the value of λ in the pdf for an exponential random variable.

   c Hence, find the probability of a Grand Final ticket being purchased after 3 or more days.

   d Find the average time before a Grand Final ticket is purchased.

3 Find the mean and standard deviation of a normal random variable X, given that
$$P(X > 13) = 0.4529 \quad \text{and} \quad P(X > 28) = 0.1573$$

4 A continuous probability density function is described as follows:

$$f(x) = \begin{cases} 0, & x < 0 \\ 6 - 18x, & 0 \leqslant x \leqslant k \\ 0, & x > k \end{cases}$$

   Find: **a** the value of k

           b the mean and standard deviation of the distribution.

5 It is known that 41% of a population support the Environment Party. A random sample of 180 people are selected from the population. If X is the random variable giving the number who support the Environment Party in this sample:

   a   **i** State the distribution of X.   **ii** Find $E(X)$ and $Var(X)$.

      iii Find $P(X \geqslant 58)$.

   b State a suitable approximation for the random variable X and use it to recalculate part **a iii**. Comment on your answer.

6 Trainee typists make on average 2.5 mistakes per page when typing a document. If the mistakes on any one page are made independently of any other page, and if X represents the number of mistakes made on one page and Y represents the number of mistakes made in a 52-page document:

    a State the distributions of X and Y.

    b Find the probability that Rana, a trainee typist, will make more than 2 mistakes on a randomly chosen page.

    c Find the probability that Rana will make more than 104 mistakes in a 52-page document.

    d State $E(X)$, $Var(X)$, $E(Y)$ and $Var(Y)$.

    e Now assume that X and Y can be approximated by normal random variables with the same means and variances as found above. Use the normal approximations to redo **b** and **c** above. Comment on your answers.

7 The continuous random variable X has a pdf $f(x) = \frac{2}{5}$ for $1 \leqslant x \leqslant k$. Find:

    a the value of k, and state the distribution of X

    b $P(1.7 \leqslant x \leqslant 3.2)$

    c $E(X)$ and $Var(X)$.

8 The continuous random variable X is uniformly distributed over the interval $a < x < b$. The 30th percentile is 3 and the 90th percentile is 12. Find:

    a the values of a and b **b** the pdf of X

    c $P(5 < X < 9)$ **d** the cdf of X.

9 **a** If the random variable $T \sim N(7, 36)$, find $P(|T - 6| < 2.3)$.

    b Four random observations of T are made. Find the probability that exactly 2 of the observations will lie in the interval $|T - 6| < 2.3$.

10 Show that the mean and variance of the continuous exponential random variable defined by $f(x) = \lambda e^{-\lambda x}$, $x \geqslant 0$, are $\frac{1}{\lambda}$ and $\frac{1}{\lambda^2}$ respectively.

    Note: This question is not required for exam purposes but may be useful for part of a portfolio piece of work as it incorporates work from the core. Using integration by parts may prove helpful.

11 Find the mean and standard deviation of the continuous random variable that is uniformly distributed over the interval:

    a 0 to 1   **b** 2 to 6

    c 0 to a **d** from m to n where $m < n$.

C | DISTRIBUTIONS OF THE SAMPLE MEAN

INFERENCES

A principal application of statistics is to make **inferences** about a **population** based on observations from a sufficiently large **sample** from the population. As the sample is used to make generalisations about the whole population it is essential to employ correct sampling methods when selecting the sample.

Reminders:

- The **mean** of a set of data is its arithmetic average, i.e., the sum of all the data values divided by the number of them. The mean is a measure of the distribution's **centre**.

  If finding the mean of a sample, $\overline{x}$ is used, whereas μ is used for a population mean.

- The **standard deviation** of a set of data measures the deviation between the data values and the mean. It is a measure of the variability or spread of the distribution.

  When finding the standard deviation of a sample, s is used, whereas σ is used for a population standard deviation.

RANDOM SAMPLING

In order to establish correct inferences about a population from a sample, we use **random sampling** where each individual in the population is equally likely to be chosen.

There are three sampling methods used to select samples.   These are:

- systematic sampling   • stratified random sampling   • cluster sampling.

PARAMETERS AND STATISTICS

A **parameter** is a numerical characteristic of a *population*.   **P**opulation **p**arameter

A **statistic** is a numerical characteristic of a *sample*.   **S**ample **s**tatistic

A parameter or a statistic could be the mean, a percentage, the range, the standard deviation, etc.

When we calculate a sample statistic which we want to use to estimate the population parameter, we do not expect it to be exactly equal to the population parameter. As a result, some measure of reliability needs to be given and this is generally in the form of a **confidence interval**. To obtain such an interval, we need to know how the sample statistic is distributed.

The distribution of a sampling statistic is called its **sampling distribution.**

SAMPLING DISTRIBUTIONS

Consider tossing a coin where $x = 0$ corresponds to '0 head'
                                  and $x = 1$ corresponds to '1 head'.

The probability distribution for the random variable X is:

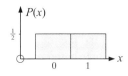

Now suppose we are interested in the sampling **mean**, $\overline{x}$, for the possible samples when tossing a coin *twice* $(n = 2)$, i.e., the mean result for two tosses.

Possible samples	$\overline{x}$
T, T is 0, 0	0
T, H is 0, 1	$\frac{1}{2}$
H, T is 1, 0	$\frac{1}{2}$
H, H is 1, 1	1

The **sampling distribution** of $\overline{x}$ is:

$\overline{x}$	0	$\frac{1}{2}$	1
Frequency	1	2	1
$P(\overline{x})$	$\frac{1}{4}$	$\frac{2}{4}$	$\frac{1}{4}$

And the graph is:

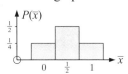

Note: $P(\overline{x})$ is the probability of a particular value
              of $\overline{x}$ occurring.

Now suppose we are interested in the sampling **mean**, $\overline{x}$, for the possible samples when tossing a coin *three times* ($n = 3$), i.e., the mean result for three tosses.

Possible samples	$\overline{x}$	Possible samples	$\overline{x}$
T, T, T is $0, 0, 0$	0	H, H, T is $1, 1, 0$	$\frac{2}{3}$
T, T, H is $0, 0, 1$	$\frac{1}{3}$	H, T, H is $1, 0, 1$	$\frac{2}{3}$
T, H, T is $0, 1, 0$	$\frac{1}{3}$	T, H, H is $0, 1, 1$	$\frac{2}{3}$
H, T, T is $1, 0, 0$	$\frac{1}{3}$	H, H, H is $1, 1, 1$	1

The **sampling distribution** of $\overline{x}$ is:

$\overline{x}$	0	$\frac{1}{3}$	$\frac{2}{3}$	1
Frequency	1	3	3	1
$P(\overline{x})$	$\frac{1}{8}$	$\frac{3}{8}$	$\frac{3}{8}$	$\frac{1}{8}$

The sampling distribution of x for this case is even closer to the shape of a normal distribution.

And the graph is:

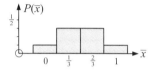

Now consider a spinner with possible outcomes $x = 1$, 2 or 3 and when it is spun 3 times i.e., $n = 3$.

Possible samples	$\overline{x}$	Possible samples	$\overline{x}$	Possible samples	$\overline{x}$	Possible samples	$\overline{x}$
$\{1, 1, 1\}$	1	$\{1, 3, 2\}$	2	$\{2, 2, 3\}$	$\frac{7}{3}$	$\{3, 2, 1\}$	2
$\{1, 1, 2\}$	$\frac{4}{3}$	$\{1, 3, 3\}$	$\frac{7}{3}$	$\{2, 3, 1\}$	2	$\{3, 2, 2\}$	$\frac{7}{3}$
$\{1, 1, 3\}$	$\frac{5}{3}$	$\{2, 1, 1\}$	$\frac{4}{3}$	$\{2, 3, 2\}$	$\frac{7}{3}$	$\{3, 2, 3\}$	$\frac{8}{3}$
$\{1, 2, 1\}$	$\frac{4}{3}$	$\{2, 1, 2\}$	$\frac{5}{3}$	$\{2, 3, 3\}$	$\frac{8}{3}$	$\{3, 3, 1\}$	$\frac{7}{3}$
$\{1, 2, 2\}$	$\frac{5}{3}$	$\{2, 1, 3\}$	2	$\{3, 1, 1\}$	$\frac{5}{3}$	$\{3, 3, 2\}$	$\frac{8}{3}$
$\{1, 2, 3\}$	2	$\{2, 2, 1\}$	$\frac{5}{3}$	$\{3, 1, 2\}$	2	$\{3, 3, 3\}$	3
$\{1, 3, 1\}$	$\frac{5}{3}$	$\{2, 2, 2\}$	2	$\{3, 1, 3\}$	$\frac{7}{3}$		

The **sampling distribution** of $\overline{x}$ is:

$\overline{x}$	1	$\frac{4}{3}$	$\frac{5}{3}$	2	$\frac{7}{3}$	$\frac{8}{3}$	3
Frequency	1	3	6	7	6	3	1
$P(\overline{x})$	$\frac{1}{27}$	$\frac{3}{27}$	$\frac{6}{27}$	$\frac{7}{27}$	$\frac{6}{27}$	$\frac{3}{27}$	$\frac{1}{27}$

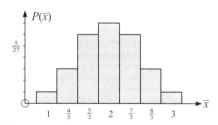

Once again we observe that the sampling distribution for this small value of n has a basic bell shape.

In this section we will be mainly interested in the **sampling distribution of the sample mean**.

EXERCISE 8C.1

1 A square spinner is used to generate the digits 1, 2, 3 and 4 at random. A sample of *two* digits is generated.

    a List the possible samples of two digits ($n = 2$).

    b For each possible sample, calculate the sample mean $\overline{x}$.

    c Construct a table which summarises the sampling distribution of $\overline{x}$ and the probabilities associated with it.

    d   Draw a sampling distribution histogram to display the information.

2   Repeat question **1 c** and **d**, but this time consider samples of *three* digits, i.e., $n = 3$.

3   A random variable X has two possible values (2 and 3), with equal chance of each occurring.

    a   List all possible samples when $n = 4$, and for each possible sample find the sample mean $\overline{x}$.

    b   Write down in table form the sampling distribution of $\overline{x}$, complete with probabilities.

4   Two ordinary dice are rolled. The mean $\overline{x}$ of every possible set of results is calculated. Find the sampling distribution of $\overline{x}$.

ERRORS IN SAMPLING

The statistics calculated from a sample should provide an accurate picture of the population. If the sample is large enough then the errors should be small.

One of the characteristics of a 'good' sample is that it is just large enough so that its mean is a reliable indication of the mean of the population. Likewise, proportions in the sample should reasonably match proportions within the population.

Whenever sample data is collected, differences in sample characteristics, for example, means and proportions, do occur. These differences are called **errors**.

Errors which may be due to faults in the sampling process are **systematic errors**, resulting in **bias**. However, errors which may be due to natural variability are **random errors**, sometimes called **statistical errors**.

Systematic errors are often due to poor sample design, or are errors made when measurements are taken.

In the following investigation we examine how well actual samples represent a population. A close look at how samples differ from each other helps us better understand the sampling error due to natural variation (random error).

INVESTIGATION 1   **A COMPUTER BASED RANDOM SAMPLER**

In this investigation we will examine samples from a symmetrical distribution as well as one that is skewed.

We will examine how the random process causes variations in:

- the raw data which makes up different samples
- the frequency counts of specific outcome proportions
- a measure of the centre (mean)
- a measure of spread (standard deviation).

The simulation is **spreadsheet** based.

STATISTICS
PACKAGE

What to do:

1   Click on the icon given alongside. The given distribution (in column A) consists of 487 data values. The five-number summary is given and the data has been tabulated. Record the five-number summary and the frequency table given.

2   At the bottom of the screen click on samples . Notice that the starting *sample size* is

10 and the *number of random samples* is 30. Change the *number of random samples* to 200.

3 Click on   find samples   and when this is complete click on   find sample means .

	A	B	C	D	E	F	G	H	I	J
	Sample Size: 10 ▼		Number of Random Samples:		30 ▼		find samples		find sample means	
1										
2										
3	Samples:	1	2	3	4	5	6	7	8	9
4		41	46	54	46	37	14	28	78	78
5		50	61	51	58	75	68	80	90	63
6		47	79	57	48	73	58	58	72	78
7		5	44	53	66	80	69	36	19	32
8		44	62	50	28	72	41	62	39	49
9		37	27	28	59	88	36	23	53	38
10		35	15	30	31	23	32	14	77	57
11		41	50	36	64	67	69	43	54	87
12		51	88	45	76	73	29	36	54	99
13		64	50	26	50	45	72	39	45	16
14	Means:	41.50	52.20	43.00	52.60	63.30	48.80	41.90	58.10	59.7

4 Click on   analyse . Then:

   a record the population mean (μ) and standard deviation (σ) for the population

   b record the *mean of sample means* and *standard deviation of the sample means*.

   c Examine the associated histogram.

	A	B	C
1	*Population:*	*Mean:*	49.65
2		*Standard Deviation:*	19.46
3			
4	*Samples:*	*Sample Size:*	10
5		*Mean of Means:*	51.14
6		*Standard Deviation of Means:*	5.85
7			
8	*Number of Samples:*	30	
9			
10		*Mean of Sample 1:*	41.50
11		*Mean of Sample 2:*	52.20
12		*Mean of Sample 3:*	43.00

5 Click on   samples   again and change the *sample size* to 20. Repeat steps **3** and **4** to gather information about the random samples of size 20.

6 Repeat with samples of size 30, 40 and 50. Comment on the variability.

7 What do you observe about the mean of sample means in each case and the population mean μ?

8 Is the *standard deviation of the sample means* equal to the standard deviation (σ) for the population?

9 If we let the *standard deviation of the sample means* be represented by $s_{\bar{x}}$, then from a summary of your results, copy and complete a table like the one given.

Determine the model which links $s_{\bar{x}}$ and the sample size, n.

n	$s_{\bar{x}}^2$
10	
20	
30	
40	
50	

10 Now click on the icon for data from a skewed distribution. Complete an analysis of this data by repeating the above procedure and recording all results.

STATISTICS PACKAGE

From the investigation, you should have discovered that:

- the samples consist of randomly selected members of the population
- there is great variability in samples and their means
- in larger samples there is less variability, i.e., smaller values of $s_{\overline{x}}$
- there is greater accuracy in reflecting the population means if we take larger samples
- the *mean of sample means* approximates the population mean, i.e., mean$_{\overline{x}} \approx \mu$
- the *standard deviation of the sample means*, $s_{\overline{x}} \approx \frac{\sigma}{\sqrt{n}}$, n is the size of each sample
- the distribution of sample means $\overline{x}$, for non-normally distributed populations is approximately normally distributed for large values of n. The larger the value of n the better the approximation.

THE CENTRAL LIMIT THEOREM

From the conclusions of the previous investigation we state the **Central Limit Theorem** (CLT). This theorem is based on the distribution of the sample mean and relates this distribution to the population mean.

The Central Limit Theorem

If we take samples from a non-normal population X with mean μ and variance σ^2, then providing the sample is large enough, the sample mean $\overline{X}$ is approximately normal and $\overline{X} \sim N\left(\mu, \frac{\sigma^2}{n}\right)$.   The larger the value of n, the better the approximation will be.

Note:
- Many texts provide a "rule of thumb" of $n \geqslant 30$ (for n large enough).
- If X is a random variable of a normal distribution to begin with, the size of n is not important,   i.e., $\overline{X} \sim N\left(\mu, \frac{\sigma^2}{n}\right)$ for all values of n.
- The syllabus states that "Distributions that do not satisfy the Central Limit Theorem" are excluded, making the rule of thumb above virtually redundant. It also states that the "Proof of the Central Limit Theorem" is not required.
- The distribution of the sample means has a reducing standard deviation as n increases, but the mean $\overline{x}$ is constant and equal to the population mean μ.

As sample size n increases:

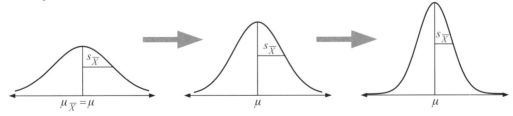

$s_{\overline{X}}$ decreases as $s_{\overline{X}} = \frac{\sigma}{\sqrt{n}}$ and   mean$_{\overline{X}} = \mu$ always.

Remember with the Central Limit Theorem we are looking at the distributions of the **sample means** $\overline{X}$, not at the distribution of individual scores.

Example 26

Consider rolling a die where the random variable X is the number of dots on a face.
a   Tabulate the probability distribution of x. Graph the distribution.
b   Find the mean and standard deviation of the distribution.
c   Many hundreds of random samples of size 36 are taken. Find:
    i   the mean of the sampling distribution of the sample mean ($\text{mean}_{\overline{x}}$)
    ii $s_{\overline{x}}$, the standard deviation of the sampling distribution of the sample mean.
d   Comment on the shape of the distribution of $\overline{x}$.

a   The probability distribution of X
    which is *uniform* is:

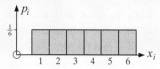

x_i	1	2	3	4	5	6
p_i	$\frac{1}{6}$	$\frac{1}{6}$	$\frac{1}{6}$	$\frac{1}{6}$	$\frac{1}{6}$	$\frac{1}{6}$

b $\mu = \sum p_i x_i = \frac{1}{6}(1) + \frac{1}{6}(2) + \frac{1}{6}(3) + \ldots\ldots + \frac{1}{6}(6) = 3.5$

$\sigma^2 = \sum x_i^2 p_i - \mu^2$

$\quad = 1(\frac{1}{6}) + 4(\frac{1}{6}) + 9(\frac{1}{6}) + 16(\frac{1}{6}) + 25(\frac{1}{6}) + 36(\frac{1}{6}) - (3.5)^2$

$\quad = 2.916\,666....$

$\therefore \quad \sigma \approx 1.708$

c   i $\text{mean}_{\overline{x}} = \mu = 3.5$ ii $s_{\overline{x}} = \dfrac{\sigma}{\sqrt{36}} \approx \dfrac{1.708}{6} \approx 0.285$ {CL theorem}

d   Since n is large, at 36, we can apply the Central Limit theorem.
    So, the distribution of $\overline{x}$ would very closely resemble the normal curve.

Why is the distribution of the sample mean $\overline{X}$ approximately normal for large n even if the distribution of the random variable X is not normal? (A formal proof for this is not required.)

Consider this:

If we take *independent* random samples of size n, the sample mean for any given sample of size n will be either "larger", or "smaller than or equal to" the true population mean.

We have a binomial distribution,   i.e., 2 outcomes: $\overline{x}$ is larger than μ,   i.e., $\overline{x} > \mu$
or $\overline{x}$ is smaller than or equal to μ,   i.e., $\overline{x} \leqslant \mu$.

Whether or not we finish with $\overline{x} > \mu$ or $\overline{x} \leqslant \mu$ obviously depends on the sample that has been selected. The weighted values of the scores selected in the sample compared to the value of μ will determine whether $\overline{x} > \mu$ or $\overline{x} \leqslant \mu$.   Irrespective, this is a *binomial distribution* as we are taking n independent samples, and we have already seen in section B that a binomial distribution approximates a normal distribution for large n.

THE SAMPLING ERROR

The **sampling error** is an estimate of the margin by which the sample mean might differ from the population mean.

$s_{\overline{X}}$ is used to represent the **sampling error** (or **standard error**) of the mean

and $s_{\overline{X}} = \dfrac{\sigma}{\sqrt{n}}$.   **Note:** $\text{mean}_{\overline{X}} = \mu$.

In summary, there are two factors which help us to decide if a sample provides useful and accurate information. These are:

- The **sample size**.

  If the sample size is too small, the statistics obtained from it may be unreliable. A sufficiently large sample should reflect the same mean as the population it comes from.

- The **sample error**.

  The sampling error indicates that for a large population, a large sample may be unnecessary. For example, the reliability of the statistics obtained from a sample of size 1000 can be almost as good as those obtained from a sample of size 4000. The additional data may provide only slightly more reliable statistics.

EXERCISE 8C.2

1   Random samples of size 36 are selected from a population with mean 64 and standard deviation 10. For the sampling distribution of the sample means, find:

   a   the mean   b   the standard deviation.

2   Random samples of size n are selected from a population where the standard deviation is 24.

   a   Write $s_{\overline{X}}$ in terms of n.
   b   Find $s_{\overline{X}}$ when   i $n = 4$ ii   16   iii   64.
   c   How large must a sample be for the sampling error to equal 4?
   d   Graph $s_{\overline{X}}$ against n.
   e   Discuss $s_{\overline{X}}$ as n increases in value. Explain the significance of this result.

3   The IQ measurements of a population have mean 100 and a standard deviation of 15. Many hundreds of random samples of size 36 are taken from the population and a relative frequency histogram of the sample means is formed.

   a   What would we expect the mean of the samples to be?
   b   What would we expect the standard deviation of the samples to be?
   c   What would we expect the shape of the histogram to look like?

4   If a coin is tossed, the random variable X could be 'the number of heads which appear'.

   So, $X = 0$ or 1 and the probability function for x is:

x_i	0	1
p_i	$\frac{1}{2}$	$\frac{1}{2}$

   a   Find the μ and σ for the X-distribution.
   b   Now consider the sampling distribution of $\overline{X}$.
       List the 16 possible samples of size $n = 4$ and construct a probability function table.
   c   For the sampling distribution of means in **b**, find   i $\text{mean}_{\overline{X}}$ ii $s_{\overline{X}}$

   d   Check that $\text{mean}_{\overline{X}} = \mu$ (from **a**)   and $s_{\overline{X}} = \dfrac{\sigma}{\sqrt{n}}$ (from **a**).

Example 27

The age of business men in Sweden is distributed with mean 43 and standard deviation 8. If 16 business men are randomly selected from the population, what is the probability that the sample mean of these measurements is:

a   less than 40   **b**   greater than 45   **c**   between 37 and 47?

By the CLT, $X \sim N\left(43, \left(\frac{8}{\sqrt{16}}\right)^2\right)$ i.e., $X \sim N(43, 2^2)$

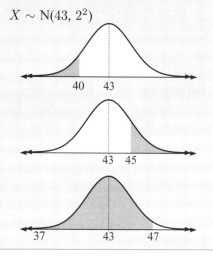

a $P(\overline{X} < 40)$
= normalcdf($-$E99, 40, 43, 2)
≈ 0.0668

b $P(\overline{X} > 45)$
= normalcdf(45, E99, 43, 2)
≈ 0.159

c $P(37 < \overline{X} < 47)$
= normalcdf(37, 47, 43, 2)
≈ 0.976

Example 28

The contents of soft drink cans is distributed with mean 378 mL and standard deviation 7.2 mL. Find the likelihood that:

a   an individual can contains less than 375 mL
b   a box of 36 cans has average contents less than 375 mL.

In this example, we must see the difference between the scores for *individual cans* and scores for the *means of samples of size 36*. X represents an individual score, $\overline{X}$ represents sample mean scores. $X \sim N(378, 7.2^2)$ and $\overline{X} \sim N(378, \frac{7.2^2}{36})$

a $P(X < 375)$
= normalcdf($-$E99, 375, 378, 7.2)
≈ 0.338

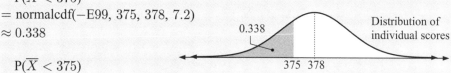

Distribution of individual scores

b $P(\overline{X} < 375)$
= normalcdf($-$E99, 375, 378, $\frac{7.2}{\sqrt{36}}$)
$\approx 0.006\,21$

So, there is a 0.6% chance (approximately) of getting a box of 36 with average contents less than 375 mL compared with a 33.9% chance of an individual can having contents less than 375 mL.

Distribution of sample means

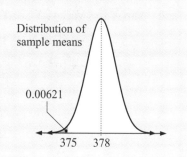

In the following example we revisit **Example 2**, but this time employ the Central Limit Theorem.

Example 29

The weights of male employees in a bank are normally distributed with a mean $\mu = 71.5$ kg and standard deviation $\sigma = 7.3$ kg. The bank has an elevator with a maximum recommended load of 444 kg for safety reasons. Six male employees enter the elevator. Calculate the probability p that their combined weight exceeds the maximum recommended load.

$X \sim N(71.5, 7.3^2)$.

By the CLT, $\overline{X} \sim N\left(71.5, \frac{7.3^2}{6}\right)$ {as samples of size 6, $n = 6$}

$$p = P\left(\overline{X} > \frac{444}{6}\right)$$

$$= \text{normalcdf}\left(\frac{444}{6}, \text{E99}, 71.5, \frac{7.3}{\sqrt{6}}\right)$$

$$\doteqdot 0.201, \quad \text{which is the same answer as in } \textbf{Example 2.}$$

In the following example, we justify why the mean and standard deviation of $\overline{X}$ are μ and $\frac{\sigma}{\sqrt{n}}$ respectively.

Example 30

Consider all random samples of size n taken from a population described by the random variable X with mean μ and variance σ^2. Now consider the distribution of the means of these samples, described by $\overline{X}$. Show that $E(\overline{X}) = \mu$ and $\text{Var}(\overline{X}) = \frac{\sigma^2}{n}$.

Suppose X has independent scores $X_1, X_2, X_3, X_4, \dots, X_n$

$$\therefore \ E(\overline{X}) = E\left(\frac{1}{n}(X_1 + X_2 + X_3 + X_4 + \dots + X_n)\right)$$

$$= \frac{1}{n}(E(X_1) + E(X_2) + E(X_3) + \dots + E(X_n))$$

$$= \frac{1}{n}(\mu + \mu + \mu + \dots + \mu) \qquad \{n \text{ of them}\}$$

$$= \frac{1}{n} \times n\mu$$

$$= \mu$$

and $\text{Var}(\overline{X}) = \text{Var}\left(\frac{1}{n}(X_1 + X_2 + X_3 + \dots + X_n)\right)$

$$= \frac{1}{n^2}(\text{Var}(X_1) + \text{Var}(X_2) + \text{Var}(X_3) + \dots + \text{Var}(X_n))$$

$$= \frac{1}{n^2}(\sigma^2 + \sigma^2 + \sigma^2 + \dots + \sigma^2) \qquad \{n \text{ of them}\}$$

$$= \frac{1}{n^2} \times n\sigma$$

$$= \frac{\sigma^2}{n}$$

This justifies why the mean and standard error of $\overline{X}$ are μ and $\frac{\sigma}{\sqrt{n}}$ respectively.

Example 31

A population is known to have a standard deviation of 8 but has an unknown mean. In order to estimate the mean μ, a random sample of 60 is taken. Find the probability that the estimate is in error by less than 2.

As $n = 60$, the CLT applies.

As the error is either $\overline{X} - \mu$ or $\mu - \overline{X}$, we need to find $P(|\overline{X} - \mu| < 2)$

Now $P(|\overline{X} - \mu| < 2)$

$= P(-2 < \overline{X} - \mu < 2)$

$= P\left(\dfrac{-2}{\frac{\sigma}{\sqrt{n}}} < \dfrac{\overline{X} - \mu}{\frac{\sigma}{\sqrt{n}}} < \dfrac{2}{\frac{\sigma}{\sqrt{n}}} \right)$ {setting up $Z = \dfrac{\overline{X} - \mu}{\frac{\sigma}{\sqrt{n}}}$}

$= P\left(\dfrac{-2}{\frac{8}{\sqrt{60}}} < Z < \dfrac{2}{\frac{8}{\sqrt{60}}} \right)$

$= P\left(-\dfrac{\sqrt{60}}{4} < Z < \dfrac{\sqrt{60}}{4} \right)$

$= \text{normalcdf}\left(-\dfrac{\sqrt{60}}{4}, \dfrac{\sqrt{60}}{4} \right)$

≈ 0.947

INVESTIGATION 2   CHOCBLOCKS

Chocblock produce mini chocolate bars which vary a little in weight. The machine used to make them produces bars whose weight is normally distributed with mean 18.2 grams and standard deviation 3.3 grams. 25 bars are then placed in a packet for sale. Hundreds of thousands of packets are produced each year.

What to do:

1 What are the mean$_{\overline{x}}$ and $s_{\overline{x}}$ values for this situation?

2 Printed on each packet is the nett weight of contents. This is 425 grams. What is the manufacturer claiming about the mean weight of each bar?

3 What percentage of their packets will be rejected because they fail to meet the 425 gram claim?

4 An additional bar is added to each packet with the nett weight claim retained at 425 grams.

    a What is the minimum acceptable claim now?

    b What are the mean$_{\overline{x}}$ and $s_{\overline{x}}$ now?

    c What percentage of these packets would we expect to reject?

EXERCISE 8C.2 (Continued)

5 The values of homes in a wealthy suburb of a small city are skewed high with a mean of \$320 000 and a standard deviation of \$80 000. A sample of 25 homes was taken and the mean of the sample was found to be \$343 000.

    a Find the probability that a random sample of 25 homes in this suburb has a mean of at least \$343 000, using the Central Limit Theorem.

    b Comment on the reliability of your answer to part **a**.

6 An elevator has a maximum recommended load of 650 kg. What is the maximum recommended number of adult males that might be allowed to use the elevator at any one time, if the weights of adult males are distributed normally with a mean of 73.5 kg and standard deviation of 8.24 kg, and if you want to be at least 99.5% certain that the total weight does not exceed the maximum recommended load. **Hint:** Start with $n = 9$.

7 Suppose the duration of human pregnancies can be modelled by a normal distribution with mean 267 days and a standard deviation of 15 days.

    a What percentage of pregnancies should be overdue between 1 and 2 weeks? (Overdue means any time lasting more than 267 days.)

    b At least how many days should the longest 20% of all pregnancies last (i.e., what is the 80th percentile for pregancy times)?

    c A certain obstretician is providing prenatal care for 64 pregnant women. Describe the sampling distribution for the sample mean of all random samples of size 64 $(\overline{X})$. Specify the model, mean and standard deviation for the distribution of the random variable $\overline{X}$.

    d What is the probability that the mean duration of the obstretician's patients' pregnancies will be premature by at least one week?

    e If the duration of these pregnancies no longer follows a normal model, but is skewed to the left, does that change the answers to parts **a** to **d** above?

8 Ayrshire cows average 49 units of milk per day with a standard deviation of 5.87 units, whereas Jersey cows average 44.8 units of milk each day with a standard deviation of 5.12 units. If milk production for each of these breeds can be modelled by a normal distribution:

    a What is the probability that a randomly selected Ayrshire will average more than 50 units of milk daily?

    b What is the probability that a randomly selected Jersey will give more milk than a randomly selected Ayrshire cow?

    c A dairy farmer has 25 Jerseys. What is the probability that the average production for this small herd exceeds 46 units per day?

    d A neighbouring farmer has 15 Ayshires. What is the probability that her herd averages at least 4 units more than the average for the Jersey herd?

THE PROPORTION OF SUCCESSES IN A LARGE SAMPLE

We are frequently presented by the media with estimates of population proportions, often in the form of percentages.

For example: • if an election was held tomorrow, 52% of the population would vote Labor
• 17% of the African population tested positive to HIV
• 73% of company executives say they will not employ smokers.

To help with estimating a **population proportion** p, we need to consider taking a random sample and looking at the distribution of the random variable $\hat{p}$ that represents the distribution of all the possible sample proportions of samples of size n.

Consider the election example.

To estimate the proportion of voters who intend to vote for the "Do Good" party, a random sample of 3500 voters was taken and 1820 indicated they would vote "Do Good".

The **sample proportion** of "Do Good" voters is denoted $\hat{p} = \frac{1820}{3500} = 0.52$.

The question arises:

"How is $\hat{p}$ distributed and what is the mean $\mu_{\hat{p}}$ and standard deviation $s_{\hat{p}}$ of the $\hat{p}$ distribution?"

To answer part of this question, we will examine a sample proportion in greater detail.

Firstly, we see that $\hat{p} = \dfrac{X}{n}$ where $\begin{cases} \hat{p} = \text{the sample proportion} \\ X = \text{number of successes in the sample} \\ n = \text{sample size.} \end{cases}$

The random variable X which stands for the number of successes in the sample (the number who vote "Do Good" in our example) has a binomial distribution,

i.e., $X \sim B(n,\, p)$.   (We assume samples are made *with replacement*.)

Now $\hat{p} \sim N\left(p,\, \dfrac{pq}{n}\right)$ where $q = 1 - p$ and n is large.

Proof: $E(\hat{p}) = E\left(\frac{1}{n}X\right) = \frac{1}{n}E(X) = \frac{1}{n} \times np = p$ {as X is $B(n,\, p)$}

and $\text{Var}(\hat{p}) = \text{Var}\left(\frac{1}{n}X\right) = \left(\frac{1}{n}\right)^2 \text{Var}(X) = \frac{1}{n^2} \times npq = \dfrac{pq}{n}$

So, by the Central Limit Theorem, as n is large, $\hat{p} \sim N\left(p,\, \dfrac{pq}{n}\right)$.

Example 32

Ms Claire Buford gained 43% of the votes in the local Council elections.
a   Find the probability that a poll of 150 randomly selected voters would show over 50% in favour of Ms Buford.
b   Find the corresponding probability if the sample consisted of 750 randomly selected voters.
c   A sample of 100 voters was taken and 62% of these voted for Ms Burford. Find the probability of this occurring and comment on the result.

a The population proportion $p = 0.43$,   so $q = 0.57$.

Also, we are given that $n = 150$.

Now $\hat{p} \sim N\left(0.43, \frac{0.43 \times 0.57}{150}\right)$

$\therefore$ $P(\hat{p} > 0.5) = \text{normalcdf}\left(0.5, 1, 0.43, \sqrt{\frac{0.43 \times 0.57}{150}}\right)$
≈ 0.0417 (the standard error ≈ 0.0404)

Note: A more accurate answer can be obtained using a continuity correction but the teachers notes from the syllabus indicate that this is not required in examinations. However the continuity correction can make a large difference to the answer.

More accurately, $P(\hat{p} > 0.5)$ $= P\left(\hat{p} \geqslant 0.5 + \frac{1}{2}\left(\frac{1}{150}\right)\right)$
$\approx P(\hat{p} \geqslant 0.503\,33)$
$\approx \text{normalcdf}\left(0.503\,33, 1, 0.43, \sqrt{\frac{0.43 \times 0.57}{150}}\right)$
≈ 0.0348

b $\hat{p} \sim N\left(0.43, \frac{0.43 \times 0.57}{750}\right)$

$\therefore$ $P(\hat{p} > 0.5) = \text{normalcdf}\left(0.5, 1, 0.43, \sqrt{\frac{0.43 \times 0.57}{750}}\right)$
$\approx 0.000\,054\,0$

Note: Using the continuity correction $P(\hat{p} > 0.5) = 0.000\,0463$

c $\hat{p} \sim N\left(0.43, \frac{0.43 \times 0.57}{100}\right)$

$P(\hat{p} \geqslant 0.62) = \text{normalcdf}\left(0.62, 1, 0.43, \sqrt{\frac{0.43 \times 0.57}{100}}\right)$
$\approx 0.000\,062\,1$

This is so unlikely that we would doubt the truth of Ms Burford only getting 43% of the vote.

Using the continuity correction, $P(\hat{p} \geqslant 0.62) = P\left(\hat{p} \geqslant 0.62 - \frac{1}{200}\right)$
$\approx 0.000\,0932$

EXERCISE 8C.3

1 A random sample of size $n = 5$ is selected from a normal population which has a mean μ of 40 and standard deviation σ of 4. Find the following probabilities:
   a $P(\overline{X} < 42)$ **b** $P(\overline{X} > 39)$ **c** $P(38 < \overline{X} < 43)$

2 During a one week period in Sydney the average price of an orange was 42.8 cents with standard deviation 8.7 cents. Find the probability that the average price per orange from a case of 60 oranges is less than 45 cents.

3 The average energy content of a fruit bar is 1067 kJ with standard deviation 61.7 kJ. Find the probability that the average energy content of a sample of 30 fruit bars is more than 1050 kJ/bar.

4   The average sodium content of a box of cheese rings is 1183 mg with standard deviation 88.6 mg. Find the probability that the average sodium content per box for a sample of 50 boxes lies between 1150 mg and 1200 mg.

5   Genuine customers at a clothing store are in the shop for an average time of 18 minutes with standard deviation 5.3 minutes. What is the probability that in a sample of 37 customers the average stay in the shop is between 17 and 20 minutes?

6   The average contents of a can of beer is 382 mL, even though it says 375 mL on a can. The statistician at the brewery says that the standard deviation is steady at 16.2 mL. Assuming the contents of a can are normally distributed, find the probability that:

   a   an individual can contains less than 375 mL

   b   a slab of two dozen cans has an average less than 375 mL per can.

7   Returning to the fruit bar problem of question **3**, find the probability that:

   a   an individual fruit bar contains at least 1060 kJ of energy, if energy content is normally distributed

   b   a carton of 50 fruit bars has average energy content in excess of 1060 kJ.

8   A concerned union person wishes to estimate the hourly wage of shop assistants in Adelaide. He decides to randomly survey 300 shop assistants to calculate the sample mean. Assuming that the standard deviation is $1.27, find the probability that the estimate of the population mean is in error by 10 cents or more.

9   An egg manufacturer claims that eggs delivered to a supermarket are known to contain no more than 4% that are broken. On a given busy day, 1000 eggs are delivered to this supermarket and 7% are broken. What is the probability that this could happen? Briefly comment on the manufacturer's claim.

10   Two sevenths of households in a country town are known to own computers. Find the probability that of a random sample of 100 households, no more than 29 households own a computer.

11   Eighty five percent of the plum trees grown in a particular area produce more than 700 plums.

   a   State the sampling distribution for the proportion of plum trees that produce more than 700 plums in this area where the sample is of size n.

   b   State the conditions under which the sampling distribution can be approximated by the normal distribution.

   c   In a random sample of 200 plum trees selected, find the probability that:
      i   less than 75%   **ii**   between 75% and 87%   produce more than 700 plums.

   d   In a random sample of 500 plum trees, 350 were found to produce more than 700 plums.
      i   What is the likelihood of 350 or fewer trees producing more than 700 plums?
      ii   Comment, giving two reasons why this sample is possible.

12   A regular pentagon has sectors numbered 1, 1, 2, 3, 4. Find the probability that, when the pentagon is spun 400 times, the result of a 1 occurs:

   a   more than 150 times   **b**   at least 150 times   **c**   less than 175 times.

13 A tyre company in Moscow claims that at least 90% of the tyres they sell will last at least 30 000 km. To test this, a consumer protection service sampled 250 tyres and found that 200 of the tyres did not last for at least 30 000 km.

    a State the distribution of the sample proportions with any assumptions made.

    b Find the proportion of samples of 250 tyres that would have no more than 200 tyres lasting at least 30 000 km.

    c Comment on this result.

D | CONFIDENCE INTERVALS FOR MEANS AND PROPORTIONS

Trying to find a population parameter such as the mean weekly salary of Austrian adults (over 18) would be an extremely difficult task but the Central Limit Theorem allows us to use our sample means to estimate quantities like this.

By the CLT we can assume that approximately 95% of the sample means would lie within 2 standard errors of the population mean.

$$E(\overline{X}) = \mu, \qquad \text{Var } (\overline{X}) = \frac{\sigma}{\sqrt{n}}$$

The diagram shows the distribution of sample means, $\overline{X}$.

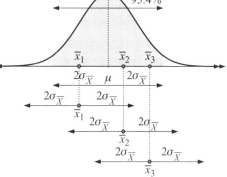

A statement like:

"We are 95% confident that the mean weekly salary is between 637 euros and 691 euros."

clearly indicates that the mean most likely lies in an interval between 637 euros and 691 euros. The level of confidence is 95%, i.e., the probability that the interval contains the parameter μ is 0.95 .

> A **confidence interval estimate of a parameter** (in this case, the population mean, μ) is an interval of values between two limits together with a percentage indicating our confidence that the parameter lies in the interval.

The Central Limit Theorem is used as a basis for finding all confidence intervals.

By the Central Limit Theorem, the sample mean, $\overline{X}$, is normally distributed with mean μ and standard deviation $\frac{\sigma}{\sqrt{n}}$.

The corresponding standard normal random variable is $\quad Z = \dfrac{\overline{X} - \mu}{\frac{\sigma}{\sqrt{n}}} \quad$ and $\quad Z \sim N(0, 1)$.

For a **95% confidence level** we need to find a for which $\ P(-a < Z < a) = 0.95 \ .... (*)$

Because of the symmetry of the graph of the normal distribution, the statement reduces to

$P(Z < -a) = 0.025 \quad \text{or} \quad P(Z < a) = 0.975$

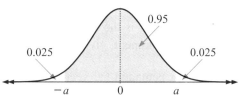

From a graphics calculator (or a table of standard normal probabilities) we find that $\quad a \approx 1.96$

Therefore, in $*$ $P(-1.96 < Z < 1.96) = 0.95$ or $P\left(-1.96 < \dfrac{\overline{x} - \mu}{\frac{\sigma}{\sqrt{n}}} < 1.96\right) = 0.95$

which means $\dfrac{\overline{x} - \mu}{\frac{\sigma}{\sqrt{n}}} < 1.96$ and $\dfrac{\overline{x} - \mu}{\frac{\sigma}{\sqrt{n}}} > -1.96$

$\therefore$ $\overline{x} - \mu < 1.96\dfrac{\sigma}{\sqrt{n}}$ and $\overline{x} - \mu > -1.96\dfrac{\sigma}{\sqrt{n}}$

$\therefore$ $\mu > \overline{x} - 1.96\dfrac{\sigma}{\sqrt{n}}$ and $\mu < \overline{x} + 1.96\dfrac{\sigma}{\sqrt{n}}$

So, we see that $\overline{x} - 1.96\dfrac{\sigma}{\sqrt{n}} < \mu < \overline{x} + 1.96\dfrac{\sigma}{\sqrt{n}}$.

This interval gives a 95% confidence interval for the population mean μ for any given sample of size n and population standard deviation σ.

So,   the **95% confidence interval for** μ is from $\boldsymbol{\overline{x} - 1.96\dfrac{\sigma}{\sqrt{n}}}$ to $\boldsymbol{\overline{x} + 1.96\dfrac{\sigma}{\sqrt{n}}}$.

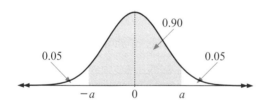

Note: The exact centre of the confidence interval is the value of $\overline{x}$ for the sample taken.

OTHER CONFIDENCE INTERVALS FOR μ

The 90% confidence interval for μ

This time $P(Z < -a) = 0.05$ or
$$P(Z < a) = 0.95$$
and from tables or calculator $a \doteqdot 1.645$
and as a is the coefficient of $\frac{\sigma}{\sqrt{n}}$, in the following confidence interval,

the **90% confidence interval for** μ is $\boldsymbol{\overline{x} - 1.645\dfrac{\sigma}{\sqrt{n}} < \mu < \overline{x} + 1.645\dfrac{\sigma}{\sqrt{n}}}$

In summary,

Confidence level	a	Confidence interval
90%	1.645	$\overline{x} - 1.645\frac{\sigma}{\sqrt{n}} < \mu < \overline{x} + 1.645\frac{\sigma}{\sqrt{n}}$
95%	1.960	$\overline{x} - 1.960\frac{\sigma}{\sqrt{n}} < \mu < \overline{x} + 1.960\frac{\sigma}{\sqrt{n}}$
98%	2.326	$\overline{x} - 2.326\frac{\sigma}{\sqrt{n}} < \mu < \overline{x} + 2.326\frac{\sigma}{\sqrt{n}}$
99%	2.576	$\overline{x} - 2.576\frac{\sigma}{\sqrt{n}} < \mu < \overline{x} + 2.576\frac{\sigma}{\sqrt{n}}$

The values of a are determined by a graphics calculator or tables.

The **confidence level** is the amount of confidence we place in μ being within the calculated confidence interval.

The **width** of a confidence interval is $2 \times a \times \dfrac{\sigma}{\sqrt{n}}$ where a is the level of confidence in the table above.

The sample mean is the **centre** of the confidence interval.

INVESTIGATION 3   CONFIDENCE LEVELS AND INTERVALS

To obtain a greater understanding of confidence intervals and levels   **DEMO**
click on the icon to visit a random sampler demonstration which cal-
culates confidence intervals at various levels of your choice (90%,
95%, 98% or 99%) and counts the intervals which include the population mean.

Note: Consider samples of different size but all with mean 10 and standard deviation 2.

The 95% confidence interval is $10 - \dfrac{1.960 \times 2}{\sqrt{n}} < \mu < 10 + \dfrac{1.960 \times 2}{\sqrt{n}}$.

For various values of n we have:

n	Confidence interval
20	$9.123 < \mu < 10.877$
50	$9.446 < \mu < 10.554$
100	$9.608 < \mu < 10.392$
200	$9.723 < \mu < 10.277$

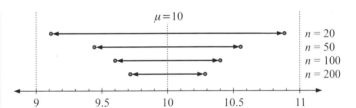

We see that increasing the sample size produces confidence intervals of shorter width.

Example 33

A drug company produces tablets with mass that is normally distributed with a
standard deviation of 0.038 mg. A random sample of ten tablets was found to have
an average (mean) mass of 4.87 mg. Calculate a 95% CI for the mean mass of
these tablets based on this sample.

Even though n is relatively small, the fact that the mass is normally distributed
means that $\overline{X} \sim N\left(4.87, \dfrac{0.038}{\sqrt{10}}\right)$

$\therefore$ a 95% CI for mean mass, μ, is
$$4.87 - 1.96 \times \frac{0.038}{\sqrt{10}} < \mu < 4.87 + 1.96 \times \frac{0.038}{\sqrt{10}}$$

i.e., $4.846 < \mu < 4.894$

$\therefore$ we are 95% confident that the population mean lies in the interval
$4.85 < \mu < 4.89$.

Example 34

A sample of 60 yabbies was taken from a dam. The
sample mean weight of the yabbies was 84.6 grams
and the standard deviation of the population was
16.8 grams.

Find for the yabbie population:

a the 95% confidence interval for the population
mean

b the 99% confidence interval for the population
mean.

We are given the sample mean $\overline{X} = 84.6$ and standard deviation $\sigma = 16.8$.

a The 95% confidence interval is: $\overline{x} - 1.960\frac{\sigma}{\sqrt{n}} < \mu < \overline{x} + 1.960\frac{\sigma}{\sqrt{n}}$

i.e., $84.6 - \frac{1.960 \times 16.8}{\sqrt{60}} < \mu < 84.6 + \frac{1.960 \times 16.8}{\sqrt{60}}$

$\therefore \quad 80.349 < \mu < 88.851$

So, we are 95% confident that the population mean weight of the yabbies lies
between 80.3 grams and 88.9 grams.

b The 99% confidence interval is: $\overline{x} - 2.576\frac{\sigma}{\sqrt{n}} < \mu < \overline{x} + 2.576\frac{\sigma}{\sqrt{n}}$

i.e., $84.6 - \frac{2.576 \times 16.8}{\sqrt{60}} < \mu < 84.6 + \frac{2.576 \times 16.8}{\sqrt{60}}$

$\therefore \quad 79.01 < \mu < 90.19$

So, we are 99% confident that the population mean weight of the yabbies lies
between 79.0 grams and 90.2 grams.

Confidence intervals can be obtained directly from your graphics calculator.

CONFIDENCE INTERVALS FOR μ WHEN σ^2 IS UNKNOWN

Often we do not know the population variance σ^2. So, we use an unbiased estimate of σ^2 to
estimate it. In fact we use s_{n-1}^2 to estimate σ^2.

However in doing this, the assumption that the random variable $\overline{X}$ is distributed normally is
now not quite correct, especially for relatively small samples.

We know that with **known** σ^2, $Z = \dfrac{\overline{X} - \mu}{\frac{\sigma}{\sqrt{n}}} \sim N(0, 1)$

So, what is the distribution of $\dfrac{\overline{X} - \mu}{\frac{s_{n-1}}{\sqrt{n}}}$ if σ^2 **is unknown**?

The answer is, the random variable $T = \dfrac{\overline{X} - \mu}{\frac{s_{n-1}}{\sqrt{n}}}$ is a t-**distribution**, sometimes called

"students" t-**distribution** (named after William Gosset who wrote under a pseudonym of
"student").

t- DISTRIBUTIONS

All t-distributions are symmetrical about the origin. They are just like standardised normal bell-shaped curves, but fatter. Each curve has a single parameter ν (pronounced "new") which is a positive integer. ν is known as *the number of degrees of freedom* of the distribution.

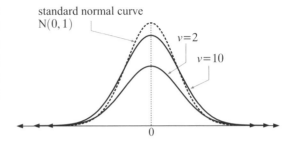

standard normal curve
N(0, 1)
$v=2$
$v=10$

If random variable T has 7 degrees of freedom we write $\quad T \sim \mathrm{t}(7)$.

In general, $\quad \boldsymbol{\nu = n - 1},\quad$ so for a sample of size 8, $\quad \nu = 7$.

The graphs illustrated are those of $\quad \mathrm{t}(2),\quad \mathrm{t}(10)\quad$ and $\quad Z\quad$ i.e., $\quad$N(0, 1).

In general, $\quad \nu = n - 1,\quad$ so for a sample of size 8, $\quad \nu = 7$.

The graphs illustrated are those of $\quad \mathrm{t}(2),\quad \mathrm{t}(10)\quad$ and $\quad Z\quad$ i.e., $\quad$N(0, 1).

In general, as ν increases, the curves begin to look more and more like the standardised normal Z-curve.

For samples of size n where σ is unknown, it can be shown that $\quad T = \dfrac{\overline{X} - \mu}{\frac{s_{n-1}}{\sqrt{n}}}\quad$ follows a **t-distribution** with $n - 1$ degrees of freedom, i.e., $T \sim \mathrm{t}(n - 1)$.

Example 35

The fat content (in grams) of 30 randomly selected pies at the local bakery was determined and recorded as:

15.1 14.8 13.7 15.6 15.1 16.1 16.6 17.4 16.1 13.9 17.5 15.7 16.2 16.6 15.1
12.9 17.4 16.5 13.2 14.0 17.2 17.3 16.1 16.5 16.7 16.8 17.2 17.6 17.3 14.7

Determine a 98% confidence interval for the average fat content of all pies made.

Entering the data into a calculator using the list and statistical functions, we obtain $\quad \overline{x} \approx 15.9\quad$ and $\quad s_{n-1} \approx 1.365$

σ is unknown and $\quad T = \dfrac{\overline{X} - \mu}{\frac{s_{n-1}}{\sqrt{n}}}\quad$ is $\quad \mathrm{t}(29)$

Using a graphics calculator, a 98% CI for μ is $\quad 15.28 < \mu < 16.51$.

Note: As $n = 30$, i.e., n is sufficiently large, the normal CI is acceptable

$$\text{i.e.,}\quad 15.9 - 2.326\tfrac{\sigma}{\sqrt{n}} < \mu < 15.9 + 2.326\tfrac{\sigma}{\sqrt{n}}$$

$$\text{i.e.,}\ 15.9 - 2.326 \times \tfrac{1.365}{\sqrt{30}} < \mu < 15.9 + 2.326 \times \tfrac{1.365}{\sqrt{30}}$$

$$\text{i.e.,}\quad 15.32 < \mu < 16.48$$

So, using either distribution, we are 98% confident that μ lies between 15.3 and 16.5 .

Example 36

A random sample of eight independent observations of a normal random variable gave $\sum x = 72.8$ and $\sum x^2 = 837.49$. Calculate:

a an unbiased estimate of the population mean

b an unbiased estimate of the population standard deviation

c a 90% confidence interval for the population mean.

a $\overline{x} = \dfrac{\sum x}{n} = \dfrac{72.8}{8} = 9.1$ and so 9.1 is an unbiased estimate of μ.

b $s_n^2 = \dfrac{\sum x^2}{n} - \overline{x}^2 = \dfrac{837.49}{8} - 9.1^2 \approx 21.876$

The unbiased estimate of σ^2 is $s_{n-1}^2 = \dfrac{n}{n-1} s_n^2 = \dfrac{8}{7} \times 21.876 \approx 25.00$

$\therefore$ the unbiased estimate of $\sigma \approx 5.00$

c Using a graphics calculator, we input $\overline{x} = 9.1$ and $s_{n-1} = 5.00$ to get the 90% confidence interval for μ.

This is $5.75 < \mu < 12.45$ {using the t-distribution}

DETERMINING HOW LARGE A SAMPLE SHOULD BE

When designing an experiment in which we wish to estimate the population mean, the size of the sample is an important consideration.

Finding the sample size is a problem that can be solved using the confidence interval.

Let us revisit **Example 35** on the fat content of pies.

The question arises: 'How large should a sample be if we wish to be 98% confident that the sample mean will differ from the population mean by less than 0.3 grams if we know the population standard deviation $\sigma = 1.365$, i.e., $-0.3 < \mu - \overline{x} < 0.3$?'

Now the 98% confidence interval for μ is:

$$\overline{x} - 2.326\tfrac{\sigma}{\sqrt{n}} < \quad \mu \quad < \overline{x} + 2.326\tfrac{\sigma}{\sqrt{n}}$$

i.e., $-2.326\tfrac{\sigma}{\sqrt{n}} < \mu - \overline{x} < 2.326\tfrac{\sigma}{\sqrt{n}}$

So, we need to find n when $2.326\tfrac{\sigma}{\sqrt{n}} = 0.3$

i.e., $\sqrt{n} = \dfrac{2.326\sigma}{0.3} = \dfrac{2.326 \times 1.365}{0.3} \approx 10.583$

$\therefore$ $n \approx 112$

So, a sample of 112 should be taken.

Example 37

Revisit the yabbies from the dam problem of **Example 34**. We now wish to find the sample size needed to be 95% confident that the sample mean differs from the population mean by less than 5 grams. What sample size should be taken?

From the previous sample of 60, $\sigma = 16.8$ was used.
The 95% confidence interval for μ is:

$$\bar{x} - 1.960\frac{\sigma}{\sqrt{n}} < \quad \mu \quad < \bar{x} + 1.960\frac{\sigma}{\sqrt{n}}$$

i.e., $-1.96\frac{\sigma}{\sqrt{n}} < \mu - \bar{x} < 1.96\frac{\sigma}{\sqrt{n}}$

Note: To ensure that no mistakes are made it is good practice to use the final value of n and see what confidence interval this gives for the sample mean.

Now, we need to find n such that $1.96\dfrac{\sigma}{\sqrt{n}} = 5$

i.e., $\dfrac{1.96 \times 16.8}{\sqrt{n}} = 5$

$\therefore \quad n = \left(\dfrac{1.96 \times 16.8}{5}\right)^2 \approx 43.37$

So, a sample of 44 should be used.

CONFIDENCE INTERVALS FOR PROPORTIONS

Recall that the sample proportions of successes $\hat{p}$ is distributed normally,

i.e.,   for large n, $\hat{p} \sim N(p, \dfrac{pq}{n})$.

The distribution of $\hat{p}$ is called the **sampling distribution of proportions**.

As proportions from samples are distributed normally for large n, we can find confidence intervals for proportions in exactly the same way we have done for the population mean.

The value of $\hat{p}$ is an **unbiased estimate** of p, the true population proportion, and $\hat{q} = 1 - \hat{p}$ is an **unbiased estimate** of q.

Hence, if we are attempting to find a 95% CI for the unknown proportion of a population, we take a sufficiently large sample (the rule suggested in the teaching notes is $np \geqslant 10$, $n(1 - p) \geqslant 10$ or $nq \geqslant 10$).

Using previous arguments:

> The **large sample 95% confidence interval for p** is
>
> $$\hat{p} - 1.96\sqrt{\frac{\hat{p}\,\hat{q}}{n}} < p < \hat{p} + 1.96\sqrt{\frac{\hat{p}\,\hat{q}}{n}} \quad \text{where } \hat{q} = 1 - \hat{p}.$$
>
> For a 90% confidence interval,   we replace 1.96 by 1.645.
> For a 98% confidence interval,   we replace 1.96 by 2.326.
> For a 99% confidence interval,   we replace 1.96 by 2.576.

Example 38

A random sample of 200 residents from Munich showed that 53 supported the Bayern Munich football team.

a   Find the sample proportion of Bayern Munich supporters.

b   Find a 95% CI for the proportion of residents of Munich who support Bayern Munich.

c   Interpret your answer to **b**.

---

a   The sample proportion of Bayern Munich supporters is $\hat{p} = \frac{53}{200} = 0.265$.

Thus we estimate that 26.5% of the residents of Munich support Bayern Munich.

Note: This estimate is called a **point estimate** as distinct from an **interval estimate** (confidence interval).

b   The 95% CI for p is $\hat{p} - 1.96\sqrt{\dfrac{\hat{p}\,\hat{q}}{n}} < p < \hat{p} + 1.96\sqrt{\dfrac{\hat{p}\,\hat{q}}{n}}$

i.e., $0.265 - 1.96\sqrt{\dfrac{0.265 \times 0.735}{200}} < p < 0.265 + 1.96\sqrt{\dfrac{0.265 \times 0.735}{200}}$

$\therefore\quad 0.203\,83 < p < 0.326\,16$

c   So, we expect p to lie between 0.204 and 0.326 with 95% confidence, **or** we are 95% confident that the actual proportion of Bayern Munich supporters throughout Munich lies between 20.4% and 32.6%.

Example 39

Random samples of households are used to estimate the proportion of them who own at least one dog. Jason sampled 300 households and found that 123 had at least one dog. Kelly sampled 600 households and found that 252 had at least one dog.

a   Find a 95% confidence interval for each sample.

b   Illustrate the limits on a number line.   c   Comment on the limits.

---

a   **Jason's sampling:** $\hat{p} = \frac{123}{300} = 0.41$

and so his 95% confidence interval for the population proportion p is

$$\hat{p} - 1.96\sqrt{\frac{\hat{p}\,\hat{q}}{n}} < p < \hat{p} + 1.96\sqrt{\frac{\hat{p}\,\hat{q}}{n}}$$

i.e., $0.41 - 1.96\sqrt{\dfrac{0.41 \times 0.59}{300}} < p < 0.41 + 1.96\sqrt{\dfrac{0.41 \times 0.59}{300}}$

$\therefore\quad 0.3543 < p < 0.4657$

Kelly's sampling: $\hat{p} = \frac{252}{600} = 0.42$

and so her 95% confidence interval for the population proportion p is

i.e., $0.42 - 1.96\sqrt{\dfrac{0.42 \times 0.58}{600}} < p < 0.42 + 1.96\sqrt{\dfrac{0.42 \times 0.58}{600}}$

$\therefore\quad 0.3805 < p < 0.4595$

b

c   Kelly's larger sample produced a narrower interval. Jason estimates the actual proportion to lie between 35.4% and 46.6% with 95% confidence, whereas Kelly estimates the actual proportion to lie between 38.1% and 46.0%, also with 95% confidence.

ASSESSING CLAIMS USING A CONFIDENCE INTERVAL

Assessing a claim with a confidence interval is now possible, but we must be very careful in stating any conclusions.

For example,   consider tossing a coin 1000 times to see if it is 'fair'.

Fair coins have $P(\text{heads}) = p = \frac{1}{2}$,   and $q = 1 - p = \frac{1}{2} = P(\text{tails})$

If 536 heads result, the 95% confidence interval for p is

$$0.536 - 1.96\sqrt{\tfrac{0.536\times0.464}{1000}} < p < 0.536 + 1.96\sqrt{\tfrac{0.536\times0.464}{1000}}   \text{ i.e., }   0.505 < p < 0.567$$

Thus we are 95% confident that the true value of p lies between 0.505 and 0.567. We might say "there is strong evidence that the coin is biased towards heads", but must not say "this proves that the coin is biased" because a very rare event could have occurred, i.e., there is less than 5% chance that we would get 536 heads if we tossed a fair coin 1000 times.

The significant departure from 0.5 may be due to chance (albeit very small) alone.

Example 40

The manufacturer of *Perfect Strike* matches claimed that 80% of their match boxes contained 50 or more matches. To check this claim a consumer randomly chose 250 boxes and counted the contents. The consumer found that 183 boxes contained 50 or more matches.

a   Find a 98% confidence interval for the proportion of match boxes in the population which contain 50 or more matches.

b   Does the consumer's data support the manufacturer's claim?

a   The estimate of the proportion is $\widehat{p} = \frac{183}{250} = 0.732$ and a 98% confidence interval for p is

$$0.732 - 2.326\sqrt{\tfrac{0.732\times0.268}{250}} < p < 0.732 + 2.326\sqrt{\tfrac{0.732\times0.268}{250}}$$

$$\therefore   0.667 < p < 0.797$$

b   We are 98% confident that the true proportion lies between 66.7% and 79.7% based on our sample. The manufacturer's claim lies outside the interval.
So, there is strong evidence that the manufacturer's claim is false.

SAMPLING ERROR FOR PROPORTIONS

Since 95% confidence limits for the population proportion p are $\widehat{p} \pm 1.96\sqrt{\dfrac{\widehat{p}\,\widehat{q}}{n}}$,

we could say that the **sampling error** $= \pm \mathbf{1.96}\sqrt{\dfrac{\widehat{p}\,\widehat{q}}{n}}$ with 95% confidence.

In a case where $\widehat{p}$ is not known $\widehat{p}\,\widehat{q}$ has a maximum value of $\frac{1}{4}$ which occurs when $\widehat{p}$ and $\widehat{q}$ are both $\frac{1}{2}$.   [Consider $f(x) = x(1-x)$ where $0 \leqslant x \leqslant 1$.]

$\therefore$ if $\widehat{p}$ is unknown,

the maximum **sampling error** for 95% confidence $= \pm 1.96\sqrt{\dfrac{\left(\frac{1}{2}\right)\left(\frac{1}{2}\right)}{n}}$

$$= \pm \mathbf{1.96}\left(\dfrac{1}{2\sqrt{n}}\right)$$

Example 41

For financial reasons, a newspaper decides they will survey only 2000 voters to ask their voting intentions at the next elections. What accuracy could they expect from the survey with 95% confidence?

the sampling error $= \pm 1.96\left(\dfrac{1}{2\sqrt{2000}}\right) \doteqdot \pm 0.022$ i.e., $\pm 2.2\%$

So, if they sample 2000 voters the results should be accurate within 2.2% with 95% confidence.

CHOOSING THE SAMPLE SIZE

We can use the sampling error formula at whatever level of confidence we require to determine the sample size we should use in **sampling for proportions**.

Example 42

A researcher wishes to estimate, with a probability of 0.95, the proportion to within 3% of mosquitos which carry a virus. How large must the sample be?

We notice that $\widehat{p}$ is unknown and the sampling error is to be at most $3\% = 0.03$.

So, $1.96\left(\dfrac{1}{2\sqrt{n}}\right) = 0.03$ $\therefore$ $2\sqrt{n} = \dfrac{1.96}{0.03}$

$\therefore$ $\sqrt{n} = 32.6666....$

Therefore the sample size, $n \approx 1067$.

EXERCISE 8D

In each of the following examples, state whether you are using a standard normal (Z-distribution), a t-distribution, the distribution for a sampling proportion ($\hat{p}$) or the binomial distribution.

1   The mean μ, of a population is unknown, but its standard deviation is 10. In order to estimate μ a random sample of size $n = 35$ was selected. The mean of the sample was found to be 28.9.

   a   Find a 95% confidence interval for μ.   b   Find a 99% confidence interval for μ.
   c   In changing the confidence level from 95% to 99%, how does the width of the confidence interval change?

2   The choice of the confidence level to be used is made by an experimenter. Why do experimenters not always choose to use confidence intervals of at least 99%?

3   A random sample of n is selected from a population with known standard deviation 11. The sample mean is 81.6.

   a   Find a 95% confidence interval for μ if: i $n = 36$ ii $n = 100$.
   b   In changing n from 36 to 100, how does the width of the confidence interval change?

4   If the $P\%$ confidence interval for μ is $\bar{x} - a \left(\frac{\sigma}{\sqrt{n}} \right) < \mu < \bar{x} + a \left(\frac{\sigma}{\sqrt{n}} \right)$ then

   for $P = 95$, $a = 1.960$.   Find a if P is: a   99   b   80   c   85   d   96.
   Hint: Use the Z-distribution tables.

5   A random sample of size $n = 50$ is selected from a population with standard deviation σ and the sample mean is 38.7, or a graphics calculator with a diagram.

   a   Find a 95% confidence interval for the mean μ if: i $\sigma = 6$ ii $\sigma = 15$.
   b   What effect does changing σ from 6 to 15 have on the width of the confidence interval?

6   Neville kept records of the time that he had to wait to receive telephone support for his accounting software. During a six month period he made 167 calls and the mean waiting time was 8.7 minutes. The shortest waiting time was 2.6 minutes and the longest was 15.1 minutes.

   a   Estimate σ using $\sigma \approx$ range $\div$ 6.
   b   Find a 98% confidence interval for estimating the mean waiting time for all telephone customer calls for support.
   c   Use the normal distribution to briefly explain why the formula in a for an estimate of σ is a reasonable one.

7   A breakfast cereal manufacturer uses a machine to deliver the cereal into plastic packets which then go into cardboard boxes. The quality controller randomly samples 75 packets and obtains a sample mean of 513.8 grams with sample standard deviation 14.9 grams. Construct a 99% confidence interval in which the true population mean should lie.

8   A sample of 42 patients from a drug rehabilitation program showed a mean length of stay on the program of 38.2 days with a standard deviation of 4.7 days. Estimate with a 90% confidence interval the average length of stay for all patients on the program.

9 A researcher wishes to estimate the mean weight of
   adult crayfish in Indonesian waters. From previous
   records she knows that adult crayfish vary in weight
   between 625 grams and 2128 grams.

   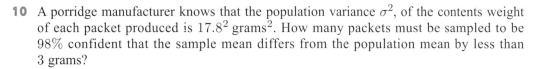

   a Estimate the standard deviation using the range
      of weights given.
   b How large must a sample be so that she is 95%
      confident that the sample mean differs from the population mean by less than 70
      grams, that is, $|\overline{X} - \mu| < 70$? State any assumptions made.

10 A porridge manufacturer knows that the population variance σ^2, of the contents weight
    of each packet produced is 17.8^2 grams^2. How many packets must be sampled to be
    98% confident that the sample mean differs from the population mean by less than
    3 grams?

11 A sample of 48 patients from an alcohol rehabilitation program showed participation time
    on the program had a population variance of 22.09 days^2. How many patients would
    have to be sampled to be 99% confident that the sample mean number of days on the
    program differs from the population mean by less than 1.8 days?

12 When 2839 Russians were randomly sampled, 1051 said they feared living close to
    overhead electricity power lines because of possible 'increased cancer risk'. Use the
    results of this survey to estimate with a 95% confidence interval the proportion of all
    Russians with this fear.

13 In a game of chance, one player suspected the coin being used was unfair. To test this
    he tossed the coin 500 times and observed 281 heads and 219 tails as the only outcomes.
    Estimate with a 99% confidence interval the probability of getting a head when tossing
    this coin. Comment on your answer.

14 A random sample of 2587 Irish adults were asked if they are better off now than they
    were ten years ago. 1822 said that they were not.
    a What proportion of the sample said that they were not better off now?
    b Estimate with a 99% confidence interval the proportion of all Irish adults who claim
       not to be better off now.
    c In a town of 5629 adults in Ireland how many would you expect to be better off
       now? State a weakness in your answer.

15 What is the large sample 80% confidence interval for estimating a population proportion,
    p, for a sample of size n with proportion $\widehat{p}$?

16 The manufacturer of Chocfruits claims that 90% of the one kilogram boxes have apricot
    centres in more than half of the Chocfruits. To check this claim a consumer purchased at
    random 80 boxes and found the percentage of each box with apricot centres. She found
    that 70 of the boxes had apricot centres in more than half of the Chocfruits.
    a What proportion of the sample of boxes had more than half of the Chocfruits with
       apricot centres?
    b Estimate with a 95% confidence interval the proportion of all boxes produced by
       the manufacturer which have more than half of the Chocfruits with apricot centres.
    c Does the consumer's data support the manufacturer's claim?

17 Growhair is the latest product of a pharmaceutical company. The company claims that their tests show that 43% of users of the product showed significant hair gain after a period of four months.

To test the claim Consumer Affairs randomly sampled 187 users and found that 68 of them did show significant hair gain. At a 95% confidence level, does the sample support the company's claim?

18 Publishers Karras Pty Ltd decide to survey 1500 of their readers to ask their opinion on the new format and layout of their fortnightly magazine. What accuracy would you expect from the survey with:

   a   95% confidence   **b**   99% confidence?

19 A poll on voting intentions for the upcoming state election is to be carried out at a 95% confidence level. Find the sampling error when the sample size is:

   a   500   **b**   1000   **c**   2000   **d**   4000

20 A scientist wishes to estimate the proportion of abnormally large peas in a new hybrid crop. He wishes to be accurate to 2% with a probability of 0.95.

   a   How large should the sample be?

   b   If the probability is raised to 0.99, how large would the sample now have to be?

21 When 2750 voters were asked whether the income tax rates were too high, 2106 said 'yes'.

   a   If the poll was at a 90% confidence level, determine the poll's margin for error (sampling error).

   b   How many voters need to be surveyed to have the same margin of error as in **a** but with an increased confidence level of 95%?

22 After the latest frost 189 apples were randomly picked and 43 were found to be not fit for sale.

   a   What is the sampling error in this case (with 95% confidence)?

   b   How large a sample would need to be taken to estimate the proportion of unsaleable apples to within 3% with 95% confidence?

23 In some countries laws are made to prevent anglers from catching fish smaller than a given length. In a random sample of 300 fish caught in a certain region, 27 were smaller than the legal limit.

   a   Estimate the proportion of fish caught below the legal limit in that region.

   b   Find a 98% confidence interval that contains the proportion of fish caught below the legal limit.

   c   Explain why this interval estimate is approximate and briefly explain what this interval estimate means.

   d   What size sample would you take to estimate the proportion to be within 2% with 98% confidence?

24 In 1995, for a random sample of 75 German residents interviewed, 43 voted in favour of the introduction of the new European currency.

    a Calculate a 95% confidence interval for the population proportion of German residents in favour of the new European currency.

    b How many German residents would you need to sample if you were to be provided with an interval of width 0.05 with 95% confidence?

    c Give two reasons why the calculation in **b** is an estimate.

    d In 1995, for another random sample of 200 German residents, a 95% CI for the population proportion in favour of the Euro was approx. $]0.441, 0.579[$. How many of the 200 voted in favour of the Euro?

E SIGNIFICANCE AND HYPOTHESIS TESTING

Visitors to the West Coast of the South Island of New Zealand are often bitten by sandflies.

A new product to repel sandflies has the statement *"will repel sandflies for an average protection time of more than six hours"* printed on its label. The current most popular brands offer *"protection for 6 hours"*.

The government tourist department wishes to preserve the tourist trade. Anxious also to provide the best sandfly protection possible, they decide to test the manufacturer's claim. How can they test the claim?

There are many circumstances where a test of a claim is appropriate. We do this by testing hypotheses.

> A **statistical hypothesis** is a statement about a population parameter. The parameter could be a population mean or a proportion.

When testing a hypothesis we:
- formulate a hypothesis involving a parameter
- sample the population to get information about the parameter
- check whether the sample supports the hypothesis.

In this section of work we will test hypotheses concerning either the **mean** μ, or a **population proportion** p.

HYPOTHESIS TESTS AND CONFIDENCE INTERVALS

A hypothesis test is like the converse of a confidence interval.

Remember that a 95% confidence interval for the mean μ based on our sample $\bar{x}$ was

$$\bar{x} - 1.960\tfrac{\sigma}{\sqrt{n}} < \mu < \bar{x} + 1.960\tfrac{\sigma}{\sqrt{n}}$$

This means that $\bar{x} - 1.960\tfrac{\sigma}{\sqrt{n}} < \mu$ and $\mu < \bar{x} + 1.960\tfrac{\sigma}{\sqrt{n}}$

$\therefore$ $-\mu - 1.960\tfrac{\sigma}{\sqrt{n}} < -\bar{x}$ and $-\bar{x} < -\mu + 1.960\tfrac{\sigma}{\sqrt{n}}$

$$\therefore \quad \mu + 1.960 \frac{\sigma}{\sqrt{n}} > \bar{x} \quad \text{and} \quad \bar{x} > \mu - 1.960 \frac{\sigma}{\sqrt{n}}$$

$$\therefore \quad \mu - 1.960 \frac{\sigma}{\sqrt{n}} < \bar{x} < \mu + 1.960 \frac{\sigma}{\sqrt{n}}$$

This is effectively a confidence interval for $\bar{x}$ based on μ.

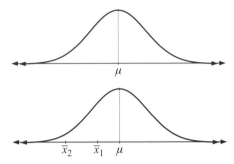

As a result, in hypothesis testing, we are setting μ and then seeing if our sample mean $\bar{x}$ suggests that μ is a reasonable mean, i.e., $\bar{x}$ falls within an **acceptable** probability range of μ.

On our diagram, a sample mean of $\bar{x}_1$ is not unlikely if μ was the true mean.

However a sample mean of $\bar{x}_2$ is indicating that μ is less likely to be the true mean.

Note: The graphs drawn above represent the distribution of the *sample means* which have mean μ and standard deviation $\frac{\sigma}{\sqrt{n}}$ (by the Central Limit Theorem).

HYPOTHESES ABOUT MEANS

When a statement is made about a product it is usually tested statistically. Because statisticians are conservative, their usual approach is to claim that the statement about the product is not correct. The statistician makes the claim that statistics will show no differences. That claim is called the **null hypothesis** (called H_0).

The alternative hypothesis (called H_1) is that the statistical evidence is sufficient to accept the claim.

So, we consider *two* hypotheses:

- a **null hypothesis** (H_0), which is a statement of *no difference* (or *no change*) and is assumed to be true until sufficient evidence is provided so that it is rejected

- an **alternative hypothesis** (H_1), which is a statement that there *is a difference* or *change* which has to be established. Supporting evidence is necessary if it is to be accepted.

In the case of the sandfly repellent,

$$H_0 \text{ is:} \quad \mu = 6 \quad \{\text{the new product has the same effectiveness as the others}\}$$
$$H_1 \text{ is:} \quad \mu > 6 \quad \{\text{the new product is superior to the others}\}$$

We then gather a random sample from the population in order to test the null hypothesis. If the test shows that H_0 should be rejected, then its alternative H_1 should be accepted.

ONE-SIDED AND TWO-SIDED ALTERNATIVE HYPOTHESES

If H_0 is that: $\quad \mu = \mu_0 \quad$ the alternative hypothesis H_1 could be

- $\mu > \mu_0$ **(one-sided)**
- $\mu < \mu_0$ **(one-sided)**
- $\mu \neq \mu_0$ **(two-sided, as $\mu \neq \mu_0$ could mean $\mu > \mu_0$ or $\mu < \mu_0$).**

Consider the sandfly repellent situation again.

- In the case where the manufacturer of a new brand wants evidence that the new product is **superior** in lasting time the hypotheses would be

  H_0 is: $\mu = 6$ {the new product has the same effectiveness as the old ones}

  H_1 is: $\mu > 6$ {the new product lasts longer than the old ones}.

- In the case where a competitor wants evidence that the new product has **inferior** lasting time the hypothesis would be

  H_0 is: $\mu = 6$ {the new product has the same effectiveness as the old ones}

  H_1 is: $\mu < 6$ {the new product lasts less than the old ones}.

- In the case where an unbiased third party wants to show that the new product **differs** from the old ones but is not concerned whether the lasting time is more or less, the hypothesis would be

  H_0 is: $\mu = 6$ {the new product has the same effectiveness as the old ones}

  H_1 is: $\mu \neq 6$ {the new product has different effectiveness from the old ones}.

Note: The null hypothesis H_0 **always** states a **specific** value of μ.

ERROR TYPES

There are two types of **error** in decision making:

- Falsely rejecting H_0,   i.e.,   rejecting a true null hypothesis. This is called a **Type I error**.
- Falsely accepting H_0,   i.e.,   accepting a false null hypothesis. This is called a **Type II error**.

An example of a Type I error is rejecting, because it is highly improbable, the event that you get 10 heads in 10 tosses of a fair coin when that event, though improbable, can occur.

An example of a Type II error is when you accept the hypothesis that you have a fair coin because you had the event of getting 7 heads in 10 tosses, which can easily happen with a fair coin due to chance, when in fact the coin may actually be biased towards getting a head. More about this later!

EXERCISE 8E.1

1   What is meant by the following:

    a   a Type I error   **b**   a Type II error

    c   the null hypothesis   **d**   the alternative hypothesis?

2   **a**   An experimenter wishes to test H_0: $\mu = 20$ against H_1: $\mu > 20$.

        i   If the mean is actually 20 and the experimenter concludes that the mean exceeds 20, what type of error has been made?

        ii   If the population mean is actually 21.8, what type of error has been committed if the experimenter concludes that the mean is 20?

    b   A researcher wishes to test H_0: $\mu = 40$ against H_1: $\mu \neq 40$.   What type of error has been made if she concludes that:

        i   the mean is 40 when it is in fact 38.1

        ii   the mean is not 40 when it actually is 40?

3   In trials where juries are used "*a person is presumed innocent until proven guilty*", so
    the null hypothesis would be H_0:   the person on trial is innocent.

    a   What would be the alternative hypothesis H_1?
    b   If an innocent person is judged guilty, what type of error has been committed?
    c   If a guilty person is judged as innocent, what type of error has been committed?

4   A researcher conducts experiments to determine the effectiveness of two anti-dandruff
    shampoos X and Y. He tests the hypotheses:

    H_0:   X and Y have the same effectiveness H_1:   X is more effective than Y.

    What decision would cause   a   a type I error   b   a type II error?

5   Globe Industries make torch globes. Current globes have a mean life of 80 hours. Globe
    Industries are considering mass production of a new globe they think will last longer.

    a   If the manufacturer wants to show that the new globe lasts longer, what set of
        hypotheses should be considered?
    b   If the new globe costs less to make, and Globe Industries will adopt it unless it
        has an inferior lifespan to the old type, what set of hypotheses would they now
        consider?

6   The top underwater speed of submarines produced
    at the dockyards is 26.3 knots. They modify the
    design to reduce drag and believe that the max-
    imum speed will now be considerably increased.
    What set of hypotheses should they consider to
    test whether or not the new design has produced a
    faster submarine?

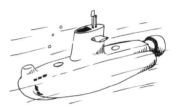

HYPOTHESIS TESTING FOR THE MEAN OF ONE SAMPLE

Here we are concerned with **testing the validity** of a **null hypothesis** about the mean of **one
sample**.

The probability value calculated from the sample casts *little* or *serious doubt* over the validity
of the null hypothesis.

A *small probability* value would suggest that the outcome observed is a freak occurrence or
the assumption of validity is misplaced. In this case we would consider rejecting H_0.

A *large probability* value would suggest that the outcome can be considered to be what could
be expected to occur by chance. In this case we would not reject H_0.

Note: We only reject or not reject (accept) H_0.

CONSTRUCTING THE NULL AND ALTERNATIVE HYPOTHESES (H_0 AND H_1)

The **null hypothesis** is a statement of *no effect*, and so the null hypothesis is usually set up
to say, for example, that 'there is no effect occurring in experimental set up' or 'the company
involved is correct, i.e., the claim they make is true'.

Usually an experiment is set up to show the effect.

For example:
- the new drug is better than the old one
- the new fertiliser results in better yield
- the company's claim is wrong.

Hence, H_1 would say
- the new drug is better
- the yield is better
- the company's claim is correct.

and H_0 would say   no effect is occurring.

It is often easier to construct H_1, first, then H_0.

Some further examples:

- A drug company claims the pain-killers it makes last for at least 3 hours. A sample of 30 tablets tried on subjects returned a mean effective time of 2.8 hours and standard deviation of 0.15 hours. Does the sample data indicate that the claim is too high?

  H_0: $\mu = 3$
  H_1: $\mu < 3$ (a one-tailed (left) test)

- A farmer knew his average yield of a certain grain while using a fertiliser was 600 kg per hectare. He changed the fertiliser believing his average yield would increase.

  H_0: $\mu = 600$
  H_1: $\mu > 600$ (a one-tailed (right) test)

- The average house price in a suburb in 2004 was known to be \$235 000. A sample was taken in 2005 to see whether or not the average price had changed.

  H_0: $\mu = 235\,000$
  H_1: $\mu \neq 235\,000$ (a two-tailed test)

For the first two examples, the probability calculation will be based on the appropriate **one tail** of the normal distribution (due to the structure of the problem), while the third, where there is no idea of whether the change will be up or down, will require a probability value that includes both left and right tails.

THE TEST STATISTIC, NULL DISTRIBUTION, p-VALUE AND THE DECISION

The **test statistic** is a value derived from the sampling process and is calculated from the sample taken.

The **null distribution** is the distribution used to determine the probability and depends on the problem. It may be:
- the Z-distribution   (if σ^2 is *known*)   or
- the t-distribution   (if σ^2 is *unknown*)

For a sampling proportion problem where n is large, we use the Z-distribution to approximate the binomial.

For example, in the house price problem above,

if 200 house prices were sampled in 2005 and the mean $\overline{x}$ was found to be \$215 000 with the unbiased estimate of the standard deviation $s_{n-1} = \$30\,000$ the test statistic would be:

$$t = \frac{\overline{x} - \mu}{\frac{s_{n-1}}{\sqrt{n}}} = \frac{215\,000 - 235\,000}{\frac{30\,000}{\sqrt{200}}} \approx -9.43 \quad \text{with 199 degrees of freedom.}$$

The **p-value** is the probability of this occurrence or something more extreme based on the assumption that H_0 **is valid**. It is the p-value that allows us to *make a decision* on the rejection or otherwise of H_0.

In this case   p-value $= P(t \geqslant 9.43) + P(t \leqslant -9.43)$ {includes 2-tails}

$\approx 1 \times 10^{-14}$ {from Casio graphics calculator, (**DIST, t, tcd**)}

or $\approx 1.11 \times 10^{-17}$ {from TI-83 graphics calculator}

The difference between the two models is probably due to the use of different calculation methods.

For this tiny probability we would think that either we are extremely unlucky or that our assumption of H_0 being valid is *not correct*. That is, we are saying that it is extremely unlikely to obtain a sample like this if H_0 is correct. Do not forget that this is still possible, whilst being extremely unlikely. In hypothesis testing of this kind there are no certainties (absolutes).

The cut off depends on the level of significance chosen and is usually 0.05 (a 5% level of significance or 95% confidence level).

So if the p-value < 0.05 then enough doubt is cast on the validity of H_0.

The **level of significance** is the threshold below which we reject H_0. It may be 5% or 1%, whichever is sensible.

The level of significance provides us with a strict rule for rejecting or accepting H_0. A level of significance of 5% means that the probability of making a Type I error is 0.05. Hence there is a 5% chance of rejecting H_0 when it is indeed true.

For the housing price example, our decision is to reject H_0, which means sufficient evidence exists to suggest that $\mu \neq 235\,000$. In fact since the sample mean was less than the previously known mean we may suggest (at the 0.05 level) that the mean is less than before. Most likely a statistician would pursue this further.

Sometimes in hypothesis testing, we refer to the **critical values** for the distribution. These refer to the cut-off values of the distribution about which the decisions are made. For example, if we have a Z-distribution and a 2-tailed test with a 5% level of significance, the critical values are $z^* \approx \pm 1.96$.   This is illustrated in the diagram below:

The shaded area which equals 0.025 in each part, adding to 0.05, is referred to as the **critical region (rejection region)**.

The values ± 1.96 are the **critical values** for a 2-tailed test. If the Z-score from the sample falls within the shaded areas, we would *reject* the null hypothesis.

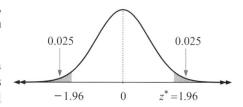

If it falls in between ± 1.96, we *accept* H_0.

In the housing problem, the critical t-values are $t^* \approx \pm 1.972$.

Check this on your calculator.

Hence, we reject H_0 because the test statistic ≈ -9.43 which is lower than -1.972.

USING A GRAPHICS CALCULATOR

Click on the icon to obtain instructions for **TI** and **Casio** calculators.

Be aware that your calculator may use different notation to that used in IB.

For example, with **Casio**, s_{n-1} is $x_{\sigma_{n-1}}$ and with **TI** s_{n-1} is s_x.

Do not forget that s_{n-1}^2 is the **unbiased estimate** of σ^2.

Summary:

There are effectively 7 steps in reporting on a hypothesis test.

These are:

Step 1: State the null and alternative hypotheses. (Specify whether it is a 1- or 2-tailed test.)

Step 2: State the type of distribution under H_0.

Step 3: Calculate the test statistic from the sample evidence.

Step 4: State the decision rule based on the significance level.

Step 5: Find the p-value using your graphics calculator *or* find the critical values and region.

Step 6: Make your decision   i.e.,   **reject** or **not reject** H_0 based on the significance level.

Step 7: Write a brief statement/conclusion giving your decision some contextual meaning.

For the housing price problem, the steps are:

1 Hypotheses: H_0: $\mu = 235\,000$ H_1: $\mu \neq 235\,000$ (2-tailed test)

2 Null distribution: t-distribution with $\nu = 199$ (as σ^2 is unknown).

3 Test Statistic: $t = \dfrac{\overline{x} - \mu}{\frac{s_{n-1}}{\sqrt{n}}} = \dfrac{215\,000 - 235\,000}{\frac{30\,000}{\sqrt{200}}} \approx -9.43$

with 199 degrees of freedom

4 Decision Rule: Reject H_0 if p-value is less than 0.05 .

5 p-value: p-value $= \text{P}(t \geqslant 9.43) + \text{P}(t \leqslant -9.43) \approx 1.11 \times 10^{-17}$

6 Decision: As the p-value is less than 0.05, then we reject H_0.

7 Conclusion: Hence, sufficient evidence exists to suggest that $\mu \neq 235\,000$, in fact since the sample mean was less than the previously known mean we suggest (at the 0.05 level) that the mean is smaller than before.

Check these values on your graphics calculator.

You can do 2 checks:
- a direct test   or
- by calculating a probability using the test statistic.

Example 43

A buyer of prawns (for a restaurant chain) goes to a seafood wholesaler and inspects a large catch of over 50 000 prawns. She has instructions to buy the catch if the mean weight exceeds 55 grams per prawn. A random sample of 60 prawns is taken and weighed. The mean weight is 56.2 grams with standard deviation 4.2 grams. Is there sufficient evidence at a 5% level to reject the catch?

1. **Hypotheses:** H_0: $\mu = 55$
                            H_1: $\mu > 55$ (1-tailed test)

2. **Null distribution:** Z-distribution (σ is known, $\sigma = 4.2$)

3. **Test Statistic:** $Z = \dfrac{56.2 - 55}{\frac{4.2}{\sqrt{60}}} \approx 2.213$

4. **Decision Rule:**   Reject H_0 if p-value is less than 0.05

5. **p-value:** $p\text{-value} = \mathrm{P}(Z \geqslant 2.213) \approx 0.0134$

6. **Decision:**   As the p-value is less than 0.05, then we reject H_0.

7. **Conclusion:**   Hence, sufficient evidence exists to accept H_1
                            i.e., mean weight exceeds 55 grams. So, on this evidence the buyer should purchase the catch.

Example 44

Fabtread manufacture motorcycle tyres. Under normal test conditions the average stopping time for motor cycles travelling at 60 km/h is 3.12 seconds. The production team have recently designed and manufactured a new tyre tread. Under the normal test conditions they took 41 stopping time measurements and found that the mean time was 3.03 seconds with standard deviation 0.27 seconds.
Is there sufficient evidence, at a 1% level, to support the team's belief that they have improved the stopping time?

1. **Hypotheses:** H_0: $\mu = 3.12$
                            H_1: $\mu < 3.12$ (1-tailed test)

2. **Null distribution:** t-distribution (σ is unknown, $s_n^2 = 0.27^2$) with $\nu = 40$

3. **Test Statistic:** $s_{n-1}^2 = \dfrac{n}{n-1} \times s_n^2 = \dfrac{41}{40} \times 0.27^2 \approx 0.07472$

                            $\therefore$ $s_{n-1} \approx 0.27335$

                            and $t = \dfrac{3.03 - 3.12}{\frac{0.27335}{\sqrt{41}}} \approx -2.108$

4. **Decision Rule:**   Reject H_0 if the p-value is less than 0.01

5. **p-value:** $p\text{-value} = \mathrm{P}(t \leqslant -2.108) \approx 0.02066$ (graphics calculator)

6. **Decision:**   As the p-value is greater than 0.01, then we do not reject H_0.

> 7. **Conclusion:**   Hence, insufficient evidence exists to accept H_1 i.e., at a 1%
> level of significance, there is not an improvement in stopping
> time due to the new tread pattern.

In this last example, we may be guilty of making a Type II error (accepting H_0 when it is false). In this case because we want a stricter level of significance (1%), we increase the possibility of making a Type II error. This is true in general!

Note:

- **Rejection of H_0**   (We can use the p-**value** or the **critical value** to do this).

  When we reject H_0, we do so because chance alone cannot plausibly explain the observed disagreement between $\overline{x}$ and μ_0. (Here, μ_0 is the value for μ under H_0.) It could nevertheless be true that H_0 is correct (we then make a Type I error). The strength of evidence against H_0 is given by the p-value.

- **Acceptance of H_0**

  When we accept H_0, we do so because the observed disagreement between $\overline{x}$ and μ_0 can plausibly be explained by chance. It may be that H_0 is not true (we then make a Type II error). There is no notion of evidence in favour of H_0. Acceptance of H_0 is simply the failure to obtain sufficient evidence to reject H_0.

- At a 5% significance level, we would reject H_0 above and possibly be guilty of making a Type I error with probability 0.05 or 5%. The probability of making the Type II error above is unknown, but we would expect it to be greater or at least different from 0.05. The significance level and the probability of making a Type I error are the same. It is important to be aware of the asymmetry between acceptance and rejection. (Refer to **Example 46** which follows.)

  The hypothesis testing approach is to accept H_0 unless we find sufficient evidence to cause us to reject it. **Accepting H_0 is not the same thing as rejecting H_1 and vice-versa**. Rejecting H_0 is a "stronger" conclusion than accepting.

- p-**values:**   The broad interpretation of the p-value is as a measure of the strength of evidence against H_0. The smaller the p-value, the stronger the evidence against H_0. A common mistake is to suppose that the p-value is the probability that H_0 is correct. The proper interpretation is that the p-value is the probability that $\overline{x}$ and μ_0 would disagree to at least the extent actually observed if H_0 were true.

SIGNIFICANCE TESTING FOR THE PROPORTION OF ONE LARGE SAMPLE

Recall that for large n, the sampling distribution of a proportion $\widehat{p} = \dfrac{x}{n}$ is approximately normal with mean $\mu_{\widehat{p}} = p$ and standard deviation $\sigma_{\widehat{p}} = \sqrt{\dfrac{pq}{n}}$.
As a consequence:

> For testing the null hypothesis H_0 that $p = p_0$,   the **test statistic** is
>
> $$Z = \frac{\widehat{p} - p_0}{\sqrt{\dfrac{p_0 \, q_0}{n}}} \quad \text{when} \quad n \geqslant 30, \quad np_0 \geqslant 5, \quad nq_0 \geqslant 5$$

The rejection region is:

For $\;H_1$: $p > p_0$,

  we reject H_0 if $\;z^* > z_\alpha$

For $\;H_1$: $p < p_0$,

  we reject H_0 if $\;z^* < -z_\alpha$

For $\;H_1$: $p \neq p_0$,

  we reject H_0 if $\;z^* < -z_{\frac{\alpha}{2}}$

      or $\;z^* > z_{\frac{\alpha}{2}}$

Example 45

A supplier of superior mixed nuts claims that only 25% of the nuts are peanuts. A consumer does not believe the claim and in a sample of 3187 nuts finds that 848 were peanuts. Does the consumer's evidence support his belief that the mix has more than 25% peanuts? [Test at a level of significance of 0.01]

1. **Hypotheses:** H_0: $p = 0.25$
                       H_1: $p > 0.25$ (1-tailed test)

2. **Null distribution:** $\hat{p}$-distribution, with $\hat{p} = \frac{848}{3187} \approx 0.2661$ (store on gdc)

3. **Test Statistic:** $Z = \dfrac{0.2661 - 0.25}{\sqrt{0.25 \times \frac{0.75}{3187}}} \approx 2.097$ (store on gdc)

4. **Decision Rule:**   Reject $\;H_0$ if p-value is less than 0.01

5. **p-value:** p-value $= \mathrm{P}(Z \geqslant 2.097) \doteq 0.017\,996$ from the gdc
                    without the continuity correction
                    or $0.018\,024$ with
                    continuity correction.

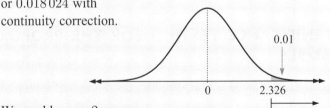

6. **Decision:**   We could argue 2 ways:
               • As the p-value is greater than 0.01, *or*
               • as the test statistic does not lie in the rejection
                 region, then we do not reject H_0 in either case.

7. **Conclusion:**   Hence, insufficient evidence exists to accept H_1
                    i.e., at the 1% level of significance, the mix does not
                    contain more than 25% of peanuts.

Example 46

A nutrition expert found that 43% of Southern Vale children ate insufficient fruit each day (at least three pieces). To check whether this figure was the same for Northern Vale children, a university research group sampled 625 Northern Vale children and found that 308 ate insufficient fruit each day. What conclusion can be made at a 0.05 level of significance?

1. **Hypotheses:**
H_0: $p = 0.43$
H_1: $p \neq 0.43$ (2-tailed test)

2. **Null distribution:** $\hat{p}$-distribution, with $\hat{p} = \frac{308}{625} \approx 0.4928$ (store on gdc)

3. **Test Statistic:**
$$Z = \frac{0.4928 - 0.43}{\sqrt{0.43 \times \frac{0.57}{625}}} \approx 3.171 \quad \text{(store on gdc)}$$

4. **Decision Rule:**   Reject H_0 if p-value is less than 0.05

5. **p-value:**
p-value $= P(Z \leqslant -3.171) + P(Z \geqslant 3.171) \approx 0.00152$
from the gdc with and without the continuity correction

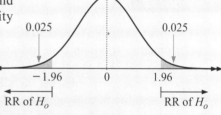

6 **Decision:**   We could argue 2 ways:
- As the p-value is less than 0.05,   *or*
- as the test statistic does lie in the rejection region, then we do reject H_0 in either case.

7. **Conclusion:**   Hence, there is sufficient evidence at the 0.05 level to conclude that the proportion of Northern Vales children's fruit consumption each day differs from that of the Southern Vales children. In fact, the sample proportion of 0.4928 suggests that the percentage figure may be higher. This may lead to another hypothesis test.

In **Example 46** above, a 95% CI for the true population proportion of children from the Northern Vales who ate insufficient fruit is:

$$0.4928 - 1.96\sqrt{\tfrac{0.43 \times 0.57}{625}} < p < 0.4928 + 1.96\sqrt{\tfrac{0.43 \times 0.57}{625}}$$

i.e., $0.454 < p < 0.532$

This is consistent with the fact that when we reject H_0 in a 2-tailed test at the 5% level of significance, then we will be 95% confident that the assumed proportion $p = 0.43$,   under H_0, will not be contained in the 95% CI for the true population proportion p.

Hypothesis Tests and Confidence Intervals

Consider the test of H_0: $\mu = \mu_0$.

We will accept H_0 at the 5% level of significance if $|Z| = \dfrac{|\overline{x} - \mu_0|}{\frac{\sigma}{\sqrt{n}}} < 1.96$.

Now consider the 95% CI for μ, $]\,\overline{x} - 1.96\frac{\sigma}{\sqrt{n}},\ \overline{x} + 1.96\frac{\sigma}{\sqrt{n}}\,[$

If the value μ_0 lies within the 95% CI then $|\overline{x} - \mu| < 1.96\frac{\sigma}{\sqrt{n}}$ $\Rightarrow$ $|Z| < 1.96$.

Similarly, if μ_0 is not within the 95% CI then $|Z| \geqslant 1.96$

Hence, the test of H_0: $\mu = \mu_0$ with 5% level of significance is equivalent to the rule:

Accept H_0 if and only if μ_0 lies within the 95% CI for μ (2-tailed tests only).

Note: This is not always true for 1-tailed tests. For example, see **Example 48** which
follows. Why is it not always true for 1-tailed tests?

Example 47   (An illustration of the asymmetry of acceptance and rejection of H_0.)

A random variable X representing the number of successes can be modelled by
a binomial distribution with parameters $n = 250$ and p, whose value is unknown.
A significance test is performed, based on a sample value of x_0, to test the
hypothesis $p = 0.6$, against the alternative, the null hypothesis $p > 0.6$.
The probability of making a Type I error is 0.05.

a   Find the critical region for x_0.

b   Find the probability of making a Type II error in the case when in actual fact
$p = 0.675$.

---

a   Given $X \sim B(250, p)$ and H_0: $p = 0.6$, H_1: $p > 0.6$.

If H_0 is true, then $p = 0.6$, so $X \sim B(250, 0.6)$.

Thus $np = 150$ and $npq = 60$ and $np, nq \geqslant 10$.

Hence, we can approximate X by:

$X \sim N(150, 60)$ and we have
a 5% significance level.
Using a 1-tailed test at 5% level,
and a Z-distribution, the critical
value is $z = 1.645$.

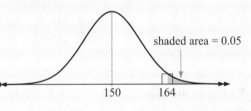

shaded area = 0.05

150   164

$\therefore$ since we are considering values in the upper tail,

$$\dfrac{x_0 - 0.5 - 150}{\sqrt{60}} > 1.645 \quad \text{(with continuity correction)}$$

or $\dfrac{x_0 - 150}{\sqrt{60}} > 1.645 \quad \text{(without continuity correction)}$

$\therefore$ $x_0 > 1.645\sqrt{60} + 150.5$, i.e., $x_0 > 163.2$ (with continuity correction) *or*
$x_0 > 162.7$ (without continuity correction).

Since x is an integer, the **critical (rejection) region** is $x \geqslant 164$ **or** $x \geqslant 163$.

$$\text{(with cc)} \qquad \text{(without cc)}$$

Checking: $\dfrac{164 - 0.5 - 150}{\sqrt{60}} \approx 1.74 > 1.645$

and $\dfrac{163 - 0.5 - 150}{\sqrt{60}} \approx 1.61 < 1.645$ (with continuity correction)

b   If $p = 0.675$,   we have H_0: $p = 0.6$, H_1: $p > 0.6$

From **a** the critical region is $X \geqslant 164$,
so H_0 is accepted when $X < 164$.

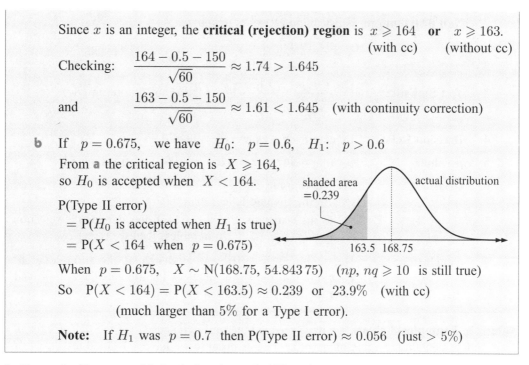

shaded area
=0.239

actual distribution

163.5   168.75

P(Type II error)

$= \text{P}(H_0 \text{ is accepted when } H_1 \text{ is true})$

$= \text{P}(X < 164 \text{ when } p = 0.675)$

When $p = 0.675$, $X \sim \text{N}(168.75,\ 54.843\,75)$ (np, $nq \geqslant 10$ is still true)

So $\text{P}(X < 164) = \text{P}(X < 163.5) \approx 0.239$ or 23.9% (with cc)

(much larger than 5% for a Type I error).

Note: If H_1 was $p = 0.7$ then P(Type II error) ≈ 0.056 (just $> 5\%$)

In **Example 47**, you could check that the probability of a type II error increases if we require a stricter significance level, for example, 0.01, i.e., a smaller type I error.

Example 48

(An example of paired samples (matched pairs) using a single sample technique.)

Prior to the 2004 Olympic Games an institute of sport took 20 fit athletes and over a one month period gave them a special diet and exercise program. This program was to try to improve their sprint times over 100 m. Below is their "best" time before and after the program. The athletes have been recorded as the letters A to T and times are in seconds.

Athlete	A	B	C	D	E	F	G	H	I	J
Before	10.3	10.5	10.6	10.4	10.8	11.1	9.9	10.6	10.6	10.8
After	10.2	10.3	10.8	10.1	10.8	9.7	9.9	10.6	10.4	10.6

Athlete	K	L	M	N	O	P	Q	R	S	T
Before	11.2	11.4	10.9	10.7	10.7	10.9	11.0	10.3	10.5	10.6
After	10.8	11.2	11.0	10.5	10.7	11.0	11.1	10.5	10.3	10.2

Has the program significantly improved the athletes' performance? Conduct a hypothesis test at the 5% level of significance.

Let $U = X_1 - X_2$ where X_1 represents the time before and X_2 represents the time after the program.

1.   **Null hypotheses:** H_0: $\mu = 0$ (i.e.,   times have not improved)

H_1: $\mu > 0$ (1-tailed test as testing to see if times have improved)

2. **Null distribution:** t-distribution   (σ^2 is unknown)

$$\bar{u} = \frac{\sum(u_i)}{20} = \frac{3.1}{20} = 0.155, \quad s_{n-1} \approx 0.344\,085$$

3. **Test Statistic:** $t = \dfrac{\bar{u} - \mu}{\frac{s_{n-1}}{\sqrt{n}}} = \dfrac{0.155 - 0}{0.0769} \approx 2.014\,56$ (store on gdc)

4. **Decision Rule:**   Reject H_0 if p-value is less than 0.05

5. **p-value:** p-value $= P(t > 2.014\,56) \approx 0.02916$ from the gdc

6. **Decision:**   We could argue 2 ways:
    - As the p-value is less than 0.05,   *or*
    - as the test statistic $t^* \approx 2.014\,56$ lies outside the rejection region ($t > 1.729$, from tables) then we reject H_0.

7. **Conclusion:**   Hence, there is sufficient evidence at the 0.05 level to conclude that the sprint times of the athletes have improved after the implementation of the program.

Note: In **Example 48** above, we have rejected the null hypothesis, yet the 95% CI for μ does contain the value of $\mu = 0$. This is because we have a 1-tailed test.

Check that the 95% CI for μ is $]-0.0257, 0.336\,[$.   Look at the 90% CI to see that $\mu = 0$ does not belong as we have a 1-tailed test.

EXERCISE 8E.2

1   For the following hypotheses find the rejection region for the test statistic for $n \geqslant 30$ and $\alpha = 0.05$:

    a H_0: $\mu = 40$ **b** H_0: $\mu = 50$ **c** H_0: $\mu = 60$
        H_1: $\mu > 40$ H_1: $\mu < 50$ H_1: $\mu \neq 60$

2   Repeat question **1** but for $\alpha = 0.01$.

3   An experimenter believes that a population which has a standard deviation of 12.9, has a mean μ that is greater than 80. To test this, a random sample of 200 measurements was made. The sample mean was 83.1 and the test significance level $\alpha = 0.01$.

    a   Write down the null and alternative hypotheses.
    b   State the null distribution.   **c**   Find the value of the test statistic.
    d   Find the rejection region and illustrate it.   **e**   State the conclusion for the test.

4   A liquor chain claimed that the mean price of a bottle of wine had fallen from what it was 12 months previously. Records showed that 12 months ago the mean price was $13.45 a 750 mL bottle. In total, a random sample of prices of 389 different bottles of wine was taken from several of its stores. (Each store in the chain has the same price for each particular product.) The mean price was $13.30 with a standard deviation of $0.25. Is there sufficient evidence at a 2% level to reject the claim? In your answer state:

    a   the null and alternative hypotheses   **b**   the null distribution
    c   the test statistic   **d**   the p-value
    e   your conclusion.

5   **a**   A random sample of $n = 237$ gave 123 successes.

Test at a significance level of 5% ($\alpha = 0.05$) the hypothesis H_0: $p = 0.5$
H_1: $p > 0.5$

   b   A random sample of $n = 382$ gave 295 successes. Test at a significance level of 1% ($\alpha = 0.01$) the hypothesis H_0: $p = 0.8$
H_1: $p \neq 0.8$

6   A coin is tossed 400 times and falls heads on 182 occasions. Do these results provide sufficient evidence that the coin is biased? (An unbiased coin has equal chance of falling 'heads' or 'tails'.) Test at a 5% level of significance.

7   The theoretical chance of rolling a sum of seven with a pair of unbiased dice is $\frac{1}{6}$.

At a casino one player rolled a pair of dice 231 times and a sum of seven appeared 57 times. Management suspected that the player had switched to 'loaded' dice.

Test at a 1% level H_0: $p = \frac{1}{6}$ against H_1: $p > \frac{1}{6}$.

8   A motor boat dealer claimed that at least 85% of its customers would recommend his boats to a friend. A student who doubted this claim decided to check the claim and surveyed 57 of the dealer's customers who were easily identified with stickers on their boats. The student found that 45 did in fact recommend the dealership. Do these results support the dealers claim (at a 1% level)?

9   A supermarket decides to buy a large quantity of apples if it is sure that less than 5% of them have skin blemishes. The survey randomly inspects 389 apples and finds skin blemishes on 16 of them. Is there sufficient evidence at an α level of 0.02 to suggest to the purchasing officer to proceed with the purchase?

10   The management of a golf club claimed that the mean income of its members was in excess of \$95 000. Therefore its members could afford to pay increased annual subscriptions. To show that this claim was invalid the members sought the help of a statistician. The statistician was to examine the current tax records of a random sample of members fairly and test the claim of the club's management at a 0.02 significance level. The statistician found, from his random sample of 113 club members, that the average income was \$96 318 with standard deviation \$14 268.

   a   Find an unbiased estimate of the population standard deviation.
   b   State the null and alternative hypotheses when testing this claim.
   c   State the null distribution.
   d   Find the test statistic.
   e   Find the p-value when testing the null hypothesis.
   f   Find the critical region for rejection of the null hypothesis and sketch it.
   g   State whether or not there is sufficient evidence to reject management's claim.
   h   Would the statistician be committing a Type I or Type II error if his assertion was incorrect?
   i   Find a 99% CI interval for the mean income of members and comment on your result. Why do we check with a 99% CI?

11 While peaches are being canned, 250 mg of preservative is supposed to be added by a dispensing device. To check the machine, the quality controller obtains 60 random samples of dispensed preservative and finds that the mean preservative added was 242.6 mg with sample standard deviation 7.3 mg, i.e., $s_n = 7.3$.

   a At a 5% level, is there sufficient evidence that the machine is not dispensing a mean of 250 mg? Set out your solution in full giving either a p-value or a critical value and state your decision.

   b Use a confidence interval to verify your answer.

12 A mathematics coaching school claims to significantly increase students' test results over a period of several coaching sessions. To test their claim a teacher tested 12 students prior to receiving coaching and recorded their results. The students were not given the answers or their results. At the conclusion of the coaching the teacher then administered the same test as before to check on the improvement. The paired results were:

Student	A	B	C	D	E	F	G	H	I	J	K	L
Before coaching	15	17	25	11	28	20	23	34	27	14	26	26
After coaching	20	16	25	18	28	19	26	37	31	13	27	20

Conduct a suitable hypothesis test to see if the mathematics coaching school claim was true.

13 A machine packs sugar into 1 kg bags. A random sample of eight filled bags was taken and the masses of the bags measured to the nearest gram. Their masses in grams were: 1001, 998, 999, 1002, 1001, 1003, 1002, 1002.   It is suspected that the machine overfills the bags. Perform a test at the 1% level, to determine whether the machine needs maintenance. It is known that the masses of the bags of sugar are normally distributed with a variance 2.25 g.

14 A machine is used to fill bottles with water. The bottles are to be filled to a volume of 500 mL. Ten random measurements of the volume give a mean of 499 mL with a standard deviation of 1.2 mL. Assuming that the volumes of water are normally distributed, test at the 1% level whether there is a significant difference from the expected value.

F   THE CHI-SQUARED DISTRIBUTION

THE 'GOODNESS OF FIT' TEST FOR ANY DISTRIBUTION

Have you ever tried to randomly generate the ten digits 0, 1, 2, 3, ..., 9?

This is easy to do on your calculator.   For example, on a **Casio** the instructions are:

   Go to   MENU $\rightarrow$ RUN $\rightarrow$ OPTN $\rightarrow$ F6(continue) $\rightarrow$ F4(NUM) $\rightarrow$ F2(Int) $\rightarrow$
        EXIT $\rightarrow$ F3(PROB) $\rightarrow$ they type 10F4(RAN#)

The question is: "Are these numbers *really* generated at random?"

With the techniques we have already seen, we are in a position to test whether or not our random number generator is indeed really a generator of numbers at random.

To begin with, if the numbers are randomly generated, if we generated say 100 different digits, we would expect to get on average the same frequency for each of the digits. That is, we would expect to get on average 10 "0's",   10 "1's",   10 "2's", etc.   In other words we are suggesting that the outcomes can be modelled by a discrete uniform distribution. If X is the RV representing the digit generated, then

$$X \sim DU(10) \quad \text{where} \quad x = 0, 1, 2, \ldots, 9,$$

and the probability mass function is $P(X = x) = \frac{1}{10}$.

I took a sample of 100 digits from my gdc using the above instructions for random generation and obtained the following results:

Score (x)	0	1	2	3	4	5	6	7	8	9
Observed frequency (f_o)	10	17	13	7	15	3	8	12	6	9
Expected frequency (f_e)	10	10	10	10	10	10	10	10	10	10

The null hypothesis is that the digits are generated at random and that the distribution of outcomes can be modelled by a discrete uniform distribution.

H_0: $X \sim DU(10)$ and H_1: X is not from a discrete uniform distribution,
i.e., the digits are not generated at random.

To test this hypothesis, we calculate what is known as the χ^2 (chi-squared) statistic.

This is $\chi^2_{calc} = \sum \dfrac{(f_o - f_e)^2}{f_e}$ where f_o is an observed frequency
and f_e is an expected frequency.

Note: All possible values of χ^2 are positive. Can you explain why?

In the above example,

$$\chi^2_{calc} = \frac{(10 - 10)^2}{10} + \frac{(17 - 10)^2}{10} + \frac{(13 - 10)^2}{10} + \ldots + \frac{(9 - 10)^2}{10}$$

We now use what is called "a χ^2 goodness-of-fit test". The chi-squared statistic χ^2_{calc} can be approximated by a χ^2 (chi-squared) distribution subject to certain conditions.

THE χ^2 (CHI-SQUARED) DISTRIBUTION

The χ^2 distribution depends on one parameter, the number of **degrees of freedom** ν (new), (similar to the student t-distribution considered earlier).

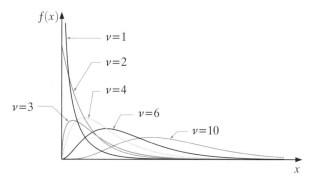

Refer to the diagram.
When $\nu = 1$ or 2, the distribution is J-shaped. When $\nu > 2$, it is positively skewed. The larger the value of ν, the more symmetric the distribution becomes and when ν is very large,

the distribution is approximately normal.

The number of degrees of freedom ν, is obtained by calculating the number of classes minus the number of restrictions,

i.e., $\nu = $ **number of classes** (n) $-$ **number of restrictions** (k)

In the above test for random generation, $\nu = n - k = 10 - 1 = 9$.

The restriction is explained by the fact that $\sum f_e = \sum f_o$.   This should always be true. Why?

The χ^2 test is conducted as a 1-tail (upper) test.

When performing the test, we need to know whether the test statistic χ^2_{calc} lies in the upper tail or **critical (rejection) region** in which case we would **reject** H_0, or in the main area of the χ^2 distribution.

The boundary value of the critical region is called the **critical value** and its value depends on the level of significance chosen (5% or 1% or whatever). This is consistent with hypothesis testing covered in section E.

In the diagram, the **critical (rejection) region** is the shaded area at the 5% significance level. We say $\alpha = 0.05$, the critical value is x_α and when $\nu = 3$, $x_\alpha \approx 7.814$.

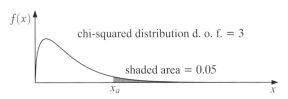

Hence, in a χ^2 test with $\nu = 3$, if $\chi^2_{calc} > 7.814$, then we would reject H_0.

So now let us test the problem about random generation introduced above. Below is a typical solution to the problem.

Example 49

> For the random number data, test at a 5% level if the data is indeed random.

1. **Hypotheses:** H_0:   the data is from a uniform distribution
                          H_1:   the data is not from a uniform distribution

2. **Null distribution:** χ^2-distribution with $\nu = 9$ (1-tailed)

3. **Test Statistic:** $\chi^2_{calc} = \sum \dfrac{(f_o - f_e)^2}{f_e} \approx 16.6$ {from graphics calc}

4. **Decision Rule:**   Reject H_0 if p-value is less than 0.05.

5. ***p*-value:** p-value $= P(\chi^2(9) > 16.6) \approx 0.0554$ {graphics calc}

6. **Decision:**   As the p-value is greater than 0.05, then we do not reject H_0.

7. **Conclusion:**   Hence, insufficient evidence exists to suggest that the calculator does not randomly generate digits from 0 to 9 (at the 0.05 level).

Example 50

It is claimed that the following data set has been selected from a uniform distribution. Test this assertion at a 5% level.

Score	5 - 9	10 - 14	15 - 19	20 - 24	25 - 29
Frequency	12	18	6	10	4

The sum of the frequencies is 50, so if the claim is true we would expect $\frac{50}{5} = 10$ as the frequency for each group.

i.e.,

Score	5 - 9	10 - 14	15 - 19	20 - 24	25 - 29
f_o	12	18	6	10	4
f_e	10	10	10	10	10

Hypotheses: H_0:   the data is from a uniform distribution
H_1:   the data is not from a uniform distribution

Null distribution: χ^2 distribution with $\nu = 4$

Test Statistic: $\chi^2_{calc} = \sum \dfrac{(f_o - f_e)^2}{f_e} = 12$ {using the lists of the gcalc.}

Decision Rule: Reject H_0 if p-value is less than 0.05

p-value: p-value $= P(\chi^2 > 12) \approx 0.0174$ {from the gcalc.}

Decision: As the p-value is less than 0.05, then we reject H_0.

Conclusion: Hence, sufficient evidence exists to suggest that the data did not come from a uniform distribution.

The χ^2-'goodness of fit' test is often used to test if data comes from
- a normal distribution   • a Poisson distribution   • a binomial distribution
- a uniform distribution   • or any other given distribution.

Example 51

It is claimed that the following data comes from a Poisson distribution with mean 5. Test this claim at a 0.01 level of significance.

Score	$\leqslant 3$	4	5	6	$\geqslant 7$	total
frequ.	6	9	10	7	4	36

First we need to prepare a table of observed and expected frequencies.

$P(X \leqslant 3) = \text{poissoncdf}(5, 3) \approx 0.2650$ and $36 \times 0.2650 \approx 9.54$
$P(X = 4) = \text{poissonpdf}(5, 4) \approx 0.1755$ and $36 \times 0.1755 \approx 6.32$
$P(X = 5) = \text{poissonpdf}(5, 5) \approx 0.1755$ and $36 \times 0.1755 \approx 6.32$
$P(X = 6) = \text{poissonpdf}(5, 6) \approx 0.1462$ and $36 \times 0.1462 \approx 5.26$
$P(X \geqslant 7) = 1 - P(X \leqslant 6)$
$\qquad\qquad = 1 - \text{poissoncdf}(5, 6) \approx 0.2378$ and $36 \times 0.2378 \approx 8.56$

Score	$\leqslant 3$	4	5	6	$\geqslant 7$
f_o	6	9	10	7	4
f_e	9.54	6.32	6.32	5.26	8.56

Note: If any of the expected frequencies are smaller than 5, we need to collapse that row and combine it with an adjacent row.

The reason for this is that if the expected frequency is < 5 it can distort the χ^2_{calc} value. This is because dividing by small values makes the fraction unnecessarily large and so χ^2_{calc} would be unnecessarily large.

$\nu = 4$ as we have one restriction   i.e., $\sum f_e = 36$.

Hypotheses: H_o: the data is from a Poisson distribution of mean 5
                    H_1:   the data is not from a Poisson distribution of mean 5

Null distribution: χ^2 distribution with $\nu = 4$

Test Statistic: $\chi^2_{calc} = \sum \dfrac{(f_o - f_e)^2}{f_e} \approx 7.60$ (using the lists of the gcalc.)

Decision Rule: Reject H_o if p-value is less than 0.01 (1% level of signif.)

p-value p-value $= P(\chi^2_{calc} > 7.60) \approx 0.107$ (from graphics calculator)

Decision: As the p-value is > 0.01, then we do not reject (accept) H_o.

Conclusion: Hence, insufficient evidence exists to suggest that the data did not come from a Poisson distribution with mean 5.

Example 52

The following data shows the number of children born to 150 Indian women in a 5-year period in the 19th Century. Test at a 5% level of significance, whether the data is binomial with parameters $n = 5$ and $p = 0.5$.

Number of children	0	1	2	3	4	5
Number of women	4	19	41	52	26	8

First we need to prepare a table of observed and expected frequencies.

$P(X = 0) = \text{bimompdf}(5, 0.5, 0) \approx 0.03125$ and $150 \times 0.03125 \approx 4.7$
$P(X = 1) = \text{bimompdf}(5, 0.5, 1) \approx 0.15625$ and $150 \times 0.15625 \approx 23.4$
$P(X = 2) = \text{bimompdf}(5, 0.5, 2) \approx 0.3125$ and $150 \times 0.3125 \approx 46.9$
$P(X = 3) = \text{bimompdf}(5, 0.5, 3) \approx 0.3125$ and $150 \times 0.3125 \approx 46.9$
$P(X = 4) = \text{bimompdf}(5, 0.5, 4) \approx 0.15625$ and $150 \times 0.15625 \approx 23.4$
$P(X = 5) = \text{bimompdf}(5, 0.5, 5) \approx 0.03125$ and $150 \times 0.03125 \approx 4.7$

Number of children	0	1	2	3	4	5
f_o	4	19	41	52	26	8
f_e	4.7	23.4	46.9	46.9	23.4	4.7

these two are < 5

Combining so no f_e is < 5 we get

Number of children	0 or 1	2	3	4 or 5	$\sum$
f_o	23	41	52	34	150
f_e	28.1	46.9	46.9	28.1	150

Hypotheses: H_o: the data is from a Binomial distribution of $n = 5$,
$p = 0.5$,   i.e., $X \sim B(5, 0.5)$

H_1:   the data is not distributed like this

Null distribution: χ^2 distribution with $\nu = 3$

Test Statistic: $\chi^2_{calc} = \sum \dfrac{(f_o - f_e)^2}{f_e} \approx 3.46$ (using the lists of the gcalc.)

Decision Rule: Reject H_o if p-value is less than 0.05 (5% level of signif.)

p-value: $p\text{-value} = P(\chi^2_{calc} > 3.46) \approx 0.326$ (from the gcalc.)

Decision: As the p-value is greater than 0.05, then we do not reject (accept) H_o.

Conclusion: Hence, insufficient evidence exists to suggest that the data did not come from a Binomial distribution with $n = 5$ and $p = 0.5$.

Example 53

Consider the Indian women/children data, but this time test if $X \sim B(5, p)$ where p is unspecified.

In order to do this, first we need to estimate p.

Notice that $\overline{x} = \dfrac{\sum fx}{\sum f} = \dfrac{4(0) + 19(1) + 41(2) + 52(3) + 26(4) + 8(5)}{150}$

$\therefore \quad \overline{x} = \dfrac{401}{150} \approx 2.673$

But, for a binomial distribution $\mu = np$

$\therefore \quad p = \dfrac{\mu}{n}$ is estimated by $\dfrac{\overline{x}}{n} \approx \dfrac{2.673}{5} \approx 0.5346$

$P(X = 0) = \text{bimompdf}(5, 0.5346, 0) \approx 0.021\,83$ and $150 \times 0.021\,83 \approx 3.3$
$P(X = 1) = \text{bimompdf}(5, 0.5346, 1) \approx 0.125\,40$ and $150 \times 0.125\,40 \approx 18.8$
$P(X = 2) = \text{bimompdf}(5, 0.5346, 2) \approx 0.288\,10$ and $150 \times 0.288\,10 \approx 43.2$
$P(X = 3) = \text{bimompdf}(5, 0.5346, 3) \approx 0.330\,93$ and $150 \times 0.330\,93 \approx 49.6$
$P(X = 4) = \text{bimompdf}(5, 0.5346, 4) \approx 0.190\,07$ and $150 \times 0.190\,07 \approx 28.5$
$P(X = 5) = \text{bimompdf}(5, 0.5346, 5) \approx 0.043\,67$ and $150 \times 0.043\,67 \approx 6.6$

Hence the table is:

Number of children	0 or 1	2	3	4	5	$\sum$
f_o	23	41	52	26	8	150
f_e	22.1	43.2	49.6	28.5	6.6	150

Hypotheses: H_o: the data is from a Binomial distribution of $n = 5$, p,
                          i.e., $X \sim B(5, p)$
                   H_1:   the data is not distributed like this

Null distribution: χ^2 distribution with $\nu = 3$ as the number of restrictions $= 2$
                         (These are, $\sum f_e = 150$ and we had to estimate p.)

Test Statistic: $\chi^2_{calc} = \sum \dfrac{(f_o - f_e)^2}{f_e} \approx 0.806$ {graphics calculator}

Decision Rule: Reject H_o if p-value is less than 0.05   (5% level of signif.)

p-value: p value $= P(\chi^2_{calc} > 0.806) \approx 0.848$ {graphics calculator}

Decision: As the p-value is greater than 0.05, then we do not reject
                (accept) H_o.

Conclusion: Hence, insufficient evidence exists to suggest that the data did
                  not come from a Binomial distribution.

MORE ON NUMBER OF DEGREES OF FREEDOM

If n is the number of classes involved (do not forget the need to collapse classes if $f_e < 5$)
then

Distribution		ν
Uniform		$n - 1$
Poisson	• if m is known	$n - 1$
	• if m is unknown and it is estimated from observed frequencies by $\overline{x} = m$	$n - 2$
Binomial	• if n and p are known	$n - 1$
	• if p is unknown and estimated from observed frequencies by $\overline{x} = np$	$n - 2$
Normal	• if μ and σ^2 are known	$n - 1$
	• if μ and σ^2 are unknown and estimated from observed frequencies by $\overline{x}$ and s_{n-1}	$n - 3$

Remember the fundamental rule:

Number of degrees of freedom = number of classes − number of restrictions

i.e., $\nu = n - k$.

'GOODNESS OF FIT' FOR CONTINUOUS RANDOM VARIABLES

Example 54

A drink bottle manufacturer sells bottled drinks with a nominal volume of 275 mL.

A consumer affairs employee measured 100 bottles and obtained the following frequency distribution:

Vol. (X) in mL	266-< 272	272-< 274	274-< 276	276<-278	278-< 280	280-< 286
Obs. bottles (f_o)	1	16	26	19	20	18

Use a χ^2 test at a 5% level of significance to determine whether or not the normal distribution is an adequate model for the data.

First we find unbiased estimates of μ and σ from the given data.

Mid-interval (x)	269	273	275	277	279	283
Frequency	1	16	26	19	20	18

$\longleftarrow \sum = 100$

From a calculator $\quad \bar{x} = 277.24 \quad$ and $\quad s_{n-1} \approx 3.4027 \quad\quad X \sim N(277.24, \, 3.4027^2)$

Expected frequency calculations:

$\quad\quad P(X < 272) \times 100 = \text{normalcdf}(-\text{E99}, \, 272, \, 277.24, \, 3.4027) \times 100 \approx 6.18$

$P(272 \leqslant X < 274) \times 100 \approx 10.87$

$P(274 \leqslant X < 276) \times 100 \approx 18.73$

$P(276 \leqslant X < 278) \times 100 \approx 23.06$

$P(278 \leqslant X < 280) \times 100 \approx 20.30 \quad$ and $\quad P(X \geqslant 280) \times 100 \approx 20.86$

Tabling these values:

Volume (mL)	< 272	272-274	274-276	276-278	278-280	$\geqslant 280$
f_o	1	16	26	19	20	18
f_e	6.18	10.87	18.73	23.06	20.30	20.86

Hypotheses: H_o: the data is from a normal distribution
                           i.e., $X \sim N(277.24, \, 3.4027^2)$
                      H_1:   the data is not distributed like this

Null distribution: χ^2 distribution with $\nu = 6 - 3 = 3$
                      $\sum f_e = 100 \quad$ and we had to estimate μ and σ

Test Statistic: $\chi^2_{calc} = \sum \dfrac{(f_o - f_e)^2}{f_e} \approx 10.696$ (using lists of the gcalc.)

Decision Rule: Reject H_o if p-value is less than 0.05   (5% level of signif.)

p-value: p value $= P(\chi^2_{calc} > 10.696 \approx 0.0135$ (from the gcalc.)

Decision: As the p-value is less than 0.05, then we do reject H_o.

Conclusion: Hence, sufficient evidence exists to suggest that the data did not come from a normal distribution. The normal distribution does not provide an adequate model of the data at a 5% level.

Example 55

The continuous random variable Y has a pdf $f(y) = 0.5e^{-0.5y}$, for $y \geqslant 0$.
A biologist in Taiwan believes that the lifetime of certain volatile microbes can
be modelled by this random variable Y measured in minutes.
The biologist carried out an experiment on the lifetime of 50 microbes and
recorded her results, given in the table below:

Lifetime (Y) in minutes	$\leqslant 1$	1-3	3-5	5-7	7-9	> 9
Observed no. of microbes (f_0)	15	16	10	5	3	1

a   Find the expected frequencies in each of the intervals.

b   At the 5% significance level, test whether the biologist's assumption is correct.

a   To find the expected frequencies under the null hypothesis, we need to
    firstly find the probabilities and multiply by 50. The probabilities are
    calculated by finding areas using definite integrals.

$$P(0 \leqslant Y \leqslant 1) = 50 \int_0^1 0.5e^{-0.5y} \, dy \approx 19.67$$

$$P(1 < Y \leqslant 3) = 50 \int_1^3 0.5e^{-0.5y} \, dy \approx 19.17$$

$$P(3 < Y \leqslant 5) = 50 \int_3^5 0.5e^{-0.5y} \, dy \approx 7.05$$

$$P(5 < Y \leqslant 7) = 50 \int_5^7 0.5e^{-0.5y} \, dy \approx 2.59$$

Likewise $P(7 < Y \leqslant 9) \approx 0.95$ and $P(Y > 9) \approx 0.57$

We form a table:

Lifetime (Y) in minutes	$\leqslant 1$	1-3	3-5	5-7	7-9	> 9
Observed no. of microbes (f_0)	15	16	10	5	3	1
Expected no. of microbes (f_e)	19.67	19.17	7.05	2.59	0.95	0.57

b   The expected number for $Y > 5$ is $\approx 2.59 + 0.95 + 0.57 \approx 4.11$ which is
    < 5. So, we combine further: for $Y > 3$,   expected number is
    $\approx 4.11 + 7.05 \approx 11.16$ and we have

Y	$\leqslant 1$	1-3	> 3
f_0	15	16	19
f_c	19.67	7.05	11.16

Hypotheses: H_o: the data is modelled by the continuous random
                          variable Y defined above
                  H_1:   the data is not distributed like this

Null distribution: χ^2 distribution with $\nu = 3 - 1 = 2$

Test Statistic: $\chi^2_{calc} = \sum \dfrac{(f_o - f_e)^2}{f_e} \approx 7.149$ {lists of the gcalc.})

Decision Rule: Reject H_o if p-value is less than 0.05   {5% level of signif.}

p-value: p-value $= P(\chi^2_{calc} > 7.149) \approx 0.0280$ {from the gcalc.}

Decision: As the p-value is smaller than 0.05, then we reject H_o.

> **Conclusion:**   Hence, insufficient evidence exists to suggest that the data did not come from a continuous exponential distribution given.
> At a 5% level of significance, we can say this distribution does provide an adequate model of the data.

THE χ^2 TEST FOR THE INDEPENDENCE OF TWO VARIABLES

The χ^2 test for the **independence of two variables** is used when data is given within a **two variable contingency table**.

The two variables could be

- 'preferred president' independent of 'race'
- 'preferred political party' independent of 'socio-economic status'
- 'degree of hypertension (high blood pressure)' independent of 'amount of smoking'.

Consider the following example.

200 Hungarian males over the age of forty had their blood pressure taken and were categorised as having either severe, mild or no hypertension. Also noted was the amount of smoking they undertook - it was categorised as none, moderate and heavy (hence categorical data). The data collected is summarised in the table below. It is wondered if hypertension and amount of smoking are independent (at the 0.05 level of significance).

Degree of hypertension	Amount of smoking			
	None	Moderate	Heavy	Total
severe	10	14	20	44
mild	20	18	31	69
none	40	22	25	87
Total	70	54	76	200

Note: This situation has $\nu = 4$ **degrees of freedom** calculated in a contingency table by:

$$\nu = (r-1)(c-1), \quad \text{where} \quad r = \text{the number of rows}$$
$$c = \text{the number of columns}$$

We need to determine the **expected cell values** *based on the assumption that the variables are independent (null hypothesis)*. To do this, calculate the row and column totals and the overall total.

Degree of hypertension	Amount of smoking			
	None	Moderate	Heavy	Total
severe	10	14	20	→ 44
mild	20	18	31	→ 69
none	40	22	25	→ 87
Total	70	54	76	200

Table of expected values:

Degree of hypertension	Amount of smoking			Total
	None	*Moderate*	*Heavy*	*Total*
severe	15.40	11.88	16.72	44
mild	24.15	18.63	26.22	69
none	30.45	23.49	33.06	87
Total	70	54	76	200

$$\text{this is } \frac{70 \times 44}{200} \qquad \text{this is } \frac{54 \times 87}{200} \qquad \text{this is } \frac{76 \times 69}{200}$$

Reason: E(severe hypertension **and** non smoking) $= np = 200 \times \frac{70}{200} \times \frac{44}{200} = \frac{70 \times 44}{200}$

We now find

$$\chi^2_{calc} = \sum \frac{(f_o - f_e)^2}{f_e} = \frac{(10 - 15.4)^2}{15.4} + \frac{(14 - 11.88)^2}{11.88} + \ldots\ldots + \frac{(25 - 33.6)^2}{33.6} \approx 9.576$$

These calculations are laborious and a graphics calculator provides a significant short cut. We enter the original contingency as a **matrix** and finally obtain a screen dump such as this.

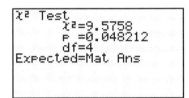

```
χ² Test
     χ²=9.5758
     P =0.048212
     df=4
Expected=Mat Ans
```

click on the appropriate icon for instructions

Finally, the solution is:

1   Null hypotheses: H_o: degree of hypertension and amount of smoking are statistically independent

H_1:   degree of hypertension and amount of smoking are statistically dependent

2   Null distribution: χ^2 distribution with $\nu = (3 - 1)(3 - 1) = 4$

3   Test Statistic: $\chi^2_{calc} = \sum \frac{(f_o - f_e)^2}{f_e} \approx 9.5758$ {test facility of the gcalc.}

4   Decision Rule: Reject H_o if p-value is less than 0.05

5 p-value: p-value $= P(\chi^2 > 9.5758) \approx 0.048\,212$ {graphics calculator}

6   Decision: As the p-value is less than 0.05, then we reject H_o.

7   Conclusion: Hence, sufficient evidence exists to suggest that degree of hypertension and amount of smoking are statistically dependent.

TWO BY TWO CONTINGENCY TABLES

If each of the variables under consideration has two levels, then **Yate's continuity correction** should be employed. However, this is no longer required in the syllabus so we can assume either we won't be tested on "Two by Two contingency tables" or we simply proceed as normal.

Note: The graphics calculator does not use Yate's continuity correction.

You must do this by hand by calculating $\sum \dfrac{(\mid f_o - f_e \mid - \frac{1}{2})^2}{f_e}$.

An example of a "Two by Two contingency tables" is provided below.

Example 56

A manager of a large life insurance company had been receiving complaints from sales managers because the company was hiring non-university qualified sales people. The sales managers suggested that the performance of the non-graduates was not as good as those who had university qualifications. 900 sales staff, 300 graduates and 600 non-graduates were sampled and their performance rated as either satisfactory or unsatisfactory.

The data is summarised alongside. Does the data support the sales managers' assertion?

Performance	Graduate	Non-graduate	Total
Satisfactory	172	311	483
Unsatisfactory	128	289	417
Total	300	600	900

Null hypotheses: H_o: Qualification and performance are statistically independent
H_1: Qualification and performance are statistically dependent

Null distribution: χ^2 distribution with $\nu = 1$

Test Statistic: $\chi^2_{calc} = \sum \dfrac{(f_o - f_e)^2}{f_e} \approx 2.43$

```
χ²-Test
 χ²=2.433084588
 P=.1187989248
 df=1

■
```

{using test facility of gcalc.}

with the Yates continuity correction
we get $\chi^2_{calc} \approx 2.22$, but this is an exclusion in the syllabus.

Decision Rule: Reject H_o if p-value is less than 0.05

p-value: p-value $= P(\chi^2 > 2.43) \approx 0.119$ (from the graphics calculator)
(with the Yates cc the p-value ≈ 0.137)

Decision: As the p-value is greater than 0.05, then we do not reject H_o.

Conclusion: Hence, insufficient evidence exists to suggest that qualification and performance are statistically dependent. So we accept the hypothesis that "Qualification and performance are statistically independent".

EXERCISE 8F

1   In "Series A" football played in Italy, the Juventus club claims its professionalism means that its results are independent of the weather.   During the season, they had the following results recorded from 50 games played:

Use a χ^2 test at both the 1% and 5% significance levels, to test the claim that the results of Juventus are independent of the weather.

	Weather		
Result	Good	Bad	Total
Win	12	4	16
Draw	8	4	11
Lose	8	14	23
Total	28	22	50

2 The Medical Association of Taiwan claims people who receive flu immunisation are less likely to suffer from colds in winter than those who do not have flu immunisation injections.

A random sample of 200 people

	No flu immunisation injections	Flu immunisation injections	Total
No colds	30	51	81
Colds	61	58	119
Total	91	109	200

was taken and the results recorded in the table given. Is the claim justified? Test at the 5% level of significance.

3 At the commencement of a school year, the Educational Authorities informed the principal that a "lack of attention to giving homework to students" by teachers was becoming a problem. The Authorities had figures that 58% of students thought this was a problem, 38% thought it was not a problem, and the rest were undecided. So, the Principal surveyed 200 students and found 97 thought this was a problem, 12 were undecided and the rest thought it was not a problem.

Use a "Goodness of fit" test at a 1% and 5% level of significance, to see if the Principal's survey results matched those of the Educational Authorities. Discuss, including a discussion of the types of possible errors, which level is the best for this problem.

4 The number of accidents reported to the local police station over a period of 52 weeks are recorded in the table:

Number of accidents	0	1	2	3
Number of weeks	26	11	10	5

   a Use the data set above to find the mean number of accidents per week.

   b Test at the 5% level of significance whether or not a Poisson distribution would adequately model this data set.

5 The results obtained by 400 students in Mathematics and English are displayed in the table below, but one entry was illegible due to spilled coffee over it.

	Pass English	Fail English
Pass Mathematics	198	92
Fail Mathematics	57	

   a Complete the missing entry.

   b Test at the 5% level of significance whether the performances in each subject are related.

6 Six coins are thrown simultaneously 275 times and the results are recorded in the table alongside:

Because a tail appeared at least once on every occasion, an observer concluded that exactly one of the coins must have had two tails whilst the other five coins were fair. In testing this assertion:

No. of tails	Frequency
1	13
2	47
3	91
4	85
5	31
6	8

   a clearly state the null and alternative hypotheses

   b test this assertion at the 5% level of significance.

7 A coin was tossed until a head appeared and the number of tosses required was recorded. This was repeated in all 100 times and the results were recorded in the given table:

Number of tosses required	Frequency
1	46
2	20
3	12
4	8
5	5
6	3
7	4
8	2

  a State the null distribution you would use to test if the coin is fair.

  b By calculating an appropriate χ^2 statistic, test at a 5% significance level, whether or not the null distribution gives a good fit to this data.

8 In a study to determine whether alcohol consumption and tobacco usage may be related, a survey of people was conducted. The table alongside details the results of the survey.

Perform a suitable test at a 5% level of significance to determine whether or not alcohol consumption and tobacco usage are related to each other.

Alcohol	Tobacco		
	None	1-15	16 or more
None	105	7	11
0.30 - 3.00	58	5	13
3.10 - 30.00	84	37	42
more than 30	57	16	17

9 The random variable X has a probability density function (pdf) $f(x)$ given by:

$$f(x) = \begin{cases} e - ke^x, & 0 \leqslant x \leqslant 1 \\ 0, & \text{otherwise} \end{cases}$$

  a Show that $k = 1$.

  b A battery producer believes that this pdf models the lifetime in years of the batteries he produces. To test his assertion he conducted an experiment by determining the lifetime of 50 of his batteries. The results are displayed in the table alongside:

  Perform a suitable test at the 5% significance level to determine whether or not the random variable defined above does adequately model his data.

Lifetime in years	Number of batteries
0 - 0.2	18
0.2 - 0.4	11
0.4 - 0.6	10
0.6 - 0.8	6
0.8 - 1	5

REVIEW SETS

REVIEW SET 8A

1 A soft drink manufacturer produces small and large bottles of drink. The volumes of both sizes of drink are distributed normally with means and standard deviations given in the table alongside.

	mean (mL)	s.d. (mL)
small drink	338	3
large drink	1010	12

  a Find the probability that one large bottle selected at random has a volume greater than the combined volume of three smaller bottles selected at random.

  b Find the probability that one large bottle selected at random has a volume three times larger than that of one smaller bottle selected at random.

2 The probability distribution for the random variable X is given in the table shown:

$X = x$	-3	-1	1	3	5
P$(X = x)$	c	c	c	c	c

Find the:

a value of c

b mean of X

c probability that X is greater than the mean

d variance of X, i.e., Var (X).

3 A student waits for a bus to take him to school. He knows that 35% of all the buses that pass his stop can take him to school. The others go elsewhere.

a If he catches the first bus that can take him to school, find:

   i the probability that it will take at most 4 buses for him to get a correct one

   ii the average number of buses it will take for him to get a correct one.

b If he catches the third bus that could take him to school, find:

   i the probability that it will take 7 buses to get him to school

   ii the average number of buses it will take for him to get to school

   iii the probability that it will take no more than 5 buses to get him to school.

4 Patients arrive at random to visit the local doctor at a rate of 14 per hour during visiting hours. Find the probability that:

a exactly five patients arrive to visit the doctor between 9:00 am and 9:45 am

b there will be fewer than seven patients arriving between 10:00 am and 10:30 am.

5 At the local supermarket, you can buy biros in packets of 12. On average, there are three faulty biros per packet. If you select two biros without replacement:

a describe the random variable F that indicates the number of faulty biros

b draw a probability distribution table for F.

c You decide that if two of the pens are faulty you will not buy the packet. If none of the pens is faulty you will buy the packet. If one of the pens is faulty, you will select another pen and if that is faulty, you will not buy the packet.

   i Find the probability that you will buy the packet.

   ii Find the probability you will buy the packet if you select two biros with replacement.

6 The weekly demand for petrol in thousands of kilolitres at a local service station is a continuous random variable with probability density function:

$$f(x) = \begin{cases} ax^3 + bx^2, & 0 \leqslant x \leqslant 1 \\ 0 & \text{elsewhere} \end{cases}$$

a If the mean weekly demand is 700 kilolitres, determine the values of a and b.

b Suppose the service station has a storage capacity of 950 kilolitres. Find the probability that the service station will run out of petrol in any given week.

7 Twelve percent of families in a certain wealthy district are known to never use the Internet. A random sample of 300 families is checked. Find the probability that the proportion of families that never use the internet is:

a less than 11%

b more than 14%

c between 11% and 14%.

8 To work out the credit limit of a prospective credit card holder a company gives points based on factors such as employment, income, home and car ownership and general credit history. A statistician working for the company randomly samples 40 applicants and determines the point total for each. These are:

> 214   211   213   213   215   212   212   212   210   211   211   211   212   213
> 214   213   211   212   214   214   214   213   215   214   211   210   211   216
> 211   212   212   210   211   210   210   212   213   213   213   212

a Determine the sample mean, $\overline{x}$, and standard deviation s_n.

b Determine a 95% confidence interval that the company would use to estimate the mean point score for the population of applicants.

9 225 randomly selected elite sports people were asked the question: "Should all elite athletes be tested for the HIV virus?" and 93% said "Yes".

a Estimate with a 95% confidence interval the percentage of all elite athletes who would say yes.

b Interpret your answer to **a**.

10 A die was rolled 420 times. A 'six' resulted on 86 occasions.

a Determine a 95% confidence interval to estimate the probability of rolling a 'six' with this die.

b Interpret your answer to **a**.

11 Quickchick grow chickens to sell to a supermarket chain. However, the buyers believe that the chickens are supplied underweight. As a consequence they consider the hypotheses:

> H_0:   Quickchick is not supplying underweight chickens
> H_1:   Quickchick is supplying underweight chickens.

What conclusion would result in: **a**   a type I error   **b**   a type II error?

12 Red and blue biros are sold in packets of six. Each biro is either red or blue. The manufacturer claims that the number of red biros in a packet can be modelled by a binomial distribution. He collects 100 packets at random and obtains the following information.

a Calculate the average (mean) number of red biros per packet.

b Hence, estimate the probability that a randomly chosen biro is red.

c By calculating an appropriate χ^2 statistic, test at a 10% significance level whether or not the binomial distribution gives a good fit to this data.

Number of red biros	Number of packets
0	1
1	3
2	9
3	17
4	31
5	28
6	11

13 In an effort to study the level of intelligence of students entering into a University, a psychologist collected data from 2000 students given an entrance test. The psychologist wished to determine whether the 2000 test scores came from a normal distribution with mean 100 and variance 100 which had been the pattern over the past 50 years. The psychologist prepared the following table but was unable to complete it through serious illness. The expected frequencies have been rounded to the nearest integer.

Score	Observed frequencies	Expected frequencies	Score	Observed frequencies	Expected frequencies
$\leqslant 75$	10	3	100.5-110.5	725	
$70.5 - 80.5$	45	48	110.5-120.5	250	253
$80.5 - 90.5$	287		120.5-130.5	40	38
$90.5 - 100.5$	641		$\geqslant 130.5$	2	2

  a Copy and complete the table, clearly explaining how you obtained your answers.

  b Test the hypothesis at the 5% level of significance.

14 A group of 10 students was given a revision course before their final IB examination. So that it could be seen if there was an improvement as a result of the revision course the students took a test at the beginning and at the end of the course. These marks were recorded in the table below.

Student	A	B	C	D	E	F	G	H	I	J
Pre-test	12	13	11	14	10	16	14	13	13	12
Post test	11	14	16	13	12	18	15	14	15	11

  a State why it would not be appropriate to work with the difference between the *means* of these two sets of scores. Hence determine a 90% confidence interval for the mean difference of the examination scores. Explain the meaning of your answer.

  b It was hoped that by doing the revision course the students' scores would improve. Perform an appropriate test at the 5% level of significance to determine whether this was the case.

REVIEW SET 8B

1 At a school fete, gamblers bet on the outcome of numbered counters X dollars chosen at random, with probability distribution given in the table.

$X = x$	-5	-1	3	6
$P(X = x)$	0.3	0.2	0.2	

  a What is the probability of getting a 6 on counter X?

  b What is the expected return per game for gamblers playing this game, if the score is the return paid to the gambler?

  c Explain why organisers should charge $1 to play this game rather than 50 cents.

A similar game involves randomly choosing counters Y with probability distribution given in the table alongside.

$Y = y$	-3	2	5
$P(Y = y)$	0.5	0.3	0.2

  d What is the expected return to gamblers for playing this game Y?

  e What is the expected return for gamblers wishing to play both games simultaneously?

  f How much would you expect the school to make if gamblers played games X and Y 500 times each, and the combined game of X and Y 1000 times if they charge $1 for any game played?

2 A coin is biased so that when it is tossed, the probability of obtaining tails is $\frac{3}{5}$. The coin is tossed 1000 times and X is the number of tails obtained. Find:

  a the mean of X **b** the standard deviation of X.

3 Pierre runs a game at a fair, where each player is guaranteed to win 10 Euros. Players pay a certain amount each time they throw an unbiased die and must keep throwing until a '6' occurs. When a '6' occurs Pierre gives the player 10 Euros. On average Pierre wishes to make a profit of 2 Euros per game. How much does he charge per throw?
Note: A game concludes when the 10 Euros are paid to the player.

4 Otto Hemmer Fishing Industries purchases fish of a certain type from fishermen in batches of 100. On average it is known that 13 of a batch of 100 fish have length less than 50 cm.

The buyers of fish for Otto Hemmer Industries are instructed to randomly sample 10 of the batch from a certain fisherman and only purchase the entire batch of 100 if the random sample has at most two fish with length less than 50 cm. Let X denote the number of fish with length less than 50 cm in this sample.

a Describe the distribution of X.

b Write down the formula for calculating $P(X = x)$ for $x = 0, \ldots, 10$.

c What is the probability that the buyer will purchase a batch of 100 fish from the fisherman on any day?

5 It is known that the proportion of times a journalist makes no errors per page is q.

a State the distribution of the random variable X that defines the number of errors made per page by that journalist.

b Find the probablity, in terms of q, that the journalist makes per page:
   i no errors   **ii** one error   **iii** more than one error.

c The journalist gets a bonus of $10 for no errors per page, $1 for just one error per page, but gets fined $8 for more than one error per page.
   i Draw a probability distribution table for the random variable Y, which describes the returns for the journalist for making different numbers of errors.
   ii Find $E(Y)$ in terms of q.
   iii Find the smallest value of q to three decimal places, $0 \leqslant q \leqslant 1$, such that the journalist will receive an overall bonus.

6 In the Japanese J-League, it is known that 75% of all the footballers in the history of the game prefer to kick with their right leg.

a In a random sample of 20 footballers from the J-League, find the probability that:
   i exactly 14 players prefer to kick with their right leg
   ii no more than five prefer to kick with their left leg.

b In a random sample of 1050 players from the J-League find the probability that:
   i exactly 70% of players prefer to kick with their right leg
   ii no more than 25% prefer to kick with their left leg.

   Hint: For **b** use a suitable approximation for the random variable
        X = the number of footballers who prefer to kick with their right leg.

7 To estimate the mean number of hours lost during a year due to sickness, a sample of 375 people will be used. Last year the standard deviation for the number of hours lost was 67 and we will use this as the standard deviation this year. What is the probability that the estimate is in error by more than ten hours?

8 The Transport Authority of Mars conducted a survey on motor vehicle accident deaths. They found that 56 out of 173 drivers tested positive for high levels of drugs or alcohol in their blood.

Estimate with a 90% confidence interval the true percentage of driver deaths on Mars where drivers have high levels of alcohol or drugs in their blood.

9 Battery manufacturers want to estimate the proportion of defective batteries produced by a machine in the workshop. A random sample of 400 batteries is tested and 32 are found to be defective.

  a Find a point estimate for the proportion of defective batteries produced by that machine.

  b Find a 95% interval estimate (CI) for the proportion of defective batteries produced by that machine.

  c If you conducted 150 such tests, how many of the 150 would you expect to contain the population proportion of defective items produced by that machine?

10 During the last Century, scientists exploring the nature of genetics recorded the following data relating to pea breeding:

Round and Yellow	Wrinkled and Yellow	Round and Green	Wrinkled and Green
306	109	92	49

According to the scientific theory of the day, the expected numbers are in the ratio $9 : 3 : 3 : 1$. Test at the 5% level of significance whether or not the scientific theory has been contradicted.

11 The table below summarises the incidence of tumours in 120 patients.

Construct a suitable test at the 1% level of significance to see if there is any association between the type of tumour and the location of the tumour.

		Type of tumour		
		Benign	Malignant	Other
Location	Lung	21	13	2
of	Breast	20	7	2
tumour	Other	18	27	10

12 A drink manufacturer produces soft drink for sale with each bottle having contents advertised at 375 kL. It is known that the machines producing these drinks are set so that the average volume per bottle produced is 376 mL with a standard devation of 1.84 mL. Given that the volumes of bottles are distributed normally, find:

    a the probability that an individual bottle randomly selected has a volume less than 373 mL

    b the probability that a randomly selected pack of a dozen bottles has an average volume less than the advertised amount.

Interpret these answers.

Government regulations are set to ensure that companies meet their advertising claims. If not, they will incur very heavy fines. The rules set for this company are either:

    I   A randomly selected bottle is allowed no less than 373 mL.   *or*

    II   A randomly selected pack of 12 bottles must have an average volume no less than the advertised amount.

    c Explain clearly by which method the company would prefer to be tested by the Government authority.

Suppose the company chose method II above. It wants less than 0.1% chance of being fined by the Government Authority.

    d Find, to the nearest mL, what the setting should be for the average volume of each bottle that the machines produce.

13 The random variable X has a normal distribution with mean μ and a randomly selected sample of size 15 is taken on X such that $\displaystyle\sum_{i=1}^{15} (x_i - \overline{x})^2 = 230$.

    a Find the sample variance for this sample.

    b Find an unbiased estimate of the population variance of the random variable X.

A confidence interval (not the 95% confidence interval) for μ taken from this sample is] 124.94, 129.05 [.

    c Find a 95% confidence interval for μ taken from this sample.

    d Determine the confidence level for the confidence interval   ] 124.94, 129.05 [.

14 A school claims to be able to teach anglers how to fish better and catch more fish. In order to test this hypothesis, the school recorded the number of fish caught by a random sample of nine anglers at a local jetty in a given time period before they started the course. After the fishing course was completed they recorded the number of fish caught by the same nine anglers at the same jetty in exactly the same time period. The results were:

Angler	A	B	C	D	E	F	G	H	I
No. fish caught before	24	23	22	30	41	30	33	18	15
after	36	32	40	27	32	34	33	28	19

    a Test at the 5% level whether the fishing school's claim is indeed correct. State the type of error you can make.

    b Find the 90% confidence interval for the mean difference of the two sets of scores and interpret the meaning of your answer.

HL Topic 9

(Further Mathematics SL Topic 3)

This topic explores the fundamental nature of algebraic structures and the relationships between them.

Included is an extension of the work covered in the **Core HL** text, on relations and functions, a formal study of sets and an introduction to group theory.

Sets, relations and groups

SETS

INTRODUCTION AND DEFINITION

Although many ideas relating to set theory had been an essential part of the growth of mathematics, it was not until **Georg Cantor** (1845-1918) that it was developed as a formal theory.

> A set is a well defined collection of objects. The objects in a set are called the **elements** or members of the set.

For example, if a set A contains the vowels in the English alphabet, then we write

$A = \{a, e, i, o, u\}$.

There is no doubt about what determines membership of this set of vowels. However, the collection of 10 best actors in the world would not be considered well defined, so this collection is not a set.

> If x is an element of a set A, then we write $x \in A$. The symbol '$\in$' means 'is an element of'. If x is not a member of A, we write $x \notin A$.

In the above example, $e \in A$ but $q \notin A$.

> A set is called a **finite set** if it contains a finite number of elements; otherwise it is termed an **infinite set**.

The number of distinct elements in a set A is denoted $n(A)$. This is sometimes written as $|A|$. Cantor called this the power of a set or its cardinal number.

Where $n(A)$ is small, it is usually easy to list all the elements in the set individually. However, an alternative notation can be used to describe sets without listing each element. The 'set-builder' notation $\{x \mid x$ has some specified property$\}$ is read as 'the set containing all elements, x, such that x has that property'.

For example, $\{x \mid x$ is an IB student enrolled in Mathematics HL$\}$ describes all IB students studying HL mathematics.

NUMBER SETS

The following infinite sets of numbers will already be familiar:

$\mathbb{N}$,   the set of natural numbers $\{0, 1, 2, ...\}$ (Note that 0 is omitted in some definitions.)

$\mathbb{Z}$,   the set of integers $\{0, \pm 1, \pm 2, ...\}$

$\mathbb{Q}$,   the set of rational numbers $\{x \mid x = \dfrac{p}{q}, \quad p, q \in \mathbb{Z}, \quad q \neq 0\}$

$\mathbb{R}$,   the set of real numbers

$\mathbb{C}$,   the set of complex numbers $\{z \mid z = a + ib, \quad a, b \in \mathbb{R}\}$

$\mathbb{Z}^+$, $\mathbb{Q}^+$, and $\mathbb{R}^+$ denote the positive elements of $\mathbb{Z}$, $\mathbb{Q}$, and $\mathbb{R}$ respectively.

For example, $\mathbb{Z}^+ = \{1, 2, 3, ...\}$.

Note that the set of real numbers is difficult to describe, but is considered to be well defined nevertheless. We know a number is real if it can be located on a number line.

Example 1

State whether each of the following is true:

a $3 \notin \mathbb{Q}$ b $\sqrt{9} \in \mathbb{Z}$ c $\pi \in \mathbb{Q}$

d $-6.9 \in \mathbb{Z}$ e $3.\overline{213} \in \mathbb{Q}$ f $\sqrt{-11} \in \mathbb{R}$

---

a False, as 3 can be written as $\frac{3}{1}$ and is therefore a rational number.

b True, as $\sqrt{9} = 3$.

c False, as π is an irrational number.

d False, as $-6.9 = -6\frac{9}{10}$, which is not an integer.

e True, as $3.\overline{213} = 3\frac{213}{999} = 3\frac{71}{333} = \frac{1070}{333}$ which makes it rational.

f False, as $\sqrt{-11}$ is an imaginary number. It belongs to $\mathbb{C}$ but not to $\mathbb{R}$.

EQUALITY OF SETS

Two sets are **equal** if and only if they contain the same elements. The order of elements in a set is not important.

For example, the set $\{a, b, c\}$ is the same set as $\{b, c, a\}$. The set $\{a, b, b, c\}$ is also equal to the previous two because repetitions of elements are ignored.

Example 2

State whether the following pairs of sets are equal:

a $\{3, 5, 7\}, \{5, 7, 3\}$ b $\{2, 2, 3, 5\}, \{2, 3, 5\}$

c {vowels in the English alphabet}, {a, e, i, o, u}

d {prime numbers between 24 and 28 inclusive}, {prime numbers between 32 and 36 inclusive}

e {integers between -3 and 7 inclusive}, {natural numbers between -3 and 7 inclusive}

---

a The order of the elements in a set does not matter, so the sets are equal.

b Repetition can be ignored, so the sets are equal.

c Both sets describe the same letters, so they are equal.

d Both sets are empty, so they are equal.

e The first set is $\{-3, -2, -1, 0, 1, 2, 3, 4, 5, 6, 7\}$ while the second is $\{0, 1, 2, 3, 4, 5, 6, 7\}$. $\therefore$ they are not equal.

EMPTY AND UNIVERSAL SETS

The **empty** or **null** set is defined as the set containing no elements, and is denoted $\varnothing$ or $\{\}$.

In any particular situation, the set containing all elements under consideration is called the **universal set**, $\mathbb{U}$. In statistics this would be the population, and in probability it corresponds to the sample space.

EXERCISE 9A.1

1 List the elements of the following sets and state the number of elements in each set:

    a $\{a, b, c\}$

    b $\{x \mid x \text{ is a prime number less than ten}\}$

    c $\{x \mid x \in \mathbb{Z},\ \ x \in [3, 8[$

    d $\{x \mid x \in \mathbb{R},\ \ x^2 = -9\}$

    e $\{3, 4, \{3\}, \{4\}\}$

    f $\{\varnothing\}$

2 State whether the following sets are finite or infinite:

    a $\{x \mid x \in \mathbb{Z},\ \ 0 < x < 100\}$

    b $\{x \mid x \in \mathbb{Q},\ \ 0 < x < 100\}$

3 Which of the following pairs of sets are equal?

    a $\{1, 2, 3, 3\}$ and $\{1, 2, 3\}$

    b $\{1, m, n\}$ and $\{m, 1, n\}$

    c $\{x \mid x \in \mathbb{Z},\ \ x^2 = 4\}$ and $\{x \mid x \in \mathbb{R},\ \ |x| = 2\}$

    d $\{\text{prime numbers of the form } 2n,\ n \in \mathbb{N},\ n > 1\}$ and $\{\text{negative numbers} > 3\}$

    e $\{x \mid x \in \mathbb{R},\ x \in]2, 5[\ \}$ and $\{x \mid x \in \mathbb{R},\ x \in [2, 5]\ \}$

SUBSETS

If set B only contains elements which are also found in set A, then B is a **subset** of A. Alternatively, we can say that B is a subset of A if, for all $x \in B$, $x \in A$.

B is a subset of A is denoted: $B \subseteq A$.

The empty set $\varnothing$ is a subset of every set, and every set is a subset of itself,

    i.e.,   for any set A: $\varnothing \subseteq A$ and $A \subseteq A$.

This latter property is called the **reflexive property** for set inclusion.

If a subset B of A is such that $B \neq A$, then B is said to be a **proper subset** of A. This is denoted: $B \subset A$.

Note also that for any set A, $A \subseteq \mathbb{U}$.

The subsets of the set $\{a, b\}$ are $\varnothing$, $\{a\}$, $\{b\}$, $\{a, b\}$.

Venn diagrams can be used for illustrating sets. The interior of a rectangle usually indicates the universal set $\mathbb{U}$, and interiors of circles are used for other sets. In illustrations of large numbers of sets, other closed figures may be used.

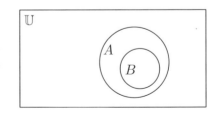

The Venn diagram alongside illustrates $B \subseteq A$.

The set of subsets of a set A is called the **power set**, $P(A)$. The number of subsets of a set with n elements is 2^n.

A proof of this is as follows:

For every subset of A, there will be two possibilities for each element $x \in A$: it will either be in the subset or it will not. Thus, for all n elements there will be 2^n different selections, and the number of subsets of A is 2^n.

> **Example 3**
>
> Find $P(A)$ if $A = \{p, q, r\}$.
>
> ---
>
> There will be $2^3 = 8$ elements of $P(A)$
> $$P(A) = \{\varnothing, \{p\}, \{q\}, \{r\}, \{p, q\}, \{p, r\}, \{q, r\}, \{p, q, r\}\}$$

Two sets A and B are **equal** if and only if $A \subseteq B$ and $B \subseteq A$.

One way to show two sets are equal is to show that:
- if $x \in A$ then $x \in B$ (this establishes that $A \subseteq B$), and
- if $y \in B$ then $y \in A$ (this establishes that $B \subseteq A$).

EXERCISE 9A.2

1 Find the power set $P(A)$ for each of the following sets:

    a $\{p, q\}$ **b** $\{1, 2, 3\}$ **c** $\{0\}$

2 For each of the following sets, state whether $A \subseteq B$ is true or false:

    a $A = \{$vowels in the English alphabet$\}$, $B = \{$letters in the word 'sequoia'$\}$
    b $A = \{0\}$, $B = \varnothing$
    c $A = \{3, 5, 9\}$, $B = \{$prime numbers$\}$
    d $A = \{x \mid a, b \in \mathbb{Z}, x = a + b\sqrt{2}\}$, $B = \{$irrational numbers$\}$

3 Prove using mathematical induction that $n(P(A)) = 2^{n(A)}$.

ALGEBRA OF SETS

INTERSECTION

The set consisting of the elements common to both set A and set B is called the **intersection** of the two sets, written $A \cap B$.

$$A \cap B = \{x \mid x \in A \text{ and } x \in B\}$$

The region shaded in the Venn diagram illustrates $A \cap B$.

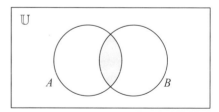

> **Example 4**
>
> Find $A \cap B$ if:
>   **a** $A = \{1, 2, 3, 4, 5, 6\}$ and $B = \{3, 5, 7, 9\}$
>   **b** $A = \{1, 2, 3, 4, 5, 6\}$ and $B = \{0, 7, 9\}$
>
> ---
>
>   **a** $A \cap B = \{3, 5\}$ **b** $A \cap B = \varnothing$

UNION

The set consisting of all the elements that are found in either *A or B* is called the **union** of the two sets, written $A \cup B$.

Note that in logic and mathematics, unless otherwise specified the word "or" is taken in its inclusive sense, i.e., it includes the "both" case.

$$A \cup B = \{x \mid x \in A \ \text{ or } \ x \in B\}$$

The shaded region illustrates $A \cup B$:

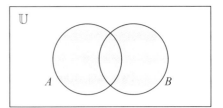

Example 5

Find $A \cup B$ if:

a $A = \{a, b, c, d, e\}$, $B = \{a, e, i, o, u\}$
b $A = \varnothing$, $B = \{1, 2, 3\}$
c $A = \{\text{even integers}\}$, $B = \{\text{odd integers}\}$
d $A = \{\text{prime numbers}\}$, $B = \mathbb{N}$

---

a $A \cup B = \{a, b, c, d, e, i, o, u\}$

b $A \cup B = \{1, 2, 3\}$ c $A \cup B = \mathbb{Z}$ d $A \cup B = \mathbb{N}$

LAWS OF INTERSECTION AND UNION

- $A \cap B \subseteq A \cup B$
- If $A \cup B = A \cap B$, then $A = B$
- $A \cup B = A$ if and only if $B \subseteq A$
- $A \cap B = A$ if and only if $A \subseteq B$
- $A \cap A = A$ (*Idempotent Law*)

- $A \cup A = A$ (*Idempotent Law*)
- $A \cap \varnothing = \varnothing$ (*Identity Law*)
- $A \cup \varnothing = A$ (*Identity Law*)
- $A \cup \mathbb{U} = \mathbb{U}$ (*Identity Law*)
- $A \cap \mathbb{U} = A$ (*Identity Law*)

Note: When we have proofs involving an equivalence statement

"if and only if"   or   iff   or $\Leftrightarrow$,   we need to perform the proof both ways.

So, if we are to prove that statement A is true if and only if statement B is true, then we have to do this both ways:

$(\Rightarrow)$ start by assuming statement A and prove that statement B is true,   **and**
$(\Leftarrow)$ assume statement B and prove that statement A is true.

For example, if we want to prove that   if a and b are positive, $a > b \ \Leftrightarrow \ a^2 > b^2$, we prove this as follows:

$(\Rightarrow)$ if $a > b$
$\Rightarrow \ a - b > 0$
$\Rightarrow \ (a - b)(a + b) > 0$ {as $a, b > 0$}
$\Rightarrow \ a^2 - b^2 > 0$
$\Rightarrow \ a^2 > b^2$

$(\Leftarrow)$ if $a^2 > b^2$
$\Rightarrow \ a^2 - b^2 > 0$
$\Rightarrow \ (a - b)(a + b) > 0$
$\Rightarrow \ a - b > 0$ {as $a + b > 0$}
$\Rightarrow \ a > b$

Example 6

Prove that $A \cup B = A$ if and only if $B \subseteq A$.

$(\Rightarrow)$ Suppose $A \cup B = A$.
   If $B = \varnothing$ then we know $B \subseteq A$
   If $B \neq \varnothing$,   then let $x \in B$
$$\therefore \quad x \in A \cup B$$
$$\therefore \quad x \in A$$
   i.e.,   if $x \in B$ then $x \in A$ $\therefore$ $B \subseteq A$.

$(\Leftarrow)$ Now let $B \subseteq A$ and suppose $A \cup B \neq A$
   $A \subseteq A \cup B$ {from the definition of a subset}
   But $A \cup B \neq A$ so $A \cup B \nsubseteq A$
   $\therefore$ there is an element $x \in A \cup B$ such that $x \notin A$
   Now if $x \in A \cup B$ and $x \notin A$,   then $x \in B$
   But this means $B \nsubseteq A$,   which is a contradiction.
   Hence $A \cup B = A$.

Therefore $A \cup B = A$ if and only if $B \subseteq A$.

DISJOINT SETS

If $A \cap B = \varnothing$, we say that A and B are **disjoint**. A and B contain no common elements.

If $A \cap B = \varnothing$ and $A \cup B = \mathbb{U}$ we say that A and B **partition** $\mathbb{U}$.

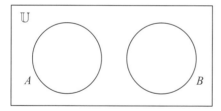

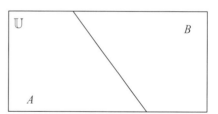

COMPLEMENT

The **complement** of A, written A', contains all elements of $\mathbb{U}$ which are not in A. This is sometimes called the **absolute complement**.

The shaded region in the diagram represents A':

Note: $A \cap A' = \varnothing$ and $A \cup A' = \mathbb{U}$

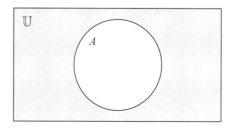

EXERCISE 9A.3

1 $A = \{1, 3, 5, 7\}, \quad B = \{0, 1, 2, 3, 4\}, \quad C = \{6, 7, 8\}, \quad \mathbb{U} = \{n \mid n \in \mathbb{N}, \ n \leqslant 9\}$

Find each of the following:

   a $A \cup B$ **b** $A \cap C$ **c** $B \cap C$ **d** $A \cap (B \cup C)$

   e $(A \cap B) \cup (A \cap C)$ **f** B' **g** $(A \cup B)'$ **h** $A' \cap B'$

2 Assuming A and B are non-empty sets, draw separate Venn diagrams to illustrate the following cases:

   a $A \cap B = \varnothing$ **b** $A \cup B = A$ **c** $A \cap B' = A$ **d** $A \cup B = \varnothing$

   e $A \cap B' = \varnothing$ **f** $A \cup B = A \cap B$ **g** $A \cup B = A \cap B'$

3 **a** Prove that $n(A \cup B) = n(A) + n(B) - n(A \cap B)$

   b In a class of 30 students, 16 play tennis and 15 play basketball. There are 6 students who play neither of these games. How many play both tennis and basketball?

4 Prove the **transitive property** of set inclusion, i.e., if $A \subseteq B$ and $B \subseteq C$, then $A \subseteq C$.

ASSOCIATIVE AND DISTRIBUTIVE PROPERTIES

Both union of sets and intersection of sets are **associative** operations. Union of sets is also said to be **distributive** over intersection and intersection is **distributive** over union,

i.e.,   • $(A \cup B) \cup C = A \cup (B \cup C)$ and $(A \cap B) \cap C = A \cap (B \cap C)$

    • $A \cup (B \cap C) = (A \cup B) \cap (A \cup C)$ and $A \cap (B \cup C) = (A \cap B) \cup (A \cap C)$

These laws can be easily shown with Venn Diagrams. A formal proof for the first of the distributive laws is as follows:

Example 7

For all sets A and B, prove that $A \cup (B \cap C) = (A \cup B) \cap (A \cup C)$

$(\Rightarrow)$ Let $x \in A \cup (B \cap C)$. Then $x \in A$ or $x \in B \cap C$

    If $x \in A$, then $x \in A \cup B$ and $x \in A \cup C$

    $\Rightarrow \quad x \in (A \cup B) \cap (A \cup C)$

    If $x \in B \cap C$, then $x \in B$ and $x \in C$.

              $\Rightarrow \quad x \in A \cup B$ and $x \in A \cup C$

              $\Rightarrow \quad x \in (A \cup B) \cap (A \cup C)$

    This establishes that $A \cup (B \cap C) \subseteq (A \cup B) \cap (A \cup C)$ ..... (1)

$(\Leftarrow)$ Now let $x \in (A \cup B) \cap (A \cup C)$

    Then $x \in A \cup B$ and $x \in A \cup C$

    If $x \in A$, then $x \in A \cup (B \cap C)$

    If $x \notin A$, then $x \in B$ and $x \in C$

    $\Rightarrow \quad x \in B \cap C \quad \Rightarrow \quad x \in A \cup (B \cap C)$

    This establishes that $(A \cup B) \cap (A \cup C) \subseteq A \cup (B \cap C)$ ..... (2)

Together, (1) and (2) give: $A \cup (B \cap C) = (A \cup B) \cap (A \cup C)$

DE MORGAN'S LAWS

Two important laws in set algebra are known as **De Morgan's Laws**. These are:

$$(A \cup B)' = A' \cap B' \quad \text{and} \quad (A \cap B)' = A' \cup B'$$

Example 8

Prove that $(A \cup B)' = A' \cap B'$

$(\Rightarrow)$ If $x \in (A \cup B)'$, then $x \notin (A \cup B)$
$\qquad\qquad\qquad\qquad \therefore \quad x \notin A$ and $x \notin B$
$\qquad\qquad\qquad\qquad$ i.e., $\quad x \in A'$ and $x \in B'$
$\qquad\qquad\qquad\qquad \therefore \quad x \in A' \cap B'$
This establishes that $(A \cup B)' \subseteq A' \cap B'$ ..... (1)

$(\Leftarrow)$ If $x \in A' \cap B'$, then $x \in A'$ and $x \in B'$
$\qquad\qquad\qquad\qquad \therefore \quad x \notin A$ and $x \notin B$
$\qquad\qquad\qquad\qquad \therefore \quad x \notin A \cup B$
$\qquad\qquad\qquad\qquad \therefore \quad x \in (A \cup B)'$
This establishes that $A' \cap B' \subseteq (A \cup B)'$ ..... (2)

Together, (1) and (2) give: $(A \cup B)' = A' \cap B'$

De Morgan's laws can also be verified using Venn diagrams.

A summary of the laws of the algebra of sets is given below:

Idempotent Laws: $A \cup A = A$	$A \cap A = A$
Associative Laws: $(A \cup B) \cup C = A \cup (B \cup C)$	$(A \cap B) \cap C = A \cap (B \cap C)$
Commutative Laws: $A \cup B = B \cup A$	$A \cap B = B \cap A$
Distributive Laws: $A \cup (B \cap C) = (A \cup B) \cap (A \cup C)$	$A \cap (B \cup C) = (A \cap B) \cup (A \cap C)$
Identity Laws: $A \cup \varnothing = A \qquad A \cup \mathbb{U} = \mathbb{U}$	$A \cap \mathbb{U} = A \qquad A \cap \varnothing = \varnothing$
Complement Laws: $A \cup A' = \mathbb{U} \qquad (A')' = A$	$A \cap A' = \varnothing \qquad \mathbb{U}' = \varnothing, \quad \varnothing' = \mathbb{U}$
De Morgan's Laws: $(A \cup B)' = A' \cap B'$	$(A \cap B)' = A' \cup B'$

DIFFERENCE

The **difference** between two sets A and B, sometimes called the **relative complement**, is defined to be

$$A \backslash B = \{x \mid x \in A \quad \text{and} \quad x \notin B\}$$

$A \backslash B$ consists of all those elements which are found in A but not in B, so

$$A \backslash B = A \cap B'$$

The region is shaded in the Venn diagram:

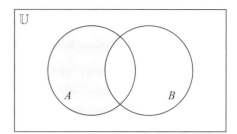

Set difference is not a commutative operation, so in general,

$$A\backslash B \neq B\backslash A.$$

Example 9

Find   **i** $A\backslash B$ and   **ii** $B\backslash A$ if:

a $A = \{1, 2, 3\}$, $B = \{4, 5\}$
b $A = \{a, b, c, d\}$, $B = \{b, d, e, f\}$
c $A = \{1, 2, 3, 4, 5\}$, $B = \{2, 4\}$

---

a   **i** $A\backslash B = \{1, 2, 3\} = A$ **ii** $B\backslash A = \{4, 5\} = B$
b   **i** $A\backslash B = \{a, c\}$ **ii** $B\backslash A = \{e, f\}$
c   **i** $A\backslash B = \{1, 3, 5\}$ **ii** $B\backslash A = \varnothing$

SYMMETRIC DIFFERENCE

The **symmetric difference** is defined by $A\Delta B = (A\backslash B) \cup (B\backslash A)$

The symmetric difference of sets A and B is the set made up of all the elements which are in A or B but not both. This is illustrated in the Venn diagram:

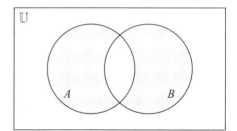

Example 10

Find $A\Delta B$ for:
a $A = \{1, 2, 3\}$, $B = \{4, 5\}$
b $A = \{a, b, c, d\}$, $B = \{b, d, e, f\}$
c $A = \{1, 2, 3, 4, 5\}$, $B = \{2, 4\}$

---

a $A\Delta B = \{1, 2, 3, 4, 5\}$ **b** $A\Delta B = \{a, c, e, f\}$

c $A\Delta B = \{1, 3, 5\}$

Note that:
- $A\Delta B = B\Delta A$ **Commutative property**
- $A\Delta(B\Delta C) = (A\Delta B)\Delta C$ **Associative property**
- $A\Delta\varnothing = A$ • $A\Delta A = \varnothing$ • $A\Delta A' = \mathbb{U}$

EXERCISE 9A.4

1 If $P = \{o, n, u, a\}$, $M = \{c, n, a, e\}$ and the universal set is $\mathbb{U} =$ letters in the word "conjugate", find:

a $P \cup M$ **b** $P \cap M$ **c** P'

d $P' \cup M'$ **e** $(P \cap M)'$ **f** $P \cap (M \cup P)$

2 In each of the Venn diagrams below, shade the region corresponding to:

  i $A \cup B$ **ii** $A \cap B$ **iii** $A \backslash B$ **iv** $A \triangle B$

a 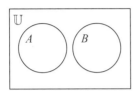 **b** 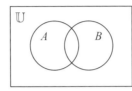 **c**

3 In the Venn diagram shown, shade the region corresponding to:

  a $A \cup B'$ **b** $A' \cap B$

  c $(A \cup B)'$ **d** $(A' \cap B')'$

  e $(A \cup B) \backslash (A \cap B)$ **f** $A \cap (B \cup A')$

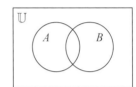

4 Find **i** $S \backslash T$ **ii** $T \backslash S$ if:

  a $S = \{1, 2, 3, 4\}$, $T = \{1, 3\}$ **b** $S = \mathbb{R}$, $T = \mathbb{Q}$

  c $S = \{0, 1, 2, 3\}$, $T = \{2, 3, 4, 5\}$ **d** $S = \{2, 3, 4\}$, $T = \{0, 1, 5\}$

5 Find $A \triangle B$ if:

  a $A = \{a, b, c, d, e\}$, $B = \{a, e\}$ **b** $A = \{1, 2, 3, 4\}$, $B = \{3, 4, 5\}$

  c $A = \{2, 4, 6\}$, $B = \{1, 3, 5\}$ **d** $A = \{9, 11, 13\}$, $B = \varnothing$

6 Prove that $A \triangle B = A \cup B$ if and only if $A \cap B = \varnothing$.

7 Prove:

  a $(A \cup B) \cap (A' \cup B) = B$ **b** $A \cap (B \backslash C) = (A \cap B) \backslash (A \cap C)$

B ORDERED PAIRS

DEFINITION

We are familiar with the concept of an ordered pair, from locating points in the Cartesian plane. However, an ordered pair need not have numbers as elements.

> An **ordered pair** (a, b) is defined to contain two components or coordinates: a first component a and a second component b.

Two ordered pairs are equal if and only if their corresponding components are equal.

i.e., $(a, b) \equiv (c, d)$ if and only if $a = c$ and $b = d$

Thus $(a, b) \equiv (b, a)$ if and only if $a = b$.

CARTESIAN PRODUCT

Given two sets A and B, the set which contains all the ordered pairs (a, b) such that $a \in A$ and $b \in B$ is called the **Cartesian product** of A and B, written $A \times B$.

$$A \times B = \{(a, b) \mid a \in A, b \in B\}$$

Thus, $\{1, 2, 3\} \times \{5, 6\} = \{(1, 5), (1, 6), (2, 5), (2, 6), (3, 5), (3, 6)\}$.

The **Cartesian plane** is $\mathbb{R} \times \mathbb{R}$, sometimes written $\mathbb{R}^2$.

In general, commutativity does not hold, i.e., $A \times B \neq B \times A$. The exceptions are when $A = B$, or when either A or B is the empty set, in which case $A \times B$ and $B \times A$ both equal the empty set.

The number of elements in $A \times B$ is found by multiplying the number of elements in each of A and B:

$$n(A \times B) = n(A) \times n(B)$$

Example 11

Prove that $A \times (B \cap C) = (A \times B) \cap (A \times C)$
i.e.,   the Cartesian product is distributive over set intersection.

$(\Rightarrow)$ Let $(x, y) \in A \times (B \cap C)$
$\Rightarrow$ $x \in A$ and $y \in B \cap C$
$\Rightarrow$ $x \in A$, $y \in B$ and $y \in C$
$\Rightarrow$ $(x, y) \in A \times B$ and $(x, y) \in A \times C$
$\Rightarrow$ $(x, y) \in (A \times B) \cap (A \times C)$
$\Rightarrow$ $A \times (B \cap C) \subseteq (A \times B) \cap (A \times C)$ ...... (1)

$(\Leftarrow)$ Let $(x, y) \in (A \times B) \cap (A \times C)$
$\Rightarrow$ $(x, y) \in A \times B$ and $(x, y) \in A \times C$
$\Rightarrow$ $x \in A$, $y \in B$ and $y \in C$
$\Rightarrow$ $x \in A$ and $y \in B \cap C$
$\Rightarrow$ $(x, y) \in A \times (B \cap C)$
$\Rightarrow$ $(A \times B) \cap (A \times C) \subseteq A \times (B \cap C)$ ...... (2)

Hence, from (1) and (2), $A \times (B \cap C) = (A \times B) \cap (A \times C)$

EXERCISE 9B.1

1 Find **i** $A \times B$ **ii** $B \times A$ if:
   a $A = \{1, 2\}$ and $B = \{3, 4, 5\}$ **b** $A = \{a\}$ and $B = \{a, b\}$
   c $A = \{1, 2, 3\}$ and $B = \varnothing$

2 Graph $A \times B$ on the Cartesian plane if:
   a $A = \{-2, 0, 2\}$, $B = \{-1, 0, 1\}$
   b $A = \{x \mid 2 \leqslant x < 5, \ x \in \mathbb{R}\}$, $B = \{x \mid -1 \leqslant x < 4, \ x \in \mathbb{R}\}$

3 Prove that $A \times (B \cup C) = (A \times B) \cup (A \times C)$.

RELATIONS

INTRODUCTION

A **relation** is any set of ordered pairs.

Any subset of the Cartesian product of two sets A and B is a relation.
If R is a relation and $(x, y) \in R$, then we sometimes write xRy.
xRy reads 'x is related to y'.
If $R \subseteq A \times B$, then R is said to be "a relation from A to B".

If $R = X \times Y$, then X is called the domain of R and Y is called the range.

The **domain** consists of all possible first components of the ordered pairs of the relation.
The **range** contains all possible second components.

If R is a relation from A to B then the domain of R is a subset of A and the range of R is a subset of B.
If $R \subseteq A \times A$, we say that R is "a relation in A".

The following are examples of relations:

$R = \{(1, 3), (2, 4), (3, 1), (3, 4)\}$ is a relation in $\mathbb{N}$
$R = \{(1, 2.5), (2, 3.7), (4, 2), (3, 7.3)\}$ is a relation from $\mathbb{N}$ to $\mathbb{Q}$
$R = \{(x, y) \mid x^2 + y^2 = 9, \ x, y \in \mathbb{R}\}$ is a relation in $\mathbb{R}$
$R = \{(x, (y, z)) \mid y^2 + z^2 = x^2, \ x, y, z \in \mathbb{Z}\}$ is a relation from $\mathbb{R}$ to $\mathbb{R}^2$

REFLEXIVE RELATIONS

A relation R in a set S is said to be **reflexive** if, for all $a \in S$, aRa.

R is a reflexive relation on the set $\{1, 2, 3, 4\}$ if and only if $\{(1, 1), (2, 2), (3, 3), (4, 4)\} \subseteq R$

Example 12

Which of the following relations are reflexive?
a   The relation R in a set of school students where xRy if and only if x and y attend the same school.
b   The relation in children in a family, "is the brother of".
c   The relation R in $\mathbb{Z}$ where xRy if and only if $x \leqslant y$.
d   The relation R in $\{1, 2, 3\}$ where $R = \{(1, 1), (1, 2), (3, 2), (3, 3)\}$.
e   The relation R in $\mathbb{R}$ where xRy if and only if $x = y$.

a   Reflexive since a student always goes to the same school as him or herself.
b   Not reflexive since you are not your own brother, especially if you are a girl.
c   Reflexive as $x \leqslant x$ for all $x \in \mathbb{Z}$.   d   Not reflexive as $(2, 2) \notin R$.
e   Reflexive by definition.

SYMMETRIC RELATIONS

A relation R in a set S is said to be **symmetric** if, for all $a, b \in S$, aRb implies bRa.

So, a relation R is symmetric if, for all $(a, b) \in R$, $(b, a) \in R$.

Example 13

Which of the following are symmetric relations?
a   A relation R in $\{1, 2, 3, 4\}$ where $R = \{(1, 2), (2, 1), (3, 3), (4, 2), (2, 4)\}$
b   The relation in a set of people, "is the sibling of".
c   The relation in a set of people, "is the brother of".
d   The relation in $\mathbb{Z}$ where xRy if and only if $x \leqslant y$.
e   The relation in $\mathbb{R}$ where xRy if and only if $x = y$.

a   Symmetric   b   Symmetric. In a set of people, not every person will have a
                           sibling. All that is required here is that if a is the brother or
                           sister of b then b will be the brother or sister of a.

c   Not symmetric. For example, Paul may be the brother of Anne, but Anne is
     not the brother of Paul.

d   Not symmetric. For example, $3 \leqslant 7$ but $7 \not\leqslant 3$ e   Symmetric.

Note that when a relation is not symmetric, we describe it as *non-symmetric* or just *not symmetric*. The term *anti-symmetric* is reserved for a special set of non-symmetric relations; in an anti-symmetric relation if xRy then it is never true that yRx unless $x = y$.

$\{(1, 2), (2, 1), (3, 2), (2, 3)\}$ is symmetric
$\{(1, 2), (2, 1), (3, 2)\}$ is non-symmetric but not anti-symmetric
$\{(1, 2), (2, 3), (3, 3)\}$ is anti-symmetric

TRANSITIVE RELATIONS

A relation R in a set S is **transitive** if, for all $a, b, c \in S$, aRc whenever aRb and bRc.

If (a, b) and (b, c) are both elements of R, then so must (a, c). Establishing this can be a time consuming process in many instances. It is often useful to make list of all possibilities and check each one.

Example 14

Which of the following relations are transitive?
a   The relation R on $\{1, 2, 3, 4\}$ where $R = \{(1, 1), (1, 2), (2, 3), (1, 3)\}$
b   The relation in a set of buildings, "is older than".
c   The relation in a set of people, "is the father of".
d   The relation R in $\mathbb{Z}$ where xRy if and only if $x \leqslant y$.
e   The relation in $\mathbb{R}$ where xRy if and only if $x = y$.

a   Transitive;   e.g., from (1, 2) and (2, 3),   (1, 3) must be in R, which is true.
b   Transitive;   if building a is older than building b, and building b is older
     than building c, then a is older than c.

> **c**   Not transitive;   if a fathers b and b fathers c, then a is the grandfather of c,
> not the father.
>
> **d**   Transitive;   if $a \leqslant b$ and $b \leqslant c$, then $a \leqslant c$.
>
> **e**   Transitive;   if $a = b$ and $b = c$, then $a = c$.

In the above examples, the relation of equality was seen to be reflexive, symmetric and transitive. This will lead us to consider a special class of relations in the next section.

EXERCISE 9B.2

1   State the domain and range of each of the following relations:

    a $\{(0,\, 5),\, (1,\, 3),\, (2,\, 2)\}$ **b** $\{(x,\, y) \mid x^2 + y^2 = 9,\ \ x \in \mathbb{Z}\}$

    c $\{(x,\, y) \mid y = \sin x,\ \ x \in \mathbb{R}\}$

2 $A = \{2,\, 3,\, 4,\, 5\}$ and $B = \{5,\, 6,\, 7,\, 8\}$.   Write R as a set of ordered pairs if:

    a $xRy \ \Leftrightarrow \ x$ is a factor of y **b** $xRy \ \Leftrightarrow \ y = x + 3$

    c $xRy \ \Leftrightarrow \ y > 2x$

3   Determine whether each of the following relations is:

        i   reflexive   **ii**   symmetric   **iii**   transitive

    a xRy if y is the brother of x **b** xRy if y is older than x

    c xRy if x and y live in the same country

    d xRy if x and y have the same mother

4   Let R be a relation on $\mathbb{N}$ defined by xRy where x and y are co-prime (share no common factors except 1). Determine whether R is:

    a   reflexive   **b**   symmetric   **c**   transitive

5   Let R be a relation in a family of sets. Determine whether R is

        i   reflexive   **ii**   symmetric   **iii**   transitive

    for the cases: **a** $ARB \ \Leftrightarrow \ A$ and B are disjoint   **b** $ARB \ \Leftrightarrow \ A \subseteq B$

                    c $ARB \ \Leftrightarrow \ n(A) = n(B)$

EQUIVALENCE RELATIONS

Definition:

> A relation in a set S which is reflexive, symmetric *and* transitive is said to be an
> **equivalence relation** in S.

Equality and congruence are obvious examples of equivalence relations.

If we graphed a relation on the Cartesian plane, then the following would apply:

    If R is reflexive, all possible points on the line $y = x$ must be included.

        For example,   if $S = \{-2,\, -1,\, 0,\, 1\}$ then $(-2,\, -2),\, (-1,\, -1),\, (0,\, 0)$,
                 and $(1,\, 1)$ must all appear on the graph.

    If R is symmetric then the graph must be symmetric about the line $y = x$.

THE EMPTY RELATION

If $A = \{1, 2, 3\}$,   examples of relations on A are:
$$R_1 = \{(1, 3), (2, 1), (1, 1)\}$$
$$R_2 = \{(1, 2)\}$$
$$R_3 = \{ \ \}$$

R_3 is the empty set. A relation R in a set is a set of ordered pairs, so any subset of a set of ordered pairs will be a relation. This includes the empty set which is referred to as the **empty relation**.

For the empty relation in a non-empty set S, the following are both true statements:

for all $a, \ b \in S$,   if aRb then bRa

for all $a, \ b, \ c \in S$,   if aRb and bRc then aRc

They are conditional statements and do not require that any element of S is related to any other.

Because there are no $a, b \in S$ such that aRb, the empty relation is symmetric and transitive by default.

However, if S is non-empty and $a \in S$, then if aRa, then R must be a non-empty relation, $\therefore$ the empty relation is not reflexive.

Hence the empty relation on a non-empty set is symmetric and transitive but is not reflexive.

A consequence of the reflexive requirement is that the empty relation on a non-empty set is not an equivalence relation. Further, as aRa for all $a \in S$,   the domain of an equivalence relation in S is S.

The empty relation is not the only instance of a relation which is symmetric and transitive but not reflexive.

e.g.,   the relation R in $A = \{a, b, c, d\}$ where
$$R = \{(a, a), (a, b), (b, a), (b, b), (a, c), (c, a), (c, c), (c, b), (b, c)\}$$

EQUIVALENCE CLASSES

If a set S is separated into subsets which are disjoint and such that their union is S, then we say S has been partitioned. An equivalence relation on S partitions S into sets which are called **equivalence classes**.

Examples:

1   Define the relation R on $\mathbb{Z}$ by

$aRb \Leftrightarrow a$ and b have the same remainder on division by 2,   where $a, b \in \mathbb{Z}$

This relation partitions $\mathbb{Z}$ into two equivalence classes; the set of odd integers and the set of even integers.

2   Let P be the set of polygons.
Define the relation R on P by

$aRb \Leftrightarrow a$ and b have the same number of sides, where $a, b \in P$.

R partitions P into an infinite number of equivalence classes; the set of triangles, the set of quadrilaterals, the set of pentagons, etc.

Theorem 1: An equivalence relation R on a set S partitions S into disjoint subsets.

Proof: As every element $a \in S$ is such that aRa (reflexive property of equivalence relations), every element must appear in the set of ordered pairs in R, and thus must appear in an equivalence class.

Hence the union of equivalence classes must be S.

Next, we prove by contradiction that the equivalence classes are disjoint:

Suppose not all sets are pairwise disjoint, so there is at least one pair of sets which is not disjoint.

We let A and B be two such sets, where $A \neq B$, $a \in A$ and $b \in B$.

Let $c \in A \cap B$. Then $a \in A$ and $c \in A$ so aRc,
and $c \in B$ and $b \in B$ so cRb.

By transitivity, aRb, so a and b belong to the same equivalence class.

But if aRb where b is any element in B, then $b \in A$

$\therefore$ every element of B is an element of A, and so $B \subseteq A$ ..... (1)

In a similar manner, we can argue that $A \subseteq B$ ..... (2)
and (1) and (2) give $A = B$

This is a contradiction. Therefore, if there is more than one equivalence class, the equivalence classes are pair-wise disjoint and the union of them is S.

Hence the set of equivalence classes is a partition of S.

The number of equivalence classes may range from one (in the case $R = S \times S$) to $n(S)$ in the case where each equivalence class contains only one element.

Example 15

Let $A = \{1, 2, 3, 4\}$ and define a relation R by: $xRy \Leftrightarrow x + y$ is even.

a Show that R is an equivalence relation.   **b** Find the equivalence classes.

---

a *Reflexive:* $x + x = 2x$
But $2x$ is even for all $x \in A$ so, xRx for all $x \in A$

Symmetric: If xRy then $x + y$ is even.
Now $x + y = y + x$ for all $x, y \in A$
$\Rightarrow y + x$ is also even $\Rightarrow yRx$ also

i.e., if xRy, then yRx

Transitive: Suppose xRy and yRz
Then $x + y$ is even and $y + z$ is even.
i.e., $x + y = 2m$ and $y + z = 2n$ where $m, n \in \mathbb{Z}$
$\Rightarrow x + y + y + z = 2m + 2n$
$\Rightarrow x + 2y + z = 2m + 2n$
$\Rightarrow x + z = 2m + 2n - 2y$
$\Rightarrow x + z = 2(m + n - y)$

But as $m, n, y \in \mathbb{Z}$ $m + n - y \in \mathbb{Z}$ also

$\therefore$ $x + z$ is even i.e., if xRy and yRz then xRz

b   Now $R = \{(1,\,1),\,(1,\,3),\,(3,\,3),\,(3,\,1),\,(2,\,2),\,(2,\,4),\,(4,\,4),\,(4,\,2)\}$

Notice that the first four ordered pairs contain only the elements 1 and 3 from A, and the remaining four ordered pairs contain 2 and 4.

So, there are two equivalence classes: $\{1,\,3\}$ and $\{2,\,4\}$.

R can be graphed on the Cartesian plane:

Notice that every possible point of $A \times A$ on the line $y = x$ is plotted; this is a consequence of the reflexive property. The symmetry property guarantees symmetry in the line $y = x$ for all other points.

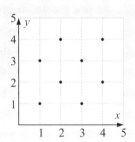

Example 16   **Similar triangles**

Let S be the set of all triangles. Define the relation R such that if $x,\,y \in S$, then xRy if and only if x is similar to y.

Show that R is an equivalence relation and describe the equivalence classes.

Reflexive: A triangle is similar to itself since, for

any triangle   ABC, $\dfrac{AB}{AB} = \dfrac{BC}{BC} = \dfrac{AC}{AC}$.

Therefore xRx for all $x \in S$.

Symmetric: If x is similar to y, then its corresponding angles are equal.
∴ y is also similar to x.
Hence for all $x,\,y \in S$, if xRy then yRx.

Transitive: Given triangles x, y and $z \in S$, if x is similar to y, then the corresponding angles of x and y are equal. Also, if y is similar to z, the corresponding angles of y and z are equal. Therefore, the corresponding angles of x and z must also be equal, and so x is similar to z.
∴ for all $x,\,y,\,z \in S$, if xRy and yRz then xRz.

Hence R is an equivalence relation on S. The equivalence classes would be sets of triangles, each set containing all triangles which are similar to each other. Notice in this instance that there are infinitely many equivalence classes, each with an infinite number of members.

Example 17   **Regular polygons**

Let S be the set of regular polygons where R is the relation defined by xRy if x is similar to y.

Show that R is an equivalence relation and describe the equivalence classes.

Reflexive: Each regular polygon is similar to itself, so xRx for all $x \in S$.

Symmetric: Two regular polygons are similar if they have the same number of sides. Therefore, if xRy then yRx for all $x, y \in S$.

Transitive: If xRy and yRz, then the number of sides of x and y are equal and the number of sides of y and z are equal.

∴ the number of sides of x and z are equal,

i.e., for all $x, y, z \in S$, if xRy and yRz then xRz.

Hence R is an equivalence relation on S. The equivalence classes would be S_3, S_4, S_5, ..., where S_n is the set of all regular n-sided polygons.

For example, S_3 is the set of equilateral triangles while S_4 is the set of squares. It is easy to see in this example that these sets are pair-wise disjoint, and that every regular polygon will be in one of these sets,

i.e., $S_3 \cup S_4 \cup S_5 \cup .... = S$, so $\{S_n\}$ partitions S.

Example 18

Consider the relation R on $\mathbb{R}$, where for all $x, y \in \mathbb{R}$, xRy if $x > y$.

Show that R is not an equivalence relation.

Clearly, the relation is not reflexive as 5 is not greater than itself.

Symmetry is also ruled out since, for example, $7 > 2$ but 2 is not greater than 7.

Transitivity applies since, if $x > y$ and $y > z$, then $x > z$.

Changing R such that xRy if $x \geqslant y$ would make R reflexive since $x \geqslant x$ for all $x \in R$. However, symmetry would still not apply.

RESIDUE CLASSES

The integers $\{0, 3, 6, 9, ...\}$ give remainder 0 on division by 3.

The integers $\{1, 4, 7, 10, ...\}$ give remainder 1 on division by 3.

The integers $\{2, 5, 8, 11, ...\}$ give remainder 2 on division by 3.

These sets of integers are the **residue classes modulo 3**. Together they make up the set of integers $\mathbb{Z}^+$.

4 and 7 have remainder 1 when divided by 3.

We say that 4 and 7 are congruent modulo 3, and $4 \equiv 7 \pmod 3$.

Also, $4 - 7 = 3$, which is a multiple of 3.

In general:

If we take any integer and divide it by any $n \in \mathbb{Z}^+$, the possible remainders are the integers $0, 1, 2, 3, ..., n - 1$.

We could place in one set all those integers which give remainder 0 on division by n, in another set all those integers with remainder 1, in another those with remainder 2 and so on.

All the sets would be different, and every integer would be in only one set for a given n.

The sets are called the **residue classes**, modulo n. Because the sets are pair-wise disjoint and their union is $\mathbb{Z}$, they partition $\mathbb{Z}$.

For example, consider the relation on $\mathbb{Z}$: xRy if and only if $y - x$ is divisible by 5. This is the same as saying that xRy is the residue class of modulo 5 with remainder 0.

> If x and y have the same remainder on division by an integer n, then we say that x is **congruent** to y modulo n and write:
>
> $$x \equiv y \pmod{n} \quad \text{if and only if} \quad x - y \text{ is a multiple of } n.$$

For example, $19 \equiv 40$ (mod 7)   as 19 and 40 both have remainder 5 when divided by 7. Alternatively, $19 - 40 = -21$ which is a multiple of 7.

Example 19

Show that the relation xRy if and only if $y - x$ is divisible by 5 is an equivalence relation, and describe the equivalence classes.

Reflexive: $x - x = 0$ and as 0 is a multiple of 5, xRx
$\Rightarrow$ R is reflexive.

Symmetric: If xRy,   then $y - x = 5m$ where $m \in \mathbb{Z}$
$\Rightarrow$ $x - y = -5m = 5(-m)$
Now $-m \in \mathbb{Z}$,   so $x - y$ is divisible by 5
$\therefore$ yRx,   and so R is symmetric.

Transitive: Suppose xRy and yRz.
Then x and y have the same remainder on division by 5,
so $y - x = 5m$ for some $m \in \mathbb{Z}$,
and y and z have the same remainder on division by 5,
so $z - y = 5n$ for some $n \in \mathbb{Z}$.
$\Rightarrow$ $z - x = (z - y) + (y - x)$
$\Rightarrow$ $z - x = 5n + 5m$
$\Rightarrow$ $z - x = 5(n + m)$ where $(n + m) \in \mathbb{Z}$
$\Rightarrow$ xRz,   so R is transitive.

As R is reflexive, symmetric and transitive, it is an equivalence relation.

Equivalence classes:

If $a \in \mathbb{Z}$ then the other elements of the equivalence class to which a belongs will be $a \pm 5$, $a \pm 10$, $a \pm 15$ etc.

There will be 5 such classes:

$\{.... -10, -5, 0, 5, 10, ...$ i.e., all integers which are divisible by 5$\}$
$\{.... -9, -4, 1, 6, 11, ...$ i.e., all integers which leave remainder 1 on division by 5$\}$
$\{.... -8, -3, 2, 7, 12, ...$ i.e., all integers which leave remainder 2 on division by 5$\}$
$\{.... -7, -2, 3, 8, 13, ...$ i.e., all integers which leave remainder 3 on division by 5$\}$
$\{.... -6, -1, 4, 9, 14, ...$ i.e., all integers which leave remainder 4 on division by 5$\}$

SETS, RELATIONS AND GROUPS (Topic 9)   **129**

From the example above:

It can easily be seen that every integer belongs to one and only one of these sets.
The sets are therefore pair-wise disjoint and their union is $\mathbb{Z}$.
The set of these residue classes is called $\mathbb{Z}_5$ and is written

$$\{[0],\ [1],\ [2],\ [3],\ [4]\} \quad \text{or just} \quad \{0,\ 1,\ 2,\ 3,\ 4\}.$$

In general, $$\mathbb{Z}_n = \{0,\ 1,\ 2,\ ...,\ n-2,\ n-1\}$$

Example 20

R is a relation on $\mathbb{R} \times \mathbb{R}$ such that for $(a,\ b),\ (x,\ y) \in \mathbb{Z} \times \mathbb{Z},\ (a,\ b)R(x,\ y)$ if and only if $x + 5y = a + 5b$.

a Show that R is an equivalence relation.

b Describe how R partitions $\mathbb{R} \times \mathbb{R}$ and state the equivalence classes.

a *Reflexive:* Letting $a = x$ and $b = y$,

$x + 5y = x + 5y$ which is true for all $(x,\ y) \in \mathbb{Z} \times \mathbb{Z}$

$\Rightarrow$ R is reflexive.

Symmetric: If $(a,\ b)R(x,\ y)$ then $x + 5y = a + 5b$

$\Rightarrow \quad a + 5b = x + 5y$

$\Rightarrow \quad (x,\ y)R(a,\ b)$ for all $(a,\ b),\ (x,\ y) \in \mathbb{Z} \times \mathbb{Z}$

$\Rightarrow \quad R$ is symmetric.

Transitive: Suppose $(a,\ b)R(x,\ y)$ and $(x,\ y)R(c,\ d)$

$\Rightarrow \quad x + 5y = a + 5b$

and $c + 5d = x + 5y$

$\Rightarrow \quad c + 5d = a + 5b$

$\Rightarrow \quad (a,\ b)R(c,\ d)$ for all $(a,\ b),\ (c,\ d) \in \mathbb{Z} \times \mathbb{Z}$

$\Rightarrow \quad R$ is transitive.

As R is reflexive, symmetric and transitive, it is an equivalence relation.

b For any $(a,\ b) \in \mathbb{Z} \times \mathbb{Z}$, we know that $x + 2y = a + 5b$

i.e., $a + 5b$ is an integer $c \in \mathbb{Z}$

$\therefore$ the relation R partitions $\mathbb{R} \times \mathbb{R}$ into an infinite number of equivalence classes, each equivalence class containing the different points $(a,\ b)$ that result in $a + 5b$ being a particular value.

For example,

$\{(0,\ 0),\ (5,\ -1),\ (10,\ -2),\ ....\}$ form the equivalence class corresponding to $a + 5b = 0$,

$\{(1,\ 0),\ (6,\ -1),\ (11,\ -2),\ ....\}$ form the equivalence class corresponding to $a + 5b = 1$,

etc.

EXERCISE 9B.3

1 If $a \equiv b \pmod{n}$ and $c \equiv d \pmod{n}$, prove that:

   a $a + c \equiv b + d \pmod{n}$ **b** $ac \equiv bd \pmod{n}$

2 Find the smallest positive integer x that is a solution of the congruence $ax \equiv 1 \pmod{11}$ for each of the values $a = 1,\ 2,\ 3,\ 4,\ 5,\ 6,\ 7,\ 8,\ 9,\ 10.$

3 R is a relation in a family of lines such that $xRy \iff x$ and y have the same gradient.

   a Show that R is an equivalence relation.   **b** Describe the equivalence classes.

4 Determine whether the relation R on $\{1,\ 2,\ 3,\ 4\}$ where
$R = \{(1,\ 1),\ (1,\ 2),\ (2,\ 2),\ (2,\ 3),\ (3,\ 3),\ (3,\ 4),\ (4,\ 4),\ (4,\ 3)\}$ is:

   a   reflexive   **b**   symmetric   **c**   transitive.

5 If $A = \{a,\ b,\ c\}$, find relations in A which are:

   a   reflexive but neither symmetric nor transitive

   b   symmetric but neither reflexive nor transitive

   c   transitive but neither reflexive nor symmetric

   d   reflexive and symmetric but not transitive

   e   reflexive and transitive but not symmetric

   f   symmetric and transitive but not reflexive.

6 $S = \{1,\ 2,\ 3,\ 4\}$ and R is an equivalence relation on S.

   If $(1, 2),\ (2, 3),\ (4, 4) \in R,$ what other ordered pairs must be in R?

7 Show that R is an equivalence relation in $\mathbb{N}$ if $xRy \iff x - y$ is divisible by 7.

8 Determine whether the relation R on $\mathbb{N}$ is an equivalence relation if:
$$xRy \iff x^2 \equiv y^2 \pmod{3}$$

9 R is a relation on $\mathbb{Z} \times \mathbb{Z}$ such that for $(a,\ b),\ (x,\ y) \in \mathbb{Z} \times \mathbb{Z},$
$(a,\ b)R(x,\ y)$ if and only if $x = a.$

   a Show that R is an equivalence relation.

   b Describe how R partitions $\mathbb{Z} \times \mathbb{Z}$ and state the equivalence classes.

10 R is a relation on $\mathbb{R} \times \mathbb{R} \setminus \{(0,\ 0)\}$ such that for $(a,\ b),\ (x,\ y) \in \mathbb{R} \times \mathbb{R} \setminus \{(0,\ 0)\},$
$(a,\ b)R(x,\ y)$ if and only if $ay = bx.$

   a Show that R is an equivalence relation.

   b Describe how R partitions $\mathbb{R} \times \mathbb{R} \setminus \{(0,\ 0)\}$ and state the equivalence classes.

11 R is a relation on $\mathbb{R} \times \mathbb{R}$ such that for $(a,\ b),\ (x,\ y) \in \mathbb{R} \times \mathbb{R},$
$(a,\ b)R(x,\ y)$ if and only if $y - b = 3x - 3a.$

   a Show that R is an equivalence relation.

   b Describe how R partitions $\mathbb{R} \times \mathbb{R}$ and state the equivalence classes.

FUNCTIONS

INTRODUCTION AND DEFINITION

Some of the work in this section expands the work covered in **Chapter 1** of the Core HL text.

A relation f from set A to set B, is said to be a **function** from A to B if, for each $x \in A$, there is only one element $y \in B$ such that $(x, y) \in f$.

Functions are sometimes referred to as **mappings**. A is the **domain** of the function and B the **codomain**. The **range** of f will be a subset of B.

Rather than write $(x, y) \in f$ or xfy, the standard notation used is $y = f(x)$ or $f : x \mapsto y$.

Example 21

Determine whether the relation from
$A = \{1, 2, 3, 4\}$ to $B = \{1, 2, 3, 4\}$
illustrated in the diagram is a function.

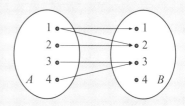

This is not a function as 1 in A is mapped to two elements, 1 and 2, in B.

Example 22

Determine whether the relation in $\mathbb{N}$, $\{(1, 3), (2, 5), (2, 3), (3, 7)\}$ is a function.

This is not a function as 2 is mapped to two different elements.

Example 23

Is the relation in $\mathbb{R}$ defined by $\{(x, y) \mid y > x\}$ a function?

No, as each element in the domain is mapped to an infinite number of elements in the range.

Example 24

The diagram below illustrates a relation from
$A = \{1, 2, 3, 4\}$ to $B = \{1, 2, 3, 4\}$.
a   Is the relation a function?
b   State the domain, co-domain and range.

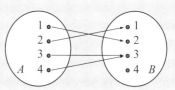

a   As each element of A is mapped to just one element of B, the relation is a function.

b   The domain of the function is $\{1, 2, 3, 4\}$, the co-domain is also $\{1, 2, 3, 4\}$, and the range is $\{1, 2, 3\}$.

Example 25

Determine whether the relation R from $A = \{1, 2, 3, 4\}$ to $B = \{1, 2, 3, 4\}$ where $R = \{(1, 4), (2, 4), (3, 4), (4, 1)\}$ is a function.

This is a function as, for each different first component of the ordered pairs, there is only one possible second component.

Example 26

Determine whether the relation $f : \mathbb{R} \to \mathbb{R}$ where $f(x) = 2x^2 - 3$ is a function.

This is a function as for each value of x there is only one value of $2x^2 - 3$.

A test for functions which can be graphed in the Cartesian plane is the **vertical line test**.

Any vertical line will never cross the graph of a function more than once.

INJECTIONS

If a function f is such that each element in the range corresponds to only one element in the domain, then f is said to be **one-to-one** or an **injection**. To show that a function is an injection, it is sufficient to prove that $f(x_1) = f(x_2)$ implies $x_1 = x_2$.

Alternatively, if f is differentiable then showing that either $f'(x) > 0$ or $f'(x) < 0$ for all x, will prove that f is an injection.

Example 27

Is the illustrated function from $A = \{1, 2, 3\}$ to $B = \{1, 2, 3, 4\}$ an injection?

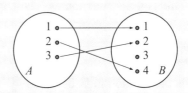

This is an injection since each element in the range can result from only one element in the domain,
i.e., no two elements in the domain are mapped to the same element in the range.

Example 28

Prove that the function $f : \mathbb{Z}^+ \to \mathbb{Z}^+$ where $f(x) = x^2$ is an injection.

To show this, suppose there is an element in the range which corresponds to two distinct elements in the domain, i.e., x_1 and x_2 where $x_1 \neq x_2$.

$$\therefore \quad f(x_1) = f(x_2) \quad \Rightarrow \quad x_1^2 = x_2^2$$
$$\Rightarrow \quad x_1 = x_2 \quad \{\text{as } x_1, \ x_2 \in \mathbb{Z}^+\}$$

This is a contradiction, so f is an injection.

If any horizontal line crosses a function graphed on the Cartesian plane at most once, the function is an injection.

SURJECTIONS

For a function f from A to B, f is said to be **onto** or a **surjection** if the range of f is B. Every element in B will be the image of an element in A, so the co-domain is the same as the range.

Example 29

Determine whether the function from
$A = \{1, 2, 3, 4\}$ to $B = \{1, 2, 3\}$
illustrated below is a surjection.

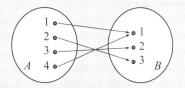

This is a surjection as every element of B corresponds to some element of A.

Example 30

Is the function $f \colon \mathbb{R} \to \mathbb{R}^+ \cup \{0\}$ where $f(x) = x^2$ a surjection?

f is a surjection because every non-negative real number is the square of a real number.

Example 31

Is the function $f \colon \mathbb{Z}^+ \to \mathbb{Z}^+$ where $f(x) = 2x$ a surjection.

If we take any positive integer and double it, we get an even positive integer.
$\Rightarrow$ no elements of $\mathbb{Z}^+$ will map onto the odd positive integers.
$\Rightarrow$ not all elements in the co-domain correspond to elements in the domain.
$\Rightarrow$ f is not a surjection.

BIJECTIONS

A function which is both an injection and a surjection, i.e., *one-to-one* and *onto*, is said to be a **bijection**.

Example 32

Is the function from
$A = \{1, 2, 3, 4\}$ to $B = \{1, 2, 3, 4\}$
illustrated in the diagram below a
bijection?

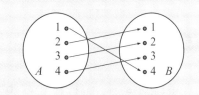

The function is a bijection because each element of the domain maps to only one element in the range (one-to-one), and each element in the co-domain corresponds to an element in the range (onto).

Example 33

Is the function $f \colon \mathbb{R} \to \mathbb{R}$ where $f(x) = x^3$ a bijection?

Every real number has a unique cube which is a real number, so f is an injection, and every real number is the cube of a unique real number, so f is a surjection.
$\therefore$ f is a bijection.

Example 34

Is the function $f \colon \mathbb{R} \to \mathbb{R}$ where $f(x) = x^2$ a bijection?

This function is not an injection since several elements of the domain can map onto the same element of the range, e.g., $f(-2) = f(2) = 4$. Also, no negative real number is the square of a real number, so the range is not the same as the co-domain. $\therefore$ the function is also not a surjection. f is not a bijection.

Example 35

Is the function $f \colon \mathbb{R}^+ \to \mathbb{R}^+$ where $f(x) = x^2$ a bijection?

This is an injection as each element of the range is the square of only one element in the domain. It is also a surjection as each real positive number is the square of a real positive number. $\therefore$ f is a bijection.

COMPOSITION OF FUNCTIONS

If f is a function from A to B and g is a function from B to C, we can define a function from a subset of A to C by $g(f(x))$ or $g \circ f$ provided the domain of g contains the range of f.

Example 36

Suppose f maps $\{1, 2, 3, 4\}$ to $\{5, 6, 7\}$ and g maps $\{5, 6, 7\}$ to $\{8, 9\}$ where $f = \{(1, 6), (2, 6), (3, 5), (4, 7)\}$ and $g = \{(5, 8), (6, 9), (7, 8)\}$.
Find: **a** $g \circ f$ **b** $f \circ g$

a $g \circ f = \{(1, 9), (2, 9), (3, 8), (4, 8)\}$
b $f \circ g$ is not defined because the domain of f does not contain the range of g.

Example 37

Let $f \colon \mathbb{R} \to \mathbb{R}$ and $g \colon \mathbb{R} \to \mathbb{R}$ where $f(x) = x + 2$ and $g(x) = x^3$.
Find: **a** $(g \circ f)(x)$ **b** $(f \circ g)(x)$

a $(g \circ f)(x) = g(f(x)) = g(x + 2) = (x + 2)^3$
b $(f \circ g)(x) = f(g(x)) = f(x^3) = x^3 + 2$

INVERSE FUNCTIONS

If f is a bijection from A to B such that $\quad f : x \mapsto y,\quad$ then it is possible to define a function such that y is mapped to x. This function is called the **inverse** of f, denoted f^{-1}.

If the order of the components of each of the ordered pairs of f is reversed, the resulting function is f^{-1}. Note that the inverse of a bijection will also be a bijection.

Example 38

Find the inverse of the function from $\quad A = \{1, 2, 3, 4\}\quad$ to $\quad B = \{1, 2, 3, 4\}$ where $\quad f = \{(1, 3), (2, 2), (3, 4), (4, 1)\}$

$$f^{-1} = \{(3, 1), (2, 2), (4, 3), (1, 4)\}$$

Example 39

Find the inverse of $\quad f : \mathbb{R} \to \mathbb{R}\quad$ if $\quad f(x) = 2x^3 + 1$

First, we note that f is both an injection and a subjection, so f is a bijection and has an inverse. Next, we put $y = 2x^3 + 1$. We interchange x and y, which has the effect of reversing the order of the components of each ordered pair of the function.

So, $\quad x = 2y^3 + 1$

Making y the subject of the equation $\quad 2y^3 = x - 1\quad$ and so $\quad y^3 = \dfrac{x-1}{2}$

$$\Rightarrow \quad y = \sqrt[3]{\frac{x-1}{2}}, \quad \text{i.e.,} \quad f^{-1}(x) = \sqrt[3]{\frac{x-1}{2}}$$

EXERCISE 9C

1   State whether each of the following relations from $\quad \{1, 2, 3, 4, 5\}\quad$ to $\quad \{1, 2, 3, 4, 5\}$ is a function, and if so, determine whether it is an injection:

   a $\{(1, 2), (2, 4), (3, 5), (1, 3), (4, 1), (5, 2)\}$

   b $\{(1, 5), (2, 4), (3, 5), (4, 5), (5, 3)\}$

   c $\{(1, 3), (2, 4), (3, 5), (4, 2), (5, 1)\}$

2   State whether each of the following relations is a function, and if so, determine whether it is: i   an injection   ii   a surjection   iii   a bijection.

   a The relation R from $\{0, 1, 2\}$ to $\{1, 2\}$ where $R = \{(0, 1), (1, 2), (2, 2)\}$

   b The relation R from $\{0, 1, 2\}$ to $\{1, 2\}$ where $R = \{(0, 1), (1, 1), (2, 1)\}$

   c The relation R from $\{0, 1, 2\}$ to $\{1, 2\}$ where $R = \{(0, 1), (1, 1), (1, 2), (2, 2)\}$

   d The relation from $\mathbb{Z}$ to $\mathbb{Z}^+$ defined by $\{(x, y) \mid y = x^2 + 1\}$

   e The relation from $\mathbb{R}^2$ to $\mathbb{R}$ defined by $(x, y)Rz$ if and only if $z = x^2 + y^2$.

   f The relation from $\mathbb{Z} \times \mathbb{Z}$ to $\mathbb{Z} \times \mathbb{Z}$ where $(a, b)R(x, y)$ if and only if $y = a$ and $x = b$.

3 For each of the following functions, state giving reasons whether it is injective, surjective or both:

   a $f: \ \mathbb{R} \to \mathbb{R}, \ \ f(x) = 2x - 1$

   b $f: \ \mathbb{R} \to \mathbb{Z}, \ \ f(x) = [x], \ \ $ where $[x]$ means   "the greatest integer less than or equal to x"

   c $f: \ \mathbb{Z} \to \mathbb{Z}^+ \cup \{0\}, \ \ f(x) = |x|$

   d $f: \ \mathbb{Q}^+ \to \mathbb{Q}^+, \ \ f(x) = x^2$

   e $f: \ \left[0, \frac{\pi}{2}\right] \to [0, \ 1], \ \ f(x) = \sin x$

   f $f: \ \mathbb{Z}^+ \to \mathbb{Z}^+, \ \ f(x) = 2x$

4 $A = \{0, 1, 2, 3\}, \ \ f$ and g are functions mapping A to A where

   $f = \{(0, 1), (1, 2), (2, 0), (3, 3)\} \ \ $ and $\ \ g = \{(0, 2), (1, 3), (2, 0), (3, 1)\}$.

   a Find each of the following:

      i $(f \circ g)(1)$ **ii** $(g \circ f)(1)$ **iii** $(f \circ g)(3)$ **iv** $(g \circ f)(3)$

   b Find:

      i f^{-1} **ii** g^{-1} **iii** $(g \circ f)^{-1}$ **iv** $(f^{-1} \circ g^{-1})$

5 f and g are functions in $\mathbb{R}^+$ such that: $\ \ f(x) = \ln(x + 1) \ \ $ and $\ \ g(x) = x^2$.

   Find each of the following:

   a $(g \circ f)(x)$ **b** $(f \circ g)(x)$ **c** $f^{-1}(x)$

   d $(g \circ f)^{-1}(x)$ **e** $(f^{-1} \circ g^{-1})(x)$

6 Prove that if $\ \ A \subseteq B \ \ $ then $\ \ f(A) \subseteq f(B)$.

D   BINARY OPERATIONS

INTRODUCTION

Given a non-empty set S, a **binary operation** on S is a rule for combining any two elements $a, b \in S$ to give a unique result c, where c is not necessarily $\in S$.

Many binary operations are familiar from operations on number. Addition, subtraction, multiplication and division are examples of binary operations.

For example, given the set of integers $\mathbb{Z}$, the binary operation of addition with 3 and 5 gives 8, and we write $\ \ 3 + 5 = 8$.

An example of subtraction on the set of natural numbers $\mathbb{N}$ is $\ \ 5 - 7 = -2$.   Note that, in this latter case, the result does not belong to the set $\mathbb{N}$. If this happens for any particular binary operation on a set, we say the set is *not closed* under that operation.

$\mathbb{Z}$ is closed under subtraction because the result of subtracting any integer from another integer is always an integer.

> **Note that some definitions of a binary operation include closure as a property.**
> **The definition used here does not and so closure must not be assumed.**

Less familiar binary operations between two elements in a set are often defined by a symbol such as $*$.

Example 40

Let a binary operation $*$ on $\mathbb{Z}$ be defined by $a * b = a + 2b - 3$

Find: **a** $3 * 5$ **b** $3 * 0$ **c** $0 * 3$ **d** $-5 * 0$

a $\quad 3 * 5 = 3 + 2 \times 5 - 3$
$\qquad\quad = 10$

b $\quad 3 * 0 = 3 + 2 \times 0 - 3$
$\qquad\quad = 0$

c $\quad 0 * 3 = 0 + 2 \times 3 - 3$
$\qquad\quad = 3$

d $\quad -5 * 0 = -5 + 2 \times 0 - 3$
$\qquad\qquad = -8$

CLOSURE

A set S is said to be **closed** under the binary operation $*$ if $a * b \in S$ for all $a, b \in S$.

A closed binary operation on a set S is a function with domain $A \times A$ and co-domain A.

Example 41

Which of the following binary operations are closed on $\mathbb{Z}$?

a $\quad a * b = \dfrac{a + b}{a^2}$ **b** $\quad a * b = 2^{a+b}$ **c** $\quad a * b = a + b - 3ab$

a Consider $a = 2$ and $b = 3$. Then $2 * 3 = \dfrac{2 + 3}{4} = \frac{5}{4} \notin \mathbb{Z}$
$\quad \Rightarrow$ the binary operation in not closed.

b Consider $a = -2$ and $b = 0$. Then $-2 * 0 = 2^{-2+0} = \frac{1}{4} \notin \mathbb{Z}$
$\quad \Rightarrow$ the binary operation is not closed.

c As a and b are in $\mathbb{Z}$, their sum $a + b$ and product ab are also in $\mathbb{Z}$.
$\quad \Rightarrow \quad a + b - 3ab$ is also in $\mathbb{Z}$
$\quad \Rightarrow \quad a * b \in \mathbb{Z}$
$\quad \Rightarrow \quad$ the binary operation is closed.

ASSOCIATIVE LAW

Consider the following example of repeated use of the binary operation multiplication on $\mathbb{Z}$:

$$3 \times (2 \times 5) = 3 \times 10 \qquad \text{and} \quad (3 \times 2) \times 5 = 6 \times 5$$
$$= 30 \qquad\qquad\qquad\qquad\quad = 30$$

Notice that the order of grouping the terms makes no difference. This is true for multiplication of all real numbers. We say that multiplication is **associative** on $\mathbb{R}$.

More generally:

A binary operation $*$ on a set S is said to be **associative** if,
$a * (b * c) = (a * b) * c$ for all $a, b, c \in S$.

If a binary operation is associative on a set, the associativity will also apply to the operation on any subset of that set. However, not all properties of an operation on a set are transferable to a subset in this way.

For example,

$8 - (3 - 5) \neq (8 - 3) - 5$ and $12 \div (6 \div 2) \neq (12 \div 6) \div 2$,   so subtraction and division are not associative operations on $\mathbb{R}$.

Example 42

Determine whether the binary operations on $\mathbb{R}$ defined below are associative.

a $a * b = 2a + 3b$ **b** $a * b = a + b + ab$

a
$$(a * b) * c = (2a + 3b) * c \qquad a * (b * c) = a * (2b + 3c)$$
$$= 2(2a + 3b) + 3c \qquad\qquad\quad = 2a + 3(2b + 3c)$$
$$= 4a + 6b + 3c \qquad\qquad\quad = 2a + 6b + 9c$$
$$\qquad\qquad\qquad\qquad\qquad\qquad\quad \neq (a * b) * c$$

Therefore $*$ is not associative.

b
$$(a * b) * c = (a + b + ab) * c$$
$$= (a + b + ab) + c + (a + b + ab)c$$
$$= a + b + ab + c + ac + bc + abc$$

$$a * (b * c) = a * (b + c + bc)$$
$$= a + (b + c + bc) + a(b + c + bc)$$
$$= a + b + c + bc + ab + ac + abc$$
$$= (a * b) * c \qquad\qquad\qquad\text{Therefore } * \text{ is associative.}$$

Although multiplication and addition of real numbers are binary operations, we usually write such statements as $3 + 6 + 17$ or $2 \times 5 \times 7$ without any need for grouping the terms into pairs.

This is true in general for associative functions, and if $*$ is associative then there is no ambiguity if we write $a * b * c$ rather than $(a * b) * c$ or $a * (b * c)$.

We will also follow the convention of writing $\underbrace{a * a * a * \ldots * a}_{n \text{ times}}$ as a^n,

so be careful not to assume that this operation is normal multiplication of real numbers.

The familiar index laws still apply for associative functions.

For example, $a^m * a^n \; = \; \underbrace{\underbrace{a * a * a * \ldots * a}_{m \text{ times}} * \underbrace{a * a * a * \ldots * a}_{n \text{ times}}}_{m + n \text{ times}} \; = a^{m+n}$.

As $(a^m)^n$ is the repeated operation of a^m, n times, it can be shown that $(a^m)^n = a^{mn}$.

COMMUTATIVE LAW

A binary operation $*$ on a set S is said to be **commutative** if $a * b = b * a$ for all $a, b \in S$.

Multiplication and addition are commutative operations on $\mathbb{R}$, whereas subtraction and division are not. As we found in **Section 14G** of the Core HL text, multiplication of square matrices of the same order is an example a binary operation which is associative but not commutative.

If $*$ is both associative and commutative then we can include the following rule as an index law:

$$(ab)^n = a^n b^n$$

Example 43	
If $*$ is both associative and commutative on a set S, show that $(ab)^2 = a^2b^2$.	$(ab)^2 = (a * b) * (a * b)$ $= a * (b * a) * b$ {Associative law} $= a * (a * b) * b$ {Commutative law} $= (a * a) * (b * b)$ {Associative law} $= a^2b^2$

Example 44

Determine whether the following operations on $\mathbb{R}$ are commutative:

a $a * b = 2a + b$ **b** $a * b = 3^{a+b}$

a $3 * 2 = 2 \times 3 + 2 = 8$ and $2 * 3 = 2 \times 2 + 3 = 7 \neq 3 * 2$
  $\therefore$ the operation is not commutative.

b $b * a = 3^{b+a}$
              $= 3^{a+b}$ {addition on $\mathbb{R}$ is a commutative operation}
              $= a * b$
  $\therefore$ the operation is commutative.

DISTRIBUTIVE LAW

Given two binary operations $*$ and $\circ$ on a set S, $*$ is said to be **distributive** over $\circ$ if $a * (b \circ c) = (a * b) \circ (a * c)$ for all $a, b, c \in S$.

In $\mathbb{R}$, multiplication is distributive over addition as $a(b + c) = ab + ac$ for all $a, b, c \in \mathbb{R}$.

Example 45

$*$ and $\circ$ are binary operations on $\mathbb{R}$ defined by $a * b = a + 2b$ and $a \circ b = 2ab$.

a   Is $*$ distributive over $\circ$?   **b**   Is $\circ$ distributive over $*$?

a $a * (b \circ c) = a * (2bc)$ and $(a * b) \circ (a * c) = (a + 2b) \circ (a + 2c)$
                      $= a + 4bc$ $= 2(a + 2b)(a + 2c)$
                                                                      $= 2a^2 + 4ac + 4ab + 8bc$
                                                                      $\neq a * (b \circ c)$

  Therefore $*$ is not distributive over $\circ$.

b $a \circ (b * c) = a \circ (b + 2c)$ and $(a \circ b) * (a \circ c) = (2ab) * (2ac)$
                      $= 2a(b + 2c)$ $= 2ab + 4ac$
                      $= 2ab + 4ac$ $= a \circ (b * c)$

  Therefore $\circ$ is distributive over $*$.

IDENTITY

For a binary operation $*$ on a set S, if there exists an element $e \in S$ such that $e * x = x * e = x$ for all $x \in S$,   then e is said to be the **identity** element for $*$ on S.

Using index notation, we can define $x^0 = e$.

The identity element for addition on $\mathbb{R}$ is the number 0.

Subtraction on $\mathbb{R}$ does not have an identity element because, although $a - 0 = a$ for all $a \in \mathbb{R}$,   it is not generally the case that $0 - a = a$.

The identity for multiplication on $\mathbb{R}$ is 1, but there is no identity for division.

If a binary operation on S is commutative, then it is sufficient to check that just one of $e * a = a$ or $a * e = a$ to establish that there is an identity element.

Theorem 2:   An identity element for a binary operation on a set is unique.

Proof: (by contradiction)

Assume that a binary operation $*$ on a set S has more than one identity element.

Let e and f be two such identity elements where $e \neq f$.

$\Rightarrow$ for all $x \in S$, $e * x = x * e = x$ ..... (1)   and $f * x = x * f = x$ ..... (2).

But as $f \in S$, we can replace x by f in (1),   so $e * f = f * e = f$.

Similarly as $e \in S$, we can replace x by e in (2), so $f * e = e * f = e$.

$\Rightarrow$ $e = f$, which contradicts the original assumption.

$\Rightarrow$ if it exists, the identity element is unique.

Example 46

Determine whether an identity element exists in $\mathbb{R}$ for each of the following operations: **a** $a * b = 3ab$ **b** $a * b = 3a + b$

a   Suppose b is an identity element for the binary operation $*$.

Then $a * b = a$ so $3ab = a$

$\Rightarrow$ $3ab - a = 0$

$\Rightarrow$ $a(3b - 1) = 0$

$\Rightarrow$ $a * b = a$ is satisfied by $b = \frac{1}{3}$ for all $a \in \mathbb{R}$.

We must now *either* show that $*$ is commutative *or* that $b * a = a$ for all $a \in \mathbb{R}$ and $b = \frac{1}{3}$.

Here we do the latter: $b * a = \frac{1}{3} * a = 3(\frac{1}{3})a = a$

$\therefore$ an identity element exists and equals $\frac{1}{3}$.

b   Suppose b is an identity element for the binary operation $*$.

Then $a * b = a$

so $3a + b = a$

$\Rightarrow$ $b = -2a$

An identity element does not exist since it would not be unique.

INVERSE

Given a binary operation $*$ on a set S with an identity element $e \in S$, an **inverse** element $x^{-1} \in S$ exists for the set if and only if $x^{-1} * x = x * x^{-1} = e$ for all $x \in S$.

The inverse for addition on $\mathbb{R}$ is $-a$ since $a + (-a) = (-a) + a = 0$ for all $a \in \mathbb{R}$. No inverse exists for addition on $\mathbb{Z}^+$.

No inverse exists for multiplication on $\mathbb{R}$ as no there is no $a \in \mathbb{R}$ such that $a * 0 = 0 * a = 1$.

However, for $\mathbb{R}/\{0\}$, each element $a \in \mathbb{Z}$ has a multiplicative inverse $\dfrac{1}{a}$.

Theorem 3:   If an associative binary operation on a set has an inverse, it is unique for each element.

Proof: (by contradiction)

Let $*$ be a binary operation on a set S with identity element e.

Suppose that an element $a \in S$ has more than one inverse, and let two of these inverses be x and y where $x \neq y$.

$$\text{Then} \quad x * a = a * x = e \ \dots \ (1) \quad \text{and} \quad y * a = a * y = e \ \dots \ (2)$$

$$\text{Using (1),} \quad (x * a) * y = e * y$$
$$\Rightarrow \quad x * (a * y) = y \qquad \{\text{Associative Law}\}$$
$$\Rightarrow \quad x * e = y \qquad \{\text{from (2)}\}$$
$$\Rightarrow \quad x = y$$

This contradicts the original assumption, so the inverse element must be unique.

The contra-positive of this theorem can be useful, i.e., if the inverse is not unique then associativity does not hold. However, note that the uniqueness of an inverse does not ensure that associativity holds.

Example 47

Let $*$ be a binary operation defined on $\mathbb{R}$ by $a * b = a + 2b$.
Determine whether:

a $*$ is associative   b $*$ is commutative   c   an identity exists in $\mathbb{R}$.

---

a $a * (b * c) = a * (b + 2c)$ and $(a * b) * c = (a + 2b) * c$
$\qquad\qquad = a + 2(b + 2c)$ $\qquad\qquad\qquad = a + 2b + 2c$
$\qquad\qquad = a + 2b + 4c$ $\qquad\qquad\qquad \neq a * (b * c)$

Therefore, $*$ is not associative.

b $a * b = a + 2b$,   whereas $b * a = b + 2a$
$\qquad \neq a * b$ Therefore $*$ is not commutative.

c   Suppose b is an identity for $*$.
Then $a * b = a$,   so $a + 2b = a$ $\Rightarrow$ $b = 0$
But $0 * a = 2a$ which $\neq 0$, $\therefore$ there is no identity element.

Example 48

Let $*$ be a binary operation defined on $\mathbb{R}$ by $a*b = a^2 + b^2$. Determine whether:

a $*$ is associative   **b** $*$ is commutative   **c**   an identity exists in $\mathbb{R}$.

a $a*(b*c) = a*(b^2 + c^2)$ $(a*b)*c = (a^2 + b^2)*c$

$\qquad\qquad = a^2 + (b^2 + c^2)^2$ $\qquad\qquad = (a^2 + b^2)^2 + c^2$

$\qquad\qquad = a^2 + b^4 + 2b^2c^2 + c^4$ $\qquad\qquad = a^4 + 2a^2b^2 + b^4 + c^2$

$\qquad\qquad\qquad\qquad\qquad\qquad\qquad\qquad\qquad\qquad \neq a*(b*c)$

Therefore $*$ is not associative.

b $a*b = a^2 + b^2$

$\qquad = b^2 + a^2$

$\qquad = b*a$ Therefore $*$ is commutative.

c   Suppose b is an identity for $*$.

Then $a*b = a$,   so $a^2 + b^2 = a$

$\qquad\qquad\qquad\quad \Rightarrow \quad b^2 = a - a^2$

$\qquad\qquad\qquad\quad \Rightarrow \quad b = \pm\sqrt{a - a^2}$

i.e.,   the value of b depends on a

$\therefore$ there is no unique identity element.

Example 49

a   Explain why the set operations *union* and *intersection* are binary operations.
b   For union of sets: **i**   is there an identity element
$\qquad\qquad\qquad\qquad\qquad$ **ii**   does each set have an inverse?
c   For intersection of sets: **i**   is there an identity element
$\qquad\qquad\qquad\qquad\qquad$ **ii**   does each set have an inverse?

a   Union and intersection are both binary operations as they have unique results.

b i   Now if $B \subseteq A$, $A \cup B = B \cup A = A$.

However, $B = \varnothing$ is the only set which is a subset of any set A.

$\therefore$ for the union of two sets, the identity element is the empty set $\varnothing$.

ii   Now for a set S, an inverse element $x^{-1} \in S$ exists for the set if and only if $x^{-1}*x = x*x^{-1} = e$ for all $x \in S$.

But $A \cup B = \varnothing$ if and only if A and B are the empty set.

$\therefore$ each set does not have an inverse under union of sets.

c i   Now if $A \subseteq B$,   then $A \cap B = A$.

However, $B = \mathbb{U}$ is the only set for which *any* A is a subset.

$\therefore$ the identity for set intersection is $\mathbb{U}$, the universal set.

ii   Now $A \cap B = \mathbb{U}$ only when $A = B = \mathbb{U}$.

$\therefore$ each set does not have an inverse under set intersection.

CAYLEY TABLES

It can be useful to set out all the possible results of a binary operation on a finite set in an operation table often referred to as a **Cayley table**, named after **Arthur Cayley** (1821 - 1895).

For a binary operation $*$ on a finite set S, the Cayley table is a square array. Each element of S appears once to the left of a row and once heading a column. The result $a * b$ is entered at the intersection of the row corresponding to a and the column corresponding to b.

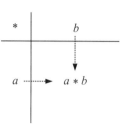

Example 50

Let a binary operation on $S = \{0, 1, 2, 3\}$ be defined by $a * b = a^2 + ab$.

a Construct the Cayley table for $*$.   **b** Is the operation closed on S?

c Is the operation commutative?

a The Cayley table is:

$*$	0	1	2	3
0	0	0	0	0
1	1	2	3	4
2	4	6	8	10
3	9	12	15	18

b From the table, it is clear that $\{0, 1, 2, 3\}$ is not closed.
For example, $3 * 2 = 15 \notin S$.

c The lack of symmetry about the leading diagonal indicates that $*$ is not commutative. For example, $3 * 2 = 15$ and $2 * 3 = 10 \neq 3 * 2$

Cayley tables do not help determine whether an operation is associative. This can sometimes be a tedious process.

EXERCISE 9D

1 Define two binary operations in $\mathbb{Q}$ by $a * b = a - b + 1$ and $a \Diamond b = ab - a$.

  a Find:

    i $3 * 4$ **ii** $4 * 3$ **iii** $(-2) \Diamond 3$ **iv** $6 \Diamond 0$

    v $0 \Diamond 7$ **vi** $4 * ((-5) \Diamond 2)$ **vii** $(4 * (-5)) \Diamond 2$

  b Solve for x:

    i $4 * x = 7$ **ii** $x \Diamond 3 = -2$

2 Determine whether closure applies to each of the following sets under multiplication:

  a $\{a + bi \mid a, b \in \mathbb{Q}, \ b \neq 0\}$

  b $\{a + bi \mid a, b \in \mathbb{Q}, \ a \neq 0\}$

  c $\{a + bi \mid a, b \in \mathbb{Q}, \ a \text{ and } b \text{ not both equal to zero}\}$

3 State whether each of the following sets is closed under the operation given:

   a The set of even positive integers $\{2, 4, 6, ...\}$ under addition

   b The set of even positive integers $\{2, 4, 6, ...\}$ under multiplication

   c The set of odd positive integers $\{1, 3, 5, ...\}$ under addition

   d The set of odd positive integers $\{1, 3, 5, ...\}$ under multiplication

   e $\mathbb{Q}$, the set of rational numbers, under addition

   f $\mathbb{Q}$, the set of rational numbers, under multiplication.

4 Construct a Cayley table for multiplication modulo 5 on $\{1, 2, 3, 4\}$.
Use the table to solve the following for x:

   a $2x = 1$ **b** $4x = 3$ **c** $3x = 4$ **d** $4x + 3 = 4$

5 Let $\diamondsuit$ be a binary operation in $\mathbb{Q} \setminus \{1\}$ such that $a \diamondsuit b = a - ab + b$.

   a Show that $\mathbb{Q} \setminus \{1\}$ is closed under $\diamondsuit$.

   b Prove that $\diamondsuit$ is associative in $\mathbb{Q} \setminus \{1\}$.

   c Find an identity element or show that one does not exist.

   d Does each element have an inverse?

6 Where one exists, state the identity element for each of the following:

   a $\mathbb{R}$ under addition   **b** $\mathbb{Z}$ under multiplication

   c $\mathbb{R}$ under $*$ where $a * b = a$ **d** $\mathbb{R}$ under $*$ where $a * b = 3ab$

   e $\mathbb{R}$ under $*$ where $a * b = 2a + ab + 2b$

7 For each of the following, determine whether each element has an inverse in the stated set. Whenever it can be found, state the inverse.

   a $\mathbb{Q}$ under addition   **b** $\mathbb{Q}$ under multiplication

   c $\mathbb{Z}^+$ under multiplication   **d** $\mathbb{R}$ under $*$ where $a * b = 2ab$

8 A binary operation $*$ is defined on the set R^2 by $(a, b) * (c, d) = (ac - bd, ad + bc)$.

   a Is $*$ associative?   **b** Is there an identity element in S? If so, state it.

   c Does each element have an inverse?

   d Is $*$ commutative?

9 Each of the following Cayley tables describes a different closed binary operation in $S = \{a, b, c\}$. For each:

     i find an identity element if it exists

     ii find an inverse for each element if one exists

     iii state whether the operation is commutative

     iv state whether the operation is associative.

a

$*$	a	b	c
a	a	b	c
b	b	c	a
c	c	a	b

b

$*$	a	b	c
a	a	a	a
b	a	b	c
c	a	c	b

c

$*$	a	b	c
a	a	c	b
b	c	b	a
c	b	a	c

d

$*$	a	b	c
a	c	a	b
b	a	b	c
c	b	c	c

e

$*$	a	b	c
a	b	c	a
b	a	b	c
c	c	a	b

GROUPS

INTRODUCTION

A set with one or more operations defined on it is called an **algebraic structure**.

Within the set of algebraic structures there is an hierarchy of types.

For example:

An algebraic structure with one operation defined is referred to as a **groupoid**.

If the associative law is obeyed, the groupoid qualifies as a **semigroup**.

A semigroup with an identity element is known as a **monoid**.

In some of these monoids, each element will have an inverse and this leads us to **groups**.

A non-empty set G on which a binary operation $*$ is defined is said to be a **group**, written $\{G, *\}$, if each of the following four axioms hold:

- G is **closed** under $*$
  i.e., for all $a, b \in G$, $a * b \in G$

- $*$ is **associative** on G
  i.e., for all $a, b, c \in G$, $(a * b) * c = a * (b * c)$

- $*$ has an **identity** element in G
  i.e., there exists a unique $e \in G$ such that $a * e = e * a = a$ for all $a \in G$

- Each element of G has an **inverse** under $*$
  i.e., for each $a \in G$, there exists an $a^{-1} \in G$ such that $a^{-1} * a = a * a^{-1} = e$

A group $\{G, *\}$ will sometimes be referred to just as G.

CANCELLATION LAWS

The group axioms lead to the following cancellation laws. As commutativity is not a group axiom, it is necessary to consider both left and right cancellation laws.

Theorem 4:   Given a group $\{G, *\}$, the following apply for all $a, b, c \in G$:

Left cancellation law   If $a * b = a * c$ then $b = c$.

Right cancellation law   If $b * a = c * a$ then $b = c$.

Proof: (of right cancellation law)

$$b * a = c * a$$
$$\Rightarrow (b * a) * a^{-1} = (c * a) * a^{-1} \quad \{\text{where } a^{-1} \in G \text{ is the inverse of } a\}$$
$$\Rightarrow b * (a * a^{-1}) = c * (a * a^{-1}) \quad \{\text{Associative Law}\}$$
$$\Rightarrow b * e = c * e \quad \{\text{where } e \in G \text{ is the identity}\}$$
$$\Rightarrow b = c$$

A similar proof establishes the left cancellation law.

ABELIAN GROUPS

While commutativity is not one of the group axioms, a special set of groups, called **Abelian** groups, has this property. It is named after the Norwegian mathematician **Niels Henrik Abel** (1802-1829).

A group $\{G, *\}$ is **Abelian** if $a * b = b * a$ for all $a, b \in G$.

CAYLEY TABLES FOR GROUPS

Cayley tables for groups have the property of being latin squares, as described in the following theorem:

Theorem 5:   If $\{G, *\}$ is a group then each element of G will appear exactly once in every row and every column of its Cayley Table.

Proof:

Let $a, p \in G$.

As $\{G, *\}$ is a group, $a^{-1} \in G$ where a^{-1} is the inverse of a

$\Rightarrow \quad a^{-1} * p \in G$ and $p * a^{-1} \in G$ for all a, p. {Closure}

Now $\quad a * (a^{-1} * p) = (a * a^{-1}) * p \quad$ {Associative}

$\qquad\qquad\qquad = e * p \qquad\qquad$ {e is the identity element}

$\qquad\qquad\qquad = p$

Therefore for any p and a it is always possible to find an element $x = a^{-1} * p$ of G such that $a * x = p$.

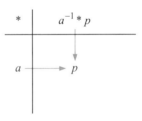

Hence p must be on the row corresponding to a. This means that every element must appear on every row.

Similarly, we can show that an element $y = p * a^{-1}$ of G can be found such that $y * a = p$, so p will appear in every column.

Now we need to show that the elements appear *only* once in each row and column.

Now for finite groups, we could note that there are only n spaces to fill in each row and column, so if each element must appear at least once, then it can appear only once. However more generally, suppose that x_1 and and x_2 are such that $a * x_1 = p$ and $a * x_2 = p$. Then $a * x_1 = a * x_2$, and so $x_1 = x_2$. {left cancellation law} We can argue similarly for each column.

Hence p must appear exactly once in every row and column.

ORDER

The **order of a group** $\{G, *\}$ is the number of elements in G, i.e, $n(G)$ or $|G|$.

The **order of an element** a of a group $\{G, *\}$ is the smallest positive integer m for which $a^m = e$, where e is the identity element of the group.

An **infinite group** has infinite order.

A **finite group** has finite order. Every element of a finite group has finite order.

In any group, the order of the identity element is 1.

In general, we may assume the closure of the set of real numbers $\mathbb{R}$ and the set of integers $\mathbb{Z}$ under the operations $+$, $-$ and $\times$. $\mathbb{R} \setminus \{0\}$ is closed under $\div$.

Example 51

Show that $\mathbb{Z}_4 \setminus \{0\}$, i.e., $\{1, 2, 3\}$ does not form a group under multiplication modulo 4, sometimes written $\times_4$.

The Cayley table for $Z_4 \setminus \{0\}$ under $\times_4$ is:

$\times_4$	1	2	3
1	1	2	3
2	2	0	2
3	3	2	1

$Z_4 \setminus \{0\}$ is not closed under $\times_4$ as $2 \times_4 2 = 0$ and $0 \notin Z_4 \setminus \{0\}$.

It therefore does not form a group.

This leads to a more general result:

Example 52

Prove that if n is not prime, $Z_n \setminus \{0\}$ does not form a group under $\times_n$.

Proof: If n is composite then $n = pq$ where $p, q \in \mathbb{Z}^+$ and $1 < p, q < n$

Thus $p, q \in \mathbb{Z}_n$ and $p \times_n q = n \bmod n = 0$

But $0 \notin \mathbb{Z}_n \setminus \{0\}$

$\therefore$ $\mathbb{Z}_n \setminus \{0\}$ is not closed under $\times_n$

$\therefore$ $\mathbb{Z}_n \setminus \{0\}$ does not form a group under $\times_n$

Example 53

Show that the set of bijections under composition of functions forms a group.

Closure: If $f : A \mapsto B$ and $g : B \mapsto C$, then $g \circ f : A \mapsto C$.
The composition of two bijections is a bijection, therefore closure applies.

Associative: The composition of functions is associative.
Proof: $(h \circ g) \circ f = (h \circ g)(f(x))$
$= h(g(f(x)))$
$= h((g \circ f)(x))$
$= h \circ (g \circ f)$

Hence the composition of bijections is also associative.

Identity: The function $e : x \mapsto x$ is a bijection.
For all functions f, $e \circ f = f \circ e = f$ $\therefore$ there is an identity in the set of bijections under composition of functions.

Inverse: Every bijection f has an inverse f^{-1} such that
$$f \circ f^{-1} = f^{-1} \circ f = e.$$

Therefore the set of bijections forms a group under the operation composition of functions. Note that in general $f \circ g \neq g \circ f$, so the group is not Abelian.

Example 54

Show that the set $\mathbb{R}$ with the binary operation $+$ is an Abelian group.

Closure: When two real numbers are added, the result is always a real number. Therefore $\mathbb{R}$ is closed under addition.

Associative: For all a, b, $c \in \mathbb{R}$, $a + (b + c) = (a + b) + c$.
Therefore $+$ is an associative operation on $\mathbb{R}$.

Identity: There exists an element $0 \in \mathbb{R}$ such that for all $a \in \mathbb{R}$,
$a + 0 = 0 + a = a$.
Therefore there is an identity element in $\mathbb{R}$ for $+$.

Inverse: If $a \in \mathbb{R}$, then $-a \in \mathbb{R}$ and $a + (-a) = (-a) + a = 0$.
Therefore each element of $\mathbb{R}$ has an inverse in $\mathbb{R}$.

Therefore, $\{\mathbb{R}, +\}$ is a group, and is an example of an infinite group.

Because addition is a commutative operation in $\mathbb{R}$, i.e., $a + b = b + a$ for all a, $b \in \mathbb{R}$, $\{\mathbb{R}, +\}$ is an *Abelian group*.

If a binary operation on a set S is associative or commutative, it can always be assumed that these properties will be true for the same operation on any subset of S.

Example 55

a   Show that $\mathbb{Z}_4$, i.e., $\{0, 1, 2, 3\}$ under the operation of $+$ modulo 4 (sometimes written $+_4$) is a group.

b   Is the group Abelian?

c   State the order of each element of the group.

a   A Cayley table will help to determine closure and the existence of an identity and inverses.

$+_4$	0	1	2	3
0	0	1	2	3
1	1	2	3	0
2	2	3	0	1
3	3	0	1	2

Closure: It can be seen from the table that for all a, $b \in \mathbb{Z}_4$, $a + b \in \mathbb{Z}_4$.
Therefore, $\mathbb{Z}_4$ is closed under $+$ modulo 4.

Associative: Associativity follows from the associative property of $\mathbb{Z}$ under $+$.

Identity: From the table it can be seen that for all $a \in \mathbb{Z}_4$,
$0 + a = a + 0 = a$.
Therefore since $0 \in \mathbb{Z}_4$, there is an identity element in $\mathbb{Z}_4$ for $+$.

> *Inverse:*   The identity appears once in every row and every column, so each element of $\mathbb{Z}_4$ has an inverse. Each of 0 and 2 is its own inverse, while 1 and 3 are inverses of each other.
>
> Therefore $\{\mathbb{Z}_4, +\}$ is a group.
>
> **b** It can be seen from the symmetry of the table that $a + b = b + a$ for all $a, b \in \mathbb{Z}_4$. Therefore, $\{\mathbb{Z}_4, +\}$ is an Abelian group.
>
> **c** 0 is the identity and has order 1.   2 has order 2. $(2 + 2 = 0)$
>   1 has order 4. $(1 + 1 + 1 + 1 = 0)$ 3 has order 4. $(3 + 3 + 3 + 3 = 0)$

EXERCISE 9E.1

Determine, giving reasons, which of the following are groups:

1 **a** $\mathbb{Q} \setminus \{0\}$ under multiplication.

    b The set of odd integers under multiplication.

    c $\{3^n \mid n \in \mathbb{Z}\}$ under multiplication.

    d $\left\{1, \ -\frac{1}{2} + i\frac{\sqrt{3}}{2}, \ -\frac{1}{2} - i\frac{\sqrt{3}}{2}\right\}$ under multiplication.

    e $\{3n \mid n \in \mathbb{Z}\}$ under addition.

    f $\{3n \mid n \in \mathbb{Z}\}$ under multiplication.

    g $\mathbb{C}$ under addition.

    h $\mathbb{C}$ under multiplication.

    i $\{a + bi \mid a, b \in \mathbb{R}, \ |a + bi| = 1\}$ under multiplication.

    j 2×2 matrices under matrix multiplication.

2 Show that $\alpha = \frac{1}{2} + i\frac{\sqrt{3}}{2}$ generates a group under multiplication. Construct the Cayley table.

ISOMORPHISM

Definition: Two groups $\{G, *\}$ and $\{H, \circ\}$ are **isomorphic** if:

          • there is a bijection $f\colon \ G \mapsto H$

and   • $f(a * b) = f(a) \circ f(b)$ for all $a, b \in G$

We can sometimes use Cayley tables to help establish isomorphism. It requires that for every p and q in G, then if $f(p) = p' \in H$ and $f(q) = q' \in H$ then the element in the p' row and q' column of the Cayley table of $\{H, 0\}$ is $f(p * q) = (p * q)'$

$$\text{i.e., } \ p' \circ q' = (p * q)'$$

For example:

The Cayley table for the set $\mathbb{Z}_5 \setminus \{0\}$, i.e., $\{1, 2, 3, 4\}$ under multiplication modulo 5, i.e., $\times_5$, is shown as:

$\times_5$	1	2	3	4
1	1	2	3	4
2	2	4	1	3
3	3	1	4	2
4	4	3	2	1

A rearrangement of the Cayley table for $\mathbb{Z}_5 \setminus \{0\}$ yields:

$\times_5$	1	2	4	3
1	1	2	4	3
2	2	4	3	1
4	4	3	1	2
3	3	1	2	4

Now suppose we replace $\times_5$ by $+_4$ and each occurrence of 1 by 0, 2 by 1 and 4 by 2:

$+_4$	0	1	2	3
0	0	1	2	3
1	1	2	3	0
2	2	3	0	1
3	3	0	1	2

It can be seen by comparison that this is the true Cayley table for $\{\mathbb{Z}_4, +\}$, i.e., the two groups have the same structure.

Matching Cayley tables is feasible only when the order of the group is small.

Example 56

a   Show that the set $\mathbb{Z}_5 \setminus \{0\}$, i.e., $\{1, 2, 3, 4\}$ under multiplication modulo 5, i.e., $\times_5$ is a group.

b   Is this group Abelian?

c   Hence show that $\{\mathbb{Z}_4, +_4\}$ and $\{\mathbb{Z}_5 \setminus \{0\}, \times_5\}$ are isomorphic.

$\times_5$	1	2	3	4
1	1	2	3	4
2	2	4	1	3
3	3	1	4	2
4	4	3	2	1

a   *Closure:*   From the table $a \times_5 b \in \mathbb{Z}_5 \setminus \{0\}$ for all $a, b \in \mathbb{Z}_5 \setminus \{0\}$.

Associative: This follows from the associativity of multiplication of integers.

Identity: The element $1 \in \mathbb{Z}_5 \setminus \{0\}$ is such that $a \times_5 1 = 1 \times_5 a = a$.
Therefore 1 is the multiplicative identity element for $\mathbb{Z}_5 \setminus \{0\}$.

Inverse: $1 \times_5 1 = 1$ and $4 \times_5 4 = 1$, so each of 1 and 4 is its own inverse.
$3 \times_5 2 = 2 \times_5 3 = 1$. Therefore 2 and 3 are inverses of each other.
Thus for each element $a \in \mathbb{Z}_5 \setminus \{0\}$ there is an inverse $a^{-1} \in \mathbb{Z}_5 \setminus \{0\}$.

Therefore $\{\mathbb{Z}_5 \setminus \{0\}, \times\}$ forms a group.

b   The symmetry of the table about the leading diagonal indicates that $a \times b = b \times a$ for all $a, b \in \mathbb{Z}_5$. Therefore the group is Abelian.

c   The Cayley table for $\{\mathbb{Z}_5/\{0\}, \times_5\}$ is shown above.

We create a Cayley table for $\{\mathbb{Z}_4, +_4\}$.

From the working previous to this **Example** we know that on rearranging the Cayley table for $\{\mathbb{Z}_5/\{0\}, \times_5\}$ the two groups have the same structure.

$+_4$	0	1	2	3
0	0	1	2	3
1	1	2	3	0
2	2	3	0	1
3	3	0	1	2

$\therefore$ there is a bijection $f\colon \mathbb{Z}_4 \mapsto \mathbb{Z}_5 \setminus \{0\}$ where: $f\colon 0 \mapsto 1, \ 1 \mapsto 2, \ 2 \mapsto 4$ and $3 \mapsto 3$ and the similarity of the Cayley tables shows that for all $a, b \in \mathbb{Z}$, $f(a +_4 b) = f(a) \times_5 f(b)$.

Therefore, $\{\mathbb{Z}_4, +_4\}$ and $\{\mathbb{Z}_5 \setminus \{0\}, \times_5\}$ are *isomorphic*.

Example 57

Prove that the group of integers $\mathbb{Z}$ under addition is isomorphic to the group of even integers, $2\mathbb{Z}$, under addition.

Proof: Let $f\colon \mathbb{Z} \to 2\mathbb{Z}$ be defined by $f(x) = 2x$

First, establish that f is a bijection.

Suppose $f(a) = f(b)$, where $a, b \in \mathbb{Z}$

Then $2a = 2b \ \Rightarrow \ a = b \ \Rightarrow \ f$ is an injection .... (1).

Suppose $q \in 2\mathbb{Z}$, then $q = 2a$ for some $a \in \mathbb{Z}$

i.e., $f(a) = q \ \Rightarrow \ f$ is a surjection .... (2)

(1) and (2) $\Rightarrow \ f$ is a bijection

Now show that $f(a + b) = f(a) + f(b)$ for all $a, b \in \mathbb{Z}$

$f(a + b) = 2(a + b) = 2a + 2b = f(a) + f(b)$

Therefore the two groups are isomorphic.

PROPERTIES

Determining isomorphism is not always easy, and it is therefore useful to know some properties of isomorphism.

If any one of these does not apply in a particular instance then isomorphism can be ruled out.

Property 1:   If $\{G, *\}$ and $\{H, \circ\}$ are isomorphic then the identity of $\{G, *\}$ is mapped to the identity of $\{H, \circ\}$.

Proof: Let e be the identity element of $\{G, *\}$ and let $f\colon G \to H$ be the bijection.

For all $a, b \in G$, $f(a * b) = f(a) \circ f(b)$

Now $e \in G$ and $a * e = e * a = a$

$\Rightarrow \ f(a * e) = f(a) \circ f(e) = f(a)$

and $f(e * a) = f(e) \circ f(a) = f(a)$

$\Rightarrow \ f(a) = f(a) \circ f(e) = f(e) \circ f(a)$

$\therefore \ f(e)$ is the identity element of $\{H, \circ\}$.

Property 2:   If $\{G, *\}$ and $\{H, \circ\}$ are isomorphic then the inverse of an element of $\{G, *\}$ is mapped to the inverse of the corresponding element in $\{H, \circ\}$, i.e., $[f(a)]^{-1} = f(a^{-1})$ for all $a \in G$.

Proof: For all $a, b \in G$, $f(a * b) = f(a) \circ f(b)$

Now $a^{-1} \in G$ and $a * a^{-1} = a^{-1} * a = e$, the identity of G

$\Rightarrow \quad f(a * a^{-1}) = f(a) \circ f(a^{-1}) = f(e)$

and $\quad f(a^{-1} * a) = f(a^{-1}) \circ f(a) = f(e)$

$\Rightarrow \quad f(e) = f(a) \circ f(a^{-1}) = f(a^{-1}) \circ f(a)$

$\therefore \quad$ since $f(e)$ is the identity of $\{H, \circ\}$,

$f(a^{-1})$ is the inverse of $f(a)$

Property 3:   If $\{G, *\}$ and $\{H, \circ\}$ are isomorphic then for all $a \in G$, a and $f(a)$ will have the same order.

Property 4:   If $\{G, *\}$ and $\{H, \circ\}$ are isomorphic, $\{G, *\}$ is Abelian if and only if $\{H, \circ\}$ is Abelian.

Two further properties will be developed later.

EXERCISE 9E.2

1 Show that the group $\{0, 1, 2\}$ under addition modulo 3 is not isomorphic to the group $\{0, 1, 2\}$ under subtraction modulo 3.

2 Show that the group $\{1, -\frac{1}{2} + i\frac{\sqrt{3}}{2}, -\frac{1}{2} - i\frac{\sqrt{3}}{2}\}$ under multiplication is isomorphic to the group $\{1, 2, 4\}$, where 1, 2, 4 are residue classes mod 7 under multiplication.

3 Show that the group $\{0, 1, 2, 3, 4\}$ under addition modulo 5 is isomorphic to the group of the five fifth roots of unity under multiplication.

4 Prove that the group $\left\{ \begin{bmatrix} 1 & 0 \\ 0 & 1 \end{bmatrix}, \begin{bmatrix} 0 & 1 \\ 1 & 0 \end{bmatrix}, \begin{bmatrix} 0 & -1 \\ -1 & 0 \end{bmatrix}, \begin{bmatrix} -1 & 0 \\ 0 & -1 \end{bmatrix} \right\}$

under matrix multiplication is isomorphic to the group $\{1, 3, 5, 7\}$ under multiplication modulo 8.

5 Prove that the multiplicative group of positive real numbers is isomorphic to the additive group of real numbers. [**Hint:** Use $f(x) = \ln x$.]

6 Prove *Property 3* above.

CYCLIC GROUPS

INTRODUCTION

Consider the group $\{\mathbb{Z}_7 \setminus \{0\}, \times_7\}$ where $\times_7$ is multiplication modulo 7.

The Cayley table is shown alongside:

Clearly, the identity element is 1.

We determine the order of the other elements of the group:

$\times_7$	1	2	3	4	5	6
1	1	2	3	4	5	6
2	2	4	6	1	3	5
3	3	6	2	5	1	4
4	4	1	5	2	6	3
5	5	3	1	6	4	2
6	6	5	4	3	2	1

$2^1 = 2$, $2^2 = 4$, $2^3 = 1$ so the element 2 has order 3

$3^1 = 3$, $3^2 = 2$, $3^3 = 6$, $3^4 = 4$, $3^5 = 5$, $3^6 = 1$ so the element 3 has order 6

$4^1 = 4$, $4^2 = 2$, $4^3 = 1$ so the element 4 has order 3

$5^1 = 5$, $5^2 = 4$, $5^3 = 6$, $5^4 = 2$, $5^5 = 3$, $5^6 = 1$ so the element 5 has order 6

$6^1 = 6$ so the element 6 has order 2

Observe that the order of each element of the group is a factor of the order of the group. This will be proved later for all finite groups.

Note also that the order of the elements 3 and 5 is 6, the same as the order of the group. Every element of $\{\mathbb{Z}_7 \setminus \{0\}, \times_7\}$ can be written as powers of 3 or 5. The group is therefore said to be **cyclic** and 3 and 5 are called **generators** of the group.

Clearly, generators are not necessarily unique.

> A group $\{G, *\}$ is said to be **cyclic** if there exists an element $g \in G$ such that for all $x \in G$, $x = g^m$ for some $m \in \mathbb{Z}$. g is said to be the **generator** of the group.

The cyclic nature of $\{\mathbb{Z}_7 \setminus \{0\}, \times_7\}$ can be seen in a rearrangement of the Cayley table. We let $a = 3$ and replace 2 by a^2, 6 by a^3, 4 by a^4, and 5 by a^5.

$\times_7$	1	3	2	6	4	5
	1	a	a^2	a^3	a^4	a^5
1 1	1	a	a^2	a^3	a^4	a^5
3 a	a	a^2	a^3	a^4	a^5	1
2 a^2	a^2	a^3	a^4	a^5	1	a
6 a^3	a^3	a^4	a^5	1	a	a^2
4 a^4	a^4	a^5	1	a	a^2	a^3
5 a^5	a^5	1	a	a^2	a^3	a^4

For all $n \in \mathbb{Z}^+$, $\{\mathbb{Z}_n, +\}$ is a cyclic group.

THEOREMS

Theorem 6:   All cyclic groups are Abelian.

Proof: Let $\{G, *\}$ be a cyclic group and let $a \in G$ be a generator of the group.

Let $x, y \in G$.

As the group is cyclic, there exists $p, q \in \mathbb{Z}$ such that $x = a^p$ and $y = a^q$

(Remember that $a^m = a * a * a * \ldots * a * a$ (written m times) and that the associative property allows us to do this without ambiguity.)

$$\therefore \quad x * y = a^p * a^q$$
$$= a^{p+q}$$
$$= a^{q+p} \quad \{\text{addition of integers is commutative}\}$$
$$= a^q * a^p$$
$$= y * x \quad \text{Therefore all cyclic groups are Abelian.}$$

A fifth property of isomorphism can now be added:

Property 5:   If $\{G, *\}$ and $\{H, \circ\}$ are isomorphic, $\{G, *\}$ is cyclic if and only if $\{H, \circ\}$ is cyclic.

Theorem 7:   For all $n \in \mathbb{Z}^+$, there is a cyclic group of order n.

Proof: The only group of order 1 must contain the identity e, and $\{\{e\}, *\}$ is cyclic.

Let $G = \{a, a^2, a^3, \ldots\ldots a^n\}$ where n is the smallest positive integer for which $a^n = e$.

For example, when $n = 1$, $G = \{a\} = \{e\}$; when $n = 2$, $G = \{a, a^2\} = \{a, e\}$.

Closure: Let $a^p, a^q \in G$ where $p, q \in \mathbb{Z}^+$ and $1 \leqslant p, q \leqslant n$

Then $a^p * a^q = a^{p+q}$

Now *either* $2 \leqslant p + q \leqslant n$ in which case $a^{p+q} \in G$

$\quad$ or $\quad p + q = n + r$ where $1 \leqslant r \leqslant n$

$\quad\quad \Rightarrow \quad a^{p+q} = a^{n+r} = a^n * a^r = e * a^r = a^r$

$\quad\quad \Rightarrow \quad$ as $1 \leqslant r \leqslant n$, $a^r \in G$, and so $a^{p+q} \in G$

Hence G is closed under $*$.

Associative: For all $x, y, z \in G$,
$$\begin{aligned} x * (y * z) &= a^p * (a^q * a^r) \\ &= a^p * a^{q+r} \\ &= a^{p+q+r} \\ &= a^{p+q} * a^r \\ &= (a^p * a^q) * a^r \\ &= (x * y) * z \end{aligned}$$

$\Rightarrow \quad *$ is an associative operation on G.

Identity: $a^n = e$ is the identity.

Inverse: Now $a^p * a^q = a^q * a^p = a^{p+q}$

$\quad\quad \Rightarrow \quad a^{p+q} = a^n = e$ when $p + q = n$

$\quad\quad\quad\quad\quad$ i.e., when $q = n - p$

As $1 \leqslant p \leqslant n$, $0 \leqslant n - p \leqslant n - 1$ i.e., $0 \leqslant q \leqslant n - 1$

If $q = 0$, $a^p = e$, which is its own inverse.

Otherwise, $1 \leqslant q \leqslant n - 1$ gives $a^q \in G$ such that
$a^p * a^q = a^q * a^p = a^{p+q} = a^n = e$

Hence each element has an inverse.

Therefore $\{G, *\}$ is a group.

Theorem 8: For any $n \in \mathbb{Z}^+$, all cyclic groups of order n are isomorphic to each other.

Proof: Let $\{G, *\}$ and $\{H, \circ\}$ be cyclic groups of order m where
$G = \{a^0, a, a^2, ..., a^{m-1}\}$ and $H = \{x^0, x, x^2, ..., x^{m-1}\}$
There is a bijection $f: G \mapsto H$ where $f(a^i) = x^i$ for all $0 \leqslant i \leqslant m - 1$.
Let $0 \leqslant p, q \leqslant m-1$, then $f(a^p * a^q) = f(a^{p+q})$ where $0 \leqslant p + q \leqslant 2m - 2$

$\quad\quad \therefore \quad p + q = r$ or $p + q = m + r$ where $0 \leqslant r \leqslant m - 1$

$\quad\quad \therefore \quad a^{p+q} = a^r$ or $a^{p+q} = a^{m+r} = a^m * a^r = a^0 * a^r = a^r$

$\quad\quad\quad \therefore \quad a^{p+q} = a^r$ for all $0 \leqslant p, q \leqslant m - 1$

$\quad\quad\quad\quad$ Similarly, $x^{p+q} = x^r$ for all $0 \leqslant p, q \leqslant m - 1$

Now $f(a^p) = x^p$, $f(a^q) = x^q$ and $f(a^r) = x^r$

$\therefore \quad f(a^p * a^q) = f(a^{p+q}) = f(a^r) = x^r = x^{p+q} = x^p \circ x^q = f(a^p) \circ f(a^q)$

Hence $\{G, *\}$ and $\{H, \circ\}$ are isomorphic.

INFINITE CYCLIC GROUPS

Cyclic groups can be infinite. An infinite group $\{G, *\}$ is cyclic if there is an element $g \in G$ such that for all $x \in G$, $x = g^n$ where $n \in \mathbb{Z}$.

An example is $\{2\mathbb{Z}, +\}$, the group consisting of the even integers under addition.

Now $0 = n \times 2$ where $n = 0$.

For all positive elements $2n \in 2\mathbb{Z}$, $n > 0$:
$$2n = \underbrace{2 + 2 + ... + 2}_{n \text{ times}} = n \times 2$$

For all negative elements $2n \in 2\mathbb{Z}$, $n < 0$:
$$2n = \underbrace{(-2) + (-2) + ... + (-2)}_{-n \text{ times (remembering } n < 0)}$$
$$= (-n) \times (-2)$$
$$= n \times 2$$

Hence every element can be written as $n \times 2$ where $n \in \mathbb{Z}$, and so 2 is the generator of this group.

Using the familiar multiplicative notation for repetitions of an operation, a cyclic group of infinite order will be of the form $\{\{....., g^{-2}, g^{-1}, e, g, g^2, ...\}, *\}$.

EXERCISE 9E.3

1 Consider the group $\{G, \times_n\}$ where G is the set containing the $n - 1$ residue classes modulo n excluding 0. Which members are generators of $\{G, \times_n\}$ when:

    a $n = 3$ **b** $n = 5$ **c** $n = 7$ **d** $n = 11$?

2 Show that $\begin{bmatrix} -\frac{1}{2} + \frac{\sqrt{3}}{2}i & 0 \\ 0 & -1 \end{bmatrix}$ is the generator of a cyclic group under matrix multiplication.

SUBGROUPS

INTRODUCTION

$\{H, *\}$ is a **subgroup** of $\{G, *\}$ if: (1) $H \subseteq G$

and (2) H forms a group under the operation $*$.

As $G \subseteq G$, $\{G, *\}$ is a subgroup of itself.

$\{e\} \subseteq G$ and $\{\{e\}, *\}$ is a group, so $\{\{e\}, *\}$ is a subgroup of every group with the same operation.

All groups with more than one element have at least two subgroups ($\{\{e\}, *\}$ and themselves). Any subgroups of a group apart from these two are called **proper subgroups**.

THEOREMS

Theorem 9: Given a non-empty subset H of G, $\{H, *\}$ is a subgroup of the group $\{G, *\}$ if $a * b^{-1} \in H$ for all $a, b \in H$.

Proof: Now we know that for all $b \in H$, there must exist a $b^{-1} \in G$ which is the inverse of b, and that $b * b^{-1} = e$, the identity of G. If these things were not true, then G would not be a group. We will show that in fact $e \in H$ and $b^{-1} \in H$ in order for $a * b^{-1} \in H$ to be true.

However, we need to prove the requirements for H to be a group are satisfied in a different order from usual.

Identity: For all $a, b \in H$, $a * b^{-1} \in H$.
Now $b \in H$, so replacing a by b gives: $b * b^{-1} \in H$
$\Rightarrow \quad e \in H$
Hence there is an identity element in H.

Inverse: For all $a, b \in H$, $a * b^{-1} \in H$.
Now $e \in H$,   so replacing a by e gives: $e * b^{-1} \in H$
$\Rightarrow \quad b^{-1} \in H$ for all $b \in H$
Hence each element has an inverse.

Closure: For all $a, b \in H$, $a * b^{-1} \in H$.
Now if we let $c = b^{-1}$, then we know $c \in H$ and $c^{-1} = b$
$\therefore$ since $a * c^{-1} \in H$ for all $c \in H$,
$\qquad\qquad a * b \in H$ for all $b \in H$ $\Rightarrow$ H is closed under $*$.

Associative: The associativity of $*$ applies to all elements of G and it therefore must apply to all elements of H, a subset of G.

Therefore, if H is a non-empty subset of G, to show that $\{H, *\}$ is a subgroup of $\{G, *\}$ it is sufficient to show that $a * b^{-1} \in H$ for all $a, b \in H$.

Theorem 10:   If $\{G, *\}$ is a *finite* group and H is a non-empty subset of G, then $\{H, *\}$ is a subgroup of $\{G, *\}$ if $a * b \in H$ for all $a, b \in H$.

Proof: *Associative:* The associativity of $*$ applies to all elements of G and it therefore must apply to all elements of H, a subset of G.

Closure: The property $a * b \in H$ for all $a, b \in H$ means $\{G, *\}$ is closed {by definition}.

Identity: As $\{G, *\}$ is a finite group, the order of any $x \in H$ is finite, m say, where $m \in \mathbb{Z}^+$.
$\Rightarrow \quad x^m = e$, but $x^m \in H$ by closure, so $e \in H$.
$\Rightarrow \quad$ the identity element is in H.

Inverse: Firstly, we note that e is its own inverse.
For all other $x \in H$, $x^m = e$ where $m \in \mathbb{Z}^+$, $m \geqslant 2$.
$\qquad$ Now $x^m = x^{(m-1)+1} = x^{1+(m-1)}$ where $m - 1 \in \mathbb{Z}^+$
$\qquad\qquad \Rightarrow \quad e = x^{m-1} * x = x * x^{m-1}$
i.e., $x * x^{m-1} = x^{m-1} * x = e$
$\therefore$ x^{m-1} is the inverse of x.

Since we can do this for all $x \in H$ other than e, but we already know that e has its own inverse, every element $x \in H$ has an inverse.

Therefore $\{H, *\}$ is a group and since $H \subseteq G$, $\{H, *\}$ is a subgroup of $\{G, *\}$.

A sixth property of isomorphism is

Property 6:   If $\{G, *\}$ and $\{H, \circ\}$ are isomorphic then any subgroup of $\{G, *\}$ will be isomorphic to some subgroup of $\{H, \circ\}$.

Corollary   For a finite group $\{G, *\}$ of order n, if there is an element $g \in G$ with order m where $2 \leqslant m \leqslant n$ then the set $H = \{e, g, g^2, ..., g^{m-1}\}$ forms a cyclic subgroup of $\{G, *\}$.

Proof: If p and q are integers such that $0 \leqslant p, \; q \leqslant m - 1$, then $0 \leqslant p + q \leqslant 2m - 2$.

$$\therefore \quad g^p * g^q = g^{p+q}$$
$$= g^{am+r} \quad \text{where} \quad a = 0 \text{ or } 1 \quad \text{and} \quad 0 \leqslant r \leqslant m - 1$$
$$= g^{am} * g^r$$
$$= (g^m)^a * g^r$$
$$= e * g^r$$
$$= g^r \quad \text{which} \in H \quad \text{since} \quad 0 \leqslant r \leqslant m - 1$$

Hence H is closed and hence forms a subgroup of $\{G, *\}$.

Since g is a cyclic generator for the group, H is a cyclic subgroup.

THEOREM OF LAGRANGE   (Joseph Louis Lagrange, 1736-1813)

Theorem 11:   (Lagrange)   The order of a subgroup of a finite group $\{G, *\}$ is a factor of the order of $\{G, *\}$.

The proof of this theorem involves consideration of cosets and lies outside the scope of this book.

An important **corollary of Lagrange's theorem** is the following:

Corollary   The order of a finite group is divisible by the order of any element.

Proof: Let $\{G, *\}$ be a finite group of order n.

If an element $x \in G$ has order n or 1, then the theorem is proved as $n|n$ and $1|n$.

If $x \in G$ has order m where $2 \leqslant m \leqslant n - 1$, then from **Theorem 10 corollary**, $\{x^0, x, x^2, x^3, ... x^{m-1}\}$ is a subgroup of $\{G, *\}$. The order of this subgroup is m.

By Lagrange's theorem, the order of any subgroup of $\{G, *\}$ must divide the order of $\{G, *\}$, i.e., $m|n$.

Therefore the order of a finite group is divisible by the order of any element.

We can therefore conclude that if $\{G, *\}$ is a finite group of order p where p is prime, then it must be a cyclic group of order p and the order of each element can only be 1 or p. Only the identity has order 1, so any other element must have order p.

Therefore, if $a \in \{G, *\}$, then $a, a^2, a^3, ..., a^p \in G$ where $a^p = e$.

As there can only be p elements, a is a generator of the group and $G = \{a, a^2, a^3, ..., a^p\}$.

All groups of order 1 will be isomorphic to $\{\{e\}, *\}$.

All groups of order 2 will have a Cayley table with the following pattern:

$*$	e	a
e	e	a
a	a	e

Note that $a*a=e$ and the group is cyclic.

We now use a Cayley table to construct a group of order 3. We know that there will be three elements, one of which is the identity, e, so we start with:

$*$	e	a	b
e	e	a	b
a	a		
b	b		

We know that each element must appear exactly once in every row and every column. The entry in the shaded square can only be b or e, but if we use e then b must be the entry in the square alongside, and the third column would have two bs in it. The shaded square must therefore be b.

$*$	e	a	b
e	e	a	b
a	a	b	
b	b		

No choice is left but to complete the second row and second column with e and the final position with a. There can thus be only one pattern for a group of order 3.

$*$	e	a	b
e	e	a	b
a	a	b	e
b	b	e	a

Notice that $a^2=b$, so the elements of the group are e, a, a^2 and the group is clearly cyclic.

Notice also that $b^2=a$, so b is also a generator of the group. In a cyclic group of prime order, each element apart from e must have order p, so each is a generator of the group.

EXERCISE 9E.4

1   a   Show that the set $\{1, 5, 7, 11\}$ mod 12 forms an Abelian group under the operation multiplication mod 12.

   b   Is the group cyclic?

   c   List all the subgroups of the group.

2   a   Prove that the set $M = \left\{ \begin{bmatrix} a & b \\ c & d \end{bmatrix} \mid a, b, c, d \in \mathbb{C}, \ ad - bc \neq 0 \right\}$ with the operation matrix multiplication is a group.

   b   Show that the following sets of matrices are subgroups of the group in a:

   i $\left\{ \begin{bmatrix} a & c \\ b & d \end{bmatrix} \mid a, b, c, d \in \mathbb{R}, \ ad - bc \neq 0 \right\}$

   ii $\left\{ \begin{bmatrix} a & c \\ 0 & d \end{bmatrix} \mid a, b, c \in \mathbb{C}, \ ad \neq 0 \right\}$

3   Let $S = \{(x, y) \mid x, y \in \mathbb{Z}\}$ Define the operation $*$ to be the composition of points where $(a, b) * (c, d) = (a + c, (-1)^c b + d)$

   a   Prove that S is a group with respect to the operation $*$.

   b   Is the group $\{S, *\}$ Abelian?

   c   Do the following sets with the operation $*$ form subgroups of G?

      i $H_1 = \{(a, 0) \mid a \in \mathbb{Z}\}$ ii $H_2 = \{(0, b) \mid b \in \mathbb{Z}\}$

4 Let $\{G, *\}$ be a group. Show that $H = \{x \mid x \in G$ and $x * a = a * x\}$ is a subgroup of G.

5 Let $\{G, *\}$ be a group and let $\{H_1, *\}$ and $\{H_2, *\}$ be subgroups of $\{G, *\}$. Prove that $\{H_1 \cap H_2, *\}$ is a subgroup of $\{G, *\}$.

F   FURTHER GROUPS

GROUPS OF ORDER 4

One of the groups of order 4 is the cyclic group whose Cayley table is shown alongside.

$*$	e	a	b	c
e	e	a	b	c
a	a	b	c	e
b	b	c	e	a
c	c	e	a	b

Note that $a^2 = b \Rightarrow a * b = a * a^2 = a^3 = c$

and $c^2 = b \Rightarrow c * b = c * c^2 = c^3 = a$.

Hence a and c are generators of the group.

However, $b^2 = e$, so b is of order 2 and is not a generator.

Care needs to be taken when using Cayley tables. Consider the following variation of the above table:

$*$	e	a	b	c
e	e	a	b	c
a	a	e	c	b
b	b	c	a	e
c	c	b	e	a

Although different in appearance, this group is isomorphic to the previous one. In this case b and c are the generators and the bijection f: $e \mapsto e$, $a \mapsto b$, $b \mapsto a$, $c \mapsto c$ maps one table onto the other.

However, the group shown in this Cayley table is not isomorphic to the previous two:

$*$	e	a	b	c
e	e	a	b	c
a	a	e	c	b
b	b	c	e	a
c	c	b	a	e

Although it is Abelian like the previous two groups, notice that a, b and c each have order 2, so this group is not cyclic. A group with this structure is called the **Klein four-group**. All groups of order four will be isomorphic to this one or to the cyclic group of order 4.

Associativity is not always obvious from the Cayley table. Only one counter-example is needed to show that an operation is not associative, but all possibilities need to be checked if associativity is to be established.

GROUPS OF ORDER n

As shown previously, if n is prime there is only one group to which all groups of order n are isomorphic.

The number of types of isomorphic groups varies for values of n greater than 1 and not prime. The table below shows the number of partitions (p) of the set of groups of order n.

n	4	6	8	9	10	12	14	15	16	18	20	21	22	24
p	2	2	5	2	2	5	2	1	14	5	5	2	2	15

In the above examples, it is important to check for associativity and this is left as an exercise.

Example 58

The following Cayley table is for the operation $*$ on the set $S = \{e, a, b, c, d, x\}$.

Show that:

$*$	e	a	b	c	d	x
e	e	a	b	c	d	x
a	a	e	c	d	x	b
b	b	d	e	x	c	a
c	c	x	a	e	b	d
d	d	b	x	a	e	c
x	x	c	d	b	a	e

  a S is closed under $*$

  b   there is an identity element for $*$ in S

  c   each element of S has a unique inverse

  d $*$ is not associative.

  a   For all $a, b \in S$, $a * b \in S$. $\therefore$ S is closed under $*$.

  b   For all $y \in S$, $e * y = y * e = y$ $\therefore$ since $e \in S$, the identity is e.

  c   For all $y \in S$, $y * y = e$,   so each element has a unique inverse, itself.

  d $a * (b * c) = a * x = b$

       $(a * b) * c = c * c = e \neq a * (b * c)$

       Thus $*$ is not an associative operation and S does not form a group under $*$.

Notice in this example that each element has a unique inverse. So, while associativity implies that each inverse is unique, the converse does not apply.

If the Cayley table indicates the inverse is not unique, we can conclude that the operation is not associative.

PERMUTATIONS

A **permutation** is a bijection from a non-empty set to itself.

For example, consider the mapping from S to S where $S = \{1, 2, 3, 4\}$ as shown in the diagram:

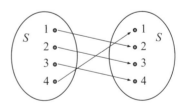

The ordered pairs of the bijection are $(1, 2)$, $(2, 3)$, $(3, 4)$, $(4, 1)$ but the permutation is commonly written in the following way:

$$p_a = \begin{pmatrix} 1 & 2 & 3 & 4 \\ 2 & 3 & 4 & 1 \end{pmatrix}$$

The entries in the second row are the values to which the entries in the first row are mapped.

IDENTITY

If $S = \{1, 2, 3, 4\}$, the number of possible such bijections will be $4! = 24$. In one of these 24 possibilities, each element will be mapped to itself, giving the identity permutation on S:

$$e = \begin{pmatrix} 1 & 2 & 3 & 4 \\ 1 & 2 & 3 & 4 \end{pmatrix}$$

COMBINING PERMUTATIONS

Let two permutations on S be $p_a = \begin{pmatrix} 1 & 2 & 3 & 4 \\ 2 & 3 & 4 & 1 \end{pmatrix}$ and $p_b = \begin{pmatrix} 1 & 2 & 3 & 4 \\ 3 & 1 & 2 & 4 \end{pmatrix}$.

The composition of two permutations is variously called **combining**, **multiplying** or **finding the product**.

Consider the composition of functions where p_a is followed by p_b as shown in the diagram:

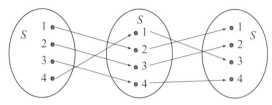

Following the arrows through gives the resulting permutation $p_b p_a = \begin{pmatrix} 1 & 2 & 3 & 4 \\ 1 & 2 & 4 & 3 \end{pmatrix}$

$p_b p_a$ could have been found by writing the combined permutation as

$$\begin{pmatrix} 1 & 2 & 3 & 4 \\ 3 & 1 & 2 & 4 \end{pmatrix} \begin{pmatrix} 1 & 2 & 3 & 4 \\ 2 & 3 & 4 & 1 \end{pmatrix}$$

and following through as shown: $\begin{pmatrix} 2 \\ \downarrow \\ 1 \end{pmatrix} \begin{pmatrix} 1 \\ \downarrow \\ 2 \end{pmatrix} = \begin{pmatrix} 1 \\ \downarrow \\ 1 \end{pmatrix}$

Note that we work from right to left when combining permutations. This is consistent with composition of functions:

$$(p_b p_a)(x) = p_b(p_a(x)) = p_b \circ p_a(x)$$

However, not all texts follow this convention.

Composition of functions is in general not commutative, and this is usually true for combining permutations. For example:

$$\begin{aligned} p_a p_b &= \begin{pmatrix} 1 & 2 & 3 & 4 \\ 2 & 3 & 4 & 1 \end{pmatrix} \begin{pmatrix} 1 & 2 & 3 & 4 \\ 3 & 1 & 2 & 4 \end{pmatrix} \\ &= \begin{pmatrix} 1 & 2 & 3 & 4 \\ 4 & 2 & 3 & 1 \end{pmatrix} \\ &\neq p_b p_a \end{aligned}$$

However, composition of functions is associative, so the process of combining permutations can be used for more than two permutations. For example:

$$p_4 p_3 p_2 p_1 = \begin{pmatrix} \cdot & 2 & \cdot & \cdot \\ \cdot & \downarrow & \cdot & \cdot \\ \cdot & 3 & \cdot & \cdot \end{pmatrix} \begin{pmatrix} \cdot & \cdot & \cdot & 4 \\ \cdot & \cdot & \cdot & \downarrow \\ \cdot & \cdot & \cdot & 2 \end{pmatrix} \begin{pmatrix} \cdot & 2 & \cdot & \cdot \\ \cdot & \downarrow & \cdot & \cdot \\ \cdot & 4 & \cdot & \cdot \end{pmatrix} \begin{pmatrix} 1 & \cdot & \cdot & \cdot \\ \downarrow & \cdot & \cdot & \cdot \\ 2 & \cdot & \cdot & \cdot \end{pmatrix}$$

gives $\begin{pmatrix} 1 & \cdot & \cdot & \cdot \\ 3 & \cdot & \cdot & \cdot \end{pmatrix}$ etc.

INVERSE

To find an inverse function, we need only to interchange the elements of the ordered pairs of the bijection. To achieve this for a permutation we swap the rows then (usually) rearrange the order of the columns so the elements in the first row are in ascending order.

For example, $\begin{pmatrix} 1 & 2 & 3 & 4 \\ 3 & 1 & 4 & 2 \end{pmatrix}^{-1} = \begin{pmatrix} 1 & 2 & 3 & 4 \\ 2 & 4 & 1 & 3 \end{pmatrix}$

as $\begin{pmatrix} 1 & 2 & 3 & 4 \\ 3 & 1 & 4 & 2 \end{pmatrix} \begin{pmatrix} 1 & 2 & 3 & 4 \\ 2 & 4 & 1 & 3 \end{pmatrix} = \begin{pmatrix} 1 & 2 & 3 & 4 \\ 2 & 4 & 1 & 3 \end{pmatrix} \begin{pmatrix} 1 & 2 & 3 & 4 \\ 3 & 1 & 4 & 2 \end{pmatrix} = \begin{pmatrix} 1 & 2 & 3 & 4 \\ 1 & 2 & 3 & 4 \end{pmatrix} = e$

EXERCISE 9F.1

1 Simplify the following compositions of permutations:

a $\begin{pmatrix} 1 & 2 & 3 & 4 \\ 1 & 4 & 2 & 3 \end{pmatrix} \begin{pmatrix} 1 & 2 & 3 & 4 \\ 4 & 2 & 3 & 1 \end{pmatrix}$ b $\begin{pmatrix} 1 & 2 & 3 & 4 \\ 2 & 3 & 1 & 4 \end{pmatrix} \begin{pmatrix} 1 & 2 & 3 & 4 \\ 4 & 3 & 1 & 2 \end{pmatrix}$

c $\begin{pmatrix} 1 & 2 & 3 & 4 \\ 2 & 1 & 4 & 3 \end{pmatrix} \begin{pmatrix} 1 & 2 & 3 & 4 \\ 2 & 1 & 4 & 3 \end{pmatrix}$ d $\begin{pmatrix} 1 & 2 & 3 & 4 \\ 3 & 4 & 1 & 2 \end{pmatrix} \begin{pmatrix} 1 & 2 & 3 & 4 \\ 2 & 3 & 1 & 4 \end{pmatrix} \begin{pmatrix} 1 & 2 & 3 & 4 \\ 4 & 1 & 2 & 3 \end{pmatrix}$

2 Find:

a $\begin{pmatrix} 1 & 2 & 3 & 4 \\ 3 & 1 & 4 & 2 \end{pmatrix}^{-1}$ b $\begin{pmatrix} 1 & 2 & 3 & 4 \\ 2 & 1 & 4 & 3 \end{pmatrix}^{-1}$

c $\left[\begin{pmatrix} 1 & 2 & 3 & 4 \\ 3 & 4 & 2 & 1 \end{pmatrix} \begin{pmatrix} 1 & 2 & 3 & 4 \\ 2 & 4 & 1 & 3 \end{pmatrix} \right]^{-1}$

3 Prove that, for all permutations p, q on $\{1, 2, 3, 4\}$, $(qp)^{-1} = p^{-1}q^{-1}$.

4 Find permutations p on $\{1, 2, 3, 4\}$ such that:

a $p \begin{pmatrix} 1 & 2 & 3 & 4 \\ 3 & 1 & 2 & 4 \end{pmatrix} = \begin{pmatrix} 1 & 2 & 3 & 4 \\ 2 & 4 & 1 & 3 \end{pmatrix}$ b $p \begin{pmatrix} 1 & 2 & 3 & 4 \\ 2 & 3 & 1 & 4 \end{pmatrix} = \begin{pmatrix} 1 & 2 & 3 & 4 \\ 2 & 4 & 1 & 3 \end{pmatrix}$

5 For each of the following, construct a Cayley table and determine whether the set of permutations is a group under composition of permutations.

a $\{A, B, C, D\}$ where $A = \begin{pmatrix} 1 & 2 & 3 & 4 \\ 1 & 2 & 3 & 4 \end{pmatrix}$, $B = \begin{pmatrix} 1 & 2 & 3 & 4 \\ 2 & 3 & 4 & 1 \end{pmatrix}$,

$C = \begin{pmatrix} 1 & 2 & 3 & 4 \\ 3 & 4 & 1 & 2 \end{pmatrix}$, $D = \begin{pmatrix} 1 & 2 & 3 & 4 \\ 4 & 1 & 2 & 3 \end{pmatrix}$

b $\{A, B, C, D\}$ where $A = \begin{pmatrix} 1 & 2 & 3 & 4 \\ 1 & 2 & 3 & 4 \end{pmatrix}$, $B = \begin{pmatrix} 1 & 2 & 3 & 4 \\ 2 & 1 & 4 & 3 \end{pmatrix}$,

$C = \begin{pmatrix} 1 & 2 & 3 & 4 \\ 3 & 4 & 1 & 2 \end{pmatrix}$, $D = \begin{pmatrix} 1 & 2 & 3 & 4 \\ 4 & 3 & 2 & 1 \end{pmatrix}$

Is either a or b a cyclic group?

6 Explain why the group consisting of all the permutations on $\{1, 2, 3, 4, 5\}$ under composition of permutations has no subgroups of order 7.

SYMMETRIC GROUP OF ORDER 3

Example 59

Consider all possible permutations on $S = \{1, 2, 3\}$.

Show that these form a group under combination of permutations.

We know that there are $3! = 6$ different permutations.

The identity, $e = \begin{pmatrix} 1 & 2 & 3 \\ 1 & 2 & 3 \end{pmatrix}$ and let $\alpha = \begin{pmatrix} 1 & 2 & 3 \\ 2 & 3 & 1 \end{pmatrix}$

$\alpha^2 = \begin{pmatrix} 1 & 2 & 3 \\ 2 & 3 & 1 \end{pmatrix} \begin{pmatrix} 1 & 2 & 3 \\ 2 & 3 & 1 \end{pmatrix} = \begin{pmatrix} 1 & 2 & 3 \\ 3 & 1 & 2 \end{pmatrix}$ which is another permutation,

and $\alpha^3 = e$.

Let $\beta = \begin{pmatrix} 1 & 2 & 3 \\ 1 & 3 & 2 \end{pmatrix}$, so $\beta^2 = e$. Let $\gamma = \begin{pmatrix} 1 & 2 & 3 \\ 3 & 2 & 1 \end{pmatrix}$, so $\gamma^2 = e$.

Finally, let $\delta = \begin{pmatrix} 1 & 2 & 3 \\ 2 & 1 & 3 \end{pmatrix}$, so $\delta^2 = e$.

So, the six permutations on S are e, α, α^2, β, γ and δ.

Call the set containing these permutations S_3.

$\alpha\beta = \begin{pmatrix} 1 & 2 & 3 \\ 2 & 3 & 1 \end{pmatrix} \begin{pmatrix} 1 & 2 & 3 \\ 1 & 3 & 2 \end{pmatrix} = \begin{pmatrix} 1 & 2 & 3 \\ 2 & 1 & 3 \end{pmatrix} = \delta$

$\alpha\gamma = \begin{pmatrix} 1 & 2 & 3 \\ 2 & 3 & 1 \end{pmatrix} \begin{pmatrix} 1 & 2 & 3 \\ 3 & 2 & 1 \end{pmatrix} = \begin{pmatrix} 1 & 2 & 3 \\ 1 & 3 & 2 \end{pmatrix} = \beta$

$\alpha\delta = \begin{pmatrix} 1 & 2 & 3 \\ 2 & 3 & 1 \end{pmatrix} \begin{pmatrix} 1 & 2 & 3 \\ 2 & 1 & 3 \end{pmatrix} = \begin{pmatrix} 1 & 2 & 3 \\ 3 & 2 & 1 \end{pmatrix} = \gamma$

Continuing in this way enables us to construct the Cayley table for combining permutations on S:

$*$	e	α	α^2	β	γ	δ
e	e	α	α^2	β	γ	δ
α	α	α^2	e	δ	β	γ
α^2	α^2	e	α	γ	δ	β
β	β	γ	δ	e	α	α^2
γ	γ	δ	β	α^2	e	α
δ	δ	β	γ	α	α^2	e

Closure: From the Cayley table, it is clear that for all a, $b \in S_3$, $a * b \in S_3$. Therefore S_3 is closed under the operation.

Associative Composition of functions is an associative operation, so the composition of permutations on S is associative.

Identity From the table, e is such that $a * b = b * a = e$ for all $a \in S_3$.
∴ since $e \in S$, e is an identity element in S_3 for $*$.

Inverse As the identity e appears once in every row and column in the table, each element in S_3 must have an inverse element under $*$. α and α^2 are inverses of each other, and each other element is its own inverse.

Therefore, $\{S_3, *\}$ forms a group.

This group is referred to as the **symmetric group of order 3**.

Notice that the order of a is 3 while β, γ and δ have order 2.

No element has order 6, so $\{S_3, *\}$ is not a cyclic group.

$\{S_3, *\}$ is therefore not isomorphic to $\{Z_7 \setminus \{0\}, \times_7\}$

The set of permutations on $S = \{1, 2, 3, \ldots, n\}$ where $n \in \mathbb{Z}^+$ is called S_n.

$\{S_n, *\}$ where $*$ is composition of permutations is referred to as the **symmetric group of order n**.

This group is often just written as S_n and consists of all possible bijections of a set with n elements onto itself.

SYMMETRIES OF AN EQUILATERAL TRIANGLE (Dihedral group of order 3)

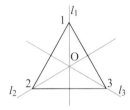

The equilateral triangle shown in the diagram has centroid O. Lines l_1, l_2 and l_3 contain the three medians of the triangle through the vertices labelled 1, 2 and 3 respectively.

There are six transformations in the plane which map the equilateral triangle onto itself.

These are the three rotations:

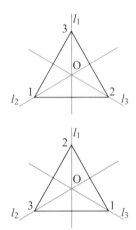

e an anti-(counter-)clockwise rotation through 0^0 about O. This is the identity or "do nothing" transformation.

r an anti-clockwise rotation through 120° about O as shown:

r^2 an anti-clockwise rotation through 240° about O. This is equivalent to two successive applications of r, i.e., $r * r$ or r^2.

Note that $r^3 = e$ is a rotation through 360° which maps every point to itself.

and the three reflections:

x a reflection in the line l_1 y a reflection in the line l_2 z a reflection in the line l_3.

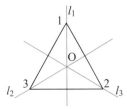
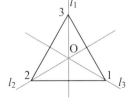
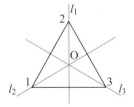

As x, y and z are reflections, $x^2 = y^2 = z^2 = e$

Let $D = \{e, r, r^2, x, y, z\}$

$\{D, *\}$ forms a group where $*$ is taken to be the combination of transformations.

We can set up the Cayley table:

For example, $r * x$ is a reflection in l_1 followed by an anti-clockwise rotation through $120°$. The result is z.

Using a cut-out copy of the triangle may help with recognition of geometric transformations.

$*$	e	r	r^2	x	y	z
e	e	r	r^2	x	y	z
r	r	r^2	e	z	x	y
r^2	r^2	e	r	y	z	x
x	x	y	z	e	r	r^2
y	y	z	x	r^2	e	r
z	z	x	y	r	r^2	e

Closure: The Cayley table shows that $a * b \in D$ for all $a, b \in D$. Therefore D is closed under $*$.

Associativity: Transformations in the plane can be considered as bijections on $\mathbb{R}^2$. Therefore, since composition of functions is associative, composition of transformations is also associative.

Identity: It can be seen from the table that $a * e = e * a = a$ for all $a \in D$. Therefore since $e \in D$, there is an identity element for $*$ in D.

Inverse: As e appears once in every row and column, every element has a unique inverse.

Therefore $\{D, *\}$ forms a group.

This group is referred to as the **dihedral group of order 3**, $\{D_3, *\}$ or just D_3.

D_n is the group consisting of all the symmetries of a regular n-sided polygon under symmetric transformations in the plane.

You may notice a similarity between this group and the group $\{S_3, *\}$. In fact, there is a bijection between D_3 and S_3 as follows:

$$r \leftrightarrow \alpha \quad r^2 \leftrightarrow \alpha^2 \quad x \leftrightarrow \beta \quad y \leftrightarrow \gamma \quad z \leftrightarrow \delta.$$

Further, replacing each occurrence of r, r^2, x, y, z in the Cayley table for $\{D_3, *\}$ with the elements they map to gives the table for $\{S_3, *\}$. $\{D, *\}$ is therefore isomorphic to $\{S_3, *\}$.

This will come as no surprise if we investigate the labelling of the vertices of the triangle. Notice that under r, for example, 1 is mapped to 2, 2 is mapped to 3 and 3 is mapped to 1.

We could write this as $\begin{pmatrix} 1 & 2 & 3 \\ 2 & 3 & 1 \end{pmatrix}$ which is α.

Under x, 1 is mapped to 1, 2 to 3 and 3 to 2. This can be written as $\begin{pmatrix} 1 & 2 & 3 \\ 1 & 3 & 2 \end{pmatrix}$ which is β.

If $H = \{e, r, r^2\}$, it is clear from the Cayley table that $\{H, *\}$ is a subgroup of $\{D_3, *\}$.

The sets $\{e, x\}$, $\{e, y\}$ and $\{e, z\}$ are also subgroups under $*$. These four groups are the only proper subgroups of $\{D_3, *\}$.

Although the symmetric group of order 3 is isomorphic to the dihedral group of order 3, this isomorphism does not extend beyond $n = 3$.

For example, S_4, the possible mappings from $\{1, 2, 3, 4\}$ has order 24 while for a square there are four rotational symmetries (including the identity) and four reflections, giving an order of 8 for D_4. Hence, a bijection cannot exist between the two sets.

EXERCISE 9F.2

1 Let ABCD be a square centred on O.   Define $T = \{I, R_1, R_2, R_3\}$ where I, R_1, R_2, R_3, are anti-clockwise rotations about O through 0°, 90°, 180° and 270° respectively.

Construct a Cayley table where combining transformations is the operation.

Prove that T is a group under the operation and show that it is cyclic.

2 State the four symmetry operations of a rectangle and show that they form a group under the operation combination of transformations.

Show that this group is isomorphic to the Klein four-group.

REVIEW SETS

REVIEW SET 9A

1 $A = \{a, b, c, d, e, f\}$, $B = \{c, e, g, h\}$ Find:

   a $A \cup B$ **b** $A \backslash B$ **c** $A \Delta B$.

2 If $A = \{1, 2, 3\}$ and $B = \{2, 4\}$,   find $A \times B$.

3 Prove $(A \cap B) \times (C \cap D) = (A \times C) \cap (B \times D)$

4 Prove $(A \setminus B) \times C = (A \times C) \setminus (B \times C)$

5 Use Venn diagrams to illustrate the following distributive laws:

   a $A \cap (B \cup C) = (A \cap B) \cup (A \cap C)$

   b $A \cup (B \cap C) = (A \cup B) \cap (A \cup C)$

6 Find the power set $P(A)$ if $A = \{1, 2, 3\}$.

Determine whether $P(A)$ forms a group under: **a** $\cap$ **b** $\cup$

7 Determine whether the binary operation $*$ on $\mathbb{R}$ is associative where $*$ is defined as

   a $a * b = \dfrac{a + b}{a^2}$ **b** $a * b = 2^{a+b}$ **c** $a * b = a + b - 3ab$

8 Let R be a relation on $\mathbb{Z}$ such that xRy if and only if $x - y$ is divisible by 6.

   a Show that R is an equivalence relation.

   b Describe the equivalence classes.

9 R is a relation on $\mathbb{R} \times \mathbb{R}$ such that for $(a, b), (x, y) \in \mathbb{R} \times \mathbb{R}$,

$$(a, b)R(x, y) \quad \text{if and only if} \quad |x| + |y| = |a| + |b|$$

   a Show that R is an equivalence relation.

   b Describe how R partitions $\mathbb{R} \times \mathbb{R}$ and state the equivalence classes.

10 R is a relation on $(\mathbb{R} \setminus \{0\}) \times \mathbb{R}^+$ such that for (a, b), $(x, y) \in (\mathbb{R} \setminus \{0\}) \times \mathbb{R}^+$
$(a, b)R(x, y)$ if and only if $bx^2 = a^2 y$.

a Show that R is an equivalence relation.

b Describe how R partitions $(\mathbb{R} \setminus \{0\}) \times \mathbb{R}^+$ and state the equivalence classes.

11 Comment on the following argument:

Given a symmetric and transitive relation R on a set S then:

if xRy then yRx for all $x, y \in \mathbb{R}$ (symmetry)

if xRy and yRx then xRx for all $x, y \in \mathbb{R}$ (transitivity)

As xRx, R must be reflexive.

Therefore a symmetric and transitive relation on a set is always an equivalence relation.

12 An operation $*$ on $\{0, 1, 2, 3, 4, 5\}$ is a composition of two binary operations, normal addition $(+)$ and multiplication modulo 6 $(\times_6)$ such that $a * b = a \times_6 (a + b)$.

Construct a Cayley table for this operation on the given set.

13 For each of the operations on real numbers, excluding 0:

i Is the operation associative?

ii Is the operation commutative?

iii If possible, find the identity element.

iv If possible, find the inverse of a.

a $a \circ b = \dfrac{1}{ab}$ **b** $a \circ b = (a+2)(b+3)$ **c** $a \circ b = a^2 b^2$

d $a \circ b = \dfrac{a}{b}$ **e** $a \circ b = a + b + 3ab$ **f** $a \circ b = ab + a$

14 Which of the following are bijections?

a $f: \mathbb{R} \to \mathbb{R}, \quad f(x) = x^3 + 5$ **b** $f: \mathbb{R}^+ \to \mathbb{R}, \quad f(x) = \ln x$

c $f: \mathbb{Z} \to \mathbb{Z}, \quad f(x) = 2x$ **d** $f: \mathbb{R} \to \mathbb{R}, \quad f(x) = 2x$

e $f: \mathbb{R} \to [-1, 1], \quad f(x) = \sin x$

In the case of each bijection, state $f^{-1}(x)$.

15 Let $f = \begin{pmatrix} 1 & 2 & 3 & 4 \\ 1 & 3 & 4 & 2 \end{pmatrix}$ and $g = \begin{pmatrix} 1 & 2 & 3 & 4 \\ 2 & 3 & 1 & 4 \end{pmatrix}$

a Find: **i** gf **ii** fg **b** Find: **i** f^{-1} **ii** g^{-1}

b Find n if $f^n = \begin{pmatrix} 1 & 2 & 3 & 4 \\ 1 & 2 & 3 & 4 \end{pmatrix}$.

16 Let M be the set of 2×2 matrices of the form $\begin{bmatrix} 1 & a \\ 0 & 1 \end{bmatrix}$ where $a \in \mathbb{Z}$.

Show that M forms an Abelian group under matrix multiplication.

17 Let S be the set of 2×2 matrices with determinant equal to 1.

Show that S forms a group under matrix multiplication.

18 Prove that if a group $\{G, *\}$ is such that $|G|$ is an odd prime number, there is only one element which is its own inverse.

19 Construct a Cayley table for $\{\mathbf{M}_1, \mathbf{M}_2, \mathbf{M}_3, \mathbf{M}_4\}$ under matrix multiplication where

$$\mathbf{M}_1 = \begin{bmatrix} 1 & 0 \\ 0 & 1 \end{bmatrix}, \quad \mathbf{M}_2 = \begin{bmatrix} 0 & -1 \\ 1 & 0 \end{bmatrix}, \quad \mathbf{M}_3 = \begin{bmatrix} -1 & 0 \\ 0 & -1 \end{bmatrix}, \quad \mathbf{M}_4 = \begin{bmatrix} 0 & 1 \\ -1 & 0 \end{bmatrix}$$

and prove that it is a group.

20 Show that each of the sets of matrices defined below forms a group under matrix multiplication:

a $\left\{ \begin{bmatrix} 1 & k & 0 \\ 0 & 1 & 0 \\ 0 & 0 & 2^n \end{bmatrix} \mid k, n \in \mathbb{R} \right\}$ **b** $\left\{ \begin{bmatrix} 1 & n & \frac{1}{2}n^2 \\ 0 & 1 & n \\ 0 & 0 & 1 \end{bmatrix} \mid n \in \mathbb{R} \right\}$

21 Show that $\{f_1, f_2, f_3, f_4\}$ is a group under the composition of functions where

$$f_1(x) = x, \quad f_2(x) = -x, \quad f_3(x) = \frac{1}{x}, \quad f_4(x) = -\frac{1}{x}.$$

22 **a** Show that $\{1, 3, 5, 9, 11, 13\}$ under multiplication modulo 14 is a group.
b State the order of each element of the group in **a**.
c Is the group in **a** cyclic?

23 Show that the matrices: $\mathbf{I} = \begin{bmatrix} 1 & 0 \\ 0 & 1 \end{bmatrix}$, $\mathbf{A} = \begin{bmatrix} 0 & 1 \\ -1 & 0 \end{bmatrix}$, $\mathbf{B} = \begin{bmatrix} 0 & -1 \\ 1 & 0 \end{bmatrix}$,

$\mathbf{C} = \begin{bmatrix} -1 & 0 \\ 0 & -1 \end{bmatrix}$, $\mathbf{D} = \begin{bmatrix} i & 0 \\ 0 & -i \end{bmatrix}$, $\mathbf{E} = \begin{bmatrix} -i & 0 \\ 0 & i \end{bmatrix}$, $\mathbf{F} = \begin{bmatrix} 0 & -i \\ -i & 0 \end{bmatrix}$,

$\mathbf{G} = \begin{bmatrix} 0 & i \\ i & 0 \end{bmatrix}$ forms a group under matrix multiplication.

24 Show that the rational numbers of the form $\dfrac{2a+1}{2b+1}$ where $a, b \in \mathbb{Z}$ form a group under multiplication.

25 The Cayley table for a set $S = \{I, A, B, C, D\}$ under the operation $*$ is shown below. Determine, with proof, which of the group axioms apply.

$*$	I	A	B	C	D
I	I	A	B	C	D
A	A	I	D	B	C
B	B	C	I	D	A
C	C	D	A	I	B
D	D	B	C	A	I

26 $\{G, *\}$ is a group with identity element e, and $\{G', \circ\}$ is a group with identity element e'. Let $S = G \times G'$. Define the "product" of pairs of elements $(a, a'), (b, b') \in S$ by $(a, a')(b, b') = (a \circ b, a' * b')$
a Prove that S is a group under the "product" operation.
b Show that the following sets are groups under the "product" operation:
i $S_1 = \{(g, e') \mid g \in G\}$ **ii** $S_2 = \{(e, g') \mid g' \in G'\}$

27 The set $G = \{a, b, c, ...\}$ under the associative operation $*$ has unique solutions x, $y \in G$ for the equations $xa = b$ and $ay = b$. Prove that $\{G, *\}$ is a group.

28 Prove that the following pairs of groups are isomorphic:

    a $\{0, 1, 2, 3\}$ under $+_4$ and $\{1, 2, 3, 4\}$ under $\times_5$

    b the multiplicative group of non-zero complex numbers $a + bi$ and the multiplicative group of matrices $\begin{bmatrix} a & -b \\ b & a \end{bmatrix}$ where $a^2 + b^2 \neq 0$.

29 Let $\{A, +_m\}$ be a group where $A = \{0, 1, 2, ..., (m-1)\}$ and let $\{B, +_{m^2}\}$ be a group where $B = \{0, 1, 2, ..., (m^2 - 1)\}$.

Prove that $G = \{(a, b)| \ a \in A, \ b \in B\}$ is a non-Abelian group of order m^3 under the operation $*$ defined by $(a, b) * (x, y) = (a + x, b + y + mxb)$.

REVIEW SET 9B

1 For the sets $A = \{0, 3, 6, 9, 12\}$, $B = \{1, 2, 3, 4, 5, 6\}$, $C = \{2, 4, 6, 8, 10\}$ and $\mathbb{U} = \{0, 1, 2, 3, 4, 5, 6, 7, 8, 9, 10, 11, 12, 13\}$. Find:

    a $A \cap (B \cup C)$ **b** $A \triangle (B \backslash C)$ **c** $B' \cup C'$

    d $A \cup (B \triangle C)$ **e** $A' \cap (B' \triangle C')$

In each case, illustrate the set on a Venn diagram.

2 Prove $(A \cap B)' = A' \cap B'$ (De Morgan)

3 Find the power set $P(A)$ if $A = \{1, 2\}$. Determine whether $P(A)$ forms a group under: **a** $\cap$ **b** $\cup$

4 A relation R in $\{0, 1, 2, 3, 4, 5\}$ is such that xRy if and only if $|x - y| < 3$.

    a Write R as a set of ordered pairs.

    b Is R **i** reflexive   **ii** symmetric   **ii** transitive?

5 R is a relation on $\mathbb{R} \times \mathbb{R}$ such that for $(a, b), (x, y) \in \mathbb{R} \times \mathbb{R}$,

    $(a, b)R(x, y)$ if and only if $x^2 + y^2 = a^2 + b^2$.

    a Show that R is an equivalence relation.

    b Describe how R partitions $\mathbb{R} \times \mathbb{R}$ and state the equivalence classes.

6 R is a relation on $\mathbb{Z} \times \mathbb{Z}$ such that for $(a, b), (x, y) \in \mathbb{Z} \times \mathbb{Z}$,

    $(a, b)R(x, y)$ if and only if $y = b$.

    a Show that R is an equivalence relation.

    b Describe how R partitions $\mathbb{Z} \times \mathbb{Z}$ and state the equivalence classes.

7 Determine whether each of the following functions is **i** an injection **ii** a surjection

    a $f: \ \mathbb{R} \to \mathbb{R}, \ f(x) = 2x^3 + 3x - 1$ **b** $f: \ \mathbb{Z} \to \mathbb{Z}^+, \ f(x) = x^2$

    c $f: \ \mathbb{C} \to \mathbb{R}^+ \cup \{0\}, \ f(x) = |x|$ **d** $f: \ \mathbb{Z}^+ \to \mathbb{R}^+, \ f(x) = \sqrt{x}$

8 A Cayley table for a binary operation $*$ is shown alongside. Find:

$\times$	1	2	3	4
1	2	1	3	1
2	3	2	4	2
3	4	1	3	2
4	1	4	2	1

  a $3*4$

  b $2*(1*3)$

  c $(2*1)*3$

9 Construct a Cayley table for $\{\textbf{A, B, C, D}\}$ under matrix multiplication where

$$\textbf{A} = \begin{bmatrix} 1 & 0 \\ 0 & 1 \end{bmatrix}, \textbf{B} = \begin{bmatrix} 1 & 0 \\ 0 & -1 \end{bmatrix}, \textbf{C} = \begin{bmatrix} -1 & 0 \\ 0 & 1 \end{bmatrix} \text{ and } \textbf{D} = \begin{bmatrix} -1 & 0 \\ 0 & -1 \end{bmatrix}.$$

Show that it is a group.

10   **a** Show that the set $\{1, 7, 9, 15\}$ forms a group under multiplication modulo 16.

    b State the order of each element of the group in **a**.

    c Is the group in **a** cyclic?

11 Show that the set $\{f_1, f_2, f_3, f_4, f_5, f_6\}$ is a group under composition of functions where $f_1(x) = x$, $f_2(x) = \dfrac{1}{1-x}$, $f_3(x) = \dfrac{x-1}{x}$, $f_4(x) = \dfrac{1}{x}$, $f_5(x) = 1 - x$,

$f_6(x) = \dfrac{x}{x-1}$.

12 Let $\{A, +_m\}$ where $A = \{0, 1, 2, ..., (m-1)\}$ be a group.

  a Prove that $\{G, *\}$ is a group where $G = \{(a, b, c) \mid a, b, c \in A\}$ and $*$ is defined by $(a, b, c) * (x, y, z) = (a + x, b + y, c + z - xb)$.

  b Is the group Abelian?

  c What is the order of the group?

13 $S = \{(a, b) \mid a, b \in \mathbb{R}\}$. The operation $*$ is defined by $(a, b) * (c, d) = (ac, bc + d)$.

  a Is $*$ associative?

  b Is $*$ commutative?

  c Is there an identity element for $*$ in S?

  d Does each element have an inverse?

14 Construct the Cayley table for the set of matrices $\{\textbf{I, A, B}\}$ where $\textbf{I} = \begin{bmatrix} 1 & 0 \\ 0 & 1 \end{bmatrix}$,

$\textbf{A} = \begin{bmatrix} -\frac{1}{2} & \frac{\sqrt{3}}{2} \\ -\frac{\sqrt{3}}{2} & -\frac{1}{2} \end{bmatrix}$ and $\textbf{B} = \begin{bmatrix} -\frac{1}{2} & -\frac{\sqrt{3}}{2} \\ \frac{\sqrt{3}}{2} & -\frac{1}{2} \end{bmatrix}$. Show that they from a group under matrix multiplication.

15 Let $\{G, *\}$ be a group and let $\{H_1, *\}$ and $\{H_2, *\}$ be subgroups of $\{G, *\}$. Prove that $\{H_1 \cap H_2, *\}$ is a subgroup of $\{G, *\}$.

16 Solve each of the following for x:

    a $x^3 \equiv 6 \pmod 7$ **b** $17x \equiv 29 \pmod{37}$

    c $x^2 + x + 3 \equiv 0 \pmod 5$ **d** $x^2 + 2x + 3 \equiv 0 \pmod{11}$

17 Find the order of each of the following elements of S_4:

    a $\begin{pmatrix} 1 & 2 & 3 & 4 \\ 3 & 1 & 2 & 4 \end{pmatrix}$ **b** $\begin{pmatrix} 1 & 2 & 3 & 4 \\ 1 & 2 & 4 & 3 \end{pmatrix}$ **c** $\begin{pmatrix} 1 & 2 & 3 & 4 \\ 2 & 1 & 4 & 3 \end{pmatrix}$

18 $\{G, \times\}$ is a group where $G = \{1, -1, i, -i\}$. $S = \{1, -1\}$ and $T = \{i, -1\}$ are subsets of G.

Under multiplication, determine whether S or T is a subgroup of $\{G, \times\}$.

19 Determine whether the following Cayley tables define groups.

    a

$*$	a	b	c	d	e
a	a	b	c	d	e
b	b	c	d	e	a
c	c	d	e	a	b
d	d	e	a	b	c
e	e	a	b	c	d

    b

$*$	a	b	c	d	e
a	a	b	c	d	e
b	b	e	d	a	c
c	c	a	b	e	d
d	d	c	e	b	a
e	e	d	a	c	b

20 Consider the group $\{G, +_n\}$ where G is the set containing the n residue classes modulo n. Which members are generators of $\{G, +_n\}$ when:

    a $n = 3$ **b** $n = 5$ **c** $n = 6$?

21 Let $G = \{(x, y) \mid x \in \mathbb{Z}, y \in \mathbb{Q}\}$ and define the composition of points in the following way: $(a, b) * (c, d) = (a + c, 2^c b + d)$.

    a Prove that G forms a group under $*$.

    b Is $\{G, *\}$ Abelian?

    c Do the following sets with the operation $*$ form subgroups of G?

        i $H_1 = \{(a, 0) \mid a \in \mathbb{Z}\}$ **ii** $H_2 = \{(0, b) \mid b \in \mathbb{Q}\}$

    d Is G a group with respect to the operation:

        i $\circ$ defined by $(a, b) \circ (c, d) = (a + c, 2^{-c} b + d)$

        ii $\square$ defined by $(a, b) \square (c, d) = (a + c, 2^c b - d)$?

22 Show that the set containing the following matrices forms a group under matrix multiplication:

$$I = \begin{bmatrix} 1 & 0 & 0 \\ 0 & 1 & 0 \\ 0 & 0 & 1 \end{bmatrix}, \quad A = \begin{bmatrix} 1 & 0 & 0 \\ 0 & 0 & 1 \\ 0 & 1 & 0 \end{bmatrix}, \quad B = \begin{bmatrix} 0 & 1 & 0 \\ 1 & 0 & 0 \\ 0 & 0 & 1 \end{bmatrix}, \quad C = \begin{bmatrix} 0 & 1 & 0 \\ 0 & 0 & 1 \\ 1 & 0 & 0 \end{bmatrix}$$

$$D = \begin{bmatrix} 0 & 0 & 1 \\ 1 & 0 & 0 \\ 0 & 1 & 0 \end{bmatrix} \quad E = \begin{bmatrix} 0 & 0 & 1 \\ 0 & 1 & 0 \\ 1 & 0 & 0 \end{bmatrix}.$$

23 The set $S = \{a, b, c, ...\}$ under the binary operation $*$ satisfies the following:
   • For each $a, b \in S$, $a * b \in S$.
   • For each $a, b, c \in S$, $(a * b) * c = a * (b * c)$.
   • There is a unique element $e \in S$ such that $e * a = a$ for each $a \in S$.
   • For each $a \in S$, there is a unique element $a' \in S$ such that $a' * a = e$.

Prove that $\{S, *\}$ is a group.

24 Prove that a cyclic group of order m is isomorphic to the additive group of residue classes modulo m.

25 Solve the following for x:

   a $4x \equiv 1 \pmod 7$ **b** $x^2 + x + 1 \equiv 0 \pmod 7$

26 For each of the following operations on real numbers:

    i   Is the operation associative?

    ii   Is the operation commutative?

    iii If possible, find the identity element.

    iv If possible, find the inverse of a.

   a $a * b = ab + 2$ **b** $a * b = (a + 2)(b + 2)$ **c** $a * b = 3(a + b)$

   d $a * b = |a + b|$ **e** $a * b = a^b$ **f** $a * b = |a - b|$

27 A system of elements with binary operation $*$ is called a **semigroup** if and only if the system is closed under the operation and $*$ is associative.

Show that the following are all semigroups and indicate which are also groups.

a

$*$	1	2
1	1	1
2	1	1

b

$*$	1	2
1	1	2
2	1	2

c

$*$	1	2
1	2	2
2	1	1

d

$*$	1	2
1	1	2
2	2	1

e

$*$	1	2	3
1	1	2	3
2	2	3	1
3	3	1	2

f

$*$	1	2	3
1	1	2	3
2	1	2	3
3	1	2	3

g

$*$	1	2	3
1	1	2	3
2	3	2	3
3	3	2	3

28 For each of the following sets:

    i Construct the Cayley table under the given operation.

    ii Prove that each set forms a group under the operation.

   a $\{1, 2, 4, 5, 7, 8\}$ under multiplication modulo 9

   b $\{1, 5, 9, 13\}$ under multiplication modulo 16

   c $\{1, 9, 11, 19\}$ under multiplication modulo 20

   d $\{1, 3, 7, 9\}$ under multiplication modulo 20

   e $\{1, 9, 13, 17\}$ under multiplication modulo 20

Are any pairs of the groups isomorphic?

29 Explain why a non-Abelian group must have at least six elements.

HL Topic

(Further Mathematics SL Topic 4)

Before beginning any work in this option, it is recommended that you revise the following areas of the **Core HL** syllabus: Sequences and Series, Differential and Integral Calculus.

These areas are identified under 'Topic 1 – Core: Algebra' and 'Topic 7 – Core: Calculus' as expressed in the syllabus guide on page 13, and pages 30-34 respectively of the IBO document on the Diploma Programme Mathematics HL for the first examination 2006.

Series and differential equations

Contents:

A Some properties of functions

B Sequences

C Infinite series

D Taylor and Maclaurin series

E First order differential equations

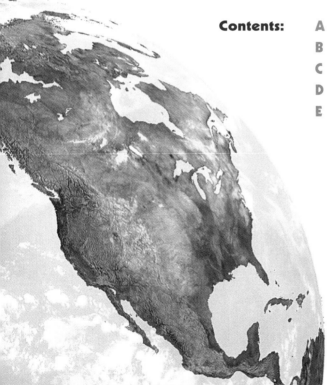

A | SOME PROPERTIES OF FUNCTIONS

THE ABSOLUTE VALUE FUNCTION

From the core Higher Level course you should be familiar with the following important hierarchy of number sets:

$$\mathbb{Z}^+ \subset \mathbb{Z} \subset \mathbb{Q} \subset \mathbb{R}$$

where: $\mathbb{Z}^+$ is the set of natural numbers, i.e., $\{1, 2, 3, \dots \}$,

$\mathbb{Z}$ is the set of integers, i.e., $\{\dots, -2, -1, 0, 1, 2, \dots \}$,

$\mathbb{Q}$ is the set of rational numbers,

i.e., numbers of the form $\dfrac{p}{q}$ where $p, q \in \mathbb{Z}$, $q \neq 0$,

$\mathbb{R}$ is the set of real numbers comprising the rational numbers $\mathbb{Q}$, and the irrational numbers that cannot be expressed as ratios of integers.

In this option topic we will be principally concerned with the set $\mathbb{R}$. Rigorous treatments of the algebraic and set theoretic properties of $\mathbb{R}$, such as the fact that $\mathbb{R}$ is a continuous set, are available in a variety of calculus and analysis books. However, we will outline here only those results of most immediate relevance to our work with limits, sequences and series.

Definition:

Let $a \in \mathbb{R}$, then the absolute value of a, denoted by $|a|$ is defined by

$$|a| = \left\{ \begin{array}{ll} a & \text{if } a \geq 0 \\ -a & \text{if } a < 0 \end{array} \right.$$

You should recognise this definition from the core part of the course. It has the following set of consequences:

1 $|a| \geq 0$ for all $a \in \mathbb{R}$.

2 $|-a| = |a|$ for all $a \in \mathbb{R}$.

3 $|ab| = |a||b|$ for all $a, b \in \mathbb{R}$.

4 $-|a| \leq a \leq |a|$ for all $a \in \mathbb{R}$.

5 If $c \geq 0$ then $|a| \leq c$ if and only if $-c \leq a \leq c$.

Proof of consequence 5:

Suppose that $|a| \leq c$. Then as $a \leq |a|$ and $-a \leq |a|$ we have $a \leq c$ and $-a \leq c$.

But $-a \leq c$ is equivalent to $-c \leq a$, so we have $-c \leq a \leq c$.

Conversely, if $-c \leq a \leq c$, then we have both $a \leq c$ and $-c \leq a$.

But $-c \leq a$ is equivalent to $-a \leq c$.

Therefore $|a| \leq c$.

THE TRIANGLE INEQUALITY

The Triangle Inequality states:

$$\text{For any } a, b \in \mathbb{R}, \; |a + b| \leqslant |a| + |b|.$$

Proof:

From **consequence 4** we have $-|a| \leqslant a \leqslant |a|$ and $-|b| \leqslant b \leqslant |b|$ for all $a, b \in \mathbb{R}$.

Adding these inequalities gives $-(|a| + |b|) \leqslant a + b \leqslant |a| + |b|$

By **consequence 5** this is equivalent to $|a + b| \leqslant |a| + |b|$.

Corollaries:

    1 $|a - b| \leqslant |a| + |b|$ for all $a, b \in \mathbb{R}$.

    2 $|a| - |b| \leqslant |a + b|$ for all $a, b \in \mathbb{R}$.

    3 $|a| - |b| \leqslant |a - b|$ for all $a, b \in \mathbb{R}$.

Proofs:

    1 By the Triangle Inequality, we have $|a + c| \leqslant |a| + |c|$ for all $a, c \in \mathbb{R}$.

        $\therefore$ letting $c = -b$, we get $|a - b| \leqslant |a| + |-b| = |a| + |b|$ for all $a, b \in \mathbb{R}$.

    2 $|a| = |(a + b) + (-b)|$

            $\leqslant |a + b| + |-b|$ for all $a, b \in \mathbb{R}$ by the Triangle Inequality.

        $\therefore$ $|a| - |b| \leqslant |a + b|$

    3 $|a| = |(a - b) + b|$

            $\leqslant |a - b| + |b|$ for all $a, b \in \mathbb{R}$ by the Triangle Inequality.

        $\therefore$ $|a| - |b| \leqslant |a - b|$

The set of real numbers can be considered as a line of infinite length:

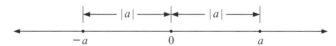

The absolute value $|a|$ of an element a can then be regarded as the distance from a to the origin. More generally the distance between two numbers a and $b \in \mathbb{R}$ can be given by $|a - b|$.

EXERCISE 10A.1

  1 Prove that $|a| \geqslant 0$ for all $a \in \mathbb{R}$.

  2 Prove that $|-a| = |a|$ for all $a \in \mathbb{R}$.

  3 Prove that $|a_1 + a_2 + \ldots + a_n| \leqslant |a_1| + |a_2| + \ldots + |a_n|$ for any $a_1, a_2, \ldots\ldots, a_n \in \mathbb{R}$.

  4 If $a < x < b$ and $a < y < b$ show that $|x - y| < b - a$.
     Interpret this result geometrically.

5 Prove that $|a - b| \leqslant |a - c| + |c - b|$.

6 Prove that if $|x - a| < \dfrac{a}{2}$ for $a > 0$ then $x > \dfrac{a}{2}$.

7 If $|x - a| < \varepsilon$ and $|y - b| < \varepsilon$ show that $|(x + y) - (a + b)| < 2\varepsilon$.

In the questions below, you are required to verify some key properties of the set of real numbers that we will use in our subsequent work.

8 The **Archimedean Property** states that for each pair of positive real numbers a and b, there is a natural number n such that $na > b$.

Use the Archimedean Property to prove that for each positive number ε there is a natural number n such that $\dfrac{1}{n} < \varepsilon$.

9 Prove the **Bernoulli Inequality** by mathematical induction, i.e., that if $x > -1$ then $(1 + x)^n \geqslant 1 + nx$ for all $n \in \mathbb{Z}^+$.

10 The Well-Ordering Principle states that every non-empty subset of $\mathbb{Z}^+$ has a least element. Show that the Well-Ordering Principle does not apply to $\mathbb{R}^+$, the set of positive reals.

11 If $r \neq 0$ is rational and x is irrational, prove that $r + x$ and rx are irrational.

THE LIMIT OF A FUNCTION AT A POINT

Consider a function $f(x)$ where the domain is a continuous subset of $\mathbb{R}$. We consider the behaviour of the function as x approaches particular values, including ∞.

Definition of the Limit of a Function at a point $x = a$:

Suppose $f(x)$ is a function defined on some domain $D \subseteq \mathbb{R}$ which includes all values of x near $x = a$ (though not necessarily $x = a$ itself). We say that l is the **limit** of $f(x)$ as x approaches a and write $\lim\limits_{x \to a} f(x) = l$ if, for each $\varepsilon > 0$, there exists $\delta > 0$ such that $|f(x) - l| < \varepsilon$ whenever $0 < |x - a| < \delta$.

This means that the values of $f(x)$ get closer and closer to the number l as x gets closer and closer to a from either side of a.

If $f(x)$ can be made as large as we please by taking x sufficiently close to a, then we say $\lim\limits_{x \to a} f(x) = \infty$ (or $-\infty$ if $f(x)$ becomes large and negative near a).

We can further refine the definition by distinguishing between a left-hand limit $\lim\limits_{x \to a^-} f(x)$, which is the value $f(x)$ tends to as we approach $x = a$ from the left, and a right-hand limit $\lim\limits_{x \to a^+} f(x)$, which is the value $f(x)$ tends to as we approach $x = a$ from the right.

We then say that $\lim\limits_{x \to a} f(x)$ exists and equals l if $\lim\limits_{x \to a^-} f(x) = \lim\limits_{x \to a^+} f(x) = l$.

Notice that limits of functions are linked with the concepts of *continuity* and *discontinuity*.

For example:

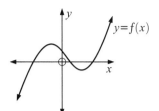

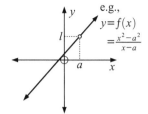

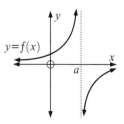

The function is continuous for all $x \in \mathbb{R}$, so $\lim\limits_{x \to a} f(x)$ exists for all $a \in \mathbb{R}$.

The function is discontinuous at $x = a$. However,

$$\lim_{x \to a^-} f(x) = \lim_{x \to a^+} f(x) = l,$$

$$\therefore \lim_{x \to a} f(x) = l.$$

The function is discontinuous at $x = a$. However,

$$\lim_{x \to a^-} f(x) \neq \lim_{x \to a^+} f(x),$$

$$\therefore \lim_{x \to a} f(x) \text{ does not exist.}$$

So in general, if we have a discontinuity or gap in a function $f(x)$ at $x = a$ and $\lim\limits_{x \to a^-} f(x) \neq \lim\limits_{x \to a^+} f(x)$, then $\lim\limits_{x \to a} f(x)$ does not exist.

It can be proved that if the limit of a function at a point exists then it is *unique*.

THEOREMS FOR LIMITS OF FUNCTIONS

If $\lim\limits_{x \to a} f(x) = l$ and $\lim\limits_{x \to a} g(x) = m$ where $|l| < \infty$ and $|m| < \infty$ then:

1 $\lim\limits_{x \to a} [cf(x)] = cl$ for any real constant c

2 $\lim\limits_{x \to a} [f(x) \pm g(x)] = l \pm m$

3 $\lim\limits_{x \to a} [f(x)g(x)] = lm$

4 $\lim\limits_{x \to a} \left[\dfrac{f(x)}{g(x)} \right] = \dfrac{l}{m}$ provided $m \neq 0$

5 $\lim\limits_{x \to a} [f(x)^n] = l^n$ for all $n \in \mathbb{Z}^+$

6 $\lim\limits_{x \to a} \left[\sqrt[n]{f(x)} \right] = \sqrt[n]{l}$ for all $n \in \mathbb{Z}^+$ provided $l \geqslant 0$

Example 1

Find $\lim\limits_{x \to 5} (2x^2 - 3x + 4)$.

$$\lim_{x \to 5} (2x^2 - 3x + 4) = \lim_{x \to 5} (2x^2) + \lim_{x \to 5} (-3x) + \lim_{x \to 5} (4)$$

$$= 2 \lim_{x \to 5} x^2 - 3 \lim_{x \to 5} x + \lim_{x \to 5} 4$$

$$= 2 \times 5^2 - 3 \times 5 + 4 = 39$$

Example 2

Find $\lim\limits_{x \to 1} \left(\dfrac{x-1}{x^2-1} \right)$.

$$\lim_{x \to 1} \left(\frac{x-1}{x^2-1} \right) = \lim_{x \to 1} \frac{(x-1)}{(x-1)(x+1)}$$

$$= \lim_{x \to 1} \frac{1}{(x+1)} \quad \text{as } x \neq 1$$

$$= \tfrac{1}{2}$$

We can use the TI-83 in **Function** mode to investigate limits such as $\lim\limits_{t \to 0} \dfrac{\sqrt{t^2+9}-3}{t^2}$:

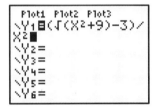

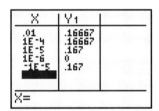

However, even with the benefit of technology, getting a reasonable estimate of such limits can be quite laborious, and the results obtained can often be perplexing.

In this particular case we can use the limit theorems to find the exact value of the limit, as shown in the next example.

Example 3

Find $\lim\limits_{t \to 0} \dfrac{\sqrt{t^2+9}-3}{t^2}$.

$$\lim_{t \to 0} \frac{\sqrt{t^2+9}-3}{t^2} = \lim_{t \to 0} \left(\frac{\sqrt{t^2+9}-3}{t^2} \times \frac{\sqrt{t^2+9}+3}{\sqrt{t^2+9}+3} \right)$$

$$= \lim_{t \to 0} \frac{t^2+9-9}{t^2 \left(\sqrt{t^2+9}+3 \right)}$$

$$= \lim_{t \to 0} \frac{t^2}{t^2 \left(\sqrt{t^2+9}+3 \right)}$$

$$= \lim_{t \to 0} \frac{1}{\sqrt{t^2+9}+3} \quad \{\text{since } t \neq 0\}$$

$$= \frac{\lim\limits_{t \to 0} 1}{\lim\limits_{t \to 0} \sqrt{t^2+9} + \lim\limits_{t \to 0} 3}$$

$$\text{But} \quad \lim_{t \to 0} \sqrt{t^2 + 9} = \sqrt{\lim_{t \to 0} (t^2 + 9)}$$

$$= \sqrt{9} = 3.$$

$$\therefore \quad \lim_{t \to 0} \frac{\sqrt{t^2 + 9} - 3}{t^2} = \frac{1}{3 + 3} = \tfrac{1}{6}.$$

INDETERMINATE FORMS

The theorems for limits of functions above do not help us to deal with *indeterminate forms*. These include:

Type	Description
$\frac{0}{0}$	$\lim\limits_{x \to a} \dfrac{f(x)}{g(x)}$ where $\lim\limits_{x \to a} f(x) = 0$ and $\lim\limits_{x \to a} g(x) = 0$
$\frac{\infty}{\infty}$	$\lim\limits_{x \to a} \dfrac{f(x)}{g(x)}$ where $\lim\limits_{x \to a} f(x) = \pm\infty$ and $\lim\limits_{x \to a} g(x) = \pm\infty$
$0 \times \infty$	$\lim\limits_{x \to a} [f(x)g(x)]$ where $\lim\limits_{x \to a} f(x) = 0$ and $\lim\limits_{x \to a} g(x) = \pm\infty$

An example of an indeterminate form is $\lim\limits_{x \to 0} \dfrac{2^x - 1}{x}$. Notice that $\lim\limits_{x \to 0} (2^x - 1) = 0$ and $\lim\limits_{x \to 0} (x) = 0$.

To address these types of limits, we use L'Hôpital's Rule.

L'HÔPITAL'S RULE

Suppose $f(x)$ and $g(x)$ are differentiable and $g'(x) \neq 0$ on an interval that contains a point $x = a$.

If $\lim\limits_{x \to a} f(x) = 0$ and $\lim\limits_{x \to a} g(x) = 0$, or, if $\lim\limits_{x \to a} f(x) = \pm\infty$ and $\lim\limits_{x \to a} g(x) = \pm\infty$,

then $\lim\limits_{x \to a} \dfrac{f(x)}{g(x)} = \lim\limits_{x \to a} \dfrac{f'(x)}{g'(x)}$ provided the limit on the right exists.

Proof of a special case of L'Hôpital's Rule:

The derivative of a function $f(x)$ at a point $x = a$, denoted by $f'(a)$, is given by the limit

$$f'(a) = \lim_{h \to 0} \frac{f(a + h) - f(a)}{h}.$$

If we write $x = a + h$ then $h = x - a$,

so alternatively we may write $f'(a) = \lim\limits_{x \to a} \dfrac{f(x) - f(a)}{x - a}$.

Using this alternative definition of the derivative, we can prove the special case of L'Hôpital's Rule in which $f(a) = g(a) = 0$, $f'(x)$ and $g'(x)$ are continuous, and $g'(a) \neq 0$. Under these conditions,

$$\lim_{x \to a} \frac{f(x)}{g(x)} = \lim_{x \to a} \frac{f(x) - f(a)}{g(x) - g(a)} \quad \text{\{since } f(a) = g(a) = 0\text{\}}$$

$$= \lim_{x \to a} \frac{\frac{f(x) - f(a)}{x - a}}{\frac{g(x) - g(a)}{x - a}} \qquad\qquad = \frac{f'(a)}{g'(a)}$$

$$= \frac{\lim\limits_{x \to a} \frac{f(x) - f(a)}{x - a}}{\lim\limits_{x \to a} \frac{g(x) - g(a)}{x - a}} \qquad\qquad = \frac{\lim\limits_{x \to a} f'(x)}{\lim\limits_{x \to a} g'(x)}$$

$$= \lim_{x \to a} \frac{f'(x)}{g'(x)}$$

Example 4

Use L'Hôpital's Rule to evaluate: **a** $\lim\limits_{x \to 0} \dfrac{2^x - 1}{x}$ **b** $\lim\limits_{x \to 0} \dfrac{\sin x}{x}$.

a $\lim\limits_{x \to 0} (2^x - 1) = 0$ and $\lim\limits_{x \to 0} x = 0$, so we can use L'Hôpital's Rule.

$$\therefore \quad \lim_{x \to 0} \frac{2^x - 1}{x} = \frac{\lim\limits_{x \to 0} \frac{d}{dx}(2^x - 1)}{\lim\limits_{x \to 0} \frac{d}{dx}(x)} \quad \text{\{L'Hôpital's Rule\}}$$

$$= \frac{\lim\limits_{x \to 0} 2^x \ln 2}{\lim\limits_{x \to 0} 1}$$

$$= \frac{\ln 2}{1} = \ln 2$$

b $\lim\limits_{x \to 0} \sin x = 0$ and $\lim\limits_{x \to 0} x = 0$, so we can use L'Hôpital's Rule.

$$\therefore \quad \lim_{x \to 0} \frac{\sin x}{x} = \frac{\lim\limits_{x \to 0} \frac{d}{dx}(\sin x)}{\lim\limits_{x \to 0} \frac{d}{dx}(x)} \quad \text{\{L'Hôpital's Rule\}}$$

$$= \frac{\lim\limits_{x \to 0} \cos x}{\lim\limits_{x \to 0} 1}$$

$$= \frac{1}{1} = 1$$

Example 5

Use L'Hôpital's Rule to evaluate:

a $\lim\limits_{x \to \infty} \dfrac{\ln x}{x}$ **b** $\lim\limits_{x \to \infty} \dfrac{e^x}{x^n}$ where $n \in \mathbb{Z}^+$.

a $\lim\limits_{x \to \infty} \ln x = \infty$ and $\lim\limits_{x \to \infty} x = \infty$, so we can use L'Hôpital's Rule.

$$\therefore \quad \lim_{x \to \infty} \frac{\ln x}{x} = \frac{\lim\limits_{x \to \infty} \frac{d}{dx}(\ln x)}{\lim\limits_{x \to \infty} \frac{d}{dx}(x)} \quad \{\text{L'Hôpital's Rule}\}$$

$$= \frac{\lim\limits_{x \to \infty} \left(\frac{1}{x}\right)}{\lim\limits_{x \to \infty} 1}$$

$$= \frac{0}{1} \quad \{\text{since} \lim_{x \to \infty} \left(\frac{1}{x}\right) = 0\}$$

$$= 0$$

b   For all $n \in \mathbb{Z}^+$, $\lim\limits_{x \to \infty} e^x = \infty$ and $\lim\limits_{x \to \infty} x^n = \infty$,

so we can use L'Hôpital's Rule.

$$\therefore \quad \lim_{x \to \infty} \frac{e^x}{x^n} = \lim_{x \to \infty} \frac{e^x}{nx^{n-1}}$$

$$= \lim_{x \to \infty} \frac{e^x}{n(n-1)x^{n-2}}$$

$$\vdots$$

$$= \lim_{x \to \infty} \frac{e^x}{n!}$$

$$= \frac{1}{n!} \lim_{x \to \infty} e^x = \infty$$

Example 6

Find $\lim\limits_{x \to 0^+} \dfrac{\ln(\cos 3x)}{\ln(\cos 2x)}$.

$\lim\limits_{x \to 0^+} \ln(\cos 3x) = 0$ and $\lim\limits_{x \to 0^+} \ln(\cos 2x) = 0$, so we apply L'Hôpital's Rule.

$$\therefore \quad \lim_{x \to 0^+} \frac{\ln(\cos 3x)}{\ln(\cos 2x)} = \lim_{x \to 0^+} \left(\frac{\frac{-3 \sin 3x}{\cos 3x}}{\frac{-2 \sin 2x}{\cos 2x}} \right)$$

$$= \lim_{x \to 0^+} \left(\frac{3 \sin 3x \cos 2x}{2 \sin 2x \cos 3x} \right)$$

$$= \left(\lim_{x \to 0^+} \frac{\sin 3x}{\sin 2x} \right) \times \left(\lim_{x \to 0^+} \frac{3 \cos 2x}{2 \cos 3x} \right)$$

$$= \left(\lim_{x \to 0^+} \frac{\sin 3x}{\sin 2x} \right) \times \frac{3}{2}$$

Now $\lim\limits_{x \to 0^+} \sin 3x = 0$ and $\lim\limits_{x \to 0^+} \sin 2x = 0$, so we use L'Hôpital's Rule again.

$$\therefore \quad \lim_{x \to 0^+} \frac{\ln(\cos 3x)}{\ln(\cos 2x)} = \left(\lim_{x \to 0^+} \frac{3 \cos 3x}{2 \cos 2x} \right) \times \frac{3}{2}$$

$$= \frac{3}{2} \times \frac{3}{2} = \frac{9}{4}$$

Example 7

Evaluate $\lim\limits_{x \to 0^+} x \ln x$.

Since $\lim\limits_{x \to 0^+} x = 0$ and $\lim\limits_{x \to 0^+} \ln x = -\infty$, we have an indeterminate form of

the $0 \times \infty$ type. We therefore apply L'Hôpital's Rule, but we first need to convert

the limit to a quotient.

Now $\quad x \ln x = \dfrac{\ln x}{\left(\frac{1}{x}\right)}$

$$\therefore \quad \lim\limits_{x \to 0^+} x \ln x = \lim\limits_{x \to 0^+} \left(\dfrac{\ln x}{\frac{1}{x}}\right)$$

$$= \lim\limits_{x \to 0^+} \left(\dfrac{\frac{1}{x}}{-\frac{1}{x^2}}\right) \quad \{\text{L'Hôpital's Rule}\}$$

$$= \lim\limits_{x \to 0^+} (-x)$$

$$= 0$$

Example 8

Evaluate $\lim\limits_{x \to \frac{\pi}{2}^-} (\sec x - \tan x)$.

We first note that $\lim\limits_{x \to \frac{\pi}{2}^-} \sec x = \infty$ and $\lim\limits_{x \to \frac{\pi}{2}^-} \tan x = \infty$.

We therefore need to convert the difference $\sec x - \tan x$ into a quotient, then

apply L'Hôpital's Rule.

Now $\quad \sec x - \tan x = \dfrac{1}{\cos x} - \dfrac{\sin x}{\cos x}$

$$= \dfrac{1 - \sin x}{\cos x}$$

where $\lim\limits_{x \to \frac{\pi}{2}^-} (1 - \sin x) = 0$ and $\lim\limits_{x \to \frac{\pi}{2}^-} \cos x = 0$.

$$\therefore \quad \lim\limits_{x \to \frac{\pi}{2}^-} (\sec x - \tan x) = \lim\limits_{x \to \frac{\pi}{2}^-} \left(\dfrac{1 - \sin x}{\cos x}\right)$$

$$= \lim\limits_{x \to \frac{\pi}{2}^-} \left(\dfrac{-\cos x}{-\sin x}\right)$$

$$= \dfrac{0}{1} = 0$$

EXERCISE 10A.2

1 Find each limit *without* using L'Hôpital's Rule:

a $\lim\limits_{x \to 1} \dfrac{x^2 + 3x - 4}{x - 1}$

b $\lim\limits_{x \to 0} \dfrac{\sin x}{e^x}$

c $\lim\limits_{x \to \pi^-} \dfrac{\sin x}{1 - \cos x}$

d $\lim\limits_{x \to 2^-} \dfrac{\ln x}{\sqrt{2 + x}}$

e $\lim\limits_{x \to 0} \dfrac{\sin 7x}{4x}$

f $\lim\limits_{x \to 0} x \cot x$

2 Evaluate each limit using L'Hôpital's Rule:

a $\lim\limits_{x \to 0} \dfrac{1 - \cos x}{x^2}$

b $\lim\limits_{x \to 0} \dfrac{e^x - 1 - x}{x^2}$

c $\lim\limits_{x \to 1} \left(\dfrac{\ln x}{x - 1} \right)$

d $\lim\limits_{x \to 0} \dfrac{\tan^{-1} x}{x}$

e $\lim\limits_{x \to 0} \dfrac{x^2 + x}{\sin 2x}$

f $\lim\limits_{x \to 0^+} \dfrac{\sin x}{\sqrt{x}}$

g $\lim\limits_{x \to 0} \dfrac{x + \sin x}{x - \sin x}$

h $\lim\limits_{x \to 0^+} x^2 \ln x$

i $\lim\limits_{x \to 0^+} \left(\dfrac{1}{x} - \dfrac{1}{\sin x} \right)$

j $\lim\limits_{x \to 0} \dfrac{a^x - b^x}{\sin x}, \quad a, b > 0$

3 Try to use L'Hôpital's Rule to find $\quad \lim\limits_{x \to \frac{\pi}{2}^-} \dfrac{\tan x}{\sec x}$.

Evaluate the limit otherwise.

4 By finding $\quad \lim\limits_{x \to \infty} x \ln \left(1 + \dfrac{1}{x} \right) \quad$ and writing $\quad \left(1 + \dfrac{1}{x} \right)^x \quad$ as $\quad e^{x \ln(1 + \frac{1}{x})}$,

prove that $\quad \lim\limits_{x \to \infty} \left(1 + \dfrac{1}{x} \right)^x = e$.

5 A function $f : D \to \mathbb{R}$ is said to be **continuous** at the point x_0 in D provided that whenever $\{x_n\}$ is a sequence in D that converges to x_0, the sequence $\{f(x_n)\} \in f(D)$ converges to $f(x_0)$.

Dirichlet's function is given by $\quad f: \mathbb{R} \to \mathbb{R} \quad$ where $\quad f(x) = \begin{cases} 1 & x \in \mathbb{Q} \\ 0 & x \notin \mathbb{Q} \end{cases}$.

Using the continuity definition above, prove that this function is discontinuous at all points in $\mathbb{R}$.

IMPROPER INTEGRALS OF TYPE $\int_a^\infty f(x)\,dx$

An **improper integral** is a definite integral that has:

- either or both limits infinite, e.g., $\int_0^\infty f(x)\,dx$, $\int_{-\infty}^\infty f(x)\,dx$, *and/or*

- an integrand that approaches infinity at one or more points in the range of integration.

  For example, $\quad \displaystyle\int_{-1}^1 \dfrac{1}{x}\,dx \quad$ is an improper integral since $\dfrac{1}{x}$ is infinite at $x = 0$.

In this section we are only concerned with improper integrals of the form $\int_a^\infty f(x)\,dx$ where a is an integer, since these are the integrals we need for sequences and series later.

Definition:

The improper integral $\int_a^\infty f(x)\,dx$ is said to be **convergent** if $\int_a^b f(x)\,dx$ exists for all b where $a \leqslant b < \infty$, and if $\int_a^\infty f(x)\,dx = \lim\limits_{b\to\infty} \int_a^b f(x)\,dx$ is finite. Otherwise the improper integral is **divergent**.

Example 9

Show that $\displaystyle\int_1^\infty \frac{1}{x}\,dx$ is divergent.

$$\int_1^\infty \frac{1}{x}\,dx = \lim_{b\to\infty} \int_1^b \frac{1}{x}\,dx$$

$$= \lim_{b\to\infty} \left[\ln x\right]_1^b$$

$$= \lim_{b\to\infty} (\ln b)$$

$$= \infty \qquad\qquad \text{Hence } \int_1^\infty \frac{1}{x}\,dx \text{ is divergent.}$$

Example 10

Investigate the convergence of $\displaystyle\int_1^\infty \frac{1}{x^p}\,dx$ where p is a real constant.

$$\int_1^\infty \frac{1}{x^p}\,dx = \lim_{b\to\infty} \int_1^b \frac{1}{x^p}\,dx = \lim_{b\to\infty} \left[\frac{1}{(1-p)x^{p-1}}\right]_1^b$$

$$= \frac{1}{1-p} \lim_{b\to\infty} \left[\left(\frac{1}{x}\right)^{p-1}\right]_1^b$$

$$= \frac{1}{1-p} \lim_{b\to\infty} \left[\left(\frac{1}{b}\right)^{p-1} - 1\right]$$

If $p > 1$ then $\dfrac{1}{1-p} \lim\limits_{b\to\infty} \left[\left(\dfrac{1}{b}\right)^{p-1} - 1\right] = \dfrac{1}{p-1}$, which is finite.

If $p < 1$ then $\lim\limits_{b\to\infty} \left(\dfrac{1}{b}\right)^{p-1} = \infty$

If $p = 1$ then we have the case presented in **Example 9**, which is divergent.

Hence $\displaystyle\int_1^\infty \frac{1}{x^p}\,dx$ converges if $p > 1$ and diverges if $p \leqslant 1$.

THE COMPARISON TEST FOR IMPROPER INTEGRALS

Suppose $0 \leqslant f(x) \leqslant g(x)$ for all $x \geqslant a$.   Then:

- if $\int_a^\infty g(x)\, dx$ is convergent, then so is $\int_a^\infty f(x)\, dx$,

or, • if $\int_a^\infty f(x)\, dx$ is divergent, then so is $\int_a^\infty g(x)\, dx$.

Example 11

Determine whether $\displaystyle\int_2^\infty \frac{1}{\sqrt{x}-1}\, dx$ is convergent or divergent.

Now we know that $\sqrt{x}-1 \leqslant \sqrt{x}$ for all $x \geqslant 2$

$$\therefore \quad \frac{1}{\sqrt{x}-1} \geqslant \frac{1}{\sqrt{x}} \quad \text{for all } x \geqslant 2.$$

Now $\displaystyle\int_2^\infty \frac{1}{x^{\frac{1}{2}}}\, dx = \int_1^\infty \frac{1}{x^{\frac{1}{2}}}\, dx - \int_1^2 \frac{1}{x^{\frac{1}{2}}}\, dx,$

where $\displaystyle\int_1^2 \frac{1}{x^{\frac{1}{2}}}\, dx$ is finite, but from **Example 10** $\displaystyle\int_1^\infty \frac{1}{x^{\frac{1}{2}}}\, dx$ is divergent.

$\therefore \quad \displaystyle\int_2^\infty \frac{1}{x^{\frac{1}{2}}}\, dx$ is divergent, and so $\displaystyle\int_2^\infty \frac{1}{\sqrt{x}-1}\, dx$ is divergent by the

Comparison Test.

Theorem:

If $\int_a^\infty |f(x)|\, dx$ converges then $\int_a^\infty f(x)\, dx$ converges.

Proof:

By definition, $-|f(x)| \leqslant f(x) \leqslant |f(x)|$

$$\therefore \quad 0 \leqslant f(x) + |f(x)| \leqslant 2\,|f(x)|$$

$$\therefore \quad 0 \leqslant \int_a^\infty f(x) + |f(x)|\, dx \leqslant 2\int_a^\infty |f(x)|\, dx$$

$\therefore$ by the Comparison Test, if $\int_a^\infty |f(x)|\, dx$ is convergent then so is $\int_a^\infty f(x) + |f(x)|\, dx$.

Supposing $\int_a^\infty |f(x)|\, dx = A < \infty$ and $\int_a^\infty f(x) + |f(x)|\, dx = B < \infty$,

$$\int_a^\infty f(x)\, dx = B - A < \infty$$

Hence $\int_a^\infty f(x)\, dx$ is convergent.

Example 12

Using integration by parts and the Comparison Test, prove that $\displaystyle\int_1^\infty \frac{\sin x}{x}\,dx$ is convergent.

$$\int_1^\infty \frac{\sin x}{x}\,dx = \lim_{b\to\infty} \int_1^b \frac{\sin x}{x}\,dx$$

$$= \lim_{b\to\infty} \left[-\frac{\cos x}{x}\right]_1^b - \lim_{b\to\infty} \int_1^b \frac{\cos x}{x^2}\,dx \quad \{\text{integrating by parts}\}$$

$$= \lim_{b\to\infty} \left(-\frac{\cos b}{b} + \cos 1\right) - \int_1^\infty \frac{\cos x}{x^2}\,dx$$

$$= \cos 1 - \int_1^\infty \frac{\cos x}{x^2}\,dx$$

Now $\quad 0 \leqslant \left|\dfrac{\cos x}{x^2}\right| \leqslant \dfrac{1}{x^2} \quad$ for all $x \geqslant 1$,

and we also know from **Example 10** that $\displaystyle\int_1^\infty \frac{1}{x^2}\,dx$ is convergent.

$\therefore \displaystyle\int_1^\infty \left|\frac{\cos x}{x^2}\right|\,dx$ is also convergent, and hence so is $\displaystyle\int_1^\infty \frac{\cos x}{x^2}\,dx$.

Hence $\displaystyle\int_1^\infty \frac{\sin x}{x}\,dx$ converges.

EVALUATING IMPROPER INTEGRALS

When an improper integral is convergent, we may be able to evaluate it using a variety of techniques. These include use of the limit rules, L'Hôpital's Rule, integration by parts, and integration by substitution.

Example 13

Evaluate $\displaystyle\int_a^\infty xe^{-x}\,dx$.

$$\int_a^\infty xe^{-x}\,dx = \lim_{b\to\infty} \int_a^b xe^{-x}\,dx$$

$$= \lim_{b\to\infty} \left(\left[-xe^{-x}\right]_a^b - \int_a^b -e^{-x}\,dx\right) \quad \{\text{integrating by parts}\}$$

$$= \lim_{b\to\infty} \left(-be^{-b} + ae^{-a} - \left[e^{-x}\right]_a^b\right)$$

$$= \lim_{b\to\infty} \left(-be^{-b} + ae^{-a} - e^{-b} + e^{-a}\right)$$

$$= e^{-a}(a+1) + \lim_{b\to\infty} \left(e^{-b}(1-b)\right)$$

$$= e^{-a}(a+1) + \lim_{b\to\infty} \left(\frac{1-b}{e^b}\right)$$

Now $\lim\limits_{b \to \infty} (1 - b) = -\infty$ and $\lim\limits_{b \to \infty} e^b = \infty$

$\therefore \int_a^\infty x e^{-x}\, dx = e^{-a}(a + 1) + \lim\limits_{b \to \infty} \dfrac{-1}{e^b}$ {L'Hôpital's Rule}

$\qquad\qquad\qquad = e^{-a}(a + 1)$

EXERCISE 10A.3

1 Use the Comparison Test for improper integrals to test for convergence:

  a $\displaystyle\int_1^\infty \dfrac{x}{2x^5 + 3x^2 + 1}\, dx$ **b** $\displaystyle\int_2^\infty \dfrac{x^2 - 1}{\sqrt{x^7 + 1}}\, dx$

2 Determine whether $\displaystyle\int_1^\infty \dfrac{\sin x}{x^3}\, dx$ is convergent.

3 Test for convergence:

  a $\displaystyle\int_1^\infty \dfrac{x^2 + 1}{x^4 + 1}\, dx$ **b** $\displaystyle\int_0^\infty e^{-x^2}\, dx$

  c $\displaystyle\int_1^\infty \dfrac{\ln x}{x}\, dx$ **d** $\displaystyle\int_1^\infty e^{-x} \ln x\, dx$

4 Prove that $\displaystyle\int_e^\infty \dfrac{\ln x}{x^p}\, dx$ is divergent for $p \leqslant 1$.

5 **a** Evaluate the integral $\int_0^\infty x^n e^{-x}\, dx$ for $n = 0, 1, 2, 3$.

   b Predict the value of $\int_0^\infty x^n e^{-x}\, dx$ when n is an arbitrary positive integer.

   c Prove your prediction using mathematical induction.

6 Evaluate: **a** $\displaystyle\int_a^\infty \dfrac{dx}{x^2 + a^2}$ **b** $\displaystyle\int_{\frac{1}{\pi}}^\infty \dfrac{1}{x^2} \sin\left(\dfrac{1}{x}\right) dx.$

7 Evaluate $\displaystyle\int_a^\infty \dfrac{dx}{e^x + e^{-x}}$ using the substitution $u = e^x$.

8 Show that $\int_0^\infty e^{-x} \cos x\, dx$ is convergent.

9 Evaluate $\displaystyle\int_1^\infty \left(\dfrac{1}{\sqrt{x}} - \dfrac{1}{\sqrt{x + 3}}\right) dx.$

10 Find the area in the first quadrant under the curve $y = \dfrac{1}{x^2 + 6x + 10}$.

APPROXIMATION TO THE IMPROPER INTEGRAL $\int_a^\infty f(x)dx$

Consider $\int_a^\infty f(x)\, dx$ where a is an integer.

Suppose we draw a graph of the function $f(x)$ and label the value of the function at different integer values:

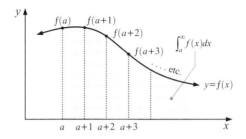

For each interval of length one along the x-axis, we can draw a rectangle of height equal to the value of the function on one side of the rectangle.

For example, the rectangle from $x = a$ to $x = a+1$ would have height $f(a)$; the rectangle from $x = a + 1$ to $x = a + 2$ would have height $f(a+1)$, and so on.

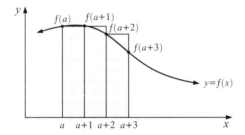

The areas of the rectangles are, respectively, f_a, f_{a+1}, f_{a+2}, ... so the areas in fact form a *sequence*.

The integral $\int_a^\infty f(x)\,dx$ may be approximated by the sum of the rectangles,

i.e., $\int_a^\infty f(x)\,dx \approx \sum_{i=a}^{\infty} f(i)$

Thus, the integral may be approximated by a *series*.

Now, let us be more particular about the side of the rectangle we choose for its height:

Suppose the function $f(x)$ is *decreasing* for all $x > a$.

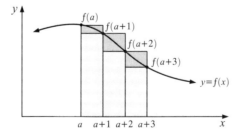

If we always take the height of each rectangle to be the value of the function at the left end of the interval, the sum of the areas of the rectangles will be greater than the integral.

This is called the *upper sum*, and $\int_a^\infty f(x)\,dx < \sum_{i=a}^{\infty} f(i)$.

Alternatively, if we use the value of the function at the right end of each interval, the sum of the areas of the rectangles will be less than the integral.

This is called the *lower sum*, and $\int_a^\infty f(x)\,dx > \sum\limits_{i=a}^{\infty} f(i+1)$.

Hence $\sum\limits_{i=a}^{\infty} f(i+1) < \int_a^\infty f(x)\,dx < \sum\limits_{i=a}^{\infty} f(i)$.

In a similar way, for any function that is *increasing* for all $x > a$, we can choose upper and lower sums such that

$$\sum\limits_{i=a}^{\infty} f(i) < \int_a^\infty f(x)\,dx < \sum\limits_{i=a}^{\infty} f(i+1).$$

Example 14

Write down a series which approximates $\int_0^\infty e^{-x^2}\,dx$.

$\int_0^\infty e^{-x^2}\,dx$ is the integral of $f(x) = e^{-x^2}$ from 0 to ∞.

$\therefore\ \int_0^\infty e^{-x^2}\,dx \approx \sum\limits_{i=0}^{\infty} e^{-i^2}$

Example 15

What integral is approximated by the sum $\sum\limits_{i=2}^{\infty} \dfrac{1}{i}$?

Now $\dfrac{1}{i}$ comes from the function $f(x) = \dfrac{1}{x}$, evaluated at $x = i$,

$\therefore$ since the summation is from 2 to ∞, the integral is from 2 to ∞ also.

Hence $\sum\limits_{i=2}^{\infty} \dfrac{1}{i} \approx \int_2^\infty \dfrac{1}{x}\,dx$.

EXERCISE 10A.4

1 Write down a series which approximates:

a $\int_0^\infty \dfrac{1}{\sqrt{x+1}}\,dx$

b $\int_4^\infty e^{-x}\,dx$

2 What integrals are approximated by these sums?

a $\sum\limits_{i=0}^{\infty} \dfrac{1}{i+2}$

b $\sum\limits_{i=3}^{\infty} \dfrac{i+1}{i^2}$

3 For the function $f(x) = e^{-x^2}$:

a show that $f(x)$ is decreasing for all $x > 0$

b write upper and lower sums that approximate $\int_0^\infty f(x)\,dx$

c write an inequality that relates the sums in b to the integral.

4 For the function $f(x) = \dfrac{1}{x^2}$:

  a show that $f(x)$ is decreasing for all $x > 0$

  b write upper and lower sums that approximate $\displaystyle\int_1^\infty \dfrac{1}{x^2}\,dx$

  c write an inequality that relates the sums in **b** to the integral.

5 For the function $f(x) = -\dfrac{1}{x^2}$:

  a show that $f(x)$ is increasing for all $x > 0$

  b write upper and lower sums that approximate $\displaystyle\int_1^\infty -\dfrac{1}{x^2}\,dx$

  c write an inequality that relates the sums in **b** to the integral.

B   SEQUENCES

Definition:

> A **number sequence** is a list of numbers in a definite order.

An **infinite number sequence** can be considered as a discrete function with domain $\mathbb{Z}^+$ and range a subset of $\mathbb{R}$.

For example, the sequence $\{a_n\}$ where $a_n = \dfrac{n}{n+1}$

denotes the infinite set of discrete points

$\left\{ \dfrac{1}{2},\ \dfrac{2}{3},\ \dfrac{3}{4},\ \dfrac{4}{5},\ \ldots\ldots \right\}$.

We can plot n against a_n to give:

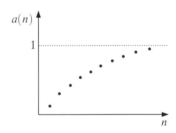

From the graph it appears that the terms of $\{a_n\}$ are approaching 1 as n becomes larger.

In fact, the difference $1 - \dfrac{n}{n+1} = \dfrac{1}{n+1}$ can be made as small as we like by taking n sufficiently large.

We indicate this using a limit by writing $\displaystyle\lim_{n\to\infty} \dfrac{n}{n+1} = 1$.   Note that this is actually the limit of the *sequence*, which is similar but not quite the same as the limit of a *function*.

However, as for functions, $\displaystyle\lim_{n\to\infty} a_n = L$ means that the terms of $\{a_n\}$ can be made arbitrarily close to L by taking n sufficiently large, but it does not necessarily mean that the values of a_n ever actually reach L. For example, $\dfrac{n}{n+1}$ never actually equals 1.

This definition formalises the limit of a sequence:

Definition:

> A sequence $\{a_n\}$ has a **limit** L if for every $\varepsilon > 0$ there exists a positive integer N such that $|a_n - L| < \varepsilon$ for all $n > N$. The limit is denoted by $\displaystyle\lim_{n\to\infty} a_n = L$.

If $\lim\limits_{n \to \infty} a_n$ exists we say the sequence **converges**. Otherwise, we say it **diverges**.

Theorem:

If the limit of a sequence exists, it is unique.

Proof:

Suppose that a given sequence $\{a_n\}$ has a limit L and also a limit L' where $L \neq L'$.

Then given any $\varepsilon > 0$ there is a positive integer N_1 such that $|a_n - L| < \dfrac{\varepsilon}{2}$ for all $n \geqslant N_1$, and there is also a positive integer N_2 such that $|a_n - L'| < \dfrac{\varepsilon}{2}$ for all $n \geqslant N_2$.

If $n > \max(N_1, N_2)$ then $|a_n - L| < \dfrac{\varepsilon}{2}$ and $|a_n - L'| < \dfrac{\varepsilon}{2}$.

Consequently if $n > \max(N_1, N_2)$,

$$|L - L'| = |L - a_n + a_n - L'|$$
$$\leqslant |L - a_n| + |a_n - L'| \quad \text{by the Triangle Inequality}$$

But $\quad |L - a_n| = |a_n - L|$

$\therefore \quad |L - L'| \leqslant |a_n - L| + |a_n - L'|$
$$< \dfrac{\varepsilon}{2} + \dfrac{\varepsilon}{2} < \varepsilon.$$

But $L \neq L'$ and hence $|L - L'| \neq 0$.

Since $|L - L'|$ is a fixed, non-zero number, this contradicts the conclusion that $|L - L'| < \varepsilon$ for any arbitrary positive number ε.

Hence $L = L'$, i.e., if the limit of a sequence exists then that limit is unique.

LIMIT THEOREMS FOR SEQUENCES

In this section, we use the formal definition of the limit of a sequence to prove limit results for some particularly important sequences. Before we can do this, however, we consider briefly the **Archimedean Property**.

Archimedes of Syracuse stated that for any two line segments, laying the shorter end-to-end only a finite number of times will always suffice to create a segment exceeding the longer of the two in length.

This means that:

Given any $\varepsilon > 0$, there exists $N \in \mathbb{Z}^+$ such that $N\varepsilon > 1$.

Result 1: For any real constant c, $\lim\limits_{n \to \infty} c = c$.

Proof: For any real constant c, $|c - c| = 0$.

$\therefore \quad |c - c| < \varepsilon$ for all $\varepsilon > 0$.

Hence $\lim\limits_{n \to \infty} c = c$ from the sequence limit definition.

Result 2: $\displaystyle\lim_{n\to\infty}\left(\frac{1}{n}\right) = 0$

Proof: From the Archimedean Property, given any $\varepsilon > 0$ there exists $N \in \mathbb{Z}^+$ such

that $\dfrac{1}{N} < \varepsilon.$

Now if $n > N$ then $\left|\dfrac{1}{n} - 0\right| = \dfrac{1}{n} < \dfrac{1}{N} < \varepsilon.$

Hence $\displaystyle\lim_{n\to\infty}\left(\frac{1}{n}\right) = 0$ from the sequence limit definition.

Result 3:   If $p > 0$ then $\displaystyle\lim_{n\to\infty}\left(\frac{1}{n^p}\right) = 0.$

Proof: Suppose $\varepsilon > 0$ is given.

Then as $\varepsilon^{\frac{1}{p}} > 0,$ by the Archimedean Property there exists an integer N

such that $N\varepsilon^{\frac{1}{p}} > 1,$ i.e., $\varepsilon^{\frac{1}{p}} > \dfrac{1}{N}.$

$\therefore \quad \dfrac{1}{N^p} < \varepsilon$

So, if we suppose that $n \geqslant N$ then $\left|\dfrac{1}{n^p} - 0\right| = \left|\dfrac{1}{n^p}\right| < \varepsilon$ for all $n \geqslant N.$

Hence $\displaystyle\lim_{n\to\infty}\left(\frac{1}{n^p}\right) = 0$ for all $p > 0$ from the sequence limit definition.

Result 4:   If $0 < |c| < 1,$ then the sequence $\{c^n\}$ converges to 0.

Proof: Since $0 < |c| < 1,$ $\dfrac{1}{|c|} > 1$ and we can let $d = \dfrac{1}{|c|} - 1$ such that $d > 0$

and $|c| = \dfrac{1}{(1+d)}.$

By the Bernoulli Inequality (see **Exercise 10A.1**), as $d > 0,$

$(1+d)^n \geqslant 1 + nd > 0$ for all $n \in \mathbb{Z}^+.$

$\therefore \quad |c|^n = \dfrac{1}{(1+d)^n} \leqslant \dfrac{1}{1+nd} < \dfrac{1}{nd}$ for all $n \in \mathbb{Z}^+.$

Given $\varepsilon > 0$ then $\varepsilon d > 0$ and by the Archimedean Property we can choose

an integer N such that $N\varepsilon d > 1,$ i.e., $\dfrac{1}{Nd} < \varepsilon.$

$\therefore \quad |c^n - 0| = |c^n| = |c|^n < \dfrac{1}{nd} \leqslant \dfrac{1}{Nd} < \varepsilon$ for all integers $n \geqslant N.$

Hence $\{c^n\}$ converges to 0   from the sequence limit definition.

The Squeeze Theorem:

Suppose we have sequences of real numbers $\{a_n\}$, $\{b_n\}$ and $\{c_n\}$ where $a_n \leqslant b_n \leqslant c_n$ for all $n \in \mathbb{Z}$. If $\lim\limits_{n \to \infty} a_n = \lim\limits_{n \to \infty} c_n = L < \infty$ then $\lim\limits_{n \to \infty} b_n = L$.

Proof:

As $L = \lim\limits_{n \to \infty} a_n = \lim\limits_{n \to \infty} c_n$, given $\varepsilon > 0$ there exists a natural number N such that

if $n \geqslant N$ then $|a_n - L| < \varepsilon$ and $|c_n - L| < \varepsilon$ for all $n \geqslant N$

$\therefore \quad -\varepsilon < a_n - L < \varepsilon$ and $-\varepsilon < c_n - L < \varepsilon$ for all $n \geqslant N$.

Now $a_n \leqslant b_n \leqslant c_n$, so $a_n - L \leqslant b_n - L \leqslant c_n - L$.

$\therefore \quad -\varepsilon < b_n - L < \varepsilon$ for all $n \geqslant N$,

i.e., $|b_n - L| < \varepsilon$ for all $n \geqslant N$.

Hence $\lim\limits_{n \to \infty} b_n = L$.

It should be clear that the Squeeze Theorem still holds if the condition $a_n \leqslant b_n \leqslant c_n$ only applies for every natural number from some point on, i.e., if there was an $n_0 \in \mathbb{Z}^+$ such that $a_n \leqslant b_n \leqslant c_n$ for all $n \geqslant n_0$.

The finite number of sequence terms from $n = 1$ to $n = n_0$ do not affect the ultimate convergence (or divergence) of the sequence.

The following definition and consequent Lemma are crucial in establishing some basic algebraic properties for limits of sequences:

Definition:

A sequence of real numbers $\{a_n\}$ is said to be **bounded** if there exists a real number $M > 0$ such that $|a_n| \leqslant M$ for all $n \in \mathbb{Z}^+$.

Lemma:

Every convergent sequence is bounded.

Proof:

Let $\{a_n\}$ be a well-defined sequence where $\lim\limits_{n \to \infty} a_n = a$.

Then if we let $\varepsilon = 1$, by the definition of convergence we can select a natural number N such that $|a_n - a| < 1$ for all $n \geqslant N$.

But from Corollary **3** of the Triangle Inequality,

$$|a_n| - |a| \leqslant |a_n - a| < 1 \quad \text{for all } n \geqslant N.$$

Hence $|a_n| \leqslant 1 + |a|$ for all $n \geqslant N$.

If we define $M = \max\{1 + |a|, |a_1|, ..., |a_{N-1}|\}$ then $|a_n| \leqslant M$ for all $n \in \mathbb{Z}^+$ so long as the series is well defined.

$\therefore$ the sequence $\{a_n\}$ is bounded.

SOME ALGEBRA OF LIMITS THEOREMS

Suppose $\{a_n\}$ converges to a real number a and $\{b_n\}$ converges to a real number b. Then:

1 $\displaystyle\lim_{n\to\infty} (a_n + b_n) = \lim_{n\to\infty} a_n + \lim_{n\to\infty} b_n = a + b.$

2 The sequence $\{a_n b_n\}$ converges and $\displaystyle\lim_{n\to\infty} (a_n b_n) = \left(\lim_{n\to\infty} a_n\right)\left(\lim_{n\to\infty} b_n\right)$

$$= ab.$$

3 If $b \neq 0$ then $\displaystyle\lim_{n\to\infty} \left(\frac{a_n}{b_n}\right) = \frac{\displaystyle\lim_{n\to\infty} a_n}{\displaystyle\lim_{n\to\infty} b_n} = \frac{a}{b}.$

These results can be extended to finite sums and products of limits using mathematical induction.

Proof of 2:

For $n \in \mathbb{Z}^+$, we have $a_n b_n - ab = a_n b_n - a_n b + a_n b - ab$

$$= a_n(b_n - b) + b(a_n - a).$$

$\therefore$ by the Triangle Inequality,

$$|a_n b_n - ab| \leqslant |a_n(b_n - b)| + |b(a_n - a)| = |a_n|\,|b_n - b| + |b|\,|a_n - a|$$

As $\{a_n\}$ and $\{b_n\}$ are convergent sequences they are bounded, by the Lemma.

Hence there exists M_1, $M_2 > 0$ such that $|a_n| \leqslant M_1$ and $|b_n| \leqslant M_2$ for all $n \in \mathbb{Z}^+$.

If we let $M = \max\{M_1, M_2\}$, then $|a_n b_n - ab| \leqslant M|b_n - b| + M|a_n - a|$ for all $n \in \mathbb{Z}^+$.

For any given $\varepsilon > 0$, since $\displaystyle\lim_{n\to\infty} a_n = a$ and $\displaystyle\lim_{n\to\infty} b_n = b$ there exist positive integers N_1, N_2 such that $|a_n - a| < \dfrac{\varepsilon}{2M}$ for all $n \geqslant N_1$ and $|b_n - b| < \dfrac{\varepsilon}{2M}$ for all $n \geqslant N_2$.

Letting $N = \max\{N_1, N_2\}$, we find $|a_n b_n - ab| \leqslant M\left(\dfrac{\varepsilon}{2M}\right) + M\left(\dfrac{\varepsilon}{2M}\right) = \varepsilon$ for all $n \geqslant N$.

Hence $\displaystyle\lim_{n\to\infty} (a_n b_n) = ab$ from the sequence limit definition.

We have applied the formal definition of the limit of a sequence to rigorously establish some key results for sequences that can now be used to deal very efficiently with more general sequence limit problems.

Example 16

If $a_n = \left(\frac{4}{5}\right)^n + \frac{3}{n} - 9$ for all $n \in \mathbb{Z}^+$, find $\lim\limits_{n \to \infty} a_n$.

By the generalised version of **1** of the Algebra of Limits Theorem,

$$\lim_{n \to \infty} \left[\left(\tfrac{4}{5}\right)^n + \frac{3}{n} - 9\right] = \lim_{n \to \infty} \left(\tfrac{4}{5}\right)^n + \lim_{n \to \infty} \frac{3}{n} + \lim_{n \to \infty} (-9)$$

Since $0 < \frac{4}{5} < 1$, $\quad \lim\limits_{n \to \infty} \left(\tfrac{4}{5}\right)^n = 0$

Also, $\lim\limits_{n \to \infty} \left(\dfrac{3}{n}\right) = \lim\limits_{n \to \infty} 3 \times \lim\limits_{n \to \infty} \dfrac{1}{n} = 0,$

and $\lim\limits_{n \to \infty} (-9) = -9$

$\therefore \quad \lim\limits_{n \to \infty} \left[\left(\tfrac{4}{5}\right)^n + \dfrac{3}{n} - 9\right] = 0 + 0 - 9 = -9$

Example 17

Let $a_n = \dfrac{2n^2 + 4n - 3}{n^2 - 4\ln n}$ for all $n \in \mathbb{Z}^+$. Find $\lim\limits_{n \to \infty} a_n$.

We first note by dividing through by n^2 that $\quad \dfrac{2n^2 + 4n - 3}{n^2 - 4\ln n} = \dfrac{2 + \dfrac{4}{n} - \dfrac{3}{n^2}}{1 - \dfrac{4\ln n}{n^2}}$

$$\therefore \quad \lim_{n \to \infty} a_n = \frac{\lim\limits_{n \to \infty} \left(2 + \dfrac{4}{n} - \dfrac{3}{n^2}\right)}{\lim\limits_{n \to \infty} \left(1 - \dfrac{4\ln n}{n^2}\right)}$$

From result **2** of the limit theorems, $\quad \lim\limits_{n \to \infty} \dfrac{1}{n^2} = 0$

$\therefore \quad \lim\limits_{n \to \infty} \left(2 + \dfrac{4}{n} - \dfrac{3}{n^2}\right) = \lim\limits_{n \to \infty} (2) + 4 \lim\limits_{n \to \infty} \left(\dfrac{1}{n}\right) - 3 \lim\limits_{n \to \infty} \left(\dfrac{1}{n^2}\right)$

$$= 2$$

Now $0 < \ln n < n$ for all $n \geqslant 1$

$\therefore \quad 0 < \dfrac{1 \ln n}{n^2} < \dfrac{1}{n}$

$\therefore \quad 0 < \dfrac{4\ln n}{n^2} < \dfrac{4}{n}$

$\therefore$ by the Squeeze Theorem, $\quad \lim\limits_{n \to \infty} \dfrac{4\ln n}{n^2} = 0$

$\therefore \quad \lim\limits_{n \to \infty} a_n = \dfrac{2}{1 - 0} = 2$

Note:

You can use the TI-83 to estimate the limit of a sequence like that above. Start by typing the sequence rule for a_n into the $\boxed{\textbf{Y=}}$ graph editor. Go to $\boxed{\textbf{TBLSET}}$ and set up this editor as shown in the second screen below. Then go to $\boxed{\textbf{TABLE}}$ and investigate with some suitably large values for n.

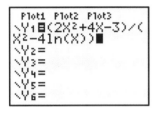      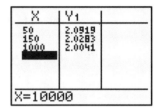

Example 18

If $a_n = \dfrac{\sin n}{n}$ for all $n \in \mathbb{Z}^+$, prove that $\displaystyle\lim_{n\to\infty} a_n = 0$.

We cannot apply the $\displaystyle\lim_{n\to\infty} \left(\dfrac{a_n}{b_n}\right) = \dfrac{a}{b}$ result as neither $\{\sin n\}$ nor $\{n\}$

are convergent sequences.

However, as $-1 \leqslant \sin n \leqslant 1$ for all $n \in \mathbb{Z}^+$,

$$-\frac{1}{n} \leqslant \frac{\sin n}{n} \leqslant \frac{1}{n} \quad \text{for all } n \in \mathbb{Z}^+.$$

$\therefore$ using the Squeeze Theorem, $\displaystyle\lim_{n\to\infty} \left(\dfrac{\sin n}{n}\right) = 0$.

EXERCISE 10B.1

1 Using the appropriate limit theorems, evaluate $\displaystyle\lim_{n\to\infty} a_n$ when it exists, if for all $n \in \mathbb{Z}^+$, a_n equals:

  a $\dfrac{1}{n + n^3}$

  b $\ln(1+n) - \ln n$

  c $\dfrac{3n^2 - 5n}{5n^2 + 2n - 6}$

  d $\dfrac{n(n+2)}{n+1} - \dfrac{n^3}{n^2+1}$

  e $\sqrt{n+1} - \sqrt{n}$

  f $\left(\dfrac{2n-3}{3n+7}\right)^4$

2 Determine if the following sequences converge:

  a $\left\{\dfrac{n!}{(n+3)!}\right\}$

  b $\left\{\dfrac{1}{\sqrt{n^2+1}-n}\right\}$

  c $\left\{\dfrac{\sqrt{n}-1}{\sqrt{n}+1}\right\}$

  d $\left\{\dfrac{\cos^2 n}{2^n}\right\}$

  e $\left\{(-1)^n \sin\left(\dfrac{1}{n}\right)\right\}$

  f $\left\{\dfrac{\sqrt[3]{2n^5 - n^2 + 4}}{n^2 + 1}\right\}$

3 Find $\lim\limits_{n \to \infty} a_n$ where $a_n = \dfrac{1}{n^2} + \dfrac{2}{n^2} + \dfrac{3}{n^2} + \ldots\ldots + \dfrac{n}{n^2}$.

4 If $n \in \mathbb{Z}^+$, find: **a** $\lim\limits_{n \to \infty} \left(\dfrac{1}{1+n}\right)^n$ **b** $\lim\limits_{n \to \infty} \left(2 + \dfrac{1}{n}\right)^n$

5 Prove part **a** of the Algebra of Limits Theorems,

i.e., if $\{a_n\}$ converges to a real number a and $\{b_n\}$ converges to a real number b,

then $\lim\limits_{n \to \infty} (a_n + b_n) = \lim\limits_{n \to \infty} a_n + \lim\limits_{n \to \infty} b_n = a + b$.

6 Use the formal definition of a limit to prove that for $n \in \mathbb{Z}^+$, $\lim\limits_{n \to \infty} \left(\dfrac{3n + 5}{7n - 4}\right) = \frac{3}{7}$.

7 If $\lim\limits_{n \to \infty} a_n = a$, $\lim\limits_{n \to \infty} b_n = b$,   and α and β are real constants,

use the Algebra of Limits Theorems to prove that $\lim\limits_{n \to \infty} (\alpha a_n + \beta b_n) = \alpha a + \beta b$.

Hence prove that $\lim\limits_{n \to \infty} (a_n - b_n) = a - b$.

A sequence $\{a_n\}$ is **monotonic** (monotone) if $a_{n+1} \geqslant a_n$ or $a_{n+1} \leqslant a_n$ for all n.

To show that a sequence is monotonic we show that either $a_{n+1} - a_n \geqslant 0$

or that $a_{n+1} - a_n \leqslant 0$ for all $n \in \mathbb{Z}^+$.

Alternatively, we can suppose a_n is represented by a continuous function $a(x)$ such that $a_n = a(n)$ for all $n \in \mathbb{Z}^+$. We then prove that for all $x \geqslant 1$, the gradient of $a(x)$ is either always positive or always negative.

The Monotone Convergence Theorem:

A monotone sequence of real numbers is convergent if and only if it is bounded.

EXERCISE 10B.2

1   **a**   Prove that the sequence with nth term $u_n = \dfrac{2n - 7}{3n + 2}$ is:

    i   monotonic increasing   **ii**   bounded.

  b   Determine whether the following sequences are monotonic and calculate their limits if they exist:

    i $\left\{\dfrac{n - 2}{n + 2}\right\}$ **ii** $\left\{\dfrac{3^n}{1 + 3^n}\right\}$ **iii** $\left\{\dfrac{1}{e^n - e^{-n}}\right\}$

  c   Prove that the series $\left\{\dfrac{1 \times 3 \times 5 \times \ldots\ldots \times (2n - 1)}{2^n n!}\right\}$ is convergent.

2   Let $u_1 = \sqrt{2}$ and define the sequence $\{u_n\}$ recursively by $u_n = \sqrt{2 + u_{n-1}}$.

Put the TI-83 into **Sequence** mode and input the recursive formula as shown:

Use **TABLE** to investigate the behaviour of $\{u_n\}$. Replace the 2 with other integer values and investigate.

3 The sequence $\{x_n\}$ is defined by $x_1 = 0$, $x_n = \sqrt{4 + 3x_{n-1}}$. Using mathematical induction, show that $\{x_n\}$ is monotonic increasing and bounded. Hence find the exact value of $\lim\limits_{n\to\infty} x_n$.

Hint: Suppose $\lim\limits_{n\to\infty} x_n = L$.

4 **a** Find the values of $\;1 + \dfrac{1}{1}, \quad 1 + \dfrac{1}{1 + \frac{1}{1}}, \quad 1 + \dfrac{1}{1 + \dfrac{1}{1 + \frac{1}{1}}}$

  b Give a recursive definition for the sequence above in terms of u_n.

  c Show that $\{u_n\}$ is bounded but not monotonic.

  d By supposing that $\lim\limits_{n\to\infty} u_n = L < \infty$, find the exact value of L.

5 **a** Expand $\left(1 + \dfrac{1}{n}\right)^n$, $n \in \mathbb{Z}^+$, using the Binomial Theorem.

  b Define $\{e_n\}$ by $e_n = \left(1 + \dfrac{1}{n}\right)^n$ and show that e_n equals:

  $$1 + 1 + \frac{1}{2!}\left(1 - \frac{1}{n}\right) + \frac{1}{3!}\left(1 - \frac{1}{n}\right)\left(1 - \frac{2}{n}\right) + \dots + \frac{1}{n!}\left(1 - \frac{1}{n}\right)\dots\left(1 - \frac{n-1}{n}\right)$$

  c Show that $2 \leqslant e_n < e_{n+1}$ for all $n \in \mathbb{Z}^+$ and

  $$e_n < 1 + 1 + \frac{1}{2!} + \frac{1}{3!} + \dots + \frac{1}{n!} < 1 + 1 + \frac{1}{2} + \frac{1}{2^2} + \dots + \frac{1}{2^{n-1}}$$

  d Using **c**, show that $\{e_n\}$ is bounded and hence convergent.

  e Given that $\lim\limits_{n\to\infty} \left(1 + \dfrac{1}{n}\right)^n = e \approx 2.718$, show that $\lim\limits_{n\to\infty} \left(1 - \dfrac{1}{n}\right)^n = e^{-1}$.

  f Use **e** and the Squeeze Theorem to find $\lim\limits_{n\to\infty} \left(\dfrac{n!}{n^n}\right)$.

INFINITE SERIES

Let $\{u_1, u_2, u_3, ...\}$ be an infinite sequence.

We can form a new sequence $S_1, S_2, S_3, ...$ i.e., $\{S_n\}$ by letting

$$S_1 = u_1$$
$$S_2 = u_1 + u_2$$
$$\vdots$$
$$S_n = u_1 + u_2 + ... + u_n = \sum_{i=1}^{n} u_i$$

where S_n, the **sum** of the first n terms of $\{u_n\}$, is called the **nth partial sum.**

Each term of $\{S_n\}$ is a **series**.

If $\displaystyle\lim_{n\to\infty} S_n = \sum_{n=1}^{\infty} u_n = S$ exists, the infinite series is **convergent**.

Otherwise it is **divergent**.

Example 19

Let $\{u_n\}$ be defined by $u_n = r^{n-1}$ where $r \neq 0 \in \mathbb{R}$, $n \in \mathbb{Z}^+$.

Find an expression for S_n, the nth partial sum of $\{u_n\}$, which does not involve a summation.

$$S_n = \sum_{i=1}^{n} u_i = \sum_{i=1}^{n} r^{i-1}$$
$$= 1 + r + r^2 + ... + r^{n-1}$$
$$\therefore \quad rS_n = r + r^2 + ... + r^n$$
$$\therefore \quad rS_n - S_n = r^n - 1$$
$$\therefore \quad S_n = \frac{r^n - 1}{r - 1}$$

It is often important to know when $\displaystyle\lim_{n\to\infty} S_n = \sum_{n=1}^{\infty} u_n$ exists, and if so, what its value is.

In general it is not possible to get an explicit expression for S_n such as that in **Example 19**. However, as we shall see, more difficult functions can often be expressed as simpler infinite series. In fact, great mathematicians such as Euler and Newton did much of their seminal work using infinite series representations of functions, though it was not until much later that other mathematicians such as Cauchy and Lagrange rigorously established when such representations were valid.

Since convergence of a series is in effect convergence of a sequence of partial sums, many of the sequence results apply. For example:

Theorem:

If $\displaystyle\sum_{n=1}^{\infty} a_n$ and $\displaystyle\sum_{n=1}^{\infty} b_n$ are convergent series, then

- $\displaystyle\sum_{n=1}^{\infty} ca_n = c \sum_{n=1}^{\infty} a_n$ where c is a constant, and

- $\displaystyle\sum_{n=1}^{\infty} (a_n \pm b_n) = \sum_{n=1}^{\infty} a_n \pm \sum_{n=1}^{\infty} b_n$ are also both convergent.

However, because the form of the sequence of partial sums is generally too unwieldy to deal with using our earlier methods, we need a special set of tests and conditions for determining when the limits of these partial sums exist.

We start with a very useful result that can tell us something either about a series $\displaystyle\sum_{n=1}^{\infty} a_n$ or its associated sequence of general terms $\{a_n\}$:

Theorem:

If the series $\displaystyle\sum_{n=1}^{\infty} a_n$ is convergent then $\displaystyle\lim_{n\to\infty} a_n = 0$.

Proof:

Let $S_n = a_1 + a_2 + \ldots + a_n$

$\therefore \quad a_n = S_n - S_{n-1}$

Now $\displaystyle\sum_{n=1}^{\infty} a_n$ is convergent, so $\{S_n\}$ is convergent (by definition).

Letting $\displaystyle\lim_{n\to\infty} S_n = S, \quad \lim_{n\to\infty} S_{n-1} = S$

$$\therefore \quad \lim_{n\to\infty} a_n = \lim_{n\to\infty} (S_n - S_{n-1}) = S - S = 0$$

We shall show later that even though $\displaystyle\lim_{n\to\infty} \frac{1}{n} = 0$, $\displaystyle\sum_{n=1}^{\infty} \frac{1}{n}$ diverges extremely slowly.

Therefore, the converse of the above theorem is not true.

However, we may establish the following Test for Divergence.

THE TEST FOR DIVERGENCE

If $\displaystyle\lim_{n\to\infty} a_n$ does not exist or $\displaystyle\lim_{n\to\infty} a_n \neq 0$, then the series $\displaystyle\sum_{n=1}^{\infty} a_n$ is divergent.

In some cases, we can use our previous work on sequences to determine if a given series is divergent.

Example 20

Show that the series $\displaystyle\sum_{n=1}^{\infty} \frac{n^2}{5n^2 + 4}$ diverges.

The nth term of the series is $a_n = \dfrac{n^2}{5n^2 + 4}$.

$$\therefore \quad \lim_{n \to \infty} a_n = \lim_{n \to \infty} \frac{n^2}{5n^2 + 4}$$

$$= \lim_{n \to \infty} \frac{1}{5 + \dfrac{4}{n^2}}$$

$$= \tfrac{1}{5} \neq 0$$

$\therefore$ the series diverges.

The Test for Divergence puts no sign restriction on each term of $\{a_n\}$. However, all of the following series tests *only apply to series of positive terms*.

THE COMPARISON TEST

Let $\{a_n\}$ be a positive series   i.e., $a_n > 0$ for all n.

If there exists a convergent series $\displaystyle\sum_{n=1}^{\infty} b_n$ such that $a_n \leqslant b_n$,

then $\displaystyle\sum_{n=1}^{\infty} a_n$ is also convergent.

Conversely, if $a_n \geqslant b_n$ and $\displaystyle\sum_{n=1}^{\infty} b_n$ diverges, then so does $\displaystyle\sum_{n=1}^{\infty} a_n$.

Proof of the first part:

Let $\{A_n\}$ and $\{B_n\}$ be the sequences of partial sums associated with a_n and b_n respectively.

As $a_n,\ b_n > 0$, $\{A_n\}$ and $\{B_n\}$ are monotonic increasing.

If $\lim_{n \to \infty} B_n = B$ then $0 \leqslant A_n \leqslant B_n \leqslant B$.

$\therefore$ A_n is also a bounded monotonic sequence and therefore converges by the Monotone Convergence Theorem.

With a minor adjustment to the proof the result can be shown to hold if $a_n \geqslant 0$ for all n.

However, the difficulty with the Comparison Test is in finding a suitable $\displaystyle\sum_{n=1}^{\infty} b_n$.

An appropriate geometric series often tends to work. Indeed, convergent geometric series are used in the proofs of some of the most general and important convergence tests.

Example 21

Test the series $\displaystyle\sum_{n=1}^{\infty} \frac{1}{2^n + 1}$ for convergence.

Now 2^n is positive for all n, and $2^n + 1 > 2^n$.

$\therefore \quad 0 < \dfrac{1}{2^n + 1} < \dfrac{1}{2^n} = \left(\tfrac{1}{2}\right)^n$ for all $n \in \mathbb{Z}^+$.

But $\displaystyle\sum_{n=1}^{\infty} \left(\tfrac{1}{2}\right)^n$ is a convergent geometric series and therefore, by the Comparison

Test, $\displaystyle\sum_{n=1}^{\infty} \frac{1}{2^n + 1}$ converges.

Now we cannot use the Comparison Test to test the series $\displaystyle\sum_{n=1}^{\infty} \frac{1}{2^n - 1}$ for convergence.

However, the next test may be useful when the Comparison Test cannot be applied directly:

THE LIMIT COMPARISON TEST

Suppose that $\displaystyle\sum_{n=1}^{\infty} a_n$ and $\displaystyle\sum_{n=1}^{\infty} b_n$ are series with positive terms.

1 If $\displaystyle\lim_{n\to\infty} \frac{a_n}{b_n} = c > 0$ then both series either converge or diverge together.

2 If $\displaystyle\lim_{n\to\infty} \frac{a_n}{b_n} = 0$ and $\displaystyle\sum_{n=1}^{\infty} b_n$ converges, then $\displaystyle\sum_{n=1}^{\infty} a_n$ converges.

3 If $\displaystyle\lim_{n\to\infty} \frac{a_n}{b_n} = \infty$ and $\displaystyle\sum_{n=1}^{\infty} b_n$ diverges, then $\displaystyle\sum_{n=1}^{\infty} a_n$ diverges.

Proof of 1:

Let $0 < \varepsilon = \dfrac{c}{2}$.

Since $\displaystyle\lim_{n\to\infty} \frac{a_n}{b_n} = c$, using the definition of a limit, there exists N such that

$$\left| \frac{a_n}{b_n} - c \right| < \frac{c}{2} \quad \text{for all } n > N$$

$$\therefore \quad -\frac{c}{2} < \frac{a_n}{b_n} - c < \frac{c}{2}$$

$$\therefore \quad \frac{c}{2} < \frac{a_n}{b_n} < \frac{3c}{2}$$

$$\therefore \quad b_n \left(\frac{c}{2} \right) < a_n < \left(\frac{3c}{2} \right) b_n \quad \text{for all } n > N$$

Now if $\sum\limits_{n=1}^{\infty} b_n$ converges then so does $\sum\limits_{n=1}^{\infty} \left(\dfrac{3c}{2}\right) b_n$.

Hence by the Comparison Test, $\sum\limits_{n=1}^{\infty} a_n$ also converges.

However, if $\sum\limits_{n=1}^{\infty} b_n$ diverges then so does $\sum\limits_{n=1}^{\infty} \left(\dfrac{c}{2}\right) b_n$.

Hence by the Comparison Test, $\sum\limits_{n=1}^{\infty} a_n$ also diverges.

Example 22

Test the series $\sum\limits_{n=1}^{\infty} \dfrac{1}{2^n - 1}$ for convergence or divergence.

We let $a_n = \dfrac{1}{2^n - 1}$ and $b_n = \dfrac{1}{2^n}$.

Then $\lim\limits_{n\to\infty} \dfrac{a_n}{b_n} = \lim\limits_{n\to\infty} \dfrac{2^n}{2^n - 1}$

$= \lim\limits_{n\to\infty} \dfrac{1}{1 - \left(\frac{1}{2}\right)^n}$

$= 1$

So by **1** above, since $\sum\limits_{n=1}^{\infty} \dfrac{1}{2^n}$ converges, $\sum\limits_{n=1}^{\infty} \dfrac{1}{2^n - 1}$ converges also.

THE INTEGRAL TEST

The Integral Test links the sum of a series to the integral of a positive function.

We remember from **Section A** that if a is an integer, $\sum\limits_{i=a}^{\infty} f(i) \approx \int_a^{\infty} f(x)\,dx$

In particular, when $a = 1$, $\sum\limits_{i=1}^{\infty} f(i) \approx \int_1^{\infty} f(x)\,dx$

Suppose that f is a continuous, positive decreasing function on $[1, \infty]$ and $a_n = f(n)$.

1 If $\int_1^{\infty} f(x)\,dx$ is convergent, then $\sum\limits_{n=1}^{\infty} a_n$ is convergent.

2 If $\int_1^{\infty} f(x)\,dx$ is divergent, then $\sum\limits_{n=1}^{\infty} a_n$ is divergent.

Clearly this test is only of practical use if $\int_1^{\infty} f(x)\,dx$ can be evaluated relatively easily.

Proof of 1:

If $f(x)$ is a positive decreasing function, then we can approximate the integral $\int_1^{\infty} f(x)\,dx$ using lower and upper sums. This process was discussed in **Section A** of the chapter, and is illustrated in the diagrams below.

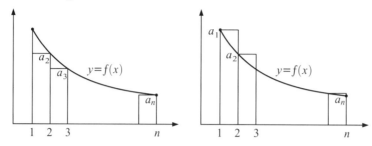

From the diagram on the left, we find that the lower sum

$$a_2 + a_3 + ... + a_n + ... \leqslant \int_1^\infty f(x)\,dx$$

$$\therefore \quad \sum_{n=1}^{\infty} a_n \leqslant a_1 + \int_1^\infty f(x)\,dx$$

And from the diagram on the right, we find that the upper sum

$$a_1 + a_2 + ... + a_n + ... \geqslant \int_1^\infty f(x)\,dx$$

$$\therefore \quad \int_1^\infty f(x)\,dx \leqslant \sum_{n=1}^{\infty} a_n$$

Hence, $\int_1^\infty f(x)\,dx \leqslant \sum_{n=1}^{\infty} a_n \leqslant a_1 + \int_1^\infty f(x)\,dx$

Therefore, if $\int_1^\infty f(x)\,dx$ converges then $\sum_{n=1}^{\infty} a_n$ is bounded and increasing, and hence convergent also.

Note:

We can use the TI-83 to help us estimate $\int_1^\infty f(x)\,dx$:

Go to **MATH** then 9:fnInt(. Press enter and put in $f(x)$ and a suitably large upper integral limit as shown:

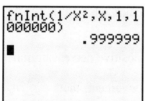

Example 23

Test $\displaystyle\sum_{n=1}^{\infty} \frac{1}{n^2 + 1}$ for convergence.

$f(x) = \dfrac{1}{x^2 + 1}$ is continuous, positive and decreasing for $x \geqslant 1$.

$\therefore$ the conditions for the Integral Test are satisfied.

Now $\int_1^\infty f(x)\,dx = \int_1^\infty \dfrac{1}{x^2+1}\,dx$

$= \lim\limits_{b\to\infty} \int_1^b \dfrac{1}{x^2+1}\,dx$

$= \lim\limits_{b\to\infty} \left[\tan^{-1} x\right]_1^b$

$= \lim\limits_{b\to\infty} \left(\tan^{-1} b - \tfrac{\pi}{4}\right)$

$= \tfrac{\pi}{2} - \tfrac{\pi}{4} = \tfrac{\pi}{4}$

$\therefore$ $\int_1^\infty f(x)\,dx$ is convergent and therefore, so is $\displaystyle\sum_{n=1}^{\infty} \dfrac{1}{n^2+1}$.

Example 24

For what values of p is the series $\displaystyle\sum_{n=1}^{\infty} \dfrac{1}{n^p}$ convergent?

Now if $p < 0$ then $\lim\limits_{n\to\infty} \dfrac{1}{n^p} = \infty$, and if $p = 0$ then $\lim\limits_{n\to\infty} \dfrac{1}{n^p} = 1$.

In both of these cases, $\lim\limits_{n\to\infty} \dfrac{1}{n^p} \neq 0$, so by the Test for Divergence, the series diverge.

But for $p > 0$, $\lim\limits_{n\to\infty} \dfrac{1}{n^p} = 0$, and since the function $f(x) = \dfrac{1}{x^p}$ is continuous, positive and decreasing on $[1, \infty]$, we can apply the Integral Test:

$\int_1^\infty \dfrac{1}{x^p}\,dx = \left[\dfrac{1}{1-p} x^{1-p}\right]_1^\infty$

$= \dfrac{1}{1-p} \lim\limits_{b\to\infty} b^{1-p} - \dfrac{1}{1-p}$

$= \begin{cases} 0 - \dfrac{1}{1-p} & \text{if } p > 1 \\ \infty & \text{if } 0 < p \leqslant 1 \end{cases}$

$\therefore$ by the Integral Test, the series $\displaystyle\sum_{n=1}^{\infty} \dfrac{1}{n^p}$ converges if $p > 1$ and diverges if $p \leqslant 1$.

The series $\displaystyle\sum_{n=1}^{\infty} \dfrac{1}{n^p}$ is called the **p-series**, and can be used to rapidly test the convergence of series of that form.

For example, the series $\displaystyle\sum_{n=1}^{\infty} \dfrac{1}{\sqrt{n}} = \sum_{n=1}^{\infty} \dfrac{1}{n^{0.5}}$ is divergent because it is the p-series with $p = \tfrac{1}{2} < 1$.

Example 25

Suppose we can use the Integral Test to show that $\sum\limits_{n=1}^{\infty} a_n$ is convergent, where $a_n = f(n)$.

a Show that the error R_k in approximating $\sum\limits_{n=1}^{\infty} a_n$ by $a_1 + a_2 + \ldots\ldots + a_k$

for some $k \in \mathbb{Z}^+$ satisfies $\int_{k+1}^{\infty} f(x)\, dx < R_k < \int_{k}^{\infty} f(x)\, dx$.

b Hence determine the number of terms necessary to approximate $\sum\limits_{n=1}^{\infty} \dfrac{1}{n^3}$ correct to two decimal places.

a The error $R_k = S - S_k = \sum\limits_{n=1}^{\infty} a_n - \sum\limits_{n=1}^{k} a_n = a_{k+1} + a_{k+2} + a_{k+3} + \ldots\ldots$

From the areas of lower rectangles in the diagram below, we deduce

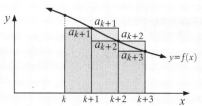

$$R_k = a_{k+1} + a_{k+2} + a_{k+3} + \cdots < \int_{k}^{\infty} f(x)\, dx$$

Then, using the upper rectangles from $x = k + 1$ onwards, we deduce

$$R_k = a_{k+1} + a_{k+2} + a_{k+3} + \cdots > \int_{k+1}^{\infty} f(x)\, dx$$

Hence $\int_{k+1}^{\infty} f(x)\, dx < R_k < \int_{k}^{\infty} f(x)\, dx$ as required.

b For the sum $\sum\limits_{n=1}^{\infty} \dfrac{1}{n^3}$, we have $f(x) = \dfrac{1}{x^3}$.

Hence $R_k < \displaystyle\int_{k}^{\infty} \dfrac{1}{x^3}\, dx = \lim_{b \to \infty} \left[-\dfrac{1}{2x^2} \right]_{k}^{b} = \lim_{b \to \infty} \left(-\dfrac{1}{2b^2} + \dfrac{1}{2k^2} \right) = \dfrac{1}{2k^2}$

To approximate the sum correctly to two decimal places, we require

$$R_k < 0.005 = \tfrac{1}{200}$$

$\therefore$ we need $\dfrac{1}{2k^2} < \tfrac{1}{200} \;\Rightarrow\; k^2 > 100 \;\Rightarrow\; k > 10 \quad \{\text{as } k > 0\}$

Hence we require 11 terms to correctly approximate $\sum\limits_{n=1}^{\infty} \dfrac{1}{n^3}$ to 2 d.p.

In part **a** of **Example 25** above, we proved the following result for **approximating an infinite series with a finite truncation**. Note that this only applies when f is a continuous, positive, decreasing function on (k, ∞), i.e., to series for which we can apply the Integral Test.

If we approximate $\sum\limits_{n=1}^{\infty} a_n$ by the sum of its first k terms,

i.e., $\sum\limits_{n=1}^{\infty} a_n \approx a_1 + a_2 + \ldots\ldots + a_k$ for some $k \in \mathbb{Z}^+$, then

the **error** R_k in approximation satisfies $\int_{k+1}^{\infty} f(x)\, dx < R_k < \int_{k}^{\infty} f(x)\, dx$.

EXERCISE 10C.1

1 Determine whether the following series are convergent or divergent using the Comparison Test or Test for Divergence.

a $\displaystyle\sum_{n=1}^{\infty} \frac{1}{e^{2n}}$

b $\displaystyle\sum_{n=1}^{\infty} \frac{n^2}{3(n+1)(n+2)}$

c $\displaystyle\sum_{n=1}^{\infty} \frac{3^n + 2^n}{6^n}$

d $\displaystyle\sum_{n=1}^{\infty} \left(\frac{1}{n} - \frac{1}{n^2}\right)$

2 Use the Limit Comparison Test with $b_n = \dfrac{2}{\sqrt{n^3}}$ to show the series $\displaystyle\sum_{n=1}^{\infty} \frac{2n^2 + 3n}{\sqrt{5 + n^7}}$ is convergent.

3 Determine whether $\displaystyle\sum_{n=1}^{\infty} \frac{1}{n^n}$ and $\displaystyle\sum_{n=1}^{\infty} \frac{1}{n!}$ are convergent using the Comparison Test.

4 Determine whether the following series converge or diverge using the Comparison Test or Limit Comparison Test.

a $\displaystyle\sum_{n=1}^{\infty} \frac{1}{\sqrt{n(n+1)(n+2)}}$

b $\displaystyle\sum_{n=2}^{\infty} \frac{1}{\sqrt[3]{n(n+1)(n-1)}}$

c $\displaystyle\sum_{n=1}^{\infty} \frac{\sin^2 n}{n\sqrt{n}}$

d $\displaystyle\sum_{n=2}^{\infty} \frac{\sqrt{n}}{n-1}$

e $\displaystyle\sum_{n=1}^{\infty} \frac{1 + 2^n}{1 + 3^n}$

f $\displaystyle\sum_{n=2}^{\infty} \frac{1}{\ln n}$

5 Find all the values of $x \in [0, 2\pi]$ for which the series $\displaystyle\sum_{n=0}^{\infty} 2^n |\sin^n x|$ converges.

6 Find c if $\displaystyle\sum_{n=2}^{\infty} (1+c)^{-n} = 2$.

7 Use the Integral Test to determine whether the following series converge:

a $\displaystyle\sum_{n=1}^{\infty} \frac{n}{n^2 + 1}$

b $\displaystyle\sum_{n=1}^{\infty} ne^{-n^2}$

c $\displaystyle\sum_{n=1}^{\infty} \frac{\ln n}{n}$

d $\displaystyle\sum_{n=2}^{\infty} \frac{1}{n \ln n}$

8 Show that $\dfrac{\pi}{4} < \displaystyle\sum_{n=1}^{\infty} \frac{1}{n^2 + 1} < \frac{1}{2} + \frac{\pi}{4}$.

9 Determine the values of p for which the series $\displaystyle\sum_{n=2}^{\infty} \frac{1}{n^p \ln n}$ converges.

10 a Estimate the error when $\displaystyle\sum_{n=1}^{\infty} \frac{1}{5n^2}$ is approximated by its first 12 terms.

b How many terms are necessary to approximate $\displaystyle\sum_{n=1}^{\infty} \frac{1}{n^4}$ correct to 6 decimal places?

11 Suppose $\sum\limits_{n=1}^{\infty} a_n$ is convergent where $a_n \neq 0$. Prove that $\sum\limits_{n=1}^{\infty} \dfrac{1}{a_n}$ is divergent.

12 The nth partial sum of a series $\sum\limits_{n=1}^{\infty} a_n$ is $S_n = \dfrac{n-1}{n+1}$.

Find a_n and write $\sum\limits_{n=1}^{\infty} a_n$ in expanded form.

13 The first few partial sums of the series $\sum\limits_{n=1}^{\infty} \dfrac{n}{(n+1)!}$

can be evaluated quickly and exactly using the TI-83:

Go to **2nd** **LIST** then OPS, 6:CumSum(and press Enter. Then **2nd** **LIST**, OPS then 5:Seq(and Enter. Then
use **MATH** and 1:Frac to obtain the screen alongside.

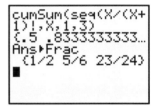

a In a similar manner, find the partial sums S_4,
S_5 and conjecture a formula for S_n for the se-

ries $\sum\limits_{n=1}^{\infty} \dfrac{n}{(n+1)!}$.

b Use mathematical induction to prove your conjecture.

c Show that the given infinite series is convergent and find its sum.

14 The harmonic series is defined by $\sum\limits_{n=1}^{\infty} \dfrac{1}{n} = 1 + \frac{1}{2} + \frac{1}{3} + \frac{1}{4} + \ldots\ldots$

Consider the following sequence of partial sums for the harmonic series:

$$S_1 = 1$$
$$S_2 = 1 + \tfrac{1}{2}$$
$$S_4 = 1 + \tfrac{1}{2} + \left(\tfrac{1}{3} + \tfrac{1}{4}\right)$$
$$> 1 + \tfrac{1}{2} + \left(\tfrac{1}{4} + \tfrac{1}{4}\right) = 1 + \tfrac{2}{2}$$
$$S_8 = 1 + \tfrac{1}{2} + \left(\tfrac{1}{3} + \tfrac{1}{4}\right) + \left(\tfrac{1}{5} + \tfrac{1}{6} + \tfrac{1}{7} + \tfrac{1}{8}\right)$$
$$> 1 + \tfrac{1}{2} + \left(\tfrac{1}{4} + \tfrac{1}{4}\right) + \left(\tfrac{1}{8} + \tfrac{1}{8} + \tfrac{1}{8} + \tfrac{1}{8}\right) = 1 + \tfrac{3}{2}$$

a Use the same method to find an inequality involving S_{16}.

b Conjecture an inequality involving S_{2^m}, $m \in \mathbb{Z}^+$. Prove your conjecture by
mathematical induction.

c Show that $S_{2^m} \to \infty$ as $m \to \infty$ and hence prove that $\{S_n\}$ is divergent.

TELESCOPING SERIES

Consider the series $\sum\limits_{n=1}^{\infty} \left(\dfrac{1}{n} - \dfrac{1}{n+1}\right)$.

We could separate it into the difference $\sum\limits_{n=1}^{\infty} \dfrac{1}{n} - \sum\limits_{n=1}^{\infty} \dfrac{1}{n+1}$. However, since both $\sum\limits_{n=1}^{\infty} \dfrac{1}{n}$

and $\displaystyle\sum_{n=1}^{\infty} \frac{1}{n+1}$ are divergent, this tells us nothing about the convergence or divergence of the whole series.

However, $\dfrac{1}{n} - \dfrac{1}{n+1} = \dfrac{1}{n(n+1)}$, and we can show $\displaystyle\sum_{n=1}^{\infty} \frac{1}{n(n+1)}$ is convergent by

comparison with $\displaystyle\sum_{n=1}^{\infty} \frac{1}{n^2}$. We therefore know that $\displaystyle\sum_{n=1}^{\infty} \left(\frac{1}{n} - \frac{1}{n+1} \right)$ is in fact con-

vergent, but do not yet know what it converges to.

Now if we expand the first n terms of the series, we obtain:

$$\sum_{r=1}^{n} \left(\frac{1}{r} - \frac{1}{r+1} \right) = \tfrac{1}{1} \cancel{-\tfrac{1}{2}} + \cancel{\tfrac{1}{2}} \cancel{-\tfrac{1}{3}} + \ldots\ldots + \cancel{\frac{1}{n-1}} \cancel{-\frac{1}{n}} + \cancel{\frac{1}{n}} - \frac{1}{n+1}$$

$$= 1 - \frac{1}{n+1} \quad \{\text{as all terms cancel except the first and last}\}$$

$$\therefore \quad \sum_{n=1}^{\infty} \left(\frac{1}{n} - \frac{1}{n+1} \right) = \lim_{n\to\infty} \sum_{r=1}^{n} \left(\frac{1}{r} - \frac{1}{r+1} \right)$$

$$= \lim_{n\to\infty} \left(1 - \frac{1}{n+1} \right)$$

$$= 1$$

This type of series is called a **telescoping series** because, like drawing in a telescope, the intermediate sections disappear.

By the telescoping process, we can not only establish the convergence of the series, but also the value of the limit.

PARTIAL FRACTIONS

If a_n is a rational function, we can often obtain a telescoping series for $\displaystyle\sum_{n=1}^{\infty} a_n$ by express-

ing a_n in terms of **partial fractions**. Using this method, we take the rational function and rewrite it as the sum of several fractions with linear denominators.

Example 26

Use partial fractions to express $\dfrac{n-1}{n(n+1)}$ as the sum of fractions with linear denominators.

Suppose $\quad \dfrac{n-1}{n(n+1)} \equiv \dfrac{A}{n} + \dfrac{B}{n+1}$

$$\equiv \dfrac{A(n+1)+Bn}{n(n+1)}$$

$$\equiv \dfrac{(A+B)n+A}{n(n+1)}$$

Equating coefficients, $\quad A+B=1 \quad$ and $\quad A=-1.$

$$\therefore \quad B=2$$

and hence $\quad \dfrac{n-1}{n(n+1)} = -\dfrac{1}{n} + \dfrac{2}{n+1}$

Example 27

Evaluate $\quad \dfrac{1}{1\times 3} + \dfrac{1}{3\times 5} + \dfrac{1}{5\times 7} + ... = \displaystyle\sum_{n=1}^{\infty} \dfrac{1}{(2n-1)(2n+1)}.$

Suppose $\quad \dfrac{1}{(2n-1)(2n+1)} \equiv \dfrac{A}{(2n-1)} + \dfrac{B}{(2n+1)}$

$$\equiv \dfrac{A(2n+1)+B(2n-1)}{(2n-1)(2n+1)}$$

$$\equiv \dfrac{(2A+2B)n+(A-B)}{(2n-1)(2n+1)}$$

Equating coefficients, $\quad 2A+2B=0 \quad$ and $\quad A-B=1$

Solving these simultaneously, $\quad A=\tfrac{1}{2}$ and $B=-\tfrac{1}{2}.$

So $\quad \dfrac{1}{(2n-1)(2n+1)} \equiv \tfrac{1}{2}\left[\dfrac{1}{(2n-1)} - \dfrac{1}{(2n+1)}\right]$

$\therefore \quad \displaystyle\sum_{r=1}^{n} \dfrac{1}{(2r-1)(2r+1)} = \tfrac{1}{2}\left[\left(\tfrac{1}{1} - \tfrac{1}{3}\right) + \left(\tfrac{1}{3} - \tfrac{1}{5}\right) + ...\right.$

$$\left. + \left(\dfrac{1}{2n-3} - \dfrac{1}{2n-1}\right) + \left(\dfrac{1}{2n-1} - \dfrac{1}{2n+1}\right)\right]$$

$$= \tfrac{1}{2}\left[1 - \dfrac{1}{2n+1}\right]$$

$\therefore \quad \displaystyle\sum_{n=1}^{\infty} \dfrac{1}{(2n-1)(2n+1)} = \tfrac{1}{2}\lim_{n\to\infty}\left[1 - \dfrac{1}{2n+1}\right] = \tfrac{1}{2}$

ALTERNATING SERIES

Thus far, we have only dealt with series with only positive terms.

An **alternating series** is one whose terms are alternately positive and negative.

e.g. $1 - \frac{1}{2} + \frac{1}{4} - \frac{1}{8} + \frac{1}{16} - \frac{1}{32} + \dots\dots$

THE ALTERNATING SERIES TEST

> If the alternating series $\sum_{n=1}^{\infty} (-1)^{n-1} b_n = b_1 - b_2 + b_3 - \dots.$ satisfies
>
> $\qquad 0 \leqslant b_{n+1} \leqslant b_n \quad$ for all $\quad n \in \mathbb{Z}^+$, and if $\quad \lim_{n\to\infty} b_n = 0$,
>
> then the series is convergent.

Note: The theorem also applies if the first term is negative, since we could simply consider the series without the first term.

Proof:

Now the $(2n + 2)$th partial sum of the series is

$\qquad S_{2n+2} = b_1 - b_2 + \dots\dots - b_{2n} + b_{2n+1} - b_{2n+2},$

where the b_i are all non-negative and non-increasing.

We therefore find that $\quad S_{2n+1} = S_{2n} + b_{2n+1}$

$\qquad\qquad\qquad\qquad\qquad S_{2n+2} = S_{2n} + b_{2n+1} + b_{2n+2}$

$\qquad\qquad\qquad\qquad\qquad S_{2n+3} = S_{2n+1} + b_{2n+2} + b_{2n+3}$

$\qquad\qquad\qquad\qquad\qquad\quad\; = S_{2n+2} + b_{2n+3}$

Since $b_{2n+1} \geqslant b_{2n+2} \geqslant b_{2n+3}$, we have $S_{2n+1} \geqslant S_{2n+3} \geqslant S_{2n+2} \geqslant S_{2n}$.

Also, $S_{2n+2} = (b_1 - b_2) + (b_3 - b_4) + (b_5 - \dots\dots - b_{2n}) + (b_{2n+1} - b_{2n+2}).$

Because the b_i are non-increasing, each expression in brackets is $\geqslant 0$.

Hence $S_n \geqslant 0$ for any even n, and since $S_{2n+1} \geqslant S_{2n+2}$, $S_n \geqslant 0$ for all n.

Finally, since $S_{2n+1} \leqslant b_1$,   we conclude that

$\qquad b_1 \geqslant S_{2n+1} \geqslant S_{2n+3} \geqslant S_{2n+2} \geqslant S_{2n} \geqslant 0.$

Hence the even partial sums S_{2n} and the odd partial sums S_{2n+1} are bounded. The S_{2n} are monotonically non-decreasing, while the odd sums S_{2n+1} are monotonically non-increasing. Thus the even and odd series both converge.

We note that since $S_{2n+1} - S_{2n} = b_{2n+1}$,   the sums converge to the same limit if and only if $\lim_{n\to\infty} b_n = 0$.

The convergence process is illustrated in the following diagram.

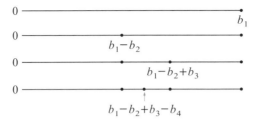

Note that if $0 \leqslant b_{n+1} \leqslant b_n$ for all $n \in \mathbb{Z}^+$ but $\lim\limits_{n \to \infty} b_n \neq 0$, then the series will eventually oscillate between two points. These points are those to which the even partial sums S_{2n} and the odd partial sums S_{2n+1} converge, i.e., $\lim\limits_{n \to \infty} S_{2n}$ and $\lim\limits_{n \to \infty} S_{2n+1}$.

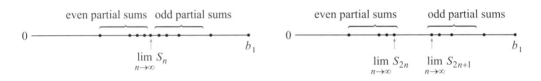

Example 28

Show that $1 - \frac{1}{2} + \frac{1}{3} - \frac{1}{4} + \ldots = \sum\limits_{n=1}^{\infty} \frac{(-1)^{n-1}}{n}$ converges.

This is an alternating series for which $b_n = \dfrac{1}{n}$.

Since $\dfrac{1}{n+1} < \dfrac{1}{n}$, the series satisfies $0 < b_{n+1} < b_n$ for all $n \in \mathbb{Z}^+$.

Also $\lim\limits_{n \to \infty} b_n = \lim\limits_{n \to \infty} \dfrac{1}{n} = 0$

$\therefore \quad \sum\limits_{n=1}^{\infty} \dfrac{(-1)^{n-1}}{n}$ converges by the Alternating Series Test

(even though we have already shown that $\sum\limits_{n=1}^{\infty} \dfrac{1}{n}$ is not convergent).

Definition:

Suppose a convergent infinite series converges to a sum S.

The **truncation error** R_n involved in using the nth partial sum S_n as an estimate of the sum S is defined by $R_n = |S - S_n|$.

The Alternating Series Estimation Theorem:

If $S = \sum\limits_{n=1}^{\infty} (-1)^{n-1} b_n$ is the sum of an alternating series satisfying

$$0 \leqslant b_{n+1} \leqslant b_n \quad \text{for all} \quad n \in \mathbb{Z}^+ \quad \text{and} \quad \lim\limits_{n \to \infty} b_n = 0$$

then $R_n = |S - S_n| \leqslant b_{n+1}$.

Proof:

$$S - S_n = \sum_{k=1}^{\infty} (-1)^{k-1} b_k - \sum_{k=1}^{n} (-1)^{k-1} b_k$$

$$= (-1)^n b_{n+1} + (-1)^{n+1} b_{n+2} + ...$$

$$= (-1)^n \left[(b_{n+1} - b_{n+2}) + (b_{n+3} - b_{n+4}) + ... \right]$$

But since $b_{r+1} \leqslant b_r$ for all $r \in \mathbb{Z}^+$,

$$b_{n+r+1} \leqslant b_{n+r} \quad \text{for all} \quad r \in \mathbb{Z}^+.$$

$$\therefore \quad b_{n+r} \geqslant b_{n+r+1} \quad \text{for all} \quad r \in \mathbb{Z}^+.$$

$$\therefore \quad (b_{n+1} - b_{n+2}) + (b_{n+3} - b_{n+4}) + ... \geqslant 0$$

i.e, $\quad R_n = |S - S_n| = (b_{n+1} - b_{n+2}) + (b_{n+3} - b_{n+4}) + ...$

Rearranging the brackets, we could alternatively write

$$R_n = b_{n+1} - (b_{n+2} - b_{n+3}) - (b_{n+4} - b_{n+5}) - .....$$

$$= b_{n+1} - \left[(b_{n+2} - b_{n+3}) + (b_{n+4} - b_{n+5}) + ... \right]$$

$$\leqslant b_{n+1} \quad \text{since} \quad \left[(b_{n+2} - b_{n+3}) + (b_{n+4} - b_{n+5}) + ... \right] \geqslant 0$$

Example 29

Find the sum of $\displaystyle\sum_{n=1}^{\infty} \frac{(-1)^{n-1}}{n!}$ correct to 3 decimal places.

This is an alternating series for which $b_n = \dfrac{1}{n!}$

Now $\quad 0 < \dfrac{1}{(n+1)!} < \dfrac{1}{n!}$

$\therefore \quad 0 < b_{n+1} < b_n \quad$ for all $\quad n \in \mathbb{Z}^+$

Also, $\quad 0 < \dfrac{1}{n!} < \dfrac{1}{n}$

$\therefore$ since $\displaystyle\lim_{n\to\infty} \frac{1}{n} = 0$ and $\displaystyle\lim_{n\to\infty} \frac{1}{n!} = \lim_{n\to\infty} b_n = 0$ by the Squeeze Theorem

$\therefore$ the series converges by the Alternating Series Test.

$$S = 1 - \tfrac{1}{2} + \tfrac{1}{6} - \tfrac{1}{24} + \tfrac{1}{120} - \tfrac{1}{720} + \tfrac{1}{5040} + ...$$

Notice that $\quad b_7 = \tfrac{1}{5040} < \tfrac{1}{2000} = 0.0005$

and $\quad S_6 = 1 - \tfrac{1}{2} + \tfrac{1}{6} - \tfrac{1}{24} + \tfrac{1}{120} - \tfrac{1}{720} = 0.631\,944$

Now by the Estimation Theorem, $\quad |S - S_6| \leqslant b_7$.

$\therefore \quad 0.631\,944 - \tfrac{1}{5040} \leqslant S \leqslant 0.631\,944 + \tfrac{1}{5040}$

i.e., $\quad 0.6317456 \leqslant S \leqslant 0.6321424$

$\therefore \quad S \doteqdot S_6 = 0.632 \quad \text{(3 d.p.)}$

ABSOLUTE AND CONDITIONAL CONVERGENCE

Given any series $\displaystyle\sum_{n=1}^{\infty} a_n$ we can consider the corresponding series

$$\sum_{n=1}^{\infty} |a_n| = |a_1| + |a_2| + \ldots$$

whose terms are the absolute values of the terms of the original series.

A series $\displaystyle\sum_{n=1}^{\infty} a_n$ is **absolutely convergent** if the series of absolute values $\displaystyle\sum_{n=1}^{\infty} |a_n|$ is convergent.

Clearly if $a_n \geqslant 0$ for all n, absolute convergence is the same as convergence.

A series such as $\displaystyle\sum_{n=1}^{\infty} \frac{(-1)^{n-1}}{n}$ which is convergent but not absolutely convergent, is called **conditionally convergent**.

So what is important about absolute and conditional convergence?

We are all familiar with the concept that $a + b = b + a$. Furthermore, if we have a finite sum $\displaystyle\sum_{n=1}^{N} a_n$, then we can also reorder the terms without affecting the sum. Infinite series which are absolute convergent behave like finite series, so for these we can again reorder the terms of the series without affecting the sum. However, the same is *not* true for conditionally convergent series!

$$\text{For example, let} \quad S = 1 - \tfrac{1}{2} + \tfrac{1}{3} - \tfrac{1}{4} + \tfrac{1}{5} - \tfrac{1}{6} + \ldots \qquad (1)$$

$$\text{Then} \quad \tfrac{1}{2}S = \tfrac{1}{2} - \tfrac{1}{4} + \tfrac{1}{6} - \tfrac{1}{8} + \ldots$$

$$\text{or} \quad \tfrac{1}{2}S = 0 + \tfrac{1}{2} + 0 - \tfrac{1}{4} + 0 + \tfrac{1}{6} + 0 - \tfrac{1}{8} + \ldots \qquad (2)$$

Adding (1) and (2) gives $\quad \tfrac{3}{2}S = 1 + 0 + \tfrac{1}{3} - \tfrac{1}{2} + \tfrac{1}{5} + 0 \ldots$

$$\text{i.e.,} \quad \tfrac{3}{2}S = 1 + \tfrac{1}{3} - \tfrac{1}{2} + \tfrac{1}{5} + \ldots$$

Thus we get a rearrangement of the original series with a different sum! In fact, Riemann showed that by taking groups of sufficiently large numbers of negative or positive terms, it is possible to rearrange a conditionally convergent series so it adds up to any arbitrary real value.

Theorem of Absolute Convergence:

If a series $\displaystyle\sum_{n=1}^{\infty} a_n$ is absolutely convergent then it is convergent.

Proof:

$$\text{By definition of absolute value,} \quad -|a_n| \leqslant a_n \leqslant |a_n|$$

$$\therefore \quad 0 \leqslant a_n + |a_n| \leqslant 2|a_n|$$

Now if $\displaystyle\sum_{n=1}^{\infty} a_n$ is absolutely convergent then $\displaystyle 2\sum_{n=1}^{\infty} |a_n|$ is convergent.

$\therefore$ by the Comparison Test, $\displaystyle\sum_{n=1}^{\infty}(a_n+|a_n|)$ is convergent.

But $\displaystyle\sum_{n=1}^{\infty}a_n = \sum_{n=1}^{\infty}(a_n+|a_n|) - \sum_{n=1}^{\infty}|a_n|$ since the series is absolutely convergent.

$\therefore$ since $\displaystyle\sum_{n=1}^{\infty}(a_n+|a_n|)$ and $\displaystyle\sum_{n=1}^{\infty}|a_n|$ are both convergent, $\displaystyle\sum_{n=1}^{\infty}a_n$ is convergent.

Example 30

Show that $\displaystyle\sum_{n=1}^{\infty}\frac{\cos n}{n^2}$ is convergent.

Now $\displaystyle\sum_{n=1}^{\infty}\frac{\cos n}{n^2} = \frac{\cos 1}{1^2} + \frac{\cos 2}{2^2} + \ldots..$ has terms with different signs, but is not an alternating series.

However, $\left|\dfrac{\cos n}{n^2}\right| \leqslant \dfrac{1}{n^2}$ for all $n \in \mathbb{R}$, and $\displaystyle\sum_{n=1}^{\infty}\frac{1}{n^2}$ is convergent.

$\therefore$ by the Comparison Test, $\displaystyle\sum_{n=1}^{\infty}\left|\frac{\cos n}{n^2}\right|$ is convergent, and by the Theorem

of Absolute Convergence, so is $\displaystyle\sum_{n=1}^{\infty}\frac{\cos n}{n^2}$.

THE RATIO TEST

The **Ratio Test** is very useful for determining whether a general series is absolutely convergent, and hence convergent:

1 If $\displaystyle\lim_{n\to\infty}\left|\frac{a_{n+1}}{a_n}\right| < 1$, then $\displaystyle\sum_{n=1}^{\infty}a_n$ is absolutely convergent.

2 If $\displaystyle\lim_{n\to\infty}\left|\frac{a_{n+1}}{a_n}\right| > 1$, then $\displaystyle\sum_{n=1}^{\infty}a_n$ is divergent.

3 If $\displaystyle\lim_{n\to\infty}\left|\frac{a_{n+1}}{a_n}\right| = 1$, the Ratio Test is inconclusive.

Proof of 1:

Let $u_n = |a_n|$, with $a_n \neq 0$ for all $n \in \mathbb{Z}^+$.

Suppose that $\displaystyle\lim_{n\to\infty}\frac{u_{n+1}}{u_n} = L < 1$, so given $\varepsilon > 0$ there exists a positive integer N

such that $\left|\dfrac{u_{n+1}}{u_n} - L\right| < \varepsilon$ for all $n \geqslant N$.

In particular, as $L < 1$ we can choose r such that $L < r < 1$ and let $\varepsilon = r - L > 0$.

Now $\left| \dfrac{u_{n+1}}{u_n} - L \right| < \varepsilon$

$\therefore$ $\dfrac{u_{n+1}}{u_n} - L < \varepsilon$

$\therefore$ $\dfrac{u_{n+1}}{u_n} < \varepsilon + L$

i.e., $\dfrac{u_{n+1}}{u_n} < r$

$\therefore$ since $n \geqslant N$, $u_{N+1} < r u_N$

$u_{N+2} < r u_{N+1} < r^2 u_N$

$u_{N+3} < r u_{N+2} < r^3 u_N$ etc.

$\therefore$ $u_{N+1} + u_{N+2} + u_{N+3} + \cdots < u_N(r + r^2 + r^3 + \cdots)$

Since $0 < r < 1$, $r + r^2 + r^3 + \ldots\ldots$ is a convergent geometric series.

$\therefore$ by the Comparison Test, $u_{N+1} + u_{N+2} + u_{N+3} + \ldots\ldots$ is also convergent.

$\therefore$ since $u_1 + u_2 + u_3 + \cdots + u_N < \infty$, $\displaystyle\sum_{n=1}^{\infty} u_n = \sum_{n=1}^{\infty} |a_n|$ is convergent.

Example 31

Test $a_n = (-1)^n \dfrac{n^3}{3^n}$ for absolute convergence.

Using the Ratio Test, $\left| \dfrac{a_{n+1}}{a_n} \right| = \left| \dfrac{\dfrac{(n+1)^3}{3^{n+1}}}{\dfrac{n^3}{3^n}} \right|$

$= \dfrac{(n+1)^3}{3^{n+1}} \times \dfrac{3^n}{n^3}$

$= \tfrac{1}{3} \left(\dfrac{n+1}{n} \right)^3$

$= \tfrac{1}{3} \left(1 + \dfrac{1}{n} \right)^3$

Now $\displaystyle\lim_{n \to \infty} \tfrac{1}{3} \left(1 + \dfrac{1}{n} \right)^3 = \tfrac{1}{3} < 1$

$\therefore$ $\displaystyle\sum_{n=1}^{\infty} (-1)^n \dfrac{n^3}{3^n}$ is absolutely convergent.

EXERCISE 10C.2

1   Use telescoping series to find: **a** $\displaystyle\sum_{r=1}^{\infty} \dfrac{1}{r(r+2)}$ **b** $\displaystyle\sum_{r=1}^{\infty} \dfrac{1}{r(r+1)(r+2)}$

2 The Fibonacci sequence is defined by the equations: $f_1 = 1$

$$f_2 = 1$$

$$f_n = f_{n-1} + f_{n-2}, \quad n \geqslant 3$$

Prove: **a** $\dfrac{1}{f_{n-1}f_{n+1}} = \dfrac{1}{f_{n-1}f_n} - \dfrac{1}{f_n f_{n+1}}$ **b** $\displaystyle\sum_{n=2}^{\infty} \dfrac{1}{f_{n-1}f_{n+1}} = 1$

3 Find a simplified form for $\displaystyle\sum_{r=1}^{n} \left(\sqrt{r+1} - \sqrt{r}\right)$.

Hence prove that $\displaystyle\sum_{r=1}^{\infty} \left(\sqrt{r+1} - \sqrt{r}\right)$ diverges.

4 Evaluate $\displaystyle\sum_{n=1}^{\infty} \left[\sin\left(\tfrac{1}{n}\right) - \sin\left(\tfrac{1}{n+1}\right)\right]$.

5 Find the values of x for which the series $\displaystyle\sum_{n=1}^{\infty} \dfrac{1}{(x+n)(x+n-1)}$ converges.

6 Show that $\displaystyle\sum_{n=1}^{\infty} \dfrac{1-n}{n^2}$ and $\displaystyle\sum_{n=1}^{\infty} \dfrac{1}{n} - \sum_{n=1}^{\infty} \dfrac{1-n}{n^2}$ diverge, but

$\displaystyle\sum_{n=1}^{\infty} \dfrac{1}{n} - \sum_{n=1}^{\infty} \dfrac{n-1}{n^2}$ converges.

7 Test these series for convergence or divergence:

a $\dfrac{1}{\ln 2} - \dfrac{1}{\ln 3} + \dfrac{1}{\ln 4} - \dfrac{1}{\ln 5} + \ldots\ldots$ **b** $\displaystyle\sum_{n=1}^{\infty} (-1)^{n-1} \dfrac{\sqrt{n}}{n+4}$

c $\displaystyle\sum_{n=1}^{\infty} (-1)^n \dfrac{n^n}{n!}$ **d** $\displaystyle\sum_{n=1}^{\infty} (-1)^n \sin\left(\tfrac{\pi}{n}\right)$

e $\displaystyle\sum_{n=2}^{\infty} \dfrac{(-1)^{n-1}}{\sqrt[3]{\ln n}}$ **f** $\displaystyle\sum_{n=1}^{\infty} \dfrac{\sin\left(\tfrac{n\pi}{2}\right)}{n!}$

g $\displaystyle\sum_{n=0}^{\infty} \dfrac{(-1)^n}{2^n n!}$ **h** $\displaystyle\sum_{n=1}^{\infty} (-1)^{n+1} \dfrac{n^2}{n^3+1}$

8 Approximate the sum of each series to the indicated level of accuracy:

a $\displaystyle\sum_{n=1}^{\infty} \dfrac{(-1)^{n+1}}{n!}$ (error < 0.01)   **b** $\displaystyle\sum_{n=1}^{\infty} \dfrac{(-1)^{n-1}}{(2n-1)!}$ (4 d.p.)

c $\displaystyle\sum_{n=0}^{\infty} \dfrac{(-1)^n}{2^n n!}$ (4 d.p.)

9　Find the first 10 partial sums of the series $\displaystyle\sum_{n=1}^{\infty} \frac{(-1)^{n-1}}{n^3}$　using the TI-83 or otherwise.

Estimate the error in using the 10th partial sum to approximate the total sum.

10　Work through the following proof of the Alternating Series test:

a　We first consider the even partial sums:

i　Explain why $S_2 = b_1 - b_2 \geqslant 0$.

ii　Show that　$S_4 \geqslant S_2$.　Hence prove that in general　$S_{2n} \geqslant S_{2n-2}$　and
$0 \leqslant S_2 \leqslant S_4 \leqslant \ .... \leqslant S_{2n} \leqslant \ ......$

iii　Show that　$S_{2n} = b_1 - (b_2 - b_3) - (b_4 - b_5) .... (b_{2n-2} - b_{2n}) - b_{2n}$　and
$S_{2n} \leqslant b_1$.

Hence prove that S_{2n} is convergent.　Let　$\displaystyle\lim_{n\to\infty} S_{2n} = S$.

b　Now for the odd partial sums:

i　Show that　$S_{2n+1} = S_{2n} + b_{2n+1}$.

ii　Show that if $\displaystyle\lim_{n\to\infty} b_n = 0$ then $\displaystyle\lim_{n\to\infty} S_{2n+1} = S$ and hence $\displaystyle\lim_{n\to\infty} S_n = S$.

11　Determine whether these series are absolutely convergent, conditionally convergent, or divergent:

a　$\displaystyle\sum_{n=1}^{\infty} \frac{(-3)^n}{n!}$

b　$\displaystyle\sum_{n=1}^{\infty} (-1)^n \frac{2^n}{n^2+1}$

c　$\displaystyle\sum_{n=1}^{\infty} (-1)^n \frac{\arctan n}{n^3}$

d　$\displaystyle\sum_{n=1}^{\infty} \left(\frac{1-3n}{3+4n}\right)^n$

12　**a**　Show that $\displaystyle\sum_{n=0}^{\infty} \frac{x^n}{n!}$　converges for all　$x \in \mathbb{R}$.

b　Deduce that　$\displaystyle\lim_{n\to\infty} \frac{x^n}{n!} = 0$　for all　$x \in \mathbb{R}$.

13　Test these series for convergence or divergence:

a　$\displaystyle\sum_{n=0}^{\infty} \frac{10^n}{n!}$

b　$\displaystyle\sum_{n=1}^{\infty} \frac{1}{\sqrt{n(n+1)}}$

c　$\displaystyle\sum_{n=1}^{\infty} \frac{2n}{8n-5}$

d　$\displaystyle\sum_{n=1}^{\infty} \frac{\cos\left(\frac{n}{2}\right)}{n^2+4n}$

e　$\displaystyle\sum_{n=2}^{\infty} \frac{n^3+1}{n^4-1}$

f　$\displaystyle\sum_{n=0}^{\infty} \frac{n!}{2 \times 5 \times 8 \times \ ...... \times (3n+2)}$

14　Test the series $\displaystyle\sum_{n=1}^{\infty} \frac{1}{n^2}$ and $\displaystyle\sum_{n=1}^{\infty} \frac{1}{n}$ for absolute convergence using the Ratio Test.

POWER SERIES

An important application of the Ratio Test is determining convergence of **Power Series**. These are series of the form

$$\sum_{n=0}^{\infty} c_n x^n = c_0 + c_1 x + c_2 x^2 + \dots \dots$$

or more generally $\sum_{n=0}^{\infty} c_n (x - a)^n = c_0 + c_1 (x - a) + c_2 (x - a)^2 + \dots \dots$

The convergence of a Power Series will usually depend on the value of x.

For example, consider the power series $\sum_{n=0}^{\infty} c_n x^n$ where $c_n = 1$ for all n. This is in fact

the geometric series $1 + x + x^2 + x^3 + x^4 + \dots \dots$,   which converges for all $|x| < 1$.

Example 32

For what values of x is $\displaystyle\sum_{n=1}^{\infty} \frac{(x-3)^n}{n}$ convergent?

Let $a_n = \dfrac{(x-3)^n}{n}$,   so $\left| \dfrac{a_{n+1}}{a_n} \right| = \left| \dfrac{(x-3)^{n+1}}{n+1} \times \dfrac{n}{(x-3)^n} \right|$

$$= \left| \frac{(x-3)\, n}{n+1} \right|$$

$$= \left| \frac{(x-3)}{1 + \frac{1}{n}} \right|$$

$$\therefore \quad \lim_{n \to \infty} \left| \frac{a_{n+1}}{a_n} \right| = |x - 3|$$

By the Ratio Test, $\displaystyle\sum_{n=1}^{\infty} a_n$ is divergent if $|x - 3| > 1$,   but is absolutely

convergent and hence convergent if $|x - 3| < 1$

$$\therefore \quad -1 < x - 3 < 1$$

$$\therefore \quad 2 < x < 4 \qquad \text{i.e.,} \quad x \in\ ]2, 4[$$

For $|x - 3| = 1$,   the Ratio Test is inconclusive, so we consider the $x = 2$
and $x = 4$ cases separately:

For $x = 2$, $\displaystyle\sum_{n=1}^{\infty} a_n = \sum_{n=1}^{\infty} \frac{(-1)^n}{n}$,   which is conditionally convergent by the

Alternating Series Test.

For $x = 4$, $\displaystyle\sum_{n=1}^{\infty} a_n = \sum_{n=1}^{\infty} \frac{1}{n}$ which is the p-series with $p = 1$ and hence is

divergent.

So, $\displaystyle\sum_{n=1}^{\infty} a_n$ converges for $2 \leqslant x < 4$,   i.e., $x \in [2, 4[$.

Theorem:

If a power series $\displaystyle\sum_{n=0}^{\infty} a_n x^n$ is absolutely convergent when $x = b$ $(b \neq 0)$ then it is convergent whenever $0 \leqslant |x| < |b|$.

Proof:

$$|a_n x^n| = \left| \frac{a_n b^n x^n}{b^n} \right|$$

$$= |a_n b^n| \times \left| \left(\frac{x}{b} \right)^n \right|$$

$$< |a_n b^n| \quad \text{since} \quad |x| < |b|$$

But $\displaystyle\sum_{n=0}^{\infty} |a_n b^n|$ is convergent, so by the Comparison Test,

$$\sum_{n=0}^{\infty} |a_n x^n| \quad \text{is also convergent.}$$

$\therefore \displaystyle\sum_{n=0}^{\infty} a_n x^n$ is absolutely convergent.

Theorem:

For a power series $\displaystyle\sum_{n=0}^{\infty} c_n (x - a)^n$, there exist only three possibilities for convergence:

- the series converges only when $x = a$
- the series converges for all $x \in \mathbb{R}$
- there exists $R \in \mathbb{R}^+$ such that the series converges if $|x - a| < R$ and diverges if $|x - a| > R$.

Definition:

A power series has a **radius of convergence** R if R is the greatest number such that the series converges for all $|x - a| < R$ and diverges for all $|x - a| > R$.

The radius of convergence may be determined by the Ratio Test.

If the power series converges for all $x \in \mathbb{R}$ we say that $R = \infty$.

If it diverges, or converges only for the single point $x = a$ we say that $R = 0$.

Definition:

The **interval of convergence** I is the set of all points for which the power series converges.

Most of the interval of convergence may be deduced from the radius of convergence. However, we need to consider convergence for the cases $|x - a| = R$ separately.

Example 33

Find the radius and interval of convergence for $\displaystyle\sum_{n=0}^{\infty} \frac{(-3)^n x^n}{\sqrt{n+1}}$.

Let $\quad a_n = \dfrac{(-3)^n x^n}{\sqrt{n+1}}, \quad$ so $\quad \left| \dfrac{a_{n+1}}{a_n} \right| = \left| \dfrac{(-3)^{n+1} x^{n+1}}{\sqrt{n+2}} \times \dfrac{\sqrt{n+1}}{(-3)^n x^n} \right|$

$$= 3\,|x|\,\sqrt{\frac{n+1}{n+2}}$$

$$= 3\,|x|\,\sqrt{\frac{1+\frac{1}{n}}{1+\frac{2}{n}}}$$

$$\therefore \quad \lim_{n\to\infty} \left| \frac{a_{n+1}}{a_n} \right| = 3\,|x|$$

$\therefore$ by the Ratio Test, $\displaystyle\sum_{n=0}^{\infty} a_n$ converges if $3\,|x| < 1$, i.e., $|x| < \frac{1}{3}$,

and diverges if $3\,|x| > 1$, i.e., $|x| > \frac{1}{3}$.

$\therefore$ the radius of convergence $R = \frac{1}{3}$.

For the interval of convergence, we consider what happens when $x = \pm\frac{1}{3}$.

If $x = -\frac{1}{3}$, $\displaystyle\sum_{n=0}^{\infty} a_n = \sum_{n=0}^{\infty} \frac{(-3)^n \left(-\frac{1}{3}\right)^n}{\sqrt{n+1}} = \sum_{n=0}^{\infty} \frac{1}{\sqrt{n+1}}$

Letting $r = n+1$,

$$\sum_{n=0}^{\infty} a_n = \sum_{r=1}^{\infty} \frac{1}{r^{0.5}} \quad \text{which diverges by the } p\text{-series test.}$$

If $x = \frac{1}{3}$, $\displaystyle\sum_{n=0}^{\infty} a_n = \sum_{n=0}^{\infty} \frac{(-3)^n \left(\frac{1}{3}\right)^n}{\sqrt{n+1}}$

$$= \sum_{n=0}^{\infty} \frac{(-1)^n}{\sqrt{n+1}} \quad \text{which converges by the Alternating Series Test.}$$

So, the interval of convergence of $\displaystyle\sum_{n=0}^{\infty} a_n$ is $\left]-\frac{1}{3}, \frac{1}{3}\right]$.

DIFFERENTIATION AND INTEGRATION OF POWER SERIES

Theorem:

A power series can be differentiated or integrated term by term over any interval lying entirely within its interval of convergence.

If $f(x) = \displaystyle\sum_{n=0}^{\infty} a_n x^n$ then $f'(x) = \displaystyle\sum_{n=1}^{\infty} n\, a_n x^{n-1}$ and $\displaystyle\int f(x)\,dx = \sum_{n=0}^{\infty} \frac{a_n}{n+1}\, x^{n+1}$.

Example 34

Find $\displaystyle\int_0^{0.1} \left(\sum_{n=0}^{\infty} \frac{(-3)^n x^n}{\sqrt{n+1}} \right) dx$

From **Example 33**, the series $\displaystyle\sum_{n=0}^{\infty} \frac{(-3)^n x^n}{\sqrt{n+1}}$ has interval of convergence $\left] -\frac{1}{3}, \frac{1}{3} \right]$.

$\therefore$ since $[0, 0.1]$ lies entirely within the interval of convergence,

$$\int_0^{0.1} \left(\sum_{n=0}^{\infty} \frac{(-3)^n x^n}{\sqrt{n+1}} \right) dx = \sum_{n=0}^{\infty} \left(\int_0^{0.1} \frac{(-3)^n x^n}{\sqrt{n+1}} \, dx \right)$$

$$= \sum_{n=0}^{\infty} \frac{(-3)^n}{\sqrt{n+1}} \left[\frac{x^{n+1}}{n+1} \right]_0^{0.1}$$

$$= \sum_{n=0}^{\infty} \frac{(-3)^n (0.1)^{n+1}}{(n+1)^{\frac{3}{2}}}$$

EXERCISE 10C.3

1 Find the radius and interval of convergence of the following series:

a $\displaystyle\sum_{n=0}^{\infty} \frac{x^n}{n!}$

b $\displaystyle\sum_{n=1}^{\infty} n 5^n x^n$

c $\displaystyle\sum_{n=0}^{\infty} \frac{3^n x^n}{(n+1)^2}$

d $\displaystyle\sum_{n=1}^{\infty} \frac{(-1)^n x^{2n-1}}{(2n-1)!}$

e $\displaystyle\sum_{n=2}^{\infty} (-1)^n \frac{(2x+3)^n}{n \ln n}$

2 Find the radius and interval of convergence of $\displaystyle\sum_{n=1}^{\infty} \frac{2 \times 4 \times 6 \times \dots \times (2n) x^n}{1 \times 3 \times 5 \times \dots \times (2n-1)}$.

3 A function f is defined by $f(x) = 1 + 2x + x^2 + 2x^3 + x^4 + \dots$,   so f is a power series with $c_{2n-1} = 1$ and $c_{2n} = 2$ for all $n \in \mathbb{Z}^+$.
Find the interval of convergence for the series and an explicit formula for $f(x)$.

4 Suppose that the radius of convergence of a power series $\displaystyle\sum_{n=0}^{\infty} c_n x^n$ is R.

What is the radius of convergence of the power series $\displaystyle\sum_{n=0}^{\infty} c_n x^{2n}$?

5 Suppose the series $\displaystyle\sum_{n=0}^{\infty} c_n x^n$ has radius of convergence 2 and $\displaystyle\sum_{n=0}^{\infty} d_n x^n$ has radius of convergence 3.

What can you say about the radius of convergence of the series $\displaystyle\sum_{n=0}^{\infty} (c_n + d_n) x^n$?

6 Show that the power series $\sum\limits_{n=1}^{\infty} \dfrac{x^n}{n^2 3^n}$ and the series of derivatives $\sum\limits_{n=1}^{\infty} \dfrac{n x^{n-1}}{n^2 3^n}$ have the same radius of convergence but not the same interval of convergence.

7 Find $\dfrac{d}{dx}\left(\sum\limits_{n=1}^{\infty} \dfrac{x^n}{n!}\right)$ and $\displaystyle\int_0^x \left(\sum\limits_{n=0}^{\infty} \dfrac{t^n}{n!}\right) dt$. For what x values do these series converge?

D   TAYLOR AND MACLAURIN SERIES

Let $\sum\limits_{n=0}^{\infty} c_n(x-a)^n$ be a power series with radius of convergence $R > 0$. If I is its interval of convergence then, for example, $I = \mathbb{R}$ (when $R = \infty$) or $I = [a - R, a + R]$ (when $R < \infty$).

Now for each $x \in I$, the limit $\sum\limits_{n=0}^{\infty} c_n(x-a)^n$ exists and is finite. The series may therefore define a function with domain I, and we can write $f(x) = \sum\limits_{n=0}^{\infty} c_n(x - a)^n$.

Functions defined in this way may look awkward. However, as we have seen, power series can be added, differentiated, and integrated, just like ordinary polynomials. Furthermore, they are particularly useful because we can express many different functions as power series expansions.

Suppose $f(x) = \sum\limits_{n=0}^{\infty} c_n(x-a)^n = c_0 + c_1(x-a) + c_2(x-a)^2 + \ldots\ldots$ where $|x - a| < R$.

We note that at $x = a$, $f(a) = c_0$.

Since we can differentiate the power series on I we have

$$f'(x) = c_1 + 2c_2(x - a) + 3c_3(x - a)^2 + \ldots\ldots$$

$\therefore$ when $x = a$, $f'(a) = c_1$

Differentiating again, we find $f''(x) = 2c_2 + 6c_3(x - a) + \ldots\ldots$

$\therefore$ when $x = a$, $f''(a) = 2c_2 = 2!\, c_2$

Continuing inductively, we find $f^{(n)}(a) = n!\, c_n$

$$\therefore \quad c_n = \frac{f^{(n)}(a)}{n!} \quad \text{where } 0! = 1 \text{ and } f^{(0)}(x) = f(x)$$

So, if $f(x) = \sum\limits_{n=0}^{\infty} c_n(x - a)^n$, $\quad |x - a| < R$

then $f(x) = f(a) + \dfrac{f'(a)}{1!}(x - a) + \dfrac{f''(a)}{2!}(x - a)^2 + \dfrac{f'''(a)}{3!}(x - a)^3 \ldots\ldots$

This is known as the **Taylor series expansion of $f(x)$ about a.**

The special case where $a = 0$ gives the expansion

$$f(x) = f(0) + xf'(0) + \frac{x^2}{2!}f''(0) + \frac{x^3}{3!}f'''(0) + \ldots\ldots$$

which is called the **Maclaurin series expansion of $f(x)$**.

Important notes about Taylor series expansions:

- A function $f(x)$ will only have a Taylor expansion if its derivatives of all orders exist on I.

- If a function has a power series expansion about a, then it must be in the form of a Taylor series.

Finally, we need to know when the Taylor series expansion is exactly equal to the function $f(x)$. Before we can discuss this, however, we need to consider truncations of the Taylor Series.

Definition:

> The **nth degree Taylor polynomial** approximation to $f(x)$ about a is:
>
> $$T_n(x) = f(a) + f'(a)(x - a) + \ldots\ldots + \frac{f^{(n)}(a)}{n!}(x - a)^n$$
>
> $$= \sum_{k=0}^{n} \frac{(x - a)^k}{k!} f^{(k)}(a)$$

Consider the function $f(x) = e^x$. Then $f^{(n)}(x) = e^x$ exists for all n and $x \in \mathbb{R}$.

The nth degree Taylor approximation to e^x about 0 is:

$$T_n(x) = 1 + \frac{x}{1!} + \frac{x^2}{2!} + \ldots\ldots + \frac{x^n}{n!}$$

Graphs of $f(x) = e^x$, $T_1(x) = 1 + x$,

$T_2(x) = 1 + x + \dfrac{x^2}{2!}$, and

$T_5(x) = 1 + x + \dfrac{x^2}{2!} + \dfrac{x^3}{3!} + \dfrac{x^4}{4!} + \dfrac{x^5}{5!}$

are shown alongside:

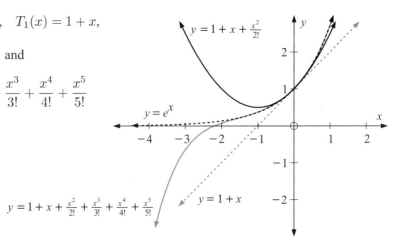

It appears that as n increases, $T_n(x)$ fits $f(x) = e^x$ better for an increasing subset of $I = \mathbb{R}$.

If we denote $R_n(x : a)$ to be the error involved in using $T_n(x)$ to approximate $f(x)$ about $x = a$ on I, then $f(x) = T_n(x) + R_n(x : a)$.

The graphs for the case of $f(x) = e^x$ expanded about $x = 0$ suggest that as n increases, $R_n(x : 0)$ decreases and $T_n(x)$ becomes closer to $f(x)$. This result is formalised in the following theorem:

Taylor's Theorem:

If $f(x)$ has derivatives of all orders on I then:

- $f(x) = T_n(x) + R_n(x)$ for all $x \in I$

- $f(x) = \sum_{n=0}^{\infty} \dfrac{f^{(n)}(a)(x-a)^n}{n!}$ if $\lim_{n \to \infty} R_n(x : a) = 0$

  where $R_n(x : a) = \dfrac{f^{(n+1)}(c)(x-a)^{n+1}}{(n+1)!}$,   where c is a constant, $c \in\ ] a,\, x\ [$,

  or $R_n(x : a) = \dfrac{1}{n!} \displaystyle\int_a^x f^{(n+1)}(t)(x-t)^n\, dt$.

Example 35

Prove that $f(x) = e^x$ is equal to its Maclaurin series expansion for all $x \in \mathbb{R}$.

As $f(x) = e^x$ is infinitely differentiable on $\mathbb{R}$ we have
$$e^x = T_n(x) + R_n(x : 0) \quad \text{for all } x \in \mathbb{R}.$$

We need to prove that $\lim_{n \to \infty} R_n(x : 0) = 0$ for all $x \in \mathbb{R}$

$$\text{where} \quad R_n(x : 0) = \frac{e^c x^{n+1}}{(n+1)!}, \quad \text{for any} \quad c \in\ ] a,\, x\ [$$

Consider $\displaystyle\sum_{n=1}^{\infty} \frac{e^c x^{n+1}}{(n+1)!}$ which has $a_n = \dfrac{e^c x^{n+1}}{(n+1)!}$.

Using the Ratio Test, $\left| \dfrac{a_{n+1}}{a_n} \right| = \left| \dfrac{e^{c+1} x^{n+2}}{(n+2)!} \times \dfrac{(n+1)!}{e^c x^{n+1}} \right|$

$$= e\,|x|\,\frac{1}{n+2}$$

$$\therefore \quad \lim_{n \to \infty} \left| \frac{a_{n+1}}{a_n} \right| = 0$$

and so $\displaystyle\sum_{n=1}^{\infty} \frac{e^c x^{n+1}}{(n+1)!}$ converges for all $x \in \mathbb{R}$.

$$\therefore \quad \lim_{n \to \infty} \frac{e^c x^{n+1}}{(n+1)!} = 0 \quad \text{for all } x \in \mathbb{R}.$$

$$\therefore \quad \lim_{n \to \infty} R_n(x : 0) = 0 \quad \text{for all } x \in \mathbb{R}.$$

$$\therefore \quad \text{by Taylor's Theorem,} \quad e^x = \sum_{n=0}^{\infty} \frac{x^n}{n!} \quad \text{for all } x \in \mathbb{R}.$$

Example 36

Find the Maclaurin series expansion for $f(x) = \cos x$, including its radius of convergence. *Hence* find Maclaurin series expansions for $f(x) = \sin x$ and $f(x) = \cos(2x)$, including their radii of convergence.

$$f(x) = \cos x \qquad \therefore \quad f(0) = 1$$
$$f'(x) = -\sin x \qquad \therefore \quad f'(0) = 0$$
$$f''(x) = -\cos x \qquad \therefore \quad f''(0) = -1$$
$$f'''(x) = \sin x \qquad \therefore \quad f'''(0) = 0$$
$$f^{(4)}(x) = \cos x \qquad \therefore \quad f^{(4)}(0) = 1$$

$\therefore$ by Taylor's Theorem,

$$f(x) = \cos x$$

$$= f(0) + \frac{f'(0)}{1!}x + \frac{f''(0)}{2!}x^2 + \frac{f'''(0)}{3!}x^3 + \ldots\ldots + R_n(x:0)$$

$$= 1 - \frac{x^2}{2!} + \frac{x^4}{4!} - \frac{x^6}{6!} + \ldots\ldots + (-1)^k \frac{x^{2k}}{(2k)!} + R_n(x:0), \quad n \in \mathbb{Z}^+$$

where $R_n(x:0) = \frac{1}{n!}\int_0^x f^{(n+1)}(t)(x-t)^n dt$ and $k = \begin{cases} \frac{n}{2} & \text{if } n \text{ is even} \\ \frac{n-1}{2} & \text{if } n \text{ is odd} \end{cases}$

Since $\left| \int_a^b f(t)\, dt \right| \leqslant \int_a^b |f(t)|\, dt$ for all $f(x)$ defined on $]\,a, b\,[$,

$$|R_n(x:0)| \leqslant \frac{1}{n!}\int_0^x \left| (x-t)^n f^{(n+1)}(t) \right|\, dt$$

$$\therefore \quad |R_n(x:0)| \leqslant \frac{1}{n!}\int_0^x |(x-t)^n|\left| f^{(n+1)}(t) \right|\, dt$$

However, $\left| f^{(n+1)}(t) \right| = |\cos t|$ or $|\sin t|$ for all $n \in \mathbb{Z}^+$

$$\therefore \quad \left| f^{(n+1)}(t) \right| \leqslant 1$$

$$\therefore \quad |R_n(x:0)| \leqslant \frac{1}{n!}\int_0^x |(x-t)^n| \times 1\, dt = \frac{1}{n!}\int_0^x |(x-t)^n|\, dt$$

$$= \frac{1}{n!}\left| \left[-\frac{|x-t|^{n+1}}{n+1} \right]_0^x \right|$$

$$= \frac{|x|^{n+1}}{(n+1)!}$$

Using the Ratio Test, we can show that $\displaystyle\sum_{n=0}^{\infty} \frac{|x|^{n+1}}{(n+1)!}$ converges for all $x \in \mathbb{R}$.

$$\therefore \quad \lim_{n\to\infty} \frac{|x|^{n+1}}{(n+1)!} = 0 \quad \text{for all } x \in \mathbb{R}.$$

$\therefore$ by the Squeeze Theorem, $\displaystyle\lim_{n\to\infty} |R_n(x:0)| = 0$ for all $x \in \mathbb{R}$.

$$\therefore \quad f(x) = \cos x = \sum_{n=0}^{\infty} \frac{(-1)^n\, x^{2n}}{(2n)!}, \quad \text{and the radius of convergence is } \infty.$$

Now the Maclaurin series expansion of $\cos x$ is integrable on $\mathbb{R}$,

$$\therefore \quad \sin t = \int_0^x \cos t \, dt$$

$$= \int_0^x \left(\sum_{n=0}^{\infty} \frac{(-1)^n \, t^{2n}}{(2n)!} \right) dt$$

$$= \sum_{n=0}^{\infty} \left(\int_0^x \frac{(-1)^n \, t^{2n}}{(2n)!} \, dt \right)$$

$$= \left[\sum_{n=0}^{\infty} \frac{(-1)^n \, t^{2n+1}}{(2n+1)!} \right]_0^x$$

$$= \sum_{n=0}^{\infty} \frac{(-1)^n \, x^{2n+1}}{(2n+1)!} \quad \text{for all } x \in \mathbb{R}$$

$$= x - \frac{x^3}{3!} + \frac{x^5}{5!} - \frac{x^7}{7!} + \ldots\ldots \quad \text{for all } x \in \mathbb{R}$$

Also, since $\cos x = \sum_{n=0}^{\infty} \frac{(-1)^n \, x^{2n}}{(2n)!}$,

$$\cos(2x) = \sum_{n=0}^{\infty} \frac{(-1)^n \, (2x)^{2n}}{(2n)!} \quad \text{for all } x \in \mathbb{R}.$$

EXERCISE 10D

1 Find the Maclaurin series expansion for $f(x) = \ln(1+x)$ and its associated interval of convergence. Show that $\lim\limits_{n \to \infty} R_n(x:0) = 0$ for all $x \in I$.

2 Find the Maclaurin series expansion for $f(x) = (1+x)^p$ and the radius of convergence that works for all $p \in \mathbb{R}$.

Hence find the Maclaurin series expansion for $(1+x^2)^{-1}$.

3 Find the Taylor series expansion about $x = 2$ for $f(x) = \ln x$ and its associated radius of convergence.

4 Use substitution to find the Maclaurin series expansions for each of the functions below, along with their associated intervals of convergence:

    a $f(x) = x \sin x$ **b** $f(x) = e^{-x^2}$ **c** $f(x) = \cos(x^3)$

5 What is the maximum error possible in using the approximation $\sin x \doteqdot x - \dfrac{x^3}{3!} + \dfrac{x^5}{5!}$ on the interval $-0.3 \leqslant x \leqslant 0.3$?

6 Use the Maclaurin series for $\sin x$ to compute $\sin 3^o$ correct to 5 d.p.

7 Using the power series expansion of e^{-x^2}, evaluate $\int_0^1 e^{-x^2} \, dx$ to 3 d.p.

8 Using the power series expansion of e^{x^2}, evaluate $\int_0^1 e^{x^2} \, dx$ to 3 d.p.

9 Using the Maclaurin series expansion of $(1 + x^2)^{-1}$, find the Maclaurin series expansion for $\arctan x$.

10 Find the Maclaurin series expansion for $f(x) = 2^x$ and its associated interval of convergence.

11 Using the Maclaurin series expansion for $f(x) = \dfrac{1}{1 + x^3}$, estimate $\displaystyle\int_0^{\frac{1}{3}} \dfrac{1}{1 + x^3}\, dx$ to 4 d.p.

12 Obtain the power series representation of $\ln\left(\dfrac{1 + x}{1 - x}\right)$ and use its first 3 terms to estimate the value of $\ln 2$.

13 Estimate the value of e^{-1} to 6 d.p. using the Alternating Series Estimation Theorem.

14 Prove that $1 + x \leqslant e^x$ for all $x \geqslant 0$. Hence show that if $u_k \geqslant 0$ for all k,

$$\prod_{k=1}^{n} (1 + u_k) = (1 + u_1)(1 + u_2)......(1 + u_n) \leqslant e^{u_1 + u_2 + ... + u_n}$$

Deduce the behaviour of $\displaystyle\prod_{k=1}^{n} (1 + u_k)$ if $\displaystyle\sum_{n=1}^{\infty} u_k$ converges.

15 In this question, use the following steps for Euler's proof of $\displaystyle\sum_{n=1}^{\infty} \dfrac{1}{n^2} = \dfrac{\pi^2}{6}$.

You may assume that $\sin x = x - \dfrac{x^3}{3!} + \dfrac{x^5}{5!} - \dfrac{x^7}{7!} + ...$ for all $x \in \mathbb{R}$.

a Find *all* the zeros of $\sin x$ and of $\dfrac{\sin x}{x}$ for $x \in \mathbb{R}$.

b Find the power series expansion for $\dfrac{\sin x}{x}$ and its interval of convergence.

c Find all the zeros of $\left(1 - \dfrac{x}{\pi}\right)\left(1 + \dfrac{x}{\pi}\right)\left(1 - \dfrac{x}{2\pi}\right)\left(1 + \dfrac{x}{2\pi}\right)......$

d Show that:

$$\left(1 - \tfrac{x}{\pi}\right)\left(1 + \tfrac{x}{\pi}\right)\left(1 - \tfrac{x}{2\pi}\right)\left(1 + \tfrac{x}{2\pi}\right)..... = \left(1 - \tfrac{x^2}{\pi^2}\right)\left(1 - \tfrac{x^2}{4\pi^2}\right)\left(1 - \tfrac{x^2}{9\pi^2}\right).....$$

and comment on Euler's claim that

$$1 - \dfrac{x^2}{3!} + \dfrac{x^4}{5!} - \dfrac{x^6}{7!} + ... = \left(1 - \tfrac{x^2}{\pi^2}\right)\left(1 - \tfrac{x^2}{4\pi^2}\right)\left(1 - \tfrac{x^2}{9\pi^2}\right).....$$

e By equating the coefficients of x^2 in this last equation, prove that:

$$\sum_{n=1}^{\infty} \dfrac{1}{n^2} = \dfrac{1}{1^2} + \dfrac{1}{2^2} + \dfrac{1}{3^2} + \dfrac{1}{4^2} + ... = \dfrac{\pi^2}{6}.$$

f As $\displaystyle\sum_{n=1}^{\infty} \dfrac{1}{n^2}$ is absolutely convergent, we can write

$$\sum_{n=1}^{\infty} \frac{1}{n^2} = \underbrace{\sum_{r=1}^{\infty} \frac{1}{(2r)^2}}_{\text{even } n} + \underbrace{\sum_{r=1}^{\infty} \frac{1}{(2r-1)^2}}_{\text{odd } n}$$

Use this last equation to find the exact values of $\displaystyle\sum_{n=1}^{\infty} \frac{1}{(2n)^2}$ and $\displaystyle\sum_{n=1}^{\infty} \frac{1}{(2n-1)^2}$

Note: Euler was able to derive a way to sum **all** series of the form $\displaystyle\sum_{n=1}^{\infty} \frac{1}{n^{2k}}, \ k \in \mathbb{Z}^+$.

However, the exact value of $\displaystyle\sum_{n=1}^{\infty} \frac{1}{n^{2k+1}}$, for **any** $k \in \mathbb{Z}^+$ is still an open question.

E FIRST ORDER DIFFERENTIAL EQUATIONS

A **differential equation** is an equation which connects the derivative(s) of an unknown function to the variables in which the function is defined which may include the function itself.

Examples of differential equations are:

$$\frac{dy}{dx} = \frac{x^2}{y} \qquad\qquad \frac{dy}{dx} = -0.075y^3 \qquad\qquad \frac{d^2y}{dx^2} - 3\frac{dy}{dx} + 4y = 0$$

Such equations not only arise in pure mathematics, but are also used to model and solve problems in physics, engineering and the other sciences.

For example:

| **A falling object** | **A parachutist** | **Object on a spring** |

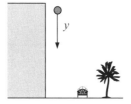  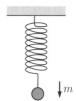

$$\frac{d^2y}{dx^2} = 9.8 \qquad\qquad m\frac{dv}{dt} = mg - av^2 \qquad\qquad m\frac{d^2y}{dt^2} = -ky$$

| **Current in an RL Circuit** | **Water from a tank** | **Dog pursuing cat** |

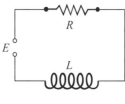 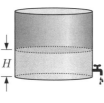 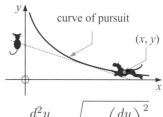

$$L\frac{dI}{dt} + RI = E \qquad\qquad \frac{dH}{dt} = -a\sqrt{H} \qquad\qquad x\frac{d^2y}{dx^2} = \sqrt{1 + \left(\frac{dy}{dx}\right)^2}$$

However, in this course we will only deal with differential equations of the form

$$f(x, y)\,\frac{dy}{dx} + g(x, y) = 0$$

These are known as **first order** differential equations since there is only one derivative in the equation, and it is a first derivative.

A function $y(x)$ is said to be a solution of a differential equation if it satisfies the differential equation for all values of x in the domain.

Example 37

Show that $y = ce^{3x} - 1$ is a solution of $\dfrac{dy}{dx} - 3y = 3$ for any constant c. Sketch the solution curves for $c = \pm 1, \pm 2, \pm 3$.

If $y = ce^{3x} - 1$

then $\dfrac{dy}{dx} = 3ce^{3x}$

$\therefore \dfrac{dy}{dx} - 3y = 3ce^{3x} - 3\left(ce^{3x} - 1\right)$

$= 3ce^{3x} - 3ce^{3x} + 3$

$= 3$, so the differential equation is satisfied for all x.

The solution curves for $c = \pm 1, \pm 2, \pm 3$ are shown below:

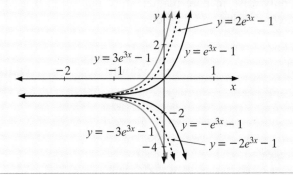

In the example, $y = ce^{3x} - 1$ is a called a **general solution** of the differential equation, since it involves the unknown constant c.

If we are given **initial conditions** for the problem, i.e., a value of y or $\dfrac{dy}{dx}$ for a specific value of x, then we can evaluate c. This gives us a **particular solution** to the problem.

So, the solution curves for $c = \pm 1, \pm 2, \pm 3$ graphed in **Example 37** are all particular solutions of $\dfrac{dy}{dx} - 3y = 3$. However, the initial conditions of the problem determine which solution curve is the correct one.

Example 38

Find a particular solution to $\dfrac{dy}{dx} - 3y = 3$ given $y = 2$ when $x = 0$.

From **Example 37**, we know that $y = ce^{3x} - 1$ is a general solution to the differential equation.

Now if $y = 2$ when $x = 0$, then $2 = ce^{3 \times 0} - 1$

$$\therefore \quad c = 3$$

$\therefore$ the particular solution is $y = 3e^{3x} - 1$

SLOPE FIELDS

If we have a first order differential equation of the form

$$f(x, y) \frac{dy}{dx} + g(x, y) = 0,$$

$$\text{then} \quad \frac{dy}{dx} = -\frac{g(x, y)}{f(x, y)}$$

$$\text{i.e.,} \quad \frac{dy}{dx} = h(x, y)$$

We may therefore deduce the slope of the solution curves to the differential equation at any point (x, y), and hence the equations of the tangents to the solution curves.

The set of tangents at all points (x, y) is called the **slope field** of the differential equation.

For example, the table below shows the values of $\dfrac{dy}{dx} = x(y - 1)$ for the integer grid points $x, y \in [-2, 2]$.

		x				
		-2	-1	0	1	2
	-2	6	3	0	-3	-6
	-1	4	2	0	-2	-4
y	0	2	1	0	-1	-2
	1	0	0	0	0	0
	2	-2	-1	0	1	2

By representing these gradients as line segments at the different (x, y) grid points, we obtain a **slope field** of the tangents to the solution curves as shown:

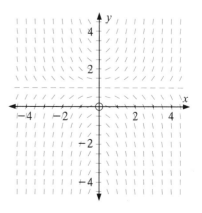

GRAPHING PACKAGE

Now the tangent to a curve approximates that curve at and near the points of tangency. Therefore, by adding more grid points or linking line segments, the slope field can be used to graphically obtain approximate solution curves of the differential equation:

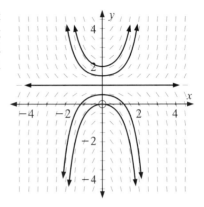

The horizontal line in the figure is the solution curve corresponding to the initial conditions $y = 1$ when $x = 0$. Although it is quite straightforward to obtain a few slope field points by hand, a larger or more refined field is best obtained using technology. You can click on the icon on your CD to run software for plotting slope fields. Alternatively, if may be possible to download software for your graphics calculator.

Note that the display of some slope field packages may be unclear at points where $\dfrac{dy}{dx}$ is either zero or undefined.

For example, for $\quad \dfrac{dy}{dx} = \dfrac{1 - x^2 - y^2}{y - x + 2},$

- $\dfrac{dy}{dx}$ is discontinuous when $\quad y - x + 2 = 0$, i.e., $\quad y = x - 2$. We show this as a distinctive line in the slope field below.

- $\dfrac{dy}{dx}$ is zero when $\quad 1 - x^2 - y^2 = 0$,

  i.e., $\quad x^2 + y^2 = 1$. We show this as a distinctive circle in the slope field alongside.

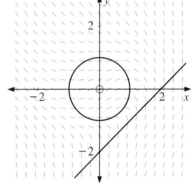

EULER'S METHOD OF NUMERICAL INTEGRATION

Euler's Method uses the same principle as slope fields to find a numerical approximation to the solution of the differential equation $\quad \dfrac{dy}{dx} = f(x, y).$

Since the slope $\dfrac{dy}{dx}$ indicates the direction in which the solution curve goes at any point, we reconstruct the graph of the solution as follows:

We start at a point (x_0, y_0) and move a small distance in the direction of the slope field to find a new point (x_1, y_1). We then move a small distance in the direction of the slope field at this new point, and so on.

If we step h units to the right each time, then

$$x_1 = x_0 + h \quad \text{and} \quad y_1 = y_0 + h\,f(x_0,\,y_0)$$

and more generally,

$$x_{n+1} = x_n + h \quad \text{and} \quad y_{n+1} = y_n + h\,f(x_n,\,y_n).$$

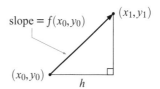

Clearly, Euler's Method only gives an approximate solution to an initial-value problem. However, by decreasing the step size h and hence increasing the number of course corrections, we can usually improve the accuracy of the approximation.

Example 39

For the initial value problem $\dfrac{dy}{dx} = x + y, \quad y(0) = 1,$ use Euler's Method with step size of 0.2 to find an approximate value for $y(1)$.

Now $x_{n+1} = x_n + h \quad$ and $\ y_{n+1} = y_n + h\,f(x_n,\,y_n)$

$\therefore$ given $f(x,\,y) = \dfrac{dy}{dx} = x + y$ and step size $h = 0.2,$

$$x_{n+1} = x_n + 0.2 \quad \text{and} \quad y_{n+1} = y_n + 0.2(x_n + y_n)$$

Using the initial conditions,

$x_0 = 0$	$y_0 = 1$
$x_1 = 0 + 0.2 = 0.2$	$y_1 = 1 + 0.2(0 + 1) = 1.2$
$x_2 = 0.2 + 0.2 = 0.4$	$y_2 = 1.2 + 0.2(0.2 + 1.2) = 1.48$
$x_3 = 0.4 + 0.2 = 0.6$	$y_3 = 1.48 + 0.2(0.4 + 1.48) = 1.856$
$x_4 = 0.6 + 0.2 = 0.8$	$y_4 = 1.856 + 0.2(0.6 + 1.856) = 2.3472$
$x_5 = 0.8 + 0.2 = 1$	$y_5 = 2.3472 + 0.2(0.8 + 2.3472) = 2.9766$

So, $y(1) \doteqdot 2.98$ to 2 d.p.

EXERCISE 10E.1

1 Consider the differential equation $\dfrac{dy}{dx} = 10y\tan x.$ Draw the slope field using integer grid points for x and y between ± 2. Assume x is measured in degrees.

2 Slope fields for two differential equations are plotted below for $x,\ y \in [-3,\ 3]$.
Use the slope fields to graph the solution curves satisfying $y(1) = 1$.

a
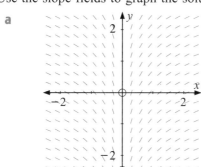

b
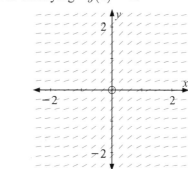

3 Sketch the slope field for the differential equation $\dfrac{dy}{dx} = x^2 + y - 1$.

Hence sketch the solution curve satisfying $y(0) = 1$.

4 Sketch the slope field for the differential equation $\dfrac{dy}{dx} = \dfrac{-1 + x^2 + 4y^2}{y - 5x + 10}$, indicating

points of discontinuity and equilibrium, i.e., where $\dfrac{dy}{dx}$ is undefined or zero.

5 Use Euler's Method with step size 0.2 to estimate $y(1)$ for the initial value problem
$\dfrac{dy}{dx} = 1 + 2x - 3y$, $y(0) = 1$.

6 Use Euler's Method with step size 0.1 to estimate $y(0.5)$ for the initial value problem
$\dfrac{dy}{dx} = \sin(x + y)$, $y(0) = 0.5$. Assume x and y are in radians.

SEPARABLE DIFFERENTIAL EQUATIONS

Differential equations which can be written in the form $\dfrac{dy}{dx} = \dfrac{f(x)}{g(y)}$ are known as **separable differential equations**.

Notice that if $\dfrac{dy}{dx} = \dfrac{f(x)}{g(y)}$ then $g(y)\dfrac{dy}{dx} = f(x)$.

If we integrate both sides of this equation with respect to x we get

$$\int g(y)\frac{dy}{dx}\,dx = \int f(x)\,dx$$

But using the Chain Rule, $\dfrac{dy}{dx}\,dx$ is just dy.

$$\therefore \quad \int g(y)\,dy = \int f(x)\,dx$$

and the problem of solving the differential equations then reduces to the problem of finding two integrals.

Example 40

Solve the initial value problem $\quad 2x\dfrac{dy}{dx} - 1 = y^2$, $\quad y(1) = 1$.

$$2x\frac{dy}{dx} - 1 = y^2$$

$$\therefore \quad 2x\frac{dy}{dx} = y^2 + 1$$

$$\therefore \quad \frac{1}{y^2 + 1}\frac{dy}{dx} = \frac{1}{2x}$$

Integrating both sides with respect to x gives

$$\int \frac{1}{y^2 + 1} \frac{dy}{dx} \, dx = \int \frac{1}{2x} \, dx$$

$$\therefore \quad \int \frac{1}{y^2 + 1} \, dy = \int \frac{1}{2x} \, dx$$

$$\therefore \quad \tan^{-1} y = \tfrac{1}{2} \ln |x| + c$$

$$\therefore \quad y = \tan \left(\tfrac{1}{2} \ln |x| + c \right)$$

But $y(1) = 1$, so $1 = \tan \left(\tfrac{1}{2} \ln 1 + c \right)$

i.e., $1 = \tan c$

$$\therefore \quad c = \tfrac{\pi}{4}$$

$\therefore$ the particular solution of the differential equation is $y = \tan \left(\ln \sqrt{x} + \tfrac{\pi}{4} \right)$.

Example 41

Find the general solution of the differential equation $\dfrac{dy}{dx} = \dfrac{x^2 y + y}{x^2 - 1}$.

$$\frac{dy}{dx} = \frac{x^2 y + y}{x^2 - 1}$$

$$= \frac{y(x^2 + 1)}{x^2 - 1}$$

$$\therefore \quad \frac{1}{y} \frac{dy}{dx} = \frac{x^2 + 1}{x^2 - 1}$$

$$= \frac{x^2 - 1 + 2}{x^2 - 1}$$

$$= 1 + \frac{2}{x^2 - 1}$$

Using partial fractions, suppose

$$\frac{2}{x^2 - 1} \equiv \frac{A}{x - 1} + \frac{B}{x + 1}$$

$$\equiv \frac{A(x + 1) + B(x - 1)}{x^2 - 1}$$

$$\therefore \quad 2 \equiv (A + B) x + (A - B)$$

Equating coefficients,

$$A + B = 0 \quad \text{and} \quad A - B = 2$$

Solving simultaneously,

$$A = 1 \quad \text{and} \quad B = -1$$

So, $\dfrac{1}{y} \dfrac{dy}{dx} = 1 + \dfrac{1}{x - 1} - \dfrac{1}{x + 1}$

Integrating both sides with respect to x gives

$$\int \frac{1}{y} \frac{dy}{dx} \, dx = \int \left(1 + \frac{1}{x - 1} - \frac{1}{x + 1} \right) dx$$

$$\therefore \quad \int \frac{1}{y} \, dy = x + \ln |x - 1| - \ln |x + 1| + c$$

$$\ln |y| = x + \ln \left(A \left| \frac{x - 1}{x + 1} \right| \right) \quad \text{where} \quad \ln A = c$$

$$\therefore \quad y = A e^x \left(\frac{x - 1}{x + 1} \right) \quad \text{is the general solution of the differential equation.}$$

The following examples show how separable variable differential equations can be constructed:

Example 42

When an object travels through a resistive medium, the rate at which it loses speed at any given instant is given by kv ms^{-2}, where v is the speed of the body at that instant and k is a positive constant.

If the initial speed is u ms^{-1}, show by formulating and solving an appropriate differential equation that the time taken for the body to decrease its speed to $\frac{1}{2}u$ ms^{-1} is $\frac{1}{k}\ln 2$ seconds.

The rate of change of speed is given by $\dfrac{dv}{dt}$.

Our differential equation must reflect that the body *loses* speed, and is therefore given by: $\dfrac{dv}{dt} = -kv$.

Separating the variables, the equation becomes:

$$\frac{1}{v}\frac{dv}{dt} = -k$$

Integrating both sides with respect to t gives

$$\int \frac{1}{v}\, dv = -k \int dt$$
$$\therefore \quad \ln|v| = -kt + c$$
$$\therefore \quad v = Ae^{-kt}$$

This is the general solution of the differential equation, so we can now make use of the extra information given to find the value of the constant A.

Since the initial speed (at $t = 0$) is u, $v = u = Ae^{-k \times 0} = A$.

So $v = ue^{-kt}$ is the particular solution of the differential equation.

When $v = \frac{1}{2}u$ we have $\frac{1}{2}u = ue^{-kt}$

$$\therefore \quad \tfrac{1}{2} = e^{-kt}$$
$$\therefore \quad -\ln 2 = -kt$$
$$\therefore \quad t = \frac{1}{k}\ln 2 \quad \text{as required.}$$

Example 43

The tangent at any point P on a curve in the first quadrant cuts the x-axis at Q. Given that OP = PQ, where O is the origin, and that the point $(1, 4)$ lies on the curve, find the equation of the curve.

We start by sketching a general curve in the first quadrant and include the information we know. P is the general point on the curve with coordinates (x, y).

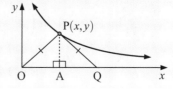

As OP $=$ OQ, triangle OPQ is isosceles.
Hence PA is the perpendicular bisector of OQ.

The coordinates of OA are $(x,\,0)$, so the
coordinates of OQ are $(2x,\,0)$.

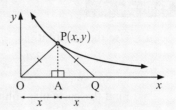

As PQ is a tangent to the curve at P, the gradient
of the curve at P is the same as the gradient of PQ.

Hence $\quad \dfrac{dy}{dx} = -\dfrac{y}{x}$

$\therefore \quad \dfrac{1}{y}\dfrac{dy}{dx} = -\dfrac{1}{x}$

Integrating both sides with respect to x gives

$$\int \frac{1}{y}\, dy = -\int \frac{1}{x}\, dx$$

$\therefore \quad \ln|y| = -\ln|x| + c$

$\therefore \quad \ln|x| + \ln|y| = c$

$\therefore \quad \ln|xy| = c$

$\therefore \quad xy = e^{c} = k \quad$ where k is a constant.

Since the curve passes through $(1,\,4)$, $\quad 1 \times 4 = k$

$\therefore \quad$ the equation of the curve is $xy = 4 \quad$ or $\quad y = \dfrac{4}{x}$, where $x > 0$.

HOMOGENEOUS DIFFERENTIAL EQUATIONS

Differential equations of the form $\dfrac{dy}{dx} = f\left(\dfrac{y}{x}\right)$ are known as **homogeneous differential equations**.

They can be solved using the substitution $y = vx$ where v is a function of x. The substitution will always reduce the differential equation to a separable form as follows:

If $y = vx$ where v is a function of x, then

$$\frac{dy}{dx} = \frac{dv}{dx}\,x + v \quad \{\text{product rule}\}$$

$\therefore \quad \dfrac{dv}{dx}\,x + v = f\left(\dfrac{vx}{x}\right) = f\left(v\right)$

$\therefore \quad \dfrac{dv}{dx} = \dfrac{f(v) - v}{x}$

$\therefore \quad \dfrac{dv}{dx} = \dfrac{\dfrac{1}{x}}{\dfrac{1}{f(v) - v}} \qquad$ which is of separable form.

Example 44

a Use the substitution $y = vx$, where v is a function of x, to solve:
$$\frac{dy}{dx} = \frac{x + 2y}{x}$$

b Find the particular solution if $y = \frac{3}{2}$ when $x = 3$.

a Now if $y = vx$, using the product rule we get $\frac{dy}{dx} = v + x\frac{dv}{dx}$.

Comparing with the differential equation, we find
$$v + x\frac{dv}{dx} = \frac{x + 2vx}{x}$$
$$\therefore \quad v + x\frac{dv}{dx} = 1 + 2v$$
$$\therefore \quad x\frac{dv}{dx} = 1 + v$$
$$\therefore \quad \frac{dv}{dx} = \frac{1 + v}{x}$$

Separating the variables and integrating, we find
$$\int \frac{1}{v + 1}\,dv = \int \frac{1}{x}\,dx$$
$$\therefore \quad \ln|v + 1| = \ln|x| + c$$
$$\therefore \quad \ln|v + 1| = \ln|Ax| \quad \text{where} \quad \ln|A| = c$$
$$\therefore \quad v + 1 = Ax$$

But $v = \frac{y}{x}$, so $\frac{y}{x} + 1 = Ax$
$$\therefore \quad y = Ax^2 - x$$

b Substituting $y = \frac{3}{2}$ and $x = 3$ into the general solution, we find
$$\frac{3}{2} = A \times 3^2 - 3$$
$$\therefore \quad 9A = \frac{9}{2}$$
$$\therefore \quad A = \frac{1}{2}$$
$$\therefore \quad \text{the particular solution is} \quad y = \frac{1}{2}x^2 - x.$$

THE INTEGRATING FACTOR METHOD

Suppose a first order linear differential equation is of the form $\frac{dy}{dx} + P(x)y = Q(x)$.

Generally this type of equation is not separable.

However, suppose there is a function $I(x)$, called an **integrating factor**, such that

$$\frac{d}{dx}\left(I(x)y\right) = I(x)\frac{dy}{dx} + I(x)\,P(x)\,y \quad \ldots\ldots (*)$$

$$= I(x)\,Q(x)$$

Then integrating both sides with respect to x would give

$$I(x)\,y = \int I(x)\,Q(x)\,dx$$

i.e., $y = \dfrac{1}{I(x)} \int I(x)\,Q(x)\,dx$ and we could hence find a solution for y.

Now if such an integrating factor exists, then from $(*)$,

$$I(x)\frac{dy}{dx} + I'(x)\,y = I(x)\frac{dy}{dx} + I(x)\,P(x)\,y$$

$$\therefore \quad I'(x) = I(x)\,P(x)$$

$$\therefore \quad \frac{I'(x)}{I(x)} = P(x)$$

Integrating both sides with respect to x,

$$\int \frac{I'(x)}{I(x)}\,dx = \int P(x)\,dx$$

$$\ln|I| + c = \int P(x)\,dx$$

i.e., $I(x) = Ae^{\int P(x)\,dx}$ where $A = e^{-c}$ and is conventionally set as 1.

Thus the **integrating factor** is $I(x) = e^{\int P(x)\,dx}$.

Note that when we calculate the integration factor, we do not need a constant of integration. This is because it becomes part of the constant A in front, which we can choose to be 1.

Example 45

Solve the differential equation $\dfrac{dy}{dx} + 3x^2 y = 6x^2$.

The integrating factor is $I(x) = e^{\int 3x^2\,dx} = e^{x^3}$

Multiplying the differential equation through by e^{x^3} gives

$$e^{x^3}\frac{dy}{dx} + 3x^2 e^{x^3}\,y = 6x^2 e^{x^3}$$

$$\therefore \quad \frac{d}{dx}\left(ye^{x^3}\right) = 6x^2 e^{x^3}$$

$$\therefore \quad ye^{x^3} = \int 6x^2 e^{x^3}\,dx$$

$$\therefore \quad ye^{x^3} = 2e^{x^3} + c$$

$$\therefore \quad y = 2 + ce^{-x^3}$$

Example 46

Solve the initial value problem $\cos x \dfrac{dy}{dx} = y \sin x + \sin(2x)$, $y(0) = 1$.

We can rewrite the differential equation as $\dfrac{dy}{dx} - \dfrac{y \sin x}{\cos x} = \dfrac{\sin(2x)}{\cos x}$

$$\therefore \quad \frac{dy}{dx} + (-\tan x)\, y = 2 \sin x$$

The differential equation is not separable, but is of a form such that we can use an integrating factor.

The integrating factor is $I(x) = e^{\int -\tan x \, dx}$

$$= e^{\ln(\cos x)} = \cos x.$$

Multiplying the equation through by the integrating factor gives

$$\cos x \, \frac{dy}{dx} + (-\cos x \tan x)\, y = 2 \sin x \cos x$$

$$\therefore \quad \frac{d}{dx}(y \cos x) = \sin(2x)$$

$$\therefore \quad y \cos x = \int \sin(2x)\, dx$$

$$= -\tfrac{1}{2} \cos(2x) + c$$

But when $x = 0, \; y = 1$

$$\therefore \quad 1 = -\tfrac{1}{2} \cos 0 + c \quad \text{and so} \quad c = \tfrac{3}{2}$$

$\therefore \quad$ the solution of the initial value problem is $y \cos x = \tfrac{3}{2} - \tfrac{1}{2}\cos(2x)$

$$\text{i.e.,} \quad y = \frac{3 - \cos(2x)}{2 \cos x}$$

EXERCISE 10E.2

1 Solve the following initial value problems:

a $(2 - x)\, \dfrac{dy}{dx} = 1$, $y(4) = 3$

b $\dfrac{dy}{dx} - 3x \sec y = 0$, $y(1) = 0$

c $e^y (2x^2 + 4x + 1)\, \dfrac{dy}{dx} = (x + 1)(e^y + 3)$, $y(0) = 2$

d $\dfrac{dy}{dx} = \dfrac{x^2 y + y}{x^2 - 1}$, $y(0) = 3$ **e** $x\, \dfrac{dy}{dx} = \cos^2 y$, $y(e) = \tfrac{\pi}{4}$

2 According to Newton's law of cooling, the rate at which a body loses temperature at time t is proportional to the amount by which the temperature $T(t)$ of the body at that instant exceeds the temperature R of its surroundings.

   a Express this information as a differential equation in terms of t, T and R.

   b If a container of hot liquid is placed in a room of temperature $18^{\circ}C$ and cools from $82^{\circ}C$ to $50^{\circ}C$ in 6 minutes, show that it takes 12 minutes for the liquid to cool from $26^{\circ}C$ to $20^{\circ}C$.

3 The tangent at any point P on a curve cuts the x-axis at the point Q.
Given that $\angle OPQ = 90^\circ$,   where O is the origin, and that the point $(1, 2)$ lies on the curve, find the equation of the curve.

4 The tangent at any point P on a curve cuts the x-axis at A and the y-axis at B.
Given that $AP : PB = 2 : 1$ and that the curve passes through $(1, 1)$, find the equation of the curve.

5 A radioactive substance decays so that the rate of decrease of mass at any time t is proportional to the mass $m(t)$ present at that time.

    a If the initial mass present is m_0, set up and solve the appropriate differential equation and hence obtain a formula for $m(t)$.

    b If the mass is reduced to $\frac{4}{5}$ of its original value in 30 days, calculate the time required for the mass to be reduced to half its original value.

6 Solve the homogeneous differential equations below using the substitution $y = vx$, where v is a function of x.

    a $\dfrac{dy}{dx} = \dfrac{x - y}{x}$
    b $\dfrac{dy}{dx} = \dfrac{x + y}{x - y}$
    c $\dfrac{dy}{dx} = \dfrac{y^2 - x^2}{2xy}$

7   **a** Show that the substitution $y = vx$ (where v is a function of x) will reduce all inhomogeneous differential equations of the form $\dfrac{dy}{dx} = \dfrac{y}{x} + f\left(\dfrac{y}{x}\right) g(x)$ to separable form.

    b Solve $x\dfrac{dy}{dx} = y + e^{\frac{y}{x}}$ using this method.

8 Solve the differential equations below using the integrating factor method.

    a $\dfrac{dy}{dx} + 4y = 12$
    b $\dfrac{dy}{dx} - 3y = e^x, \quad y(1) = 2$

    c $\dfrac{dy}{dx} + y = x + e^x, \quad y(1) = 1$
    d $x\dfrac{dy}{dx} + y = x \cos x$

9 Solve the differential equation $(x + 1)y + x\dfrac{dy}{dx} = x - x^2$.

10 Laplace transforms provide a useful link between improper integrals and differential equations.

The Laplace transform of a function $f(x)$ is defined as

$$F(s) = \mathcal{L}\{f(x)\} = \int_0^\infty e^{-sx} f(x)\, dx$$

    a Show that:

      i $\mathcal{L}\{e^{ax}\} = \dfrac{1}{s - a}, \quad s > a$
      ii $\mathcal{L}\{x\} = \dfrac{1}{s^2}, \quad s > 0$

      iii $\mathcal{L}\{\sin ax\} = \dfrac{a}{s^2 + a^2}, \quad s > 0$

    b Show that   **i** $\mathcal{L}\{f'(x)\} = s\mathcal{L}\{f(x)\} - f(0)$

                ii $\mathcal{L}\{f''(x)\} = s^2\mathcal{L}\{f(x)\} - s\,f(0) - f'(0)$

c Consider the differential equation $f''(x) + f(x) = x$, $f(0) = 0$, $f'(0) = 2$.

Assuming that $\mathcal{L}\{g(x) + h(x)\} = \mathcal{L}\{g(x)\} + \mathcal{L}\{h(x)\}$,   show that

$$\mathcal{L}\{f(x)\} = \frac{1}{s^2} + \frac{1}{s^2 + 1}.$$

Hence find a possible solution function $f(x)$ and check your answer.

REVIEW SETS

REVIEW SET 10A

1 Prove that $\lim\limits_{x \to \infty} \dfrac{\ln x}{x} = 0$.

2 Find $\lim\limits_{x \to 0} \dfrac{e^x \sin x}{x}$.

3 Find the limits, if they exist, of the sequence $\{u_n\}$ as n tends to infinity if u_n equals:

a $\dfrac{8 - 2n - 2n^2}{4 + 6n + 7n^2}$	**b** $\dfrac{(-1)^n (2n - 1)}{n}$	**c** $\dfrac{0.9^n}{1 + 0.1^n}$
d $3 + \frac{1}{n} + n[1 + (-1)^n]$	**e** $\sqrt{n + 5} - \sqrt{n - 1}$	**f** $\dfrac{n^2}{3n + 1} - \dfrac{2n^3}{6n^2 + 1}$
g $\dfrac{2n + 13}{\sqrt{6n^2 + 5n - 7}}$	**h** $n - \sqrt{n^2 + n}$	**i** $(3^n + 2^n)^{\frac{1}{n}}$
j $\arctan n$	**k** $\dfrac{e^n}{n!}$	**l** $(-1)^n n e^{-n}$
m $\dfrac{3 \times 5 \times 7 \times \dots \times (2n + 1)}{2 \times 5 \times 8 \times \dots \times (3n - 1)}$		**n** $n\left(2\cos\left(\frac{1}{n}\right) - \sin\left(\frac{1}{n}\right) - 2\right)$

REVIEW SET 10B

1 Prove that the series $\dfrac{1}{1^3 + 1} + \dfrac{2}{2^3 + 1} + \dfrac{3}{3^3 + 1} + \dfrac{4}{4^3 + 1} + \dfrac{5}{5^3 + 1} + \dots\dots$ converges.

2 Prove that the series $x + \dfrac{x^2}{2} + \dfrac{x^3}{3} + \dfrac{x^4}{4} + \dots\dots$ is convergent for $-1 < x < 1$ and divergent for $|x| > 1$.

Determine the convergence or divergence of the series for $x = \pm 1$.

3 Explain why the series $\sum\limits_{r=1}^{\infty} 3^{\frac{1}{r}}$ is not convergent.

4 Express $\dfrac{2}{r(r + 1)(r + 2)}$ in partial fractions.

Use your result to show that $\sum\limits_{r=1}^{n} \dfrac{1}{r(r + 1)(r + 2)} = \frac{1}{4} - \dfrac{1}{2(n + 1)(n + 2)}$.

Hence show that the series $u_1 + u_2 + u_3 + u_4 + \dots\dots$ where $u_r = \dfrac{1}{r(r + 1)(r + 2)}$ converges and find its sum to infinity.

5 Prove that the series $\displaystyle\sum_{n=2}^{\infty} \frac{1}{n\,(\ln n)^2}$ is convergent.

6 Determine the interval and radius of convergence of the series $\displaystyle\sum_{n=1}^{\infty} \frac{(x-3)^n}{n^{\frac{3}{2}}}$.

7 Test the series $\displaystyle\sum_{n=1}^{\infty} \sin\left(\frac{1}{n}\right)$ for convergence.

8 Determine whether or not the series $\displaystyle\sum_{k=1}^{\infty} \sin\left(\frac{(k-1)\pi}{2k}\right)$ is convergent.

9 Use the Comparison Test to prove that the series $\displaystyle\sum_{r=1}^{\infty} \frac{1+r}{1+r^2}$ diverges.

10 Determine whether $\displaystyle\sum_{n=2}^{\infty} \frac{1}{\ln n^2}$ is convergent or divergent.

11 If $\displaystyle\sum_{n=1}^{\infty} a_n$ is convergent where $a_n \geqslant 0$ for all $n \in \mathbb{Z}^+$, prove that $\displaystyle\sum_{n=1}^{\infty} a_n^2$ and

$\displaystyle\sum_{n=1}^{\infty} \left(a_n - \frac{1}{n}\right)^2$ are also convergent. Would these results follow if $a_n \in \mathbb{R}$?

12 Find the set of real numbers for which the following series converges:
$$x + \frac{x^2}{1-x} + \frac{x^3}{(1-x)^2} + \ \ldots\ldots$$

13 **a** Show that the series $S_n = \displaystyle\sum_{k=3}^{n} \frac{(-1)^{k+1}}{\ln(k-1)}$ converges as $n \to \infty$.

    b Find the maximum error involved in using S_{10} to estimate $\displaystyle\sum_{k=3}^{\infty} \frac{(-1)^{k+1}}{\ln(k-1)}$.

14 Determine if the series $\displaystyle\sum_{n=0}^{\infty} \left(\frac{n}{n+5}\right)^n$ convergence or diverges.

15 **a** Express $\dfrac{1}{x\,(x+1)}$ in terms of partial fractions.

    b Use the Integral Test to prove that the series $\displaystyle\sum_{n=1}^{\infty} \frac{1}{n\,(n+1)}$ converges.

REVIEW SET 10C

1 Find the Taylor series expansion of $(x-1)e^{x-1}$ about $x=1$ up to the term in x^3.

2 Using an appropriate Maclaurin series, evaluate correct to three decimal places:
$$\int_0^1 \sin\left(x^2\right)\,dx.$$

3 Prove that if R_n is the error term in approximating $f(x) = \ln(1+x)$ for $0 \leqslant x < 1$ using the first $n+1$ terms of its Maclaurin series, then
$$|R_n| \leqslant \frac{1}{n+1} \quad \text{for } 0 \leqslant x < 1.$$

4 Estimate $e^{0.3}$ correct to three decimal places using the Taylor aproximation:

$$f(a+x) = f(a) + xf'(a) + \ldots\ldots + \frac{x^n}{n!}f^{(n)}(a) + \frac{x^{n+1}}{(n+1)!}f^{(n+1)}(c)$$

5 Let X be a random variable such that $X \sim P_0(\lambda)$, where

$$P(X = x) = \frac{e^{-\lambda}\lambda^x}{x!} \quad \text{for } x = 0, 1, 2, \ldots.$$

Prove that $\sum\limits_{x=0}^{\infty} P(X = x) = 1$.

6 Find a simplified expression for $1 - x + x^2 - x^3 + \ldots\ldots$ where $-1 < x < 1$.
Hence find a Power Series expansion for $f(x) = \ln(1+x)$ for $-1 < x < 1$.

7 **a** Prove that $e - \sum\limits_{k=0}^{n}\frac{1}{k!} = \frac{e^c}{n+1}$ where $0 < c < 1$.

   b Using the fact that $e < 3$, show that for $n \geqslant 3$:

   i $\dfrac{1}{(n+1)!} \leqslant e - \sum\limits_{k=0}^{n}\dfrac{1}{k!} < \dfrac{3}{(n+1)!}$ and hence

   ii $\dfrac{1}{n+1} \leqslant n!\,e - \sum\limits_{k=0}^{n}\dfrac{n!}{k!} < \dfrac{3}{n+1} \leqslant \dfrac{3}{4}$

   c Using **b**, prove by contradication that e is an irrational number.

REVIEW SET 10D

1 Given that $y = ax + b$ is a solution of the differential equation $\dfrac{dy}{dx} = 4x - 2y$, find the values of the constants a and b.

2 Obtain a first order differential equation by differentiating the given equation with respect to x, then eliminating the arbitrary constant A using the original equation.

   a $y = x + \dfrac{A}{x}$ **b** $y^2 = A\cos x$

3 Draw the slope field using integer grid points for x and y between ± 4 for the differential equation $\dfrac{dy}{dx} = \dfrac{x}{y}$.

4 A curve passes through the point $(1, 2)$ and satisfies the differential equation
$$\dfrac{dy}{dx} = x - 2y.$$
Use Euler's Method with step size 0.1 to estimate the value of y when $x = 1.6$.

5 Solve the differential equation $\dfrac{dy}{dx} = \dfrac{xy}{x-1}$ given that $y = 2$ when $x = 2$.

6 Find the general solution of the differential equation $\dfrac{dy}{dx} = 2xy^2 - y^2$.

7 Use the substitution $y = vx$ where v is a function of x to solve the differential equation

$xy\dfrac{dy}{dx} = 1 + x + y^2$ given that $y = 0$ when $x = 1$.

8 By finding a suitable integrating factor, solve $\dfrac{dy}{dx} + \dfrac{3y}{x} = 8x^4$ given $y = 0$ when $x = 1$.

9 A water tank of height $1\,\text{m}$ has a square base of dimensions $2\,\text{m} \times 2\,\text{m}$. The tank is emptied by opening a tap at its base, and the water flows out at a rate that is proportional to the square root of the depth of the water at any given time.

    a If h m is the depth of the water and V is the volume of water remaining in the tank after t minutes, write down a differential equation involving $\dfrac{dV}{dt}$ and h.

    b Explain why $V = 4h$ m^3 at time t. Hence write down a differential equation involving $\dfrac{dh}{dt}$ and h.

    c Initially the tank is full, and then when the tap is opened, the water level drops by 19 cm in 2 minutes. Find the time it takes for the tank to empty.

REVIEW SET 10E

1 Match the slope fields **A**, **B** and **C** to the differential equations:

    a $\dfrac{dy}{dx} = y + 1$ **b** $\dfrac{dy}{dx} = x - y$ **c** $\dfrac{dy}{dx} = x - y^2$

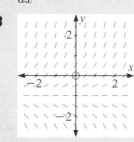 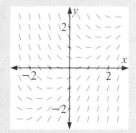

2 On the slope field for $\dfrac{dy}{dx} = 2x - y^2$

shown, sketch the solution curves through

    a $(0,\, 0)$ **b** $(2,\, 3)$.

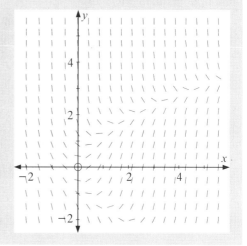

3 Use the substitution $y = vx$ where v is a function of x to solve the differential equation $\dfrac{dy}{dx} = \dfrac{x}{y} + \dfrac{y}{x}$.

4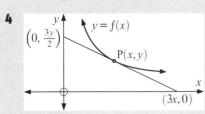

The tangent to a curve at the point P(x, y) cuts the x-axis at $(3x, 0)$ and the y-axis at $(0, \frac{3y}{2})$.

Given that $x > 0$, find the equation of the curve which passes through the point $(1, 5)$.

5 Find the equation of the curve through $(2, 1)$ given that for any point (x, y) on the curve, the y-intercept of the tangent to the curve is $3x^2 y^3$.

6 Solve using an integration factor:

a $\dfrac{dy}{dx} - \dfrac{y}{x} = \sqrt{x}$ given that $y = 0$ when $x = 4$

b $\dfrac{dy}{dx} = \cos x - y \cot x$ given that $y = 0$ when $x = \frac{\pi}{2}$.

7 The population P of an island is currently 154. The population growth in the foresee-able future is given by $\dfrac{dP}{dt} = 0.2P\left(1 - \dfrac{P}{400}\right)$ for $t > 0$.

a Find P as a function of time t years.

b Estimate the population in 20 years' time.

c Is there a limiting population size? If so, what is it?

8 The inside surface of $y = f(x)$ is a mirror. Light is emitted from O(0, 0).

All rays that strike the surface of the mirror are reflected so that they emerge parallel to the axis of symmetry (the x-axis).

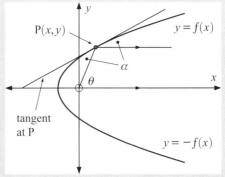

a Explain why $\theta = 2\alpha$.

b Explain why the slope of the tangent at a general point P(x, y) on the mirror is given by $\dfrac{dy}{dx} = \tan \alpha$.

c Use the identity $\tan(2\alpha) = \dfrac{2\tan\alpha}{1 - \tan^2\alpha}$ to deduce that $\tan\alpha = \dfrac{\sqrt{x^2 + y^2} - x}{y}$.

d Find a general solution to the differential equation $\dfrac{dy}{dx} = \dfrac{\sqrt{x^2 + y^2} - x}{y}$ by making the substitution $r^2 = x^2 + y^2$.

e What is the nature of $y = f(x)$?

HL Topic 11

(Further Mathematics SL Topic 5)

This Discrete Mathematics Option comprises two main parts: the first, Introductory Number Theory, has its origins in antiquity with the work of Euclid and Diophantus, and takes the theme of Diophantine Equations to the beginnings of modern Number Theory, and Fermat's Little Theorem. The second, Introductory Graph Theory, is studied from its invention, via the work of Euler, to the modern-day Travelling Salesman Problem.

These two branches are different from most traditional mathematics courses at this level, and as such, much of the material can be studied in isolation from the remainder of the **Core HL** syllabus. It can therefore be undertaken at any time in the two-year IB diploma programme.

The links between the two branches are in the areas of algorithmic processes and proof. The reader should be aware of the different methods of proof that are commonly used: induction, direct proof, proof by cases, by contrapositive and by contradiction.

Discrete mathematics

Contents:

A   NUMBER THEORY

Number theory is the study of the properties of integers.

Recall that the set of all integers is represented by $\mathbb{Z}$ and the set of all positive integers is represented by $\mathbb{Z}^+$.

So, $\mathbb{Z} = \{0, \pm 1, \pm 2, \pm 3, \pm 4, \pm 5, \ldots\}$ and $\mathbb{Z}^+ = \{1, 2, 3, 4, 5, \ldots\}$

Some **notation** used in number theory is:

$\in$ reads   *is in*   or   *is an element of*   or   *is a member of*

$\Rightarrow$ reads   *implies*

$\Leftrightarrow$ reads   *if and only if*

$a \mid b$ reads   *a divides b*   or   *a is a factor of b*

$\gcd(a, b)$ reads   *the greatest common divisor of a and b*
                    (the highest common factor of a and b)

$\operatorname{lcm}(a, b)$ reads   *the least common multiple of a and b*

A.1   NUMBER THEORY INTRODUCTION

Whilst integers would seem to be the simplest of mathematical objects, their properties lead to some very deep and satisfying mathematics.

Our study will involve:
- *techniques of proof*
- *applications of algorithms* (methods of mathematical reasoning)
- a development of the number system with *modular arithmetic*
- the "little theorem" of **Fermat**.

In this course we will address problems like the ones in the following exercise. How many of them can you solve at this stage?

EXERCISE 11A.1

At this stage do not be disappointed if you cannot solve some of these problems.

1   The numbers of the form $2^n - 1$, $n \in \mathbb{Z}^+$, $n \geqslant 2$ are thought to be prime numbers. Is this conjecture true?

2   The numbers of the form $2^p - 1$ where p is prime, are thought to be prime. Is this conjecture true? $\mathbb{P} = \{2, 3, 5, 7, 11, 13, 17, \ldots\}$

3   Find a list of:
    a   five consecutive non-prime numbers   b   six consecutive non-prime numbers

4   Prove that it is not possible to find integers x and y such that $6x + 3y = 83$.

5   Prove that a perfect square always has:
    a   an odd number of factors   b   an even number of prime factors

6 Without division, determine whether $14\,975\,028\,526\,824$ is divisible by 36.

7 Show that the equation $2x + 4y = 62$ has an infinite number of integer value solutions.
Note: $x = 1$, $y = 15$ is one such solution.

8 Are there an infinite or finite number of prime numbers? Can you prove your assertion?

9 A **rational number** is a number which can be written in the form $\frac{p}{q}$ where p and q are integers and $q \neq 0$. Prove that $\sqrt{2}$ is not rational.
Hint: Start by assuming that $\sqrt{2}$ is rational. You may find **5b** above useful.

10 Is 5041 a prime number?

In our work on number theory, the above questions will be addressed, solved and/or proven.

Before doing so, we begin with the basics, which in this case is by listing the basic **axioms** and **rules** for integers.

> An **axiom** is a reasonably obvious result which cannot be established by proof and has to be accepted as true.

A.2 ORDER PROPERTIES AND AXIOMS

Definition: $a > b \Rightarrow a - b > 0$ These are particularly useful in
  $a < b \Rightarrow b - a > 0$ establishing *order properties*.

ORDER AXIOM

If $a > 0$ and $b > 0$ then $a + b > 0$ and $ab > 0$.

ORDER PROPERTIES

These are:
- If $a < b$ and $b < c$, then $a < c$. (transitivity)
- If $a < b$, then $a + c < b + c$ and $a - c < b - c$.
- If $a < b$ and $c > 0$, then $ac < bc$.
- If $a < b$ and $c < 0$, then $ac > bc$.

Each of these is easily proven using positivity, i.e, to show $A > B$, prove $A - B > 0$.

Example 1

Prove that if $a < b$ and $c < 0$, then $ac > bc$.

As $a < b$ then $b - a > 0$
As $c < 0$ then $-c > 0$
$\therefore \quad -c(b - a) > 0$ {order axiom}
$\therefore \quad -bc + ac > 0$
$\therefore \quad ac > bc$

AXIOMS FOR INTEGERS

- If $a, b \in \mathbb{Z}$, then $a + b$, $a - b$ and $ab \in \mathbb{Z}$.

- If $a \in \mathbb{Z}$, then there does not exist $x \in \mathbb{Z}$ such that $a < x < a + 1$
  i.e., there is no integer between two successive integers.

- If $a, b \in \mathbb{Z}$ and $ab = 1$ then either $a = b = 1$ or $a = b = -1$.

- If $a, b \in \mathbb{Z}$ then either $a < b$, $a = b$ or $a > b$.

As well as these axioms we need a further principle on which many important results about subsets of positive integers depend. This is called the **Well Ordered Principle (WOP)**.

Definition:

A set S is **well ordered** $\Leftrightarrow$ every non-empty subset of S contains a least element.

Clearly $\mathbb{Z}^+$ itself contains a least element, namely 1.

The Well Ordered Principle takes this statement further by saying "Every non-empty subset of $\mathbb{Z}^+$, whether finite or infinite, contains a least element as well." So, why is this important?

THE WELL ORDERED PRINCIPLE FOR $\mathbb{Z}^+$

This principle is vital for the set of positive integers (also called **natural numbers**) as it can be used to show the validity of that most important mathematical technique of **proof by induction**.

If the Well Ordered Principle were not true for $\mathbb{Z}^+$ we would not be able to use the method of proof by induction.

The Well Ordered Principle for $\mathbb{Z}^+$ is:

every non-empty subset of $\mathbb{Z}^+$ contains at least one element.

Recall that the **Principle of Mathematical Induction (PMI)** (weak form) is:

If $P(n)$ is a proposition defined for all n in $\mathbb{Z}^+$, then if
- $P(1)$ is true   and
- the truth of $P(k) \Rightarrow$ the truth of $P(k + 1)$
  (called the **inductive step** or **inductive hypothesis**)
  then $P(n)$ is true for all $n \geqslant 1$, $n \in \mathbb{Z}^+$.

Theorem 1:   The proof by the Principle of Mathematical Induction is a valid method of mathematical proof.

Proof: (by contradiction)

Suppose that the conclusion $P(n)$ is not true for every $n \in \mathbb{Z}^+$

$\Rightarrow$ there exists at least one positive integer for which $P(n)$ is false

$\Rightarrow$ the set S, of positive integers for which $P(n)$ is false is non-empty

$\Rightarrow$ S has a least element, k say, where $P(k)$ is false.   {WOP} ...... (*)

But $P(1)$ is true $\therefore$ $k > 1$ $\Rightarrow$ $k - 1 > 0$ $\Rightarrow$ $0 < k - 1 < k$

Now since $k - 1 < k$ then $k - 1$ is not in S {as k is the least element of S}.

This implies that $P(k-1)$ is true   {from *}.

But by the inductive hypothesis $P(k-1)$ true $\Rightarrow P(k)$ true.

Hence $P(k)$ is true which contradicts *.   So, our supposition is false. QED

We see in the above proof that the WOP is necessary for Proof by Induction to be valid. It is also sufficient. The two are in fact logically equivalent.

Mathematical induction is used in many number theoretic proofs, especially in divisibility which is our major concern in this course.

Example 2

Use the Principle of Mathematical Induction to prove that $10^{n+1} + 3 \times 10^n + 5$ is divisible by 9 for all $n \in \mathbb{Z}^+$.

Proof: (By the Principle of Mathematical Induction)

(1)   If $n = 1$, $10^2 + 3 \times 10^1 + 5 = 135 = 15 \times 9$ which is divisible by 9

$\therefore$ P(1) is true.

(2)   If $P(k)$ is true, then $10^{k+1} + 3 \times 10^k + 5 = 9A$ where $A \in \mathbb{Z}$ ...... (*)

$\therefore$ $10^{[k+1]+1} + 3 \times 10^{[k+1]} + 5$

$= 10 \times 10^{k+1} + 3 \times 10 \times 10^k + 5$

$= 10(9A - 3 \times 10^k - 5) + 30 \times 10^k + 5$ {using *}

$= 90A - \cancel{30 \times 10^k} - 50 + \cancel{30 \times 10^k} + 5$

$= 90A - 45$

$= 9(10A - 5)$ where $10A - 5 \in \mathbb{Z}$ as $A \in \mathbb{Z}$

$\therefore$ $10^{[k+1]+1} + 3 \times 10^{[k+1]} + 5$ is divisible by 9

Thus $P(k+1)$ is true whenever $P(k)$ is true and $P(1)$ is true.

$\Rightarrow$ $P(n)$ is true   {P of MI}

Example 3

Use the Principle of Mathematical Induction to prove that $5^n \geqslant 8n^2 - 4n + 1$ for all n in $\mathbb{Z}^+$.

Proof: (By the Principle of Mathematical Induction)

(1)   If $n = 1$, $5^1 \geqslant 8 - 4 + 1$ i.e., $5 \geqslant 5$ is true. $\therefore$ P(1) is true.

(2)   If $P(k)$ is true, then $5^k \geqslant 8k^2 - 4k + 1$ ......(1)

i.e., $5^k - 8k^2 + 4k - 1 \geqslant 0$ ...... (*)

Now $5^{[k+1]} - 8[k+1]^2 + 4[k+1] - 1$

$= 5 \times 5^k - 8(k^2 + 2k + 1) + 4k + 4 - 1$

$= 5 \times 5^k - 8k^2 - 16k - 8 + 4k + 4 - 1$

$= (5^k - 8k^2 + 4k - 1) + 4 \times 5^k - 16k - 4$

$$\text{where} \quad 5^k - 8k^2 + 4k - 1 \geqslant 0 \qquad \{\text{using *}\}$$
$$\text{and} \quad 4 \times 5^k - 16k - 4 \geqslant 4(8k^2 - 4k + 1) - 16k - 4 \quad \{\text{using (1)}\}$$
$$\text{i.e.,} \geqslant 32k^2 - 32k$$
$$\text{i.e.,} \geqslant 32k(k-1)$$
$$\geqslant 0 \quad \text{as} \quad k \geqslant 1$$
$$\therefore \quad 5^{[k+1]} - 8[k+1]^2 + 4[k+1] - 1 \geqslant 0 \qquad \{\text{the sum of two non-negatives}\}$$
$$\therefore \quad 5^{[k+1]} \geqslant 8[k+1]^2 - 4[k+1] + 1$$

Thus $P(k+1)$ is true whenever $P(k)$ is true and $P(1)$ is true.

$\therefore \quad P(n)$ is true.

EXERCISE 11A.2.1

1   Prove, using the Principle of Mathematical Induction, that:

a $3^n > 7n$ for $n \geqslant 3$, $n \in \mathbb{Z}^+$

b $n^n > n!$ for $n \geqslant 2$, $n \in \mathbb{Z}^+$

c $3^n < n!$ for $n \geqslant 6$, $n \in \mathbb{Z}^+$

2   Prove, using the Principle of Mathematical Induction, that:

a $n^3 - 4n$ is divisible by 3 for all $n \geqslant 3$, $n \in \mathbb{Z}^+$

b $5^{n+1} + 2(3^n) + 1$ is divisible by 8 for all $n \in \mathbb{Z}^+$

c $73 \mid 8^{n+2} + 9^{2n+1}$ for all $n \in \mathbb{Z}^+$

   Note: $a \mid b$ reads a divides b or a is a factor of b.

   If $a \mid b$ where a and b are integers then $b = ka$ where $k \in \mathbb{Z}$.

3   The nth repunit is the integer consisting of n "1"s.
   For example, the third repunit is the number 111.

a   Prove that the nth repunit is $\dfrac{10^n - 1}{9}$ for all $n \in \mathbb{Z}^+$.

b   Ali claimed that all repunits, other than the second, are composite (or non-prime). Can you prove or disprove Ali's claim?

c   Ali then made a weaker statement. He claimed that if a repunit is prime, then it must have a prime number of digits. Can you prove or disprove this claim?

d   To strengthen the claim in c Ali said that all repunits with a prime number of digits must themselves be prime. Can you prove or disprove this claim?

STRONG INDUCTION (THE SECOND FORM OF MATHEMATICAL INDUCTION)

Strong induction is so called as the inductive hypothesis is far stronger than the first (weak) form.

It states that: If $P(1)$ is true and $P(k)$ is true for all $k \leqslant n \implies P(n+1)$ is true,

then $P(n)$ is true for all $n \in \mathbb{Z}^+$.

Note: $P(k)$ is true for all $k \leqslant n$ means that $P(k)$ is true for all values below a certain value,   i.e.,   P(1), P(2), P(3), ... P(k) are all true.

This form of inductive proof is logically equivalent to the weak form.

The proof of the **Unique Prime Factorisation Theorem** depends on it.

THE FIBONACCI SEQUENCE

Another area of Mathematics where proof by Strong Induction is used is that of **recurrence relationships**. These occur in the **Fibonacci sequence** of numbers.

This is   1, 1, 2, 3, 5, 8, 13, 21, 34, ...

Leonardo of Pisa (Fibonacci) (c. 1180-1228) introduces the sequence to Europe along with the Arabic notation for numerals in his book *"Liber Abaci"*. It is posed as the rabbits problem which you could source on the internet or in the library.

The Fibonacci sequence can be defined as:

$$f_1 = 1, \quad f_2 = 1 \quad \text{and} \quad f_{n+2} = f_{n+1} + f_n \quad \text{for all} \quad n \geqslant 1.$$

This is a **recurrence relationship** as we specify the initial value(s) and then give a rule for generating all future terms. This is usually a rule for finding the nth term for some of the values of the first k terms, where $1 \leqslant k \leqslant n - 1$.

Note: Many results about the Fibonacci sequence can be proven or are still to be proved. The magazine "The Fibonacci Quarterly" deals solely with newly discovered properties of the sequence. A number of proofs require **strong induction** for proof. Many sites could be visited including   http://mathworld.wolfram.com/FibonacciNumber.html

---

Example 4

A sequence is defined recursively by $a_{n+1} = \dfrac{a_n^2}{a_{n-1}}$ for all $n \geqslant 2$ with $a_1 = 1$ and $a_2 = 2$.

a   Find a_3, a_4, a_5 and a_6.

b   Hence, postulate a closed form solution for a_n.

c   Prove your postulate true using Mathematical Induction.

a $a_3 = \dfrac{a_2^2}{a_1} = \dfrac{2^2}{1} = 4$

  $a_4 = \dfrac{a_3^2}{a_2} = \dfrac{4^2}{2} = 8$

  $a_5 = \dfrac{a_4^2}{a_3} = \dfrac{8^2}{4} = 16$

  $a_6 = \dfrac{a_5^2}{a_4} = \dfrac{16^2}{8} = 32$

b   As $a_1 = 1 = 2^0$

  $a_2 = 2 = 2^1$

  $a_3 = 4 = 2^2$

  $a_4 = 8 = 2^3$

  $a_5 = 16 = 2^4$

  $a_6 = 32 = 2^5$

  we postulate that $a_n = 2^{n-1}$.

c   P(n) is   "if $a_1 = 1$, $a_2 = 2$ and $a_{n+1} = \dfrac{a_n^2}{a_{n-1}}$ for all $n \geqslant 2$ then

  $a_n = 2^{n-1}$".

Proof: (By the Principle of Mathematical Induction)

(1)   If $n = 1$, $a_1 = 2^{1-1} = 2^0 = 1$ $\therefore$ P(1) is true.

(2)   Assume that $a_n = 2^{n-1}$ is true for all $n \leqslant k$
 $\therefore$ $a_r = 2^{r-1}$ for $r = 1, 2, 3, 4, ..., k$ ...... (*)

(We are now required to prove that $a_{k+1} = 2^k$.)

Now $a_{k+1} = \dfrac{a_k^2}{a_{k-1}} = \dfrac{(2^{k-1})^2}{2^{k-2}} = \dfrac{2^{2k-2}}{2^{k-2}} = 2^k$,   as required.

Thus P(1) is true and the assumed result for $r = 1, 2, 3, 4, ..., k$

$\Rightarrow$ the same result for $r = k + 1$

then $P(n)$ is true for all $n \in \mathbb{Z}^+$.

EXERCISE 11A.2.2 (Strong Induction)

1 If a sequence is defined by $a_1 = 1$, $a_2 = 2$ and $a_{n+2} = a_{n+1} + a_n$, prove that
 $a_n \leqslant \left(\frac{5}{3}\right)^n$ for all n in $\mathbb{Z}^+$.

2 If $b_1 = b_2 = 1$ and $b_n = 2b_{n-1} + b_{n-2}$ for all $n \geqslant 2$, prove that b_n is odd
for $n \in \mathbb{Z}^+$.

The remaining questions all involve the Fibonacci sequence, f_n.

3 Evaluate $\displaystyle\sum_{k=1}^{n} f_k$ for $n = 1, 2, 3, 4, 5, 6$ and 7 and hence express $\displaystyle\sum_{k=1}^{n} f_k$ in terms
of another Fibonacci number. Prove your postulate true by induction.

4 Prove that $\left(\frac{3}{2}\right)^{n-2} < f_n < 2^{n-2}$ for all $n \in \mathbb{Z}^+$, $n \geqslant 3$.

Note: This inequality enables us to *bound* the Fibonacci numbers and tells us something about the 'exponential' growth of the numbers.

Challenge: Prove that $\left(\frac{1+\sqrt{5}}{2}\right)^{n-2} < f_n$ which leads to a closed form for f_n

(known as **Binet's formula**).   This is worth researching.

5 Rearranging $f_{n+2} = f_{n+1} + f_n$ to $f_n = f_{n+2} - f_{n+1}$ enables us to prove question
3 directly. Show how this can be done.

6 Postulate and prove a result for $\displaystyle\sum_{k=1}^{n} f_{2k-1}$ in terms of other Fibonacci numbers.

7 Postulate and prove a result for $\displaystyle\sum_{k=1}^{n} f_k^2$ in terms of other Fibonacci numbers by
expressing the result of this sum as a product of two factors, each of which can be expressed in terms of a Fibonacci number.

8 Prove that $f_{n+1} \times f_{n-1} - (f_n)^2 = (-1)^n$ for all n in $\mathbb{Z}^+$, $n \geqslant 2$.

9 Postulate and prove a result for $\displaystyle\sum_{k=1}^{n} f_{2k}$ in terms of other Fibonacci numbers.

10 Postulate and prove a result for $\displaystyle\sum_{k=1}^{2n-1} (f_k \times f_{k+1})$ in terms of the square of another Fibonacci number.

11 Given the matrix $\mathbf{F} = \begin{bmatrix} 1 & 1 \\ 1 & 0 \end{bmatrix}$,   postulate and prove a result for $\mathbf{F}^n$ in terms of the Fibonacci numbers.

Hence, by considering the determinants of $\mathbf{F}$ and $\mathbf{F}^n$ establish the result of question **8**.

12 Prove that $f_n \times f_{n-1} = (f_n)^2 - (f_{n-1})^2 + (-1)^n$,   for all $n \geqslant 2$.

This can be used to show that consecutive Fibonacci numbers have a greatest common divisor of 1. Can you see why?

THE EXISTENCE OF IRRATIONALS

Although this course deals mainly with integers, it would be remiss not to look at a brief extension to the set of irrationals. This allows us to further utilise the Well Ordered Principle.

The first number found to be irrational was probably $\sqrt{2}$. This is a classic of number theory. See the 'methods of proof' document at the start of this book. The irrationality of $\sqrt{3}$ can likewise be established using a simular technique.

However, the irrationality of $\sqrt{2}$, $\sqrt{3}$ etc can also be established using the Well Ordered Principle and contradiction.

Example 5

Use the WOP and contradiction to prove that $\sqrt{3}$ is irrational.

Suppose that $\sqrt{3}$ is rational. $\Rightarrow \sqrt{3} = \dfrac{p}{q}$ where p, q are in $\mathbb{Z}$, $q \neq 0$

$\Rightarrow \quad p = q\sqrt{3}$

We now consider the set $S = \left\{ k\sqrt{3}: \; k, \; k\sqrt{3} \text{ are in } \mathbb{Z}^+ \right\}$

By our supposition, S is a non-empty set of positive integers which by the WOP, has a smallest member s, say, and has the form $s = t\sqrt{3}$ for some integer t.

Now $s\sqrt{3} - s = s\sqrt{3} - t\sqrt{3} = (s - t)\sqrt{3}$

But $s\sqrt{3} = t\sqrt{3}\sqrt{3} = 3t$ where s and t are integers.

$\Rightarrow \quad 3t - s = (s - t)\sqrt{3}$ where s and t are integers.

$\Rightarrow \quad (s - t)\sqrt{3}$ is an integer

which is *positive* as $s - t = t\sqrt{3} - t = t(\sqrt{3} - 1)$ and $\sqrt{3} > 1$

i.e., $(s - t)\sqrt{3} \in \mathbb{Z}^+$.

However, $s(\sqrt{3} - 1) < s$ as $\sqrt{3} - 1 < 1$.

But this contradicts the definition of s as the smallest element in S.

Hence, the supposition that $\sqrt{3}$ is rational is false.

EXERCISE 11A.2.3

1 Use the Well Ordered Principle and contradication to show that $\sqrt{2}$ is irrational.

2 Use the Well Ordered Principle and contradication to show that $\sqrt{5}$ is irrational.

3 Where does the proof as in **Example 5** fail, if trying to prove the irrationality of $\sqrt{4}$?

A.3   DIVISIBILITY, PRIMALITY AND THE DIVISION ALGORITHM

Divisibility and primality are intimately linked. So, if we are to consider the primes, then we must also look at **composite numbers** (non-primes). This leads naturally to a discussion on the divisibility properties of integers. In turn, we will find that these depend on the Well Ordered Principle.

INVESTIGATION 1   HOW MANY PRIMES ARE THERE?

Do you think that there are infinitely many prime numbers or do you think that they cease as we proceed through higher positive integers?
Anne claims that the primes are infinite in number.
Can you prove or disprove her claim?

What to do:

1 What is the negation (or opposite) of the statement: "There are an infinite number of primes"?
This will be the statement we should try to contradict.

2 Surely a consequence of the negation would be that there is a largest prime P, say. Now consider the number $N = P! + 1$
   a What is the size of N compared to that of P?
   b If we assume that there is a finite number of primes (and thus a largest one), what does its size tell us about its nature (prime or composite)?

3 Consider $N = 19! + 1$.   Explain why $\dfrac{N}{2}, \dfrac{N}{3}, \dfrac{N}{4}, \dfrac{N}{5}, \ldots, \dfrac{N}{19}$ are not integers.

4 Consider what happens if we divide N by any integer k which is $\leqslant P$, and so consider the nature of N again.

5 You should now have reached the desired contradiction.

6 Now all you have to do is to write down the proof logically and in a form which cannot be disputed.

The proof you obtained from the *Investigation* is a variant on **Euclid's** proof of the infinitude of primes.

Find Euclid's proof and see how it varies from the one derived in the Investigation.

Primes and composites both have to be identified, and the search for them is not a trivial undertaking. In order to gain the insight necessary to continue, we must look at the formal rules governing divisibility and so we begin with some definitions and some properties.

ELEMENTARY DIVISIBILITY PROPERTIES

Notation: $d \mid n$ reads d *divides* n
                                    or d *is a divisor of* n
                                    or d *is a factor of* n
                                    or n *is a multiple* of d

For example, $3 \mid 12$ but $5 \nmid 12$

Definition: If d and n are integers, then $d \mid n \Leftrightarrow$ there exists $k \in \mathbb{Z}$ such that $n = dk$.

DIVISIBILITY PROPERTIES

- $n \mid n$ (every integer divides itself)
- $d \mid n$ and $n \mid m \Rightarrow d \mid m$ (transitivity)
- $d \mid n$ and $d \mid m \Rightarrow d \mid an + bm$ for all $a, b \in \mathbb{Z}$ (linearity)
- $d \mid n \Rightarrow ad \mid an$ (multiplicative)
- $ad \mid an \Rightarrow d \mid n$ if $a \neq 0$ (cancellation)
- $1 \mid n$ (1 divides every integer)
- $n \mid 1 \Rightarrow n = \pm 1$
- $d \mid 0$ for every d in $\mathbb{Z}$
- If d and n are positive integers and $d \mid n \Rightarrow d \leqslant n$.

The linearity property deserves special attention. It says that:

If d divides both n and m, then d divides **all** linear combinations of n and m.

So,   if $d \mid n$ and $d \mid m$ then in particular $d \mid n + m$ and $d \mid n - m$.

This result is particularly useful.

Example 6

Prove the transitivity property: if $d \mid n$ and $n \mid m$ then $d \mid m$.

$d \mid n \Rightarrow$ there exists k_1 such that $n = k_1 d, \ k_1 \in \mathbb{Z}$
$n \mid m \Rightarrow$ there exists k_2 such that $m = k_2 n, \ k_2 \in \mathbb{Z}$
$\therefore \ m = k_2 n = k_2(k_1 d) = k_1 k_2 d$ where $k_1 k_2 \in \mathbb{Z}$
$\therefore \ d \mid m$

Example 7   Prove that $n \mid 1 \Rightarrow n = \pm 1$.

$n \mid 1 \Rightarrow$ there exists k such that $1 = kn, \ k \in \mathbb{Z}$
So, we have to solve $kn = 1$ where k and n are integers.
The only solutions are $k = 1, \ n = 1$ or $k = -1, \ n = -1$
$\therefore \ n = \pm 1$

EXERCISE 11A.3.1

1 Prove these properties of divisibility:

    a $d \mid n \;\Rightarrow\; ad \mid an$ (a, d and n are all integers).

    b $d \mid n$ and $d \mid m \;\Rightarrow\; d \mid an + bm$ for all integers a and b.

    c If d and n are positive integers and $d \mid n \;\Rightarrow\; d \leqslant n$.

2 Prove that if $a \in \mathbb{Z}$, then the only positive divisor of both consecutive integers a and $a + 1$ is 1.

3 Prove that there do not exist integers m and n such that:

    a $14m + 20n = 101$ **b** $14m + 21n = 100$

4 If a, b and c are in $\mathbb{Z}$, prove that $a \mid b$ and $a \mid c \;\Rightarrow\; a \mid b \pm c$.

THE DIVISION ALGORITHM

The **Division Algorithm** extends our notion of divisibility to the case where **remainders** are obtained and is a formal representation of that idea. It is stated below without proof.

Theorem 2: (The Division Algorithm)

> For any two integers a and b with $b > 0$, there exists unique q and r in $\mathbb{Z}$ such that $a = bq + r$ where $0 \leqslant r < b$.

Note: In $a = bq + r$, q is the greatest integer such that $q \leqslant \dfrac{a}{b}$ and is called the **quotient**.

r is called the **remainder**, a is the **dividend** and b is the **divisor**.

For example,   for integers 27 and 4, $27 = 6 \times 4 + 3$

$$\tfrac{27}{4} = 6\tfrac{3}{4} \quad \text{and} \quad 6 \text{ is the greatest integer } \leqslant \tfrac{27}{4}.$$

Example 8

Find the quotient and remainder for:

  a $a = 133, \;\; b = 21$ **b** $a = -50, \;\; b = 8$ **c** $a = 1\,781\,293, \;\; b = 1481$

---

a $\dfrac{a}{b} = 6.333 \ldots\ldots$ $\therefore\;\; q = 6$ Now $r = a - bq$

                                             $\therefore\;\; r = 133 - 21 \times 6$

                                        i.e., $r = 7$

b $\dfrac{a}{b} = -6.25$ $\therefore\;\; q = -7$ and $r = a - bq$

                                            $= -50 - 8(-7)$

                                            $= 6$

c $\dfrac{a}{b} = 1202.76 \ldots\ldots$ $\therefore\;\; q = 1202$ and $r = a - bq$

                                            $= 1\,781\,293 - 1481 \times 1202$

                                            $= 1131$

The Division Algorithm also tells us that, if for example $b = 5$, then $a = 5q + r$ where $0 \leqslant r < 5$, i.e., $r = 0, 1, 2, 3$ or 4 and there are no other possible values. These different values of r split all integers into five disjoint sets with membership of a given set being dependent solely on the value of the remainder on division by 5.

These sets have form $5k$, $5k + 1$, $5k + 2$, $5k + 3$, $5k + 4$.

For example, 35 and 240 belong to the set $5k$,

36 and 241 belong to the set $5k + 1$, etc.

The division algorithm states that if results about divisibility by 5 apply to "2" then they apply to all numbers of the set $5k+2$.

EXERCISE 11A.3.2

1 Show that: **a** $3 \mid 66$ **b** $7 \mid 385$ **c** $654 \mid 0$

2 Find the quotient and remainder in the division process with divisor 17 and dividend:

     a 100   **b** 289   **c** -44 **d** -100

3 What can be deduced about non-zero integers a and b if $a \nmid b$ and $b \nmid a$?

4 Given a, b, c and d in $\mathbb{Z}$ where a, $c \neq 0$ show that $a \mid b$ and $c \mid d \Rightarrow ac \mid bd$.

5 Is it possible to find prime integers p, q and r such that $p \mid qr$ but $p \nmid q$ and $p \nmid r$?

6 When is it possible to find integers a, b and c such that $a \mid bc$ but $a \nmid b$ and $a \nmid c$?

7 Given $p, q \in \mathbb{Z}^+$, and $p \mid q$ prove that $p \leqslant q$.

8 Given $p, q \in \mathbb{Z}$, such that $p \mid q$, prove that $p^k \mid q^k$ where $k \in \mathbb{Z}$.

9 Prove that if the product of k integers is odd, then all the individual integers are themselves odd.

10   **a** Prove that the square of an integer takes the form $3k$ or $3k + 1$ for some $k \in \mathbb{Z}$.

     b Prove that the square of an integer is of the form $4q$ or $n = 4q + 1$ for some $q \in \mathbb{Z}$.

     c Deduce that $1\,234\,567$ is not a perfect square.

Example 9	Prove that if $a \in \mathbb{Z}$, then $3 \mid a \Leftrightarrow 3 \mid a^2$
	(i.e., $3 \mid a$ and $3 \mid a^2$ are logically equivalent statements).

Proof: ($\Rightarrow$)   If $3 \mid a$, then $a = 3q$ say, where $q \in \mathbb{Z}$

             $\Rightarrow a^2 = 9q^2$

             $\Rightarrow a^2 = 3(3q^2)$ where $3q^2 \in \mathbb{Z}$

             $\Rightarrow 3 \mid a^2$

   ($\Leftarrow$)   We can more directly prove the contrapositive, i.e., instead of showing $3 \mid a^2 \Rightarrow 3 \mid a$, we need to show $3 \nmid a \Rightarrow 3 \nmid a^2$

       Now if $3 \nmid a$, then $a = 3q + 1$ or $a = 3q + 2$ (but not $3q$)

       $\therefore$ $a^2 = 9q^2 + 6q + 1$ or $a^2 = 9q^2 + 12q + 4$

       $\Rightarrow a^2 = 3(3q^2 + 2q) + 1$ or $a^2 = 3(3q^2 + 4q + 1) + 1$

       $\Rightarrow 3 \nmid a^2$ (as in each case a remainder of 1 occurs)

Hence as $3 \nmid a \Rightarrow 3 \nmid a^2$, then $3 \mid a^2 \Rightarrow 3 \mid a$.

EXERCISE 11A.3.3

1 Prove that: an integer a is divisible by 5 $\Leftrightarrow$ $5 \mid a^2$.

2 Prove that: if a is an integer, $3 \mid a^2$ $\Leftrightarrow$ $9 \mid a^2$.

3   a   Prove that $n = 2 \;\Rightarrow\; (n+3)(n-2) = 0$ b   Is the converse in a true?

4 There are many different ways of reading the statement $p \Rightarrow q$.

These are: i   "If p then q"   ii   "q if p"   iii   "p only if q"

        iv   "p is sufficient for q"   v   "q is necessary for p"

Using the above, which of the following are true and which are not?

   a $n = 2$ only if $n^2 - n - 2 = 0$

   b $n = 2$ is sufficient for $n^2 - n - 2 = 0$

   c $n = 2$ is necessary for $n^2 - n - 2 = 0$

   d $a < b$ is sufficient for $4ab < (a+b)^2$

   e $a < b$ is necessary and sufficient for $4ab < (a+b)^2$

   f $a < b$ if and only if $4ab < (a+b)^2$

   g $a < b$ is equivalent to $4ab < (a+b)^2$

Note: *p if and only if q* is sometimes written *p iff q*.

5   a   Prove that any integer of the form $8p + 7$ is also of the form $4q + 3$.

   b   Demonstrate by using a counter example that the converse of a is not true.

6 Prove that:

   a   the cube of an integer takes either the form $9k$ or $9k \pm 1$

   b   the fourth power of an integer takes the form $5k$ or $5k + 1$

7 Prove that an integer of the form $3k^2 - 1$ is never a perfect square. Consider the contrapositive of this statement.

8 For $n \geqslant 1$, prove, by considering cases, that $\dfrac{n(n+1)(2n+1)}{6} \in \mathbb{Z}$.

Find an alternative proof. (You may also recognise the formula.)

9 Prove that no repunit, except 1, can be a perfect square. (**Hint:** If necessary, see **Exercise 11A.2.1** question 3.)

10 Prove, by using cases, that if an integer is both a perfect square and a perfect cube, then it will take one of the two forms $7k$ or $7k + 1$.

11   a   For $n \geqslant 1$, prove that the integer $7n^3 + 5n$ is even, by using the Division Algorithm and considering cases.

   b   Similarly, prove that the integer $n(7n^2 + 5)$ is of the form $3k$.

   c   Hence, prove that the integer $n(7n^2 + 5)$ is of the form $6k$. Prove this result directly, by considering the six cases.

12 Given $a \in \mathbb{Z}$, prove that $3 \mid a^3 - a$.

13   a   Show that the product of any two integers of the form $4k + 1$ also has this form.

   b   Show that the product of any two integers of the form $4k + 3$ has form $4p + 1$.

   c   What do these results tell you about the square of any odd number?

14 Using the result of the previous question, show that the fourth power of any odd integer is of the form $16k + 1$.

15 Prove by induction that the product of any three consecutive integers is divisible by 6. Prove this result directly by the Division Algorithm.

16 Prove by induction that $5 \mid n^5 - n$ for all $n \in \mathbb{Z}^+$. Prove this result using the Division Algorithm.

17 Prove by induction that the sum of the cubes of any three consecutive integers is divisible by 9. Prove this result using the Division Algorithm.

INTEGER REPRESENTATION IN VARIOUS BASES

Repeated use of the Division Algorithm, and the uniqueness of its representation of integers, is the basis of our decimal number system.

We express numbers in the decimal system as a sum of powers of 10.

For example, $34\,765 = 3 \times 10^4 + 4 \times 10^3 + 7 \times 10^2 + 6 \times 10^1 + 5 \times 10^0$

The coefficients of the powers of 10 come from the set $\{0, 1, 2, 3, 4, 5, 6, 7, 8, 9\}$ and this set is denoted as $\mathbb{Z}_{10}$.

OTHER BASES

We use 10 as our **base** as it seems to suit us. However, we could just as easily use any other integer as our base and that system of representing integers would be just as valid since the Division Algorithm is valid for all positive integer divisors. The representation of the integers so obtained is unique (in that base).

Integers written in base 2 and base 16 are very important in computer science.

Integers can be written in base 2 using powers of 2 and the digits 0 and 1 for its coefficients.

For example $101\,101_2 = 1 \times 2^5 + 0 \times 2^4 + 1 \times 2^3 + 1 \times 2^2 + 0 \times 2^1 + 1 \times 2^0$

Example 10   Convert: **a** $(1\,001\,101)_2$ to a base 10 integer.

   b   the base 10 integer 347 to a base 2 integer.

a $\begin{aligned} 1\,001\,101_2 &= 1 \times 2^6 + 1 \times 2^3 + 1 \times 2^2 + 1 \times 2^0 \\ &= 64 + 8 + 4 + 1 \\ &= 77_{10} \end{aligned}$

b   We are to write 347 in the form

$$a_k 2^k + a_{k-1} 2^{k-1} + a_{k-2} 2^{k-2} + \ldots\ldots + a_2 2^2 + a_1 2^1 + a_0$$

   where $\ 0 \leqslant a_i < 2\ $ i.e., $\ a_i \in \mathbb{Z}_2\ $ where $\ \mathbb{Z}_{\cdot 2} = \{0, 1\}$

Let $\ 347 = 2\left(a_k 2^{k-1} + a_{k-1} 2^{k-2} + \ldots\ldots + a_2 2 + a_1\right) + a_0$

i.e., $\ 347 = 2 \times 173 + 1\ $ then $\ a_0 = 1$

Since $\ a_k 2^{k-1} + a_{k-1} 2^{k-2} + \ldots\ldots + a_2 2 + a_1 \in \mathbb{Z}\ $ and the representation is unique then

$$173 = a_k 2^{k-1} + a_{k-1} 2^{k-2} + \ldots\ldots + a_2 2 + a_1$$

$$\therefore \quad 173 = 2(a_k 2^{k-2} + a_{k-1} 2^{k-3} + \ldots\ldots + a_2) + a_1$$
$$= 2 \times 86 + 1 \quad \text{and so} \quad a_1 = 1$$

and we continue this process to obtain $347_{10} = 101\,011\,011_2$

In reality we can shorten the process using repeated division by 2 and recorded the remainders, in reverse.

i.e.,

2	347	r
2	173	1
2	86	1
2	43	0
2	21	1
2	10	1
2	5	0
2	2	1
	1	0

$\longleftarrow$ 347 $= 2 \times 173 + 1$
$\longleftarrow$ 173 $= 2 \times 86 + 1$
$\longleftarrow$ 86 $= 2 \times 43 + 0$
$\longleftarrow$ 43 $= 2 \times 21 + 1$
$\longleftarrow$ 21 $= 2 \times 10 + 1$
$\longleftarrow$ 10 $= 2 \times 5 + 0$
$\longleftarrow$ 5 $= 2 \times 2 + 1$
$\longleftarrow$ 2 $= 2 \times 1 + 0$ So, $(347)_{10} = (101\,011\,011)_2$

This process can be used to convert any base 10 number to a number in another integer base.

Note: If a base number is not given, it is assumed to be base 10,   i.e.,   347 is $(347)_{10}$.

EXERCISE 11A.3.4

1   Convert $1\,001\,111\,101$ from binary to decimal notation.

2   Convert $201\,021\,102$ from ternary (base 3) to decimal notation.

3   Convert   **a** 347 to base 3   **b** 1234 to base 8   **c** 5728 to base 7.

4   Convert $87\,532$ to base 5.

5   Convert $1\,001\,111\,101$ from binary to base 4. Note that you have already converted this to base 10. Can you see a way of doing the conversion directly?

6   Convert $1\,001\,111\,101$ from binary to base 8.

7   **a** Convert $201\,021\,102$ from ternary (base 3) to base 9.
   b Convert $2\,122\,122\,102$ to base 9.

8   Detail a way of converting a given integer from base k to base k^2.

9   Convert $56\,352\,743$ from base 8 to binary.

10   Convert $313\,123\,012$ from base 4 to binary.

11   Convert $6\,326\,452\,378$ from base 9 to ternary.

12   Detail a way of converting a given integer from base k^2 to base k.

13   By repeated use of the division algorithm find the infinite decimal representation of the rational number $\frac{5}{7}$.

   (**Hint:**   Suppose $\frac{5}{7} = a_1 \times 10^{-1} + a_2 \times 10^{-2} + \ldots\ldots$ where the $a_i \in \mathbb{Z}_{10}$.)

A.4 GCD, LCM AND THE EUCLIDEAN ALGORITHM GREATEST COMMON DIVISOR (GCD)

The greatest common divisor of 6 and 15 is 3 as $3 \mid 6$ and $3 \mid 15$ and no greater number has this property of dividing into both 6 and 15. We write $\gcd(6, 15) = 3$.

> The **greatest common divisor** of integers a and b is written $\gcd(a, b)$
>
> (or simply (a, b) in some books).

Formal definition:

$$d = \gcd(a, b) \iff \begin{array}{ll} (1) & d \mid a \ \text{and} \ d \mid b \\ (2) & \text{if} \ e \mid a \ \text{and} \ e \mid b \ \text{then} \ e \mid d \end{array}$$

Examples: $\gcd(24, 36) = 12$, $\gcd(12, 0) = 12$, $\gcd(15, 28) = 1$

RELATIVELY PRIME INTEGERS

> a and b are **relatively prime** (or **coprime**) if $\gcd(a, b) = 1$

Theorem 3: If $d = \gcd(a, b)$ then (1) $\gcd\left(\dfrac{a}{d}, \dfrac{b}{d}\right) = 1$

(2) $\gcd(a, b) = \gcd(a + cb, b)$, $a, b, c \in \mathbb{Z}$

Proof: (1) If $e \in \mathbb{Z}$ and $e \mid \dfrac{a}{d}$ and $e \mid \dfrac{b}{d}$ then there exist integers k and l

such that $\dfrac{a}{d} = ke$ and $\dfrac{b}{d} = le$

$\Rightarrow \quad a = kde$ and $b = lde$

$\Rightarrow \quad a$ and b have de as a common divisor.

But $d = \gcd(a, b) \Rightarrow de \leqslant d \Rightarrow e = 1 \Rightarrow \gcd\left(\dfrac{a}{d}, \dfrac{b}{d}\right) = 1$

(2) ($\Rightarrow$) Let e be a common divisor of a and b, i.e., $e \mid a$ and $e \mid b$

$\Rightarrow \quad e \mid a + cb \quad (c \in \mathbb{Z})$ {linearity property of divisibility}

$\Rightarrow \quad e$ is a common divisor of a and $a + cb$.

($\Leftarrow$) If f is a common divisor of b and $a + cb$

$\Rightarrow \quad f$ is a common divisor of b and $(a + cb) - cb$

{again using the linearity property}

$\Rightarrow \quad f$ is a common divisor of b and a.

Note: In the above proof, we have simply shown that the sets of common divisors are the same. Do you understand that this is all that is required for the proof to be valid?

Theorem 4:

> The $\gcd(a, b)$ is the least positive integer that is a linear combination of a and b,
>
> i.e., $d = \gcd(a, b) \Rightarrow d = ma + nb$ and if $k = pa + qb$ then $k \geqslant d$.

Proof:

Let d be the least positive integer that is a linear combination of a and b.

First note that d exists since by the Well Ordered Principle, one of either $1(a) + 0(b)$ or $-1(a) + 0(b)$ is positive, $a \neq 0$ and both of these are linear combinations of a and b.

We must now show that   (1) $d \mid a$ and $d \mid b$

(2) $d = \gcd(a, b)$

(1)   Writing $d = ma + nb$ and noting that $a = dq + r$ with $0 \leqslant r < d$ by the Division Algorithm then $r = a - dq = a - q(ma + nb) = (1 - qm)a - qnb$ i.e., r is a linear combination of a and b.

But, we have defined d as the least positive linear combination of a and b and since $0 \leqslant r < d$, we can only conclude that $r = 0$.

Consequently $a = dq$ and hence $d \mid a$.

By similar argument, we also conclude that $d \mid b$.

(2)   By the linearity property, if e is any common factor of a and b then $e \mid ma + nb$. But $d = ma + nb$,   so $e \mid d$.

Consequently, by definition, $d = \gcd(a, b)$

Note 1:   The above proof is an **existence proof**. It tells us that the $\gcd(a, b)$ is a linear combination of a and b. However, it does not tell us what the linear combination is. That is the purpose of the Euclidean Algorithm which we will meet soon.

Note 2:   A corollary of the above theorem is that the set of all possible linear combinations of a and b is the set of multiples of d. You should be able to prove this since, if $d = ma + nb$ then kd can be expressed similarly. Complete the proof and remember it.

Example 11

Which of the following have a solution in $\mathbb{Z}$, and how many solutions are there?

a $24x + 36y = 12$ **b** $24x + 36y = 18$

a   Since $\gcd(24, 36) = 12$ then
$12 = m(24) + n(36)$ for some integers m and n.

So, $24m + 36n = 12$ and by inspection $m = -1, \ n = 1$ is one solution and $m = 3, \ n = -4$ is another.

(Actually, there are infinitely many solutions of the form $m = -1 + 3t$, $n = 1 - 2t$ where $t \in \mathbb{Z}$.)

However the theorem also states that there is *no other number less than 12* that can be expressed in this way. And, **Note 2** states that the only other numbers expressible like this are the multiples of 12.

So, $24x + 36y = 12$ is solvable in $\mathbb{Z}$ because $12 = \gcd(24, 36)$.

b $24x + 36y = 18$ is not solvable in $\mathbb{Z}$ as 18 is not a multiple of the $\gcd(24, 36)$.

EXERCISE 11A.4.1

1 Which of these equations has a solution in $\mathbb{Z}$? How many solutions are there?

   a $24x + 18y = 9$ **b** $2x + 3y = 67$ **c** $57x + 95y = 19$

   d $1035x + 585y = 90$ **e** $45x - 81y = 108$

2 For the equations in **1**, can you find a solution in $\mathbb{Z}$ by inspection?

3 For any equation in **1**, can you determine the form of all the other (infinite) answers?

Note: Questions **2** and **3** are those addressed by the Euclidean Algorithm.

OTHER IMPORTANT RESULTS

Using the linearity property and the previous theorem we can consider whether two integers are relatively prime in an algebraic manner by noting:

Theorem 5:

> For non-zero integers a and b,
>
> a and b are relatively prime $\Leftrightarrow$ there exist m, n in $\mathbb{Z}$ such that $ma + nb = 1$.

Proof: ($\Rightarrow$) a and b relatively prime

                $\Rightarrow$ $\gcd(a, b) = 1$

                $\Rightarrow$ there exist m, n in $\mathbb{Z}$ such that $ma + nb = 1$ {Theorem 1}

      ($\Leftarrow$)   As $d = \gcd(a, b)$

                $\Rightarrow$ $d \mid a$ and $d \mid b$

                $\Rightarrow$ $d \mid ma + nb$ {divisibility property}

                $\Rightarrow$ $d \mid 1$

                $\Rightarrow$ $d = 1$

Corollary to Theorem 5:

> If $a \mid c$ and $b \mid c$ with $\gcd(a, b) = 1$ then $ab \mid c$.

Proof:

    As $\gcd(a, b) = 1$,   there exist integers m, n such that $ma + nb = 1$

                                    then $mac + nbc = c$ ...... (1)

    Now $a \mid c$ and $b \mid c$ $\Rightarrow$ $c = ka$ and $c = lb$, $k, l \in \mathbb{Z}$

    $\therefore$ $ma(lb) + nb(ka) = c$ $\Rightarrow$ $ab(ml + nk) = c$ $\Rightarrow$ $ab \mid c$

Note: The corollary is important in a practical way since we know, for example,

          $8 \mid 144$ and $9 \mid 144$ and $\gcd(8, 9) = 1$.

          Hence $8 \times 9 \mid 144$,   i.e., $72 \mid 144$.

          However, the result is not true for divisors which are not relatively prime.

          For example, $8 \mid 144$ and $12 \mid 144$ but $8 \times 12 \nmid 144$.

The final result in this section, **Euclid's Lemma**, is of great importance.

Euclid's Lemma:

$$\text{If } a \mid bc \text{ and } \gcd(a, b) = 1, \text{ then } a \mid c.$$

Proof: As $\gcd(a, b) = 1$, there exist integers m, n such that $ma + nb = 1$
$$\therefore \quad mac + nbc = c$$

But $a \mid bc \Rightarrow bc = ka$ for some integer k.

Thus, $mac + n(ka) = c \Rightarrow a(mc + nk) = c \Rightarrow a \mid c$

Note: If the condition $\gcd(a, b) = 1$ is not true, the Lemma fails.

For example, $12 \mid 9 \times 8$, but $12 \nmid 9$.

EXERCISE 11A.4.2

1 Given $a, b, c, d \in \mathbb{Z}$, prove that:

   a if $a \mid b$ then $a \mid bc$ **b** if $a \mid b$ and $a \mid c$ then $a^2 \mid bc$

   c if $a \mid b$ and $c \mid d$ then $ac \mid bd$ **d** if $a \mid b$ then $a^n \mid b^n$.

                                                       Is the converse true?

2 Prove that for $k \in \mathbb{Z}$, one of k, $k + 2$, $k + 4$ is divisible by 3.

3 Determine the truth or otherwise of the statement:

if $p \mid (q + r)$ then either $p \mid q$ or $p \mid r$.

4 **a** Prove that:

     i the product of any three consecutive integers is divisible by 3

    ii the product of any three consecutive integers is divisible by 6

   iii the product of any four consecutive integers is divisible by 4

   iv the product of any four consecutive integers is divisible by 24.

  b Is the product of any n consecutive integers divisible by $n!$?

5 Prove that $3 \mid k(k^2 + 8)$ for all $k \in \mathbb{Z}$.

6 Heta claims that "the product of four consecutive integers is one less than a perfect square".

  a Check Heta's statement with three examples. This is *verifying the statement*.

  b Prove or disprove Heta's claim.

7 **a** Prove that for $a \in \mathbb{Z}$ and $n \in \mathbb{Z}^+$, $\gcd(a, a + n) \mid n$.

  b Hence, prove that $\gcd(a, a + 1) = 1$.

8 Use the linearity property to show that:

  a $\gcd(3k + 1, 13k + 4) = 1$

  b $\gcd(5k + 2, 7k + 3) = 1$

9 **a** Given $a, b \in \mathbb{Z}$, not both zero, prove that $\gcd(4a - 3b, 8a - 5b)$ divides b but not necessarily a.

  b Hence, prove that $\gcd(4a + 3, 8a + 5) = 1$.

10 Prove that:

  a if $\gcd(a, b) = 1$ and $c \mid a$, then $\gcd(c, b) = 1$

   b   if $\gcd(a, b) = 1$, then $\gcd(a^2, b) = \gcd(a, b^2) = 1$ and hence prove that $\gcd(a^2, b^2) = 1$.

11   **a**   Prove, using the identity $x^k - 1 = (x - 1)(x^{k-1} + x^{k-2} + x^{k-3} + \ldots\ldots + x + 1)$, and by considering repunits, that if $d \mid n$ then $(2^d - 1) \mid (2^n - 1)$.

   b   Establish that $2^{35} - 1$ is divisible by both 31 and 127.

12   Show that for $k \in \mathbb{Z}^+$ then these pairs are relatively prime.

   a $3k + 2$ and $5k + 3$ **b** $5k + 3$ and $11k + 7$

13   Given $a, b \in \mathbb{Z}$, and $\gcd(a, b) = 1$, prove that $\gcd(a + b, a - b) = 1$ or 2.

THE EUCLIDEAN ALGORITHM

The Euclidean Algorithm is the most efficient (and a rather ingenious) way of determining the greatest common divisor of two integers. It, too, was detailed in Euclid's Elements and has been known in both East and West since antiquity. It is based on the division algorithm.

The following result is fundamental to all that follows and forms the basis in proof of the Euclidean Algorithm.

Lemma:

       If $a = bq + r$ where a, b and q are integers, then $\gcd(a, b) = \gcd(b, r)$.

Proof:

If we can show that the common divisors of a and b are the same as the common divisors of b and r, we have shown $\gcd(a, b) = \gcd(b, r)$.

If $d \mid a$ and $d \mid b$ $\Rightarrow$ $d \mid (a - bq)$ {linearity property}

                           $\Rightarrow$ $d \mid r$

Hence, any common divisor of a and b is also a common divisor of b and r.

Likewise, if $d \mid b$ and $d \mid r$ $\Rightarrow$ $d \mid bq + r$ $\Rightarrow$ $d \mid a$.

Hence, any common divisor of b and r is also a common divisor of a and b.

Consequently, $\gcd(a, b) = \gcd(b, r)$.

The **Euclidean Algorithm** is the repeated use of the above Lemma, with two given integers, to find their greatest common divisor.

If a and b are positive integers with $a \geqslant b$ and we let $r_0 = a$ and $r_1 = b$ in the recursive formulae below, when we successively apply the division algorithm we obtain

$$\begin{aligned} r_0 &= r_1 q_1 + r_2, & 0 < r_2 < r_1 \\ r_1 &= r_2 q_2 + r_3, & 0 < r_3 < r_2 \\ r_2 &= r_3 q_3 + r_4, & 0 < r_4 < r_3 \\ &\;\;\vdots \\ r_{n-2} &= r_{n-1} q_{n-1} + r_n, & 0 < r_n < r_{n-1} \\ r_{n-1} &= r_n q_n + 0 \end{aligned}$$

then from the above Lemma,

$$\gcd(a, b) = \gcd(r_0, r_1) = \gcd(r_1, r_2) = \ldots\ldots = \gcd(r_{n-1}, r_n) = \gcd(r_n, 0) = r_n$$

Hence the $\gcd(a, b)$ is the last non-zero remainder in the sequence of divisions.

Note: The remainder must eventually be zero since the sequence of positive integer remainders $r_0, r_1, r_2, r_3, \ldots$ is strictly decreasing.

The systematic method to find the greatest common divisor outlined above is known as the **Euclidean Algorithm**. It is remarkable in that it does not depend on finding any of the divisors of the two numbers in question, other than, of course, the greatest common divisor.

Although it is not the only method of doing so, it also provides a method for expressing $\gcd(a, b)$ as a linear combination of a and b if this is desired.

Example 12

Find $\gcd(945, 2415)$ and then find $r, \ s \in \mathbb{Z}$ such that
$$\gcd(945, 2415) = 945r + 2415s.$$

Successive divisions give $2415 = 945(2) + 525$
$$945 = 525(1) + 420$$
$$525 = 420(1) + 105$$
$$420 = 105(4) \qquad \text{Hence } \gcd(945, 2415) = 105$$

We now work backwards, substituting the remainder at each stage

i.e., $105 = 525 - 420$
$$= 525 - (945 - 525)$$
$$= 525 \times 2 - 945$$
$$= (2415 - 945(2)) \times 2 - 945$$
$$= 2415 \times 2 - 4 \times 945 - 945$$
$$= 2415 \times 2 - 5 \times 945$$
$$\therefore \quad r = -5 \text{ and } s = 2$$

Note: r and s are not unique. $r = 41$, $s = -16$ is another solution.

EXERCISE 11A.4.3

1 Find the $\gcd(a, b)$ and integers r and s such that the $\gcd = ra + sb$ for:

   a   803, 154   **b**   12 378, 3054   **c**   3172, 793   **d**   1265, 805

   e   55, 34   **f** $f_{n+1}, \ f_n$ where f_j is the jth Fibonacci number.

2 Find $\gcd(f_{4(n+1)}, f_{4n})$ for different values of n.
   Prove that this result is true for all $n \in \mathbb{Z}^+$.

3 Postulate and prove a similar result (to **2**) for $\gcd(f_{5(n+1)}, f_{5n})$.

LEAST COMMON MULTIPLE

The multiples of 6 are   6, 12, 18, 24, 30, 36, 42, 48, 54, 60, 66, 72, ...
The multiples of 8 are   8, 16, 24, 32, 40, 48, 56, 64, ...
The common multiples of 6 and 8 are: 24, 48, 72, ...
So the least common multiple of 6 and 8 is 24.

A stricter definition follows.

Definition:

> The **least common multiple (lcm)** of integers a and b, denoted $\text{lcm}(a, b)$ is the integer m satisfying
>
> (1) $a \mid m$ and $b \mid m$
>
> (2) if $a \mid c$ and $b \mid c$ where $c > 0$, then $m \leqslant c$.

Note: For integers a, b, $\text{lcm}(a, b)$ always exists and $\text{lcm}(a, b) \leqslant |ab|$.

INVESTIGATION 2   CONNECTING GCD AND LCM

The purpose of this investigation is to find, if it exists, any relationship between the $\gcd(a, b)$ and the $\text{lcm}(a, b)$.

What to do:

1 Find the gcd and lcm of:
   a 70 and 120   **b** 37 and 60   **c** 108 and 168   **d** 450 and 325

2 Find the product of each of the pairs of numbers above.

3 Find the product of the gcd and lcm of each of the pairs of numbers above.

4 Postulate a result from the above.

Theorem 6:

> For positive integers a and b, $\gcd(a, b) \times \text{lcm}(a, b) = ab$.

Proof:

Let $d = \gcd(a, b)$ $\therefore$ $d \mid a$ and $d \mid b$

$\Rightarrow a = dr$ and $b = ds$ for $r, s \in \mathbb{Z}^+$ ...... (1)

Now consider $m = \dfrac{ab}{d}$.

We have to show that $m = \text{lcm}(a, b)$.

$\therefore m = \dfrac{(dr)b}{d}$ and $m = \dfrac{a(ds)}{d}$

i.e., $m = br$ and $m = as$

$\Rightarrow m$ is a positive common multiple of a and b.

Now let c be *any* integer positive multiple of a and b

$\Rightarrow c = au$ and $c = bv$ say, where $u, v \in \mathbb{Z}^+$.

Since $d = \gcd(a, b)$, there exist $x, y \in \mathbb{Z}$ such that $d = ax + by$

$\therefore \dfrac{c}{m} = \dfrac{c}{\dfrac{ab}{d}} = \dfrac{cd}{ab} = \dfrac{c(ax + by)}{ab} = \left(\dfrac{c}{b}\right)x + \left(\dfrac{c}{a}\right)y$

Hence $\left(\dfrac{c}{m}\right) = vx + uy$ i.e., $c = (vx + uy)m$

$\Rightarrow m \mid c \Rightarrow m \leqslant c \Rightarrow m = \text{lcm}(a, b)$

Corollary:

$$\text{For integers } a \text{ and } b, \quad \text{lcm}(a, b) = ab \iff \gcd(a, b) = 1$$

EXERCISE 11A.4.4

1 Find the gcd and lcm of:

    a 143, 227   **b** 272, 1749   **c** 3054, 12 378   **d** 267, 1121

A.5   THE LINEAR DIOPHANTINE EQUATION $ax + by = c$

The following section relates the Euclidean algorithm to the study of the simplest of all Diophantine equations, the linear Diophantine equation $ax + by = c$.

The Pythagorean equation, or its generalisation to higher powers as in **Fermat's Last Theorem**, is perhaps the most famous of the Diophantine equations.

Linear Diophantine equations are always to be solved in the integers, (or sometimes the positive integers) and have the property that there are two variables (x and y) in the equation and yet with only one equation they therefore have either an infinite number of solutions in $\mathbb{Z}$ or none.

For example, the equation $3x + 6y = 18$ has an infinite set of solutions in the integers, whereas $2x + 10y = 17$ has none at all.

One reason for the last equation having no solution is that the left hand side (LHS) is always even and the right hand side (RHS) is odd.

CONDITION FOR SOLVABILITY OF $ax + by = c$

$$ax + by = c \text{ has a solution} \iff d \mid c \text{ where } d = \gcd(a, b)$$

Proof:

  ($\Rightarrow$) $d = \gcd(a, b), \Rightarrow d \mid a$ and $d \mid b$

                      $\Rightarrow a = dr$ and $b = ds$ for integers r and s

      Now if $x = x_0$ and $y = y_0$ is a solution of $ax + by = c$ then $ax_0 + by_0 = c$

      $\Rightarrow c = ax_0 + by_0 = drx_0 + dsy_0 = d(rx_0 + sy_0)$

      $\Rightarrow d \mid c$

  ($\Leftarrow$) If $d \mid c$ then $c = dt$ for some integer t ...... (1)

      Now there exist $x_0, y_0 \in \mathbb{Z}$ such that $d = ax_0 + by_0$

                                {linearity divisibility property}

      Multiplying by t gives $dt = (ax_0 + by_0)t$

                $\therefore c = a(x_0 t) + b(y_0 t)$ {from (1)}

      Hence $ax + by = c$ has $x = tx_0, y = ty_0$ as a particular solution.

Using the above, we can prove the following theorem which gives a **method** of **solving linear Diophantine equations**.

Theorem 7:

> $ax + by = c$ has a solution $\Leftrightarrow$ $d \mid c$ where $d = \gcd(a, b)$.
>
> If x_0, y_0 is any particular solution, all other solutions are of the form
>
> $$x = x_0 + \left(\tfrac{b}{d}\right) t, \quad y = y_0 - \left(\tfrac{a}{d}\right) t \quad \text{where} \quad t \in \mathbb{Z}.$$

Proof: (of the second part)

Suppose x_0, y_0 is a known solution of $ax + by = c$.

If x', y' is another solution then $ax_0 + by_0 = c = ax' + by'$

$$\Rightarrow \quad a(x_0 - x') = b(y' - y_0) \quad ......(1)$$

Now there exist integers r and s which are relatively prime with $a = dr$ and $b = ds$

and this $\Rightarrow \quad dr(x_0 - x') = ds(y' - y_0)$

$$\Rightarrow \quad r(x_0 - x') = s(y' - y_0)$$

$$\Rightarrow \quad r \mid s(y' - y_0) \quad \text{with} \ \gcd(r, s) = 1 \ ......(2)$$

Now **Euclid's Lemma** states that if $a \mid bc$ and $\gcd(a, b) = 1$, then $a \mid c$.

So, from (2) $r \mid y_0 - y'$

$$\Rightarrow \quad y_0 - y' = rt \quad \text{say,} \quad t \in \mathbb{Z}$$

$$\Rightarrow \quad y' = y_0 - rt$$

and in (1) $a(x_0 - x') = b(-rt)$

$$\Rightarrow \quad dr(x_0 - x') = ds(-rt)$$

$$\Rightarrow \quad x_0 - x' = -st$$

$$\Rightarrow \quad x' = x_0 + st$$

i.e., $x' = x_0 + st$ and $y' = y_0 - rt$

i.e., $x' = x_0 + \left(\tfrac{b}{d}\right) t$ and $y' = y_0 - \left(\tfrac{a}{d}\right) t, \quad t \text{ in } \mathbb{Z}$

Note: Checking this solution:

$$ax + by = a\left(x_0 + \left(\tfrac{b}{d}\right) t\right) + b\left(y_0 - \left(\tfrac{a}{d}\right) t\right) = ax_0 + \tfrac{abt}{d} + by_0 - \tfrac{abt}{d} = ax_0 + by_0 = c \quad \checkmark$$

Graphically, the theorem takes this form:

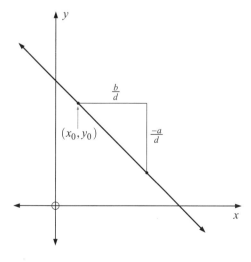

The equation $ax + by = c$ is that of a straight line and its graph has gradient $-\tfrac{a}{b}$ and since $\gcd(a, b) \mid c$, we know that there is an integer solution (x_0, y_0) on this line.

The general solution is obtained by moving a horizontal distance $\tfrac{b}{d}$ to the right (this is an integer) and moving back onto the line. Using the horizontal shift and the gradient of the line it is easy to see that the vertical distance required to regain the line is $-\tfrac{a}{d}$, which is also an integer.

Thus all such solutions are themselves integers.

Example 13

Solve $172x + 20y = 100$ in: **a** $\mathbb{Z}$ **b** $\mathbb{Z}^+$

a   We first find $\gcd(172, 20)$ using the Euclidean Algorithm.

$$172 = 8(20) + 12$$
$$20 = 1(12) + 8$$
$$12 = 1(8) + 4$$
$$8 = 2(4) \qquad \therefore \quad \gcd(172, 20) = 4$$

Now $4 \mid 1000$ $\therefore$ a solution in integers exists.

We now need to write 4 as a linear combination of 172 and 20.

Working backwards: $4 = 12 - 1(8)$
$$= 12 - (20 - 1(12))$$
$$= 12 - 20 + 12$$
$$= 2 \times 12 - 20$$
$$= 2(172 - 8(20)) - 20$$
$$= 2 \times 172 - 17 \times 20$$

Multiplying by 250 gives $1000 = 500 \times 172 - 4250 \times 20$

$\therefore$ $x_0 = 500,$ $y_0 = -4250$ is one solution.

All other solutions have form $x = 500 + \left(\frac{20}{4}\right)t,$ $y = -4250 - \left(\frac{172}{4}\right)t$

i.e., $x = 500 + 5t,$ $y = -4250 - 43t,$ $t \in \mathbb{Z}$.

b   If x and y are in $\mathbb{Z}^+$ we need to solve

$$500 + 5t > 0 \quad \text{and} \quad -4250 - 43t > 0$$

$\therefore$ $5t > -500$ and $43t < -4250$

i.e., $t > -100$ and $t < -98.33......$ $\Rightarrow$ $t = -99$

$\therefore$ $x = 500 + 5(-99)$ and $y = -4250 - 43(-99)$

i.e., $x = 5,$ $y = 7$

So, there is one and only one solution in $\mathbb{Z}^+$.   This is $x = 5,$ $y = 7$.

Corollary:

If $\gcd(a, b) = 1$ and if $x_0 = y_0$ is a solution of $ax + by = c$ then all solutions are given by $x = x_0 + bt,$ $y = y_0 - at,$ $t \in \mathbb{Z}.$

Linear Diophantine equations often are observed in word puzzles.

Following are two of these examples.

Example 14

A cow is worth 10 pieces of gold, a pig is worth 5 pieces of gold and a hen is worth 1 piece of gold. 220 gold pieces are used to buy a total of 100 cows, pigs and hens. How many of each animal is bought?

Let the number of cows be c, the number of pigs be p and the number of hens be h.

$\therefore \quad c + p + h = 100$ {the total number of all animals}

and $\quad 10c + 5p + h = 220$ {the total number of gold pieces}

Subtracting these equations gives $\quad 9c + 4p = 120$ where $\gcd(9, 4) = 1$.

By observation $\quad c_0 = 0$ and $p_0 = 30$ is one solution

$\therefore \quad c = 0 + 4t$ and $p = 30 - 9t$ is the general solution

i.e., $\quad c = 4t, \quad p = 30 - 9t, \quad h = 100 - p - c = 70 + 5t$

But $\quad c, p$ and h are all positive

$\therefore \quad 4t > 0, \qquad\qquad 30 - 9t > 0, \qquad\qquad 70 + 5t > 0$

$\therefore \quad t > 0 \qquad\qquad\quad t < \frac{30}{9} \qquad\qquad\quad \therefore \quad t > -\frac{70}{5}$

i.e., $\quad t = 1, 2$ or 3

So, there are three possible solutions.

$c = 4, p = 21, h = 75 \quad$ or $\quad c = 8, p = 12, h = 80 \quad$ or $\quad c = 12, p = 3, h = 85$

EXERCISE 11A.5

1 Find, where possible, all $x, y \in \mathbb{Z}$ such that:

    a $6x + 51y = 22$ **b** $33x + 14y = 115$ **c** $14x + 35y = 93$

    d $72x + 56y = 40$ **e** $138x + 24y = 18$ **f** $221x + 35y = 11$

2 Find all positive integer solutions of:

    a $18x + 5y = 48$ **b** $54x + 21y = 906$ **c** $123x + 360y = 99$

    d $158x - 57y = 11$

3 Split 100 into two numbers where one of them is divisible by 7 and the other by 11.

4 There are a total of 20 men, women and children at a party.

Each man has 5 drinks, whereas each woman has 4 and each child has 2. They have 62 drinks in total. How many men, women and children are at the party?

5 I wish to buy 100 animals. Cats cost me $5 each, rabbits $1 each and fish 5 cents each. I have $100 to spend and buy at least one of each animal.

If I spent all of my money on the purchase of these animals, how many of each kind of animal did I buy?

6 The cities A and M are 450 km apart. Smith travels from A to M at a *uniform* speed of 55 km/h and his friend Jones travels from M to A at a *uniform* speed of 60 km/h. When they meet, they both look at their watches and exclaim: "It is exactly half past the hour, and I started at half past!". Where do they meet?

7 A person buys a total of 100 blocks of chocolate. The blocks are available in three sizes, costing 35 cents each, 40 cents for three and 5 cents each. If the total cost is $10, how many blocks of each size does the person buy?

A.6   PRIME NUMBERS

Definitions:

An integer p is a **prime number** (or **prime**) if $p > 1$ and if the only positive numbers which divide p are 1 and p itself.

An integer greater than 1 that is not prime is said to be **composite**.

Note: 1 is neither prime nor composite.

Clearly, there are an infinite number of primes, but they appear in an undetermined manner. Thus, it would be useful to discover an efficient way of determining whether or not a given integer were prime. Unfortunately, there is no such way and this lack is the basis of the RSA encryption system, by which so many of the international financial and security transactions are protected. Put in such terms, the study of number theory becomes a highly important and applicable area of study. The basis of the RSA encryption system would be a suitable topic for an Extended Essay in Mathematics.

The primes are the building blocks of the integers and many seemingly basic questions about them, such as how to find the next largest prime, are among the oldest unanswered questions in mathematics.

Here are some fundamental results about primes that rely heavily on previous results:

Lemma 1:   (Euclid's Lemma for primes)

For integers a and b and prime p, if $p \mid ab$ then either $p \mid a$ or $p \mid b$.

Proof: If $p \mid a$ the proof is complete, so suppose $p \nmid a$. We must now show $p \mid b$.

Since $\gcd(a, p) = 1$, there exist integers r and s such that $ar + ps = 1$.

$\therefore$ $b = b \times 1 = b(ar + ps) = abr + bps$

But as $p \mid ab$, $ab = kp$ for some integer k

$\therefore$ $b = kpr + bps = p(kr + bs) \Rightarrow p \mid b$

Lemma 2:

If p is a prime and $p \mid a_1 a_2 a_3 ...... a_n$ for $a_1, a_2, a_3, ..., a_n \in \mathbb{Z}$ all $\geqslant 2$ then there exists i where $1 \leqslant i \leqslant n$ such that $p \mid a_i$.

For example,   if $p \mid 6 \times 11 \times 24$ then $p \mid 6$ or $p \mid 11$ or $p \mid 24$.

Proof: (By Induction)

(1)   If $n = 1$, i.e., $p \mid a_1$, P(1) is obviously true.

(2)   If P(k) is true, then $p \mid a_1 a_2 a_3 ..... a_k \Rightarrow p \mid a_i$ where $1 \leqslant i \leqslant k$ for some i.

Now if $p \mid a_1 a_2 a_3 ..... a_k a_{k+1}$ then $p \mid (a_1 a_2 a_3 ...... a_k) a_{k+1}$

$\Rightarrow p \mid a_1 a_2 a_3 .... a_k$ or $p \mid a_{k+1}$ {using Lemma 1}

$\Rightarrow p \mid a_i$ for some i in $1 \leqslant i \leqslant k$ or $p \mid a_{k+1}$

$\Rightarrow p \mid a_i$ for some i in $1 \leqslant i \leqslant k + 1$

Thus   P($k + 1$) is true whenever P(k) is true and P(1) is true

$\Rightarrow$ P(n) is true   {P of MI}

Now we prove what is arguably the crowning theorem of number theory "**The Fundamental Theorem of Arithmetic**". It is a result that everyone knows and accepts without a lot of questions, but without which we would have a rather different viewpoint of numbers.

THE FUNDAMENTAL THEOREM OF ARITHMETIC

Every positive integer greater than 1 is either prime or is expressible uniquely as a product of primes.

Proof:

Existence   Let S be the set of positive integers which cannot be written as a product of primes, and suppose S is non-empty.

By the Well Ordered Principle, S has a smallest number, a say.

If the only factors of a are a and 1 then a is a prime which is a contradiction.

Hence a can be factored. So, $a = a_1 a_2$ where $1 < a_1 < a$, $1 < a_2 < a$.

But, neither a_1 nor a_2 are in S since a is the smallest member of S.

Consequently, a_1 and a_2 can be factorised into primes.

$a_1 = p_1 p_2 p_3 ...... p_r$ and $a_2 = q_1 q_2 q_3 ...... q_s$ say.

$\therefore$ $a = a_1 a_2 = (p_1 p_2 p_3 ...... p_r)(q_1 q_2 q_3 ...... q_s)$ $\Rightarrow$ $a \notin S$

Uniqueness   Suppose an integer n which is $\geqslant 2$ has two different factorisations

i.e., $n = p_1 p_2 p_3 ..... p_s = q_1 q_2 q_3 ...... q_t$ where $p_i \neq q_j$ for all i, j.

However, by **Lemma 2**, $p_1 \mid q_j$ for some j.

$\Rightarrow$ $p_1 = q_j$ {as these are primes}

As this process can be continued for $p_2, p_3, ... p_s$ this leads to a contradiction.

So, the p_is are a rearrangement of the q_js and so the prime factorisation is unique.

Example 15

Discuss the prime factorisation of 360, including how many factors 360 has.

2	360
2	180
2	90
3	45
3	15
	5

$\therefore$ $180 = 2^3 \times 3^2 \times 5^1$ and this factorisation is unique apart from order of the factors.

The only prime factors of 180 are 2, 3 and 5.

Including 1 and 360,   360 has $(3+1)(2+1)(1+1)$
$= 4 \times 3 \times 2$
$= 24$ factors.

Check the last part of **Example 15** by listing all 24 factors of 360 in a systematic way.

One such factor is $2^0 \times 3^0 \times 5^0$,   another is $2^2 \times 3^1 \times 5^0$.

EXERCISE 11A.6.1

1 $2^8 \times 3^4 \times 7^2$ is a perfect square.   It equals $(2^4 \times 3^2 \times 7)^2$.

Prove that:

    a all the powers in the prime-power factorisation of $n \in \mathbb{Z}^+$ are even $\Leftrightarrow$ n is a square

    b given $n \in \mathbb{Z}^+$, the number of factors of n is odd $\Leftrightarrow$ n is a square.

2 Use the result of question **1** to prove that $\sqrt{2}$ is irrational.

    (This is yet another way of establishing that $\sqrt{2}$ is irrational.)

Here is another version of the proof of the irrationality of $\sqrt{2}$.

Example 16

Prove that $\sqrt{2}$ is irrational.

Proof: (By contradiction)

Suppose that $\sqrt{2}$ is rational. $\therefore$ $\sqrt{2} = \frac{p}{q}$ where $p, q \in \mathbb{Z}^+$, $\gcd(p, q) = 1$

Since $\gcd(p, q) = 1$,   there exist $r, s \in \mathbb{Z}^+$ such that $rp + sq = 1$

Hence, $\sqrt{2} = \sqrt{2}(rp + sq) = (\sqrt{2}p)r + (\sqrt{2}q)s$

$\Rightarrow$ $\sqrt{2} = (\sqrt{2}\sqrt{2}q)r + (\sqrt{2}\frac{p}{\sqrt{2}})s$ {using $\sqrt{2} = \frac{p}{q}$}

$\Rightarrow$ $\sqrt{2} = 2qr + ps$

$\Rightarrow$ $\sqrt{2}$ is an integer   {as p, q, r and s are in $\mathbb{Z}^+$}

     clearly a contradiction.

Finally, we present a theorem that can be used to reduce the work in identifying whether a given integer, n, is prime. In it we show that we need only attempt to divide n by all the primes $p \leqslant \sqrt{n}$. If none of these is a divisor, then n must itself be prime.

Theorem 8:

         If n is composite, then n has a prime divisor p such that $p \leqslant \sqrt{n}$.

Proof:

       Let n be a composite. Then $n = ab$ with $n > a > 1$ and $n > b > 1$.

       Suppose $a > \sqrt{n}$ and $b > \sqrt{n}$.   Then $ab > n$ i.e., $n > n$, a contradiction.

       $\therefore$ at least one of a or b must be $\leqslant n$.

       Without loss of generality, suppose $a \leqslant \sqrt{n}$.

       Since $a > 1$, there exists a prime p such that $p \mid a$.

       But $a \mid n$, $\therefore$ $p \mid n$ {$p \mid a$ and $a \mid n \Rightarrow p \mid n$} with $p \leqslant a \leqslant \sqrt{n}$.

Example 17	What is the largest possible prime factor of a composite three digit integer?

The largest 3-digit integer is 999 and $\sqrt{999} = 31.61.....$

and the largest prime factor less than this is 31.

EXERCISE 11A.6.2

1 Which are primes?   **a** 143   **b** 221   **c** 199   **d** 223

2 Prove that 2 is the only even prime.

3 **a** Prove that if $a, n \in \mathbb{Z}^+$, $n \geqslant 2$ and $a^n - 1$ is prime then $a = 2$.
       (**Hint:** Consider $1 + a + a^2 + ... + a^{n-1}$ and its sum.)
   b It is claimed that $2^n - 1$ is always prime for $n \geqslant 2$. Is the claim true?
   c It is claimed that $2^n - 1$ is always composite for $n \geqslant 2$. Is the claim true?
       (**Hint:** Consider $n = kl$ and the hint in **a**.)
   d If n is prime, is $2^n - 1$ always prime? Explain.

4 Is the third repunit a prime? Is the fourth? Is the fifth?

5 Show that if p and q are primes and $p \mid q$, then $p = q$.

6 Find the prime factorisations of: **a** 9555   **b** 989   **c** 9999   **d** 111 111

7 Which positive integers have exactly:
   a   three positive divisors   **b**   four positive divisors?

8 **a** Find all prime numbers which divide 50!
   b How many zeros are at the end of 50! when converted to an integer?
   c Find all $n \in \mathbb{Z}$ such that $n!$ ends in exactly 74 zeros.

9 Given that p is prime, prove that:
   a $p \mid a^n \Rightarrow p^n \mid a^n$ **b** $p \mid a^2 \Rightarrow p \mid a$ **c** $p \mid a^n \Rightarrow p \mid a$

10 There are infinitely many primes. 2 is the only even prime.
   a Explain why the form of odd primes can be $4n + 1$ or $4n + 3$.
   b Prove that there are infinitely many primes of the form $4n + 3$.

Note: • There are also an infinite number of primes of the form $4n + 1$, however the proof of this result is beyond the scope of our work here. Perhaps it could be investigated as an Extended Essay topic.

   • The **repunits** R_k are prime only if k is prime and then it is not necessarily so. Thus far, the only prime repunits discovered are R_2, R_{19}, R_{23}, R_{317}, and R_{1031}.

   • Another famous type of primes are those of the form $2^n - 1$, which, as we have seen, are prime only if n is prime (and that this is no guarantee). Such primes are called **Mersenne primes**, after the contemporary of **Fermat**, and the search for these continues to this day. They are linked to numbers like 6 and 28 which are the first two "**perfect numbers**". Again, this might be a fruitful area for research for an Extended Essay.

- A final type are those of the form $2^{2n}+1$; these are the Fermat primes. $n = 3, 5$ and 17 are the first three, but finding others is difficult since they become large rather quickly. Fermat believed that all such numbers were prime whenever n was prime. Clearly, with hindsight, he was mistaken.

A.7   LINEAR CONGRUENCES

The theory of congruences was developed by **Gauss**, whose saying that "Mathematics is the queen of sciences and the theory of numbers is the queen of mathematics." is much quoted. It is one of the most useful tools in number theory and we shall use it to revisit Diophantine equations and to extend our work to **Fermat's Little Theorem**.

Definition:

Two integers a and b are **congruent modulo m** if they leave the same remainder when divided by m.

We write $a \equiv b \pmod{m}$.

For example $7 = 3 \times 2 + 1$ and $64 = 3 \times 21 + 1$ $\therefore$ $64 \equiv 7 \pmod{3}$.
Notice that $64 - 7 = 57 = 3 \times 19$ i.e., $3 \mid 64 - 7$.

Examples like the one above lead to an algebraic definition:

$$a \equiv b \pmod{m} \iff m \mid (a - b) \qquad \text{or}$$

$$a \equiv b \pmod{m} \iff \text{there exists } k \in \mathbb{Z} \text{ such that } a = b + km.$$

The last statement is the most useful.

Note: • $37 \equiv 2 \pmod{5}$ as $37 - 2 = 35$ is divisible by 5.
$43 \equiv 1 \pmod{7}$ as $43 - 1 = 42$ is divisible by 7.
$a \equiv 0 \pmod{7}$ $\Rightarrow$ $a = 7m$ i.e., a is a multiple of 7.

- If $2x \equiv 3 \pmod{5}$ then $x \neq 1.5$

  In fact $x = 4$ is one solution and all others have the form $x = 4 + 5k$, $k \in \mathbb{Z}$.   We examine equations like this in a later section.

Note:

Congruences modulo m form an **equivalence relation** since they satisfy the three properties reflexivity, symmetry and transitivity and thus they impose a partition on the set of integers. The theory of equivalance relations will be covered in the abstract algebra module of the course. They are stated below:

Reflexive: If $a \in \mathbb{Z}$ then $a \equiv a \pmod{m}$.

Symmetric: If $a, \, b \in \mathbb{Z}$ with $a \equiv b \pmod{m}$ then $b \equiv a \pmod{m}$.

Transitive: If $a, \, b, \, c \in \mathbb{Z}$ with $a \equiv b \pmod{m}$ and $b \equiv c \pmod{m}$ then $a \equiv c \pmod{m}$.

It is suggested that the reader prove these results.

The partition induced by the equivalence relation gives what is referred to as the **congruence classes modulo m** or the **residue classes modulo m**.

Clearly, the form of the definition of congruences $a \equiv b \pmod m$ $\Leftrightarrow$ $a = b + km$ links nicely with the idea of the division algorithm, and using the division algorithm we can obtain the result for the "complete system of residues modulo m".

Consider the equation $a = bm + r$, where $0 \leqslant r \leqslant m - 1$, then clearly $a \equiv r \pmod m$ and we call r the least non-negative residue of $a \bmod (m)$.

Generalising this to all integers, we can state that **all** integers are congruent to one of the possible values of r, namely, one of the set $\{0, 1, 2, 3, \ldots\ldots (m-1)\}$.

This set is called the **complete system of residues modulo** m.

MODULAR ARITHMETIC

Modular arithmetic deals with the manipulation of residues.

As a general rule, we try to reduce all integers to their **least** residue equivalent at all times. This simplifies the arithmetic.

For example,

$$19 + 14 \pmod 8 \qquad\qquad 19 - 14 \pmod 8 \qquad\qquad 19 \times 14 \pmod 8$$
$$= 3 + 6 \pmod 8 \qquad\qquad = 5 \pmod 8 \qquad\qquad = 3 \times 6 \pmod 8$$
$$= 9 \pmod 8 \qquad\qquad\qquad\qquad\qquad\qquad\qquad = 18 \pmod 8$$
$$= 1 \pmod 8 \qquad\qquad\qquad\qquad\qquad\qquad\qquad = 2 \pmod 8$$

There are no problems in dealing with addition, subtraction and multiplication $\pmod m$. However, problems arise with division.

For example, consider $14 \equiv 8 \pmod 6$, a true statement

but $7 \not\equiv 4 \pmod 6$, dividing 14 and 8 by 2.

Solving equivalence equations is more difficult than we would have initially thought.

For example, can you solve these by inspection?

$$3x \equiv 4 \pmod 7, \quad 4x - 3 \equiv 5 \pmod 6 \quad \text{or} \quad x^2 \equiv 3 \pmod 6$$

Is there a unique solution to each equation?

The following Investigation helps develop the techniques needed to solve such equations.

INVESTIGATION 3   MODULAR ALGEBRA

Recall that $a \equiv b \pmod m$ $\Rightarrow$ $m \mid (a - b)$ or $a = b + km$ for $k \in \mathbb{Z}$.

What to do: Prove the following results.

1 Rules for $+$, $-$ and $\times$

Given $a \equiv b \pmod m$ and $c \equiv d \pmod m$ then:

  a $a + c \equiv b + d \pmod m$ **b** $a - c \equiv b - d \pmod m$ **c** $ka \equiv kb \pmod m$

2 Condition for division (cancellation)

  a If $ka \equiv kb \pmod m$ and $\gcd(k, m) = 1$, then $a \equiv b \pmod m$.

  b If $ka \equiv kb \pmod m$ and $\gcd(k, m) = d$, then $a \equiv b \pmod{\frac{m}{d}}$.

3 If $a \equiv b \pmod m$ then $a^n \equiv b^n \pmod m$ for all $n \in \mathbb{Z}^+$.

  (**Note:** The converse is not necessarily true.)

4 If $f(x)$ is a polynomial with integer coefficients and $a \equiv b \pmod m$, then $f(a) \equiv f(b) \pmod m$.

If you have understood the implications of the investigation you should now be able to do these.

1 Find the remainder when:

    a 65^{22} is divided by 7   **b** $2^{100} + 3^{100}$ is divided by 5.

2 Find the last two digits of 203^{20}.

3 Prove that an integer is divisible by 3 only if the sum of its digits is divisible by 3.

These questions are attempted by a trial and improvement method, in which experience plays a part. Thus, the solution will seem rather neat on initial reading, but the method will become apparent as your familiarity with the material grows.

SUMMARY OF RULES

- If $a \equiv b \pmod{m}$ and $c \equiv d \pmod{m}$ then
$a \pm c \equiv b \pm d \pmod{m}$, $ka \equiv kb \pmod{m}$, $a^n \equiv b^n \pmod{m}$.

- If $ka \equiv kb \pmod{m}$, $\gcd(k, m) = d$ then $a \equiv b \pmod{\frac{m}{d}}$.

- If $f(x)$ is a polynomial with integer coefficients then
$a \equiv b \pmod{m} \Rightarrow f(a) \equiv f(b) \pmod{m}$.

Example 18

Find the remainder when 65^{22} is divided by 7.

$$65 \equiv 2 \pmod{7} \qquad \{\text{as } 65 - 2 = 63 = 9 \times 7\}$$
$$\therefore \quad 65^{22} \equiv 2^{22} \pmod{7}$$
$$\equiv (2^3)^7 \times 2 \pmod{7}$$
$$\equiv 1 \times 2 \pmod{7} \qquad \{\text{as } 2^3 = 8 \equiv 1\}$$
$$\equiv 2 \pmod{7}$$
$$\therefore \quad 65^{22} \text{ leaves a remainder of 2 when divided by 7.}$$

Example 19

Prove that $41 \mid 2^{40} - 1$.

$$2^5 = 32 \equiv -9 \pmod{41}$$
$$\therefore \quad 2^{40} = (2^5)^8 \equiv (-9)^8 \pmod{41}$$
$$\text{But} \quad (-9)^2 = 81 \equiv -1 \pmod{41}$$
$$\therefore \quad 2^{40} \equiv (-1)^4 \pmod{41}$$
$$\text{i.e.,} \quad 2^{40} \equiv 1 \pmod{41}$$
$$\therefore \quad 2^{40} - 1 \equiv 0 \pmod{41} \quad \text{and so} \quad 41 \mid 2^{40} - 1.$$

Example 20

Find the remainder on dividing $\displaystyle\sum_{k=1}^{50} k!$ by 30.

This is equivalent to finding $\displaystyle\sum_{k=1}^{50} k!$ (mod 30)

We first note that $\quad 5! = 120 \equiv 0 \;(\text{mod}\,30)$

$$\therefore \quad k! \equiv 0 \;(\text{mod}\,30) \quad \text{for all } k \geqslant 5$$

$$\therefore \quad \sum_{k=1}^{50} k! \;(\text{mod}\,30) \equiv 1! + 2! + 3! + 4! \;(\text{mod}\,30)$$

$$\text{i.e., } \equiv 1 + 2 + 6 + 24 \;(\text{mod}\,30)$$

$$\equiv 3 \;(\text{mod}\,30)$$

$\therefore$ the remainder is 3.

EXERCISE 11A.7.1

1 Are the following pairs congruent (mod 7)?

   a   1, 15   **b** -1, 8   **c**   2, 99   **d** -1, 699

2 For which positive integers m are these true?

   a $29 \equiv 7 \;(\text{mod}\,m)$ **b** $100 \equiv 1 \;(\text{mod}\,m)$

   c $53 \equiv 0 \;(\text{mod}\,m)$ **d** $61 \equiv 1 \;(\text{mod}\,m)$

3 Find:

   a $\displaystyle\sum_{k=1}^{50} k! \;(\text{mod}\,20)$ **b** $\displaystyle\sum_{k=1}^{50} k! \;(\text{mod}\,42)$

   c $\displaystyle\sum_{k=10}^{100} k! \;(\text{mod}\,12)$ **d** $\displaystyle\sum_{k=4}^{30} k! \;(\text{mod}\,10)$

4 Find:

   a $2^{28} \;(\text{mod}\,7)$ **b** $10^{33} \;(\text{mod}\,7)$ **c** $3^{50} \;(\text{mod}\,7)$ **d** $41^{23} \;(\text{mod}\,7)$

5 Find:

   a $2^{28} \;(\text{mod}\,37)$ **b** $3^{65} \;(\text{mod}\,13)$ **c** $7^{44} \;(\text{mod}\,11)$

6 Prove that:

   a $53^{103} + 103^{53}$ is divisible by 39   **b** $333^{111} + 111^{333}$ is divisible by 7

7 **a**   Find:

         i $5^{10} \;(\text{mod}\,11)$ **ii** $3^{12} \;(\text{mod}\,13)$ **iii** $2^{18} \;(\text{mod}\,19)$ **iv** $7^{16} \;(\text{mod}\,17)$

       Can you postulate a theorem from these results?

   b   What about   **i** $4^{11} \;(\text{mod}\,12)$ **ii** $5^8 \;(\text{mod}\,9)$?

       Do these results agree with your postulate?

   c   Finally, does $13^4 \;(\text{mod}\,5)$ agree?

8 a Find:

  i $2! \pmod 3$ **ii** $4! \pmod 5$ **iii** $10! \pmod{11}$ **iv** $6! \pmod 7$

  Can you postulate a theorem from these results?

 b What about   **i** $3! \pmod 4$ **ii** $5! \pmod 6$?

  Do these results agree with your postulate?

 c Finally, does $12! \pmod{13}$ agree?

  (The proof of this result is intimately linked with the ideas of group theory that form a part of another option in the IB Higher Level Course.)

9 Prove that:

  a $7 \mid 5^{2n} + 3 \times 2^{5n-2}$ **b** $13 \mid 3^{n+2} + 4^{2n+1}$ **c** $27 \mid 5^{n+2} + 2^{5n+1}$

10 Prove that the square of any even integer $\equiv 0 \pmod 4$ and the square of any odd integer $\equiv 1 \pmod 4$.

11 Prove that the square of any integer $\equiv 0$ or $1 \pmod 3$.

12 Prove that the cube of any integer $\equiv 0$ or 1 or $8 \pmod 9$.

13 Prove that the square of any odd integer $\equiv 1 \pmod 8$.   What about the squares of even integers $\pmod 8$?

14 Show that if $a, b, c \in \mathbb{Z}^+$, such that $a \equiv b \pmod c$ then $\gcd(a, c) = \gcd(b, c)$. What does this restate?

15 Solve the congruences $x^2 \equiv 1 \pmod 3$ and $x^2 \equiv 4 \pmod 7$.

  Given that $x^2 \equiv a^2 \pmod p$ where $x, a \in \mathbb{Z}$ and p is prime, can you deduce anything about a relation between x and a?

16 Show that if n is an odd positive integer, then $\displaystyle\sum_{k=1}^{n} k \equiv 0 \pmod n$.

  Determine what happens if n is even.

17 By considering n having one of the forms $n = 4m + r$ for $r = 0, 1, 2, 3$ determine when it is true that $\displaystyle\sum_{k=1}^{n-1} k^3 \equiv 0 \pmod n$.

18 For which positive integers n is it true that $\displaystyle\sum_{k=1}^{n} k^2 \equiv 0 \pmod n$?

19 a Prove by induction that for $n \in \mathbb{Z}^+$, $3^n \equiv 1 + 2n \pmod 4$ and also that $4^n \equiv 1 + 3n \pmod 9$.

 b Is the similar result $5^n \equiv 1 + 4n \pmod{16}$ also true?   Generalise.

20 Prove that the eleventh Mersenne number $2^{11} - 1$ is divisible by 23, and thus not prime.

THE RULES FOR CANCELLATION IN CONGRUENCES

From the Investigation we saw that:

if $a \equiv b \pmod m$ then $ca \equiv cb \pmod m$,   but the converse did not necessarily hold.

We now prove the theorem observed.

Theorem 9:

$$\text{If } ca \equiv cb \ (\text{mod}\, m) \text{ and } \gcd(c,\, m) = d \text{ then } a \equiv b \ \left(\text{mod}\, \tfrac{m}{d}\right).$$

Proof: $ca \equiv cb \ (\text{mod}\, m) \ \Rightarrow \ ca = cb + km \quad \text{for some } k \in \mathbb{Z}$

But since $\gcd(c,\, m) = d,$ there exist relatively prime r and s such that
$c = rd$ and $m = sd$

$\Rightarrow \ rda = rdb + ksd$

$\Rightarrow \ ra = rb + ks$

$\Rightarrow \ r(a - b) = ks$

$\Rightarrow \ s \mid r(a - b)$ where r, s are relatively prime

$\Rightarrow \ s \mid (a - b)$ {Euclid's Lemma}

Thus $a - b = ks = k\left(\tfrac{m}{d}\right)$ i.e., $a \equiv b \bmod \left(\tfrac{m}{d}\right)$

Consequences:

- A common factor c in a congruence can be cancelled if c and the modulus m are relatively prime. This is the case since $\gcd(c,\, m) = 1,$
  i.e., if $ca \equiv cb \ (\text{mod}\, m)$ and $\gcd(c,\, m) = 1,$ then $a \equiv b \ (\text{mod}\, m).$

- If $ca \equiv cb \ (\text{mod}\, p)$ and $p \nmid c$ and p is prime then $a \equiv b \ (\text{mod}\, p).$

Example 21

Simplify if possible: **a** $33 \equiv 15 \ (\text{mod}\, 9)$ **b** $-35 \equiv 45 \ (\text{mod}\, 8)$

a	**b**
$33 \equiv 15 \ (\text{mod}\, 9)$	$-35 \equiv 45 \ (\text{mod}\, 8)$
i.e., $11 \times 3 \equiv 5 \times 3 \ (\text{mod}\, 9)$	i.e., $-7 \times 5 \equiv 9 \times 5 \ (\text{mod}\, 8)$
and $\gcd(3,\, 9) \equiv 3$	and $\gcd(5,\, 8) = 1$
$\therefore \ 11 \equiv 5 \ (\text{mod}\, \tfrac{9}{3})$	$\therefore \ -7 = 9 \ (\text{mod}\, 8)$
i.e., $11 \equiv 5 \ (\text{mod}\, 3)$	

Note:

- $ab \equiv 0 \ (\text{mod}\, n)$ may occur without $a \equiv 0 \ (\text{mod}\, n)$ or $b \equiv 0 \ (\text{mod}\, n)$.
  For example, $4 \times 3 = 0 \ (\text{mod}\, 12),$ but $4 \not\equiv 0 \ (\text{mod}\, 12)$ or $3 \not\equiv 0 \ (\text{mod}\, 12)$.

- If $ab \equiv 0 \ (\text{mod}\, n)$ and $\gcd(a,\, n) = 1,$ then $b \equiv 0 \ (\text{mod}\, n)$
  using the first consequence above.

- If $ab \equiv 0 \ (\text{mod}\, p) \ \Rightarrow \ a = 0 \ (\text{mod}\, p)$ or $b \equiv 0 \ (\text{mod}\, p)$
  using the second consequence above.

LINEAR CONGRUENCES

Linear congruences are equations of the form $ax \equiv b \ (\text{mod}\, m).$

In this section we develop the theory for the solution of these equations.

Suppose $x = x_0$ is a solution of $ax \equiv b \ (\text{mod}\, m),$ then $ax_0 \equiv b \ (\text{mod}\, m).$

So, $ax_0 = b + y_0 m$ for some $y_0 \in \mathbb{Z}$.

Thus solving a linear congruence is identical to solving a linear Diophantine equation except that there are not infinitely many solutions, as we have to work within the modulus.

Our goal is to obtain all **incongruent** solutions to $ax \equiv b \pmod{m}$ as all congruent solutions are considered to be the same.

For example, for the equation $4x \equiv 8 \pmod{12}$

$\quad\quad x = 2$, $x = -10$ and $x = 14$ are the same solution, whereas

$\quad\quad x = 2$, $x = 5$, $x = 8$ and $x = 11$ are different solutions.

$\quad\quad$ So, $4x \equiv 8 \pmod{12} \Rightarrow x = 2, 5, 8$ or 11.

A formal solution to this equation follows as a result of the next theorem.

Theorem 10:

$\quad\quad ax \equiv b \pmod{m}$ has a solution $\Leftrightarrow d \mid b$ where $d = \gcd(a, m)$ and the equation has d mutually incongruent solutions modulo m.

Proof: $\quad ax \equiv b \pmod{m}$ is equivalent to solving $ax - my = b$.

$\quad\quad$ Hence $d \mid b$ is the necessary and sufficient condition for a solution to exist. (See Diophantine equations' work.)

$\quad\quad$ Further, if x_0, y_0 is a solution then all solutions are

$\quad\quad x = x_0 + \left(\frac{m}{d}\right) t, \quad y = y_0 + \left(\frac{a}{d}\right) t, \quad t \in \mathbb{Z}.$

$\quad\quad$ We now show that the infinite solutions are partitioned into d mutually incongruent solutions due to the fact that we are now in modulo m.

$\quad\quad$ If $t = 0, 1, 2, 3, \ldots\ldots, (d-1)$ we obtain

$\quad\quad x = x_0, \ x_0 + \left(\frac{m}{d}\right), \ x_0 + 2\left(\frac{m}{d}\right), \ x_0 + 3\left(\frac{m}{d}\right), \ \ldots\ldots, \ x_0 + (d-1)\left(\frac{m}{d}\right) \ \ldots\ldots (*)$

$\quad\quad$ We now claim that these integers are incongruent modulo m and all other integers are equivalent to some of them.

$\quad\quad$ Suppose two of them are equal, i.e., $x_0 + \left(\frac{m}{d}\right) t_1 \equiv x_0 + \left(\frac{m}{d}\right) t_2 \pmod{m}$ where $0 \leqslant t_1 < t_2 \leqslant (d-1)$

$\quad\quad \Rightarrow \left(\frac{m}{d}\right) t_1 \equiv \left(\frac{m}{d}\right) t_2 \pmod{m}$ and since $\gcd\left(\frac{m}{d}, m\right) = \frac{m}{d}$ we can use the

$\quad\quad$ cancellation law to get $t_1 \equiv t_2 \pmod{m}$.

$\quad\quad$ However, $t_1 \equiv t_2 \pmod{m} \Rightarrow d \mid t_2 - t_1$ which contradicts $0 \leqslant t_1 < t_2 \leqslant (d-1)$ as $t_2 - t_1 \leqslant (d-1) < d$.

$\quad\quad$ Thus the integers in $*$ are mutually incongruent.

$\quad\quad$ It remains to prove that any other solution $x_0 + \left(\frac{m}{d}\right) t$ is congruent $\pmod{m}$ to one of the d integers in $*$. We do this by using the Division Algorithm. Since t can be written as $t = qd + r$ where t is outside the set of least positive integers, with $0 \leqslant r \leqslant (d-1)$ where r is one of the original incongruent solutions,

$\quad\quad\quad\quad$ then $x_0 + \left(\frac{m}{d}\right) t = x_0 + \left(\frac{m}{d}\right)(qd + r) = x_0 + mq + \left(\frac{m}{d}\right) r$

$\quad\quad\quad\quad \therefore \ x_0 + \left(\frac{m}{d}\right) t \equiv x_0 + \left(\frac{m}{d}\right) r \pmod{m}$

$\quad\quad\quad\quad$ with $x_0 + \left(\frac{m}{d}\right) r$ being one of the d selected solutions.

It follows that:

If x_0 is any solution of $ax \equiv b \pmod{m}$ and $d = \gcd(a, m)$, there are d incongruent solutions,
$$x = x_0, \; x_0 + \left(\tfrac{m}{d}\right), \; x_0 + 2\left(\tfrac{m}{d}\right), \; x_0 + 3\left(\tfrac{m}{d}\right), \; ......, \; x_0 + (d-1)\left(\tfrac{m}{d}\right)$$

and in the special case where a and m are relatively prime:

If $\gcd(a, m) = 1$ and $ax \equiv b \pmod{m}$ we have a unique solution.

Example 22

Solve: **a** $2x \equiv 3 \pmod 5$ **b** $12x \equiv 24 \pmod{54}$ **c** $9x \equiv 15 \pmod{24}$

a $2x \equiv 3 \pmod 5$ has $\gcd(2, 5) = 1$ $\therefore$ we have a unique solution.
By inspection, $x \equiv 4 \pmod 5$ {as $2 \times 4 = 8 \equiv 3 \pmod 5$}

b $12x \equiv 24 \pmod{54}$ has $\gcd(12, 54) = 6$ and $6 \mid 24$
So, there are exactly 6 non-congruent solutions.
Cancelling by 6 gives $2x \equiv 4 \pmod 9$
$\Rightarrow x \equiv 2 \pmod 9$
$\Rightarrow$ all solutions are $x = 2 + \left(\tfrac{54}{6}\right)t = 2 + 9t$ where $t = 0, 1, 2, 3, 4, 5$
i.e., $x \equiv 2, 11, 20, 29, 38, 47 \pmod{54}$

c $9x \equiv 15 \pmod{24}$ has $\gcd(9, 24) = 3$ and $3 \mid 15$
So, there are exactly 3 non-congruent solutions.
Now $3x \equiv 5 \pmod{\left(\tfrac{24}{3}\right)}$ {as cancellation is possible here}
$\Rightarrow 3x \equiv 5 \pmod 8$
By inspection, $x \equiv 7$
$\therefore$ all solutions have form $x = 7 + 8t \pmod{24}$
$\therefore x \equiv 7, 15$ or $23 \pmod{24}$

EXERCISE 11A.7.2

1 Solve, if possible, the following linear congruences:
a $2x \equiv 3 \pmod 7$ **b** $8x \equiv 5 \pmod{25}$ **c** $3x \equiv 6 \pmod{12}$
d $9x \equiv 144 \pmod{99}$ **e** $18x \equiv 30 \pmod{40}$ **f** $3x \equiv 2 \pmod 7$
g $15x \equiv 9 \pmod{27}$ **h** $56 \equiv 14 \pmod{21}$

2 Determine whether the following statements are true:
a $x \equiv 4 \pmod 7 \Rightarrow \gcd(x, 7) = 1$
b $12x \equiv 15 \pmod{35} \Rightarrow 4x \equiv 5 \pmod 7$
c $12x \equiv 15 \pmod{39} \Rightarrow 4x \equiv 5 \pmod{13}$
d $x \equiv 7 \pmod{14} \Rightarrow \gcd(x, 14) = 7$
e $5x \equiv 5y \pmod{19} \Rightarrow x \equiv y \pmod{19}$

f $3x \equiv y \pmod 8 \Rightarrow 15x = 5y \pmod{40}$

g $10x \equiv 10y \pmod{14} \Rightarrow x \equiv y \pmod 7$

h $x \equiv 41 \pmod{37} \Rightarrow x \pmod{41} = 37$

i $x \equiv 37 \pmod{40}$ and $0 \leqslant x < 40 \Rightarrow x = 37$

j There does not exist $x \in \mathbb{Z}$ such that $15x \equiv 11 \pmod{33}$.

A.8 THE CHINESE REMAINDER THEOREM

This is so called because there were many number puzzles of the following type posed in China, though to be fair, similar puzzles were also found in old manuscripts on the Indian subcontinent and in Greek manuscripts of the same era. They all deal with the simultaneous solution of linear congruences in different moduli.

One such problem was due to **Sun-Tsu** and is:

> Find a number which when divided by 3 leaves a remainder of 1 and when divided by 5 leaves a remainder of 2 and when divided by 7 leaves a remainder of 3.

If we put this in congruence notation, we are being asked to find x such that $x \equiv 1 \pmod 3$, $x \equiv 2 \pmod 5$ and $x \equiv 3 \pmod 7$.

The general method of solution of such simultaneous congruences is termed **The Chinese Remainder Theorem**, named in honour of the above problem and its Chinese heritage. But, before we proceed to the theory, can you solve the above problem by trial and error?

THE CHINESE REMAINDER THEOREM

If m_1, m_2, m_3, ..., m_r are pairwise relatively prime positive integers, then the system of congruences

$x \equiv a_1 \pmod{m_1}$, $x \equiv a_2 \pmod{m_2}$, $x \equiv a_3 \pmod{m_3}$, ..., $x \equiv a_r \pmod{m_r}$

has a unique solution modulo $M = m_1 m_2 m_3 ..... m_r$.

This solution is $x \equiv a_1 M_1 x_1 + a_2 M_2 x_2 + ... + a_r M_r x_r \pmod M$

where $M_k = \dfrac{M}{m_k}$ and x_i is the solution of $M_i x_i \equiv 1 \pmod{m_i}$.

Proof:

Existence First we construct a simultaneous solution to the system.

Let $M_k = \dfrac{M}{m_k} = m_1 m_2 m_3 ..... m_{k-1} m_{k+1} ..... m_r$.

Now since $\gcd(M_k, m_k) = 1$, by our theory of linear congruences it is possible to solve all r linear congruences.

The unique solution x_k is given by $M_k x_k \equiv 1 \pmod{m_k}$.

Observe that $M_i \equiv 0 \pmod{m_k}$ for $i \neq k$.

This is because $m_k \mid M_i$ in these cases.

Hence $a_1 M_1 x_1 + a_2 M_2 x_2 + ... + a_r M_r x_r \equiv a_k M_k x_k \pmod{m_k}$
$$\equiv a_k(1) \pmod{m_k}$$
$$\equiv a_k \pmod{m_k}$$

$\therefore \quad X \equiv a_1 M_1 x_1 + a_2 M_2 x_2 + \ldots\ldots + a_r M_r x_r \quad$ is a solution of

$\qquad x \equiv a_k \pmod{m_k} \quad$ for $\quad k = 1, 2, 3, \ldots., r$

$\qquad\qquad$ i.e., a solution exists.

Uniqueness $\quad$ Suppose X' is any other integer which satisfies the system

$\qquad \Rightarrow \quad X = a_1 M_1 x_1 + a_2 M_2 x_2 + \ldots\ldots + a_r M_r x_r \equiv a_k \equiv X' \pmod{m_k}$

$\qquad\qquad\qquad\qquad\qquad\qquad$ for all $\quad k = 1, 2, 3, 4, \ldots\ldots, r$

$\qquad \Rightarrow \quad m_k \mid X - X'$

and because the moduli are relatively prime

$\qquad\qquad m_1 \mid X - X', \quad m_2 \mid X - X', \quad \ldots\ldots, \quad m_r \mid X - X'$

$\qquad \Rightarrow \quad m_1 m_2 m_3 \ldots\ldots m_k \mid X - X'$

$\qquad \Rightarrow \quad M \mid X - X'$

$\qquad \Rightarrow \quad X \equiv X' \pmod{M}$

Example 23

Solve Sun-Tsu's problem
i.e., solve $\ x \equiv 1 \pmod 3$, $\ x \equiv 2 \pmod 5$, $\ x \equiv 3 \pmod 7$

3, 5, 7 are pairwise relatively prime $\ \checkmark$

and $\ M = 3 \times 5 \times 7 = 105 \quad \therefore \quad M_1 = \frac{105}{3} = 35$, $\ M_2 = 21 \ $ and $\ M_3 = 15$

To find x_1 we solve $\ 35 x_1 \equiv 1 \pmod 3 \qquad$ i.e., $\ x_1 = 2 \pmod 3$
To find x_2 we solve $\ 21 x_2 \equiv 1 \pmod 5 \qquad$ i.e., $\ x_2 = 1 \pmod 5$
To find x_3 we solve $\ 15 x_3 \equiv 1 \pmod 7 \qquad$ i.e., $\ x_3 = 1 \pmod 7$

Hence, $\ x \equiv (1)(35)(2) + (2)(21)(1) + (3)(15)(1) \pmod{105}$

$\qquad \Rightarrow \quad x \equiv 157 \pmod{105}$

$\qquad \Rightarrow \quad x \equiv 52 \pmod{105}$

So, there are infinitely many solutions $\ x = 52 \ $ (the smallest)
$x = 157$, $\ x = 209$, $\ x = 261$, etc.

Check: $\ 52 \equiv 1 \pmod 3 \ \checkmark \quad 52 \equiv 2 \pmod 5 \ \checkmark \quad 52 \equiv 3 \pmod 7 \ \checkmark$

EXERCISE 11A.8.1

1 Solve the system: $\ x \equiv 4 \pmod{11}$, $\ x \equiv 3 \pmod 7$.

2 Solve the system: $\ x \equiv 1 \pmod 5$, $\ x \equiv 2 \pmod 6$, $\ x \equiv 3 \pmod 7$.

3 Find a number which when divided by 3 leaves a remainder of 2, when divided by 5 leaves a remainder of 3 and when divided by 7 leaves a remainder of 2.

4 Solve these systems:

$\quad$ **a** $\ x \equiv 1 \pmod 2$, $\ x \equiv 2 \pmod 3$, $\ x \equiv 3 \pmod 5$

$\quad$ **b** $\ x \equiv 0 \pmod 2$, $\ x \equiv 0 \pmod 3$, $\ x \equiv 1 \pmod 5$, $\ x \equiv 6 \pmod 7$

$\quad$ **c** $\ x \equiv 1 \pmod 3$, $\ x \equiv 2 \pmod 5$, $\ x \equiv 3 \pmod 7$

Example 24

Solve Sun-Tsu's problem without using the Chinese Remainder Theorem.

The first congruence is $x \equiv 1 \pmod 3$ $\therefore$ $x = 1 + 3t, \quad t \in \mathbb{Z}$

Substituting into the 2nd congruence, $x \equiv 2 \pmod 5$ we get
$$1 + 3t \equiv 2 \pmod 5$$
$$\therefore \quad 3t \equiv 1 \pmod 5$$
$$\therefore \quad t \equiv 2 \pmod 5$$
$$\therefore \quad t \equiv 2 + 5u, \quad u \in \mathbb{Z}$$

Substituting into the 3rd congruence $x \equiv 3 \pmod 7$ we get
$$1 + 3(2 + 5u) \equiv 3 \pmod 7$$
$$\therefore \quad 7 + 15u \equiv 3 \pmod 7$$
$$\therefore \quad 15u \equiv -4 \pmod 7$$
$$\therefore \quad 15u \equiv 3 \pmod 7$$
$$\therefore \quad u \equiv 3 \pmod 7$$
$$\therefore \quad u \equiv 3 + 7v$$

$\therefore$ $x = 1 + 3t = 1 + 3(2 + 5u) = 7 + 15u = 7 + 15(3 + 7v)$

So, $x \equiv 52 + 105v$

i.e., $x \equiv 52 \pmod{105}$

Some congruence equations can be solved by converting to two or more simpler equations. The following example illustrates this procedure.

Example 25

Solve $13x \equiv 5 \pmod{276}$.

We notice that $276 = 3 \times 4 \times 23$ where   3, 4 and 23 are relatively prime.

$\therefore$ we need to solve
$$13x \equiv 5 \pmod 3 \qquad 13x \equiv 5 \pmod 4 \qquad 13x \equiv 5 \pmod{23}$$
$$\text{or} \quad x \equiv 2 \pmod 3 \qquad \quad x \equiv 1 \pmod 4 \qquad \quad x \equiv 11 \pmod{23}$$

Using the Chinese Remainder theorem
$$M = 3 \times 4 \times 23 = 276 \quad \therefore \quad M_1 = 92, \quad M_2 = 69 \quad \text{and} \quad M_3 = 12$$

To find x_1 we solve $92x_1 \equiv 1 \pmod 3$ i.e., $x_1 \equiv 2 \pmod 3$

To find x_2 we solve $69x_2 \equiv 1 \pmod 4$ i.e., $x_2 \equiv 1 \pmod 4$

To find x_3 we solve $12x_3 \equiv 1 \pmod{23}$ i.e., $x_3 \equiv 2 \pmod{23}$

Hence, $x = (2)(92)(2) + (1)(69)(1) + (11)(12)(2) \equiv 701 \pmod{276}$
$$\equiv 149 \pmod{276}$$

EXERCISE 11A.8.2

1 Solve these systems using the method shown in **Example 24**:

    a $x \equiv 4 \pmod{11}, \quad x \equiv 3 \pmod 7$

    b $x \equiv 1 \pmod 5, \quad x \equiv 2 \pmod 6, \quad x \equiv 3 \pmod 7$

    c $x \equiv 0 \pmod 2, \quad x \equiv 0 \pmod 3, \quad x \equiv 1 \pmod 5, \quad x \equiv 6 \pmod 7$

    (Each of these systems appeared in **Exercise 11A.8.1**)

2 Solve $\ 17x \equiv 3 \pmod{210}\ $ using the method shown in **Example 25**.

3 Which integers leave a remainder of 2 when divided by either 3 or 4?

4 Find an integer that leaves a remainder of 2 when divided by either 5 or 7 but is divisible by 3.

5 Find an integer that leaves a remainder of 1 when divided by 3, a remainder of 3 when divided by 5, but is divisible by 4.

6 Colin has a bag of sweets. If the sweets are removed from the bag 2, 3, 4, 5 and 6 at a time, the respective remainders are 1, 2, 3, 4 and 5. However, when they are taken out 7 at a time no sweets are left in the bag. Find the smallest number of sweets that were originally in the bag.

7 Seventeen robbers stole a bag of silver coins. They divided the coins into equal groups of 17 but 3 were left over. A fight began over the remaining coins and one of the robbers was killed. The coins were then redistributed but this time 10 were left over. Another fight broke out and another of the robbers died in the conflict. Luckily, another equal redistribution of the coins was exact. What was the least number of coins stolen by the robbers?

8 Solve the linear Diophantine equation $\ 4x + 7y = 5\ $ by considering the congruences $4x \equiv 5 \pmod 7$ and $7y \equiv 5 \pmod 4$ and showing they are equivalent to $\ x = 3 + 7t$ and $\ y = 3 + 4s\ $ and finding the relationship between t and s.

9 Repeat **8** for   **a** $\ 11x + 8y = 31$ **b** $\ 7x + 5y = 13$

10 Find the smallest integer $\ n > 2\ $ such that $\ 2 \mid a, \quad 3 \mid a + 1, \quad 4 \mid a + 2, \quad 5 \mid a + 3, \quad 6 \mid a + 4$.

11 Solve the system:

    $2x \equiv 1 \pmod 5, \quad 3x \equiv 9 \pmod 6, \quad 4x \equiv 1 \pmod 7, \quad 5x \equiv 9 \pmod{11}$.

A.9 DIVISIBILITY TESTS

One application of congruences is determining when a large integer is divisible by a smaller prime. In the following section we will look at the divisibility tests for the first 16 integers.

We will use the notation for the decimal representation for an integer a, as

$$A = a_{n-1}a_{n-2}a_{n-3}......a_1a_0 = a_{n-1}10^{n-1} + a_{n-2}10^{n-2} + a_{n-3}10^{n-3} + ... + a_1 10^1 + a_0$$

We all know the test for divisibility by 3 is:

    "If the sum of its digits is divisible by 3, then so is the original number."

We can prove the truth of such a divisibility test at this stage.

Here are the divisibility tests for divisibility by 2, 3, 5, 9 and 11.

If A is an integer then

(1) $2 \mid A \Leftrightarrow a_0 = 0, 2, 4, 6$ or 8

(2) $5 \mid A \Leftrightarrow a_0 = 0$ or 5

(3) $3 \mid A \Leftrightarrow 3 \mid (a_{n-1} + a_{n-2} + a_{n-3} + \ldots + a_1 + a_0)$

(4) $9 \mid A \Leftrightarrow 9 \mid (a_{n-1} + a_{n-2} + a_{n-3} + \ldots + a_1 + a_0)$

(5) $11 \mid A \Leftrightarrow 11 \mid (a_0 - a_1 + a_2 - a_3 + \ldots)$

Proof: Consider the polynomial $f(x) = a_{n-1}x^{n-1} + a_{n-2}x^{n-2} + \ldots + a_2x^2 + a_1x + a_0$

(1) Since $10 \equiv 0 \ (\text{mod } 2),$ then

$f(10) \equiv f(0) \ (\text{mod } 2)$ $\{a \equiv b \ (\text{mod } m) \ \Rightarrow \ f(a) \equiv f(b) \ (\text{mod } m)\}$

$\Rightarrow \quad A \equiv a_0 \ (\text{mod } 2)$

$\Rightarrow \quad A$ is divisible by 2 if a_0 is divisible by 2

$\Rightarrow \quad A$ is divisible by 2 if $a_0 = 0, 2, 4, 6, 8$

(3) Since $10 \equiv 1 \ (\text{mod } 3),$ then

$f(10) \equiv f(1) \ (\text{mod } 3)$

$\Rightarrow \quad A \equiv a_{n-1} + a_{n-2} + \ldots + a_2 + a_1 + a_0 \quad (\text{mod } 3)$

$\Rightarrow \quad A$ is divisible by 3 $\Leftrightarrow a_{n-1} + a_{n-2} + \ldots + a_2 + a_1 + a_0$
is divisible by 3.

(5) Since $10 \equiv -1 \ (\text{mod } 11),$ then

$f(10) \equiv f(-1) \ (\text{mod } 11)$

$\Rightarrow \quad A \equiv a_0 - a_1 + a_2 - a_3 + a_4 - \ldots \quad (\text{mod } 11)$

$\Rightarrow \quad A$ is divisible by 11 $\Leftrightarrow a_0 - a_1 + a_2 - a_3 + a_4 - \ldots$
is divisible by 11.

Proofs of (2) and (4) are left to the reader.

EXERCISE 11A.9.1

1 $a = 187\,261\,321\,117\,057$

  a Find $a \ (\text{mod } m)$ for $m = 2, 3, 5, 9, 11$.

  b Hence, determine if a is divisible by 2, 3, 5, 9 or 11.
     If not, find the value of the remainder of the division.

2 a Given $A = a_{n-1}10^{n-1} + a_{n-2}10^{n-2} + \ldots + a_2 10^2 + a_1 10 + a_0,$ prove that

     i $a \ (\text{mod } 10) = a_0$ ii $a \ (\text{mod } 100) = 10a_1 + a_0$

     iii $a \ (\text{mod } 1000) = 100a_2 + 10a_1 + a_0$

  b Hence, state divisibility tests for 10, 100, 1000.

  c Determine a divisibility test for 4 and 8.

  d Postulate a divisibility test for 16.

  e Find the highest power of 2 that divides:

     i $201\,984$ ii $89\,375\,744$ iii $41\,578\,912\,246$

3   **a** $n \pmod{10} = 0, 1, 2, 3, 4, \ldots, 9$.   What are the possible values of $n^2 \pmod{10}$?

    b   Why are 5437, $364\,428$, $65\,852$ and $96\,853$ not perfect squares? You must use **a**.

4   Claudia claimed that $\displaystyle\sum_{r=1}^{n} r!$ for $n \geqslant 2$ is never a perfect square. Is she correct?

5   Determine the highest power of 2 that divides:

    a $765\,432$ **b** $86\,254\,236$ **c** $62\,525\,654$ **d** $62\,525\,648$

6   For what values of k are the repunits R_k divisible by:

    a 3 **b** 9 **c** 11?

7   For each of the following binary numbers:

    i   What is the highest power of 2 that divides the number?

    ii   Is the number divisible by 3?

    a $101\,110\,101\,001$ **b** $1\,001\,110\,101\,000$ **c** $1\,010\,101\,110\,100\,100$

8   For each of the following ternary (base 3) numbers:

    i   What is the highest power of 3 that divides the number?

    ii   Is the integer divisible by 2?

    iii   Is the integer divisible by 4?

    a $10\,200\,122\,221\,210$ **b** $221\,021\,010\,020\,120$ **c** $1\,010\,101\,110\,100\,100$

DIVISIBILITY BY 7 AND 13

If $A = {}^{\backprime}a_{n-1}a_{n-2}a_{n-3}\ldots a_2 a_1 a_0{}^{\prime}$ is the decimal representation of positive integer A then

- $7 \mid A \iff 7 \mid {}^{\backprime}a_{n-1}a_{n-2}a_{n-3}\ldots a_2 a_1{}^{\prime} - 2a_0$

- $13 \mid A \iff 13 \mid {}^{\backprime}a_{n-1}a_{n-2}a_{n-3}\ldots\ldots a_2 a_1{}^{\prime} - 9a_0$

Repeated application is often necessary.

Example 26   Which of **a** 259 **b** 2481 is divisible by 7?

    a $7 \mid 259 \iff 7 \mid 25 - 2(9)$ **b** $7 \mid 2481 \iff 7 \mid 248 - 2(1)$

                    $\iff 7 \mid 7$ $\iff 7 \mid 246$

    which is true,   so $7 \mid 259$ $\iff 7 \mid 24 - 2(6)$

                                               $\iff 7 \mid 12$

                           which is not true, so $7 \nmid 2481$

Example 27   Is $12\,987$ divisible by 13?

    $13 \mid 12\,987 \iff 13 \mid 1298 - 9(7)$

                     $\iff 13 \mid 1235$

                     $\iff 13 \mid 123 - 9(5)$

                     $\iff 13 \mid 78$ which is true as $78 = 13 \times 6$

    $\therefore$ $12\,987$ is divisible by 13

Proof: (of rule for divisibility by 7)

Let $c = $ '$a_{n-1}a_{n-2}a_{n-3} \, ... \, a_2 a_1$' $\therefore$ $A = 10c + a_0$

$\therefore$ $-2A = -20c - 2a_0$

$\therefore$ $-2A = c - 2a_0 \, (\text{mod} \, 7)$ $\{$as $-20 \equiv 1 \, (\text{mod} \, 7)\}$

Thus, $7 \, | \, A$ $\Leftrightarrow$ $7 \, | \, -2A$ $\Leftrightarrow$ $7 \, | \, c - 2a_0$

EXERCISE 11A.9.2

1   Is either of 6994 and 6993 divisible by 7?

2   Complete the proof for the divisibility test for 13.

3   Find a divisibility test for 7 when the number is written in base 8. Generalise this result to base n.

4   Find a divisibility test for 9 when the number is written in base 8. Generalise this result to base n.

5   **a**   What is the divisibility test for   **i**   25   **ii**   125?

   b   Find the highest power of 5 that divides:

   i   112 250   **ii**   235 555 790   **iii**   48 126 953 125.

6   What is the divisibility test for: **a**   6   **b**   12   **c**   14   **d**   15?

7   Are these integers divisible by 11?

   a   10 763 732   **b**   8 924 310 064 537   **c**   1 086 326 715

8   Are any of these integers divisible by either 3 or 9 or 11?

   a   201 984   **b**   101 582 283   **c**   41 578 912 246

   d   433 544 319   **e**   960 991 317   **f**   48 126 953 125

9   Given the integer $n^2 - n + 7$, determine by considering different values of n, the possible values of its last digit. Prove that these are the only possible values.

A.10   FERMAT'S LITTLE THEOREM

Fermat corresponded on number theory with (amongst others) **Mersenne** and **Bernhard Frénicle**, and it was usually one or the other of these who coaxed from the rather secretive Fermat some of his most closely held results. Frénicle is responsible for bringing the Little Theorem to notice.

It states: "If p is a prime and a is any integer not divisible by p, then p divides $a^{p-1} - 1$."

Fermat communicated this result in 1640, stating also, "I would send you the demonstration, if I did not fear it being too long", a comment somewhat reminiscent of his comment about his Last Theorem.

Fermat's unwillingness to provide proofs for his assertions was all too common. Sometimes he had a proof, other times not.

Euler published the first proof of the Little Theorem in 1736, however **Leibnitz** (all too little recognised for his contributions to Number Theory, due to his lack of desire to publish) left an identical argument in a manuscript dated prior to 1683.

THEOREM (FERMAT'S LITTLE THEOREM)

If p is a prime and $p \nmid a$ then $a^{p-1} \equiv 1 \pmod{p}$.

For example, if $a = 8$ and $p = 5$, then $8^4 \equiv 1 \pmod 5$
which is true as $8^4 \equiv 4096$.

Proof: Consider these multiples of a: $a, 2a, 3a, 4a, \ldots, (p-1)a$

Suppose any two of them are congruent modulo p

i.e., $ka \equiv la \pmod{p}$ for $1 \leqslant k < l \leqslant p - 1$.

Since p is prime we can cancel $\therefore$ $k \equiv l \pmod{p}$.

Thus none of the multiples is congruent modulo p to any other numbers on the list, nor is it congruent to 0.

So, $a, 2a, 3a, 4a, \ldots, (p-1)a$ are all incongruent to each other modulo p and so they must be congruent, in some order, to the system of least residues $1, 2, 3, 4, \ldots, (p-1)$.

Thus, $a(2a)(3a)(4a)\ldots(p-1)a \equiv (1)(2)(3)(4)\ldots(p-1) \pmod{p}$

$\therefore$ $a^{p-1}(p-1)! \equiv (p-1)! \pmod{p}$

Now since $p \nmid (p-1)!$, p being prime, we can cancel by $(p-1)!$

$\therefore$ $a^{p-1} \equiv 1 \pmod{p}$

Example 28

Verify Fermat's Little Theorem for $a = 3$ and $p = 5$.

Method 1:

$1 \times 3 \equiv 3 \pmod 5$, $2 \times 3 \equiv 1 \pmod 5$, $3 \times 3 \equiv 4 \pmod 5$, $3 \times 4 \equiv 2 \pmod 5$

Multiplying these four congruences gives:

$1 \times 3 \times 2 \times 3 \times 3 \times 3 \times 3 \times 4 \equiv 3 \times 1 \times 4 \times 2 \pmod 5$

$\therefore$ $3^4 \times 4! \equiv 4! \pmod 5$

$\Rightarrow$ $3^4 \equiv 1 \pmod 5$

Method 2:

$3^4 = 81$ $\therefore$ $3^4 \equiv 1 \pmod 5$

Corollary:

If p is a prime then $a^p \equiv a \pmod{p}$ for any integer a.

Proof: If $p \mid a$,   then $a \equiv 0 \pmod{p}$ and $a^p \equiv 0^p \pmod{p}$

$\therefore$ $a^p \equiv a \pmod{p}$

If $p \nmid a$,   then by Fermat's Little Theorem

$a^{p-1} \equiv 1 \pmod{p}$

$\therefore$ $aa^{p-1} \equiv a \pmod{p}$

i.e., $a^p \equiv a \pmod{p}$

Example 29

Find the value of 3^{152} (mod 11).

Since 11 is prime, and $3^{10} \equiv 1$ (mod 11)
then $3^{152} = (3^{10})^{15} \times 3^2 \equiv 1^{15} \times 9 \equiv 9$ (mod 11)
i.e., 3^{152} (mod 11) $\equiv 9$

EXERCISE 11A.10.1

1 Find the value of:

  a 5^{152} (mod 13)   b 4^{56} (mod 7)   c 8^{205} (mod 17)   d 3^{95} (mod 13)

Fermat's Little Theorem also allows us to solve linear congruences of the form
  $ax \equiv b$ (mod p)   where p is prime.

Notice that: if $ax \equiv b$ (mod p)   then
  $\Rightarrow$ $a^{p-2} ax \equiv a^{p-2}b$ (mod p)
  $\Rightarrow$ $a^{p-1}x \equiv a^{p-2}b$ (mod p)
  $\Rightarrow$ $(1)x \equiv a^{p-2}b$ (mod p)   {as $a^{p-1} \equiv a$ (mod p)   FLT}
  $\Rightarrow$ $x \equiv a^{p-2}b$ (mod p)

So, $x \equiv a^{p-2}b$ (mod p) is the solution of $ax \equiv b$ (mod p) where p is prime.

Example 30

Solve for x: $5x \equiv 3$ (mod 11)

      $5x \equiv 3$ (mod 11) $p = 11$ is prime, $a = 5$, $b = 3$
  $\Rightarrow$ $x \equiv 5^9 \times 3$ (mod 11)
  $\Rightarrow$ $x \equiv (5^2)^4 \times 15$ (mod 11)
  $\Rightarrow$ $x \equiv 3^4 \times 4$ (mod 11) $5^2 = 25 \equiv 3$ (mod 11)
  $\Rightarrow$ $x \equiv 3^3 \times 12$ (mod 11)
  $\Rightarrow$ $x \equiv 5 \times 1$ (mod 11)
  $\Rightarrow$ $x \equiv 5$ (mod 11)

EXERCISE 11A.10.2

1 Solve: a $3x \equiv 5$ (mod 7)   b $8x \equiv 3$ (mod 13)
            c $7x \equiv 2$ (mod 11)   d $4x \equiv 3$ (mod 17)

A further use of Fermat's Little Theorem is in determining whether an integer is *not a prime*.
The contrapositive of FLT "p prime $\Rightarrow a^p \equiv a$ (mod p)   for any a"   is:

        If $a^n \not\equiv a$ (mod n)   for any $a \in \mathbb{Z}$ $\Rightarrow$ n is **not** prime.

Example 31

Test whether 123 is prime.

We minimise computation by using $a = 2$.

Now $2^{123} = (2^7)^{17} \times 2^4$ $\{2^7 = 128$ is close to $123\}$

$\therefore \quad 2^{123} \equiv 5^{17}2^4 \pmod{123}$ $\{2^7 = 128 \equiv 5\}$

$\therefore \quad 2^{123} \equiv (5^3)^5 5^2 2^4 \pmod{123}$ $\{5^3 = 125$ is close to $123\}$

$\therefore \quad 2^{123} \equiv 2^5 5^2 2^4 \pmod{123}$ $\{5^3 = 125 \equiv 2\}$

$\therefore \quad 2^{123} \equiv 5^2 \times 2^9 \pmod{123}$

$\therefore \quad 2^{123} \equiv 2^7 \times 2^2 \times 5^2 \pmod{123}$

$\therefore \quad 2^{123} \equiv 5 \times 2^2 \times 5^2 \pmod{123}$ $\{$using $2^7 \equiv 5$ again$\}$

$\therefore \quad 2^{123} \equiv 5^3 \times 2^2 \pmod{123}$

$\therefore \quad 2^{123} \equiv 2 \times 2^3 \pmod{123}$ $\{$using $5^3 \equiv 2$ again$\}$

$\therefore \quad 2^{123} \equiv 2^3 \pmod{123}$

and as $2^{123} \not\equiv 2 \pmod{123}$, 123 is not prime.

Note: The converse of Fermat's Little Theorem is false,

i.e., if $a^{n-1} \equiv 1 \pmod{n}$ then n need not be prime.

EXERCISE 11A.10.3

1 Use the method given in **Example 31** to test whether:
   a   117 is a prime   b   63 is a prime

2 Test as in **1** whether 29 is a prime. What can you conclude from the result? Think carefully.

3 Show directly that $3^{10} \equiv 1 \pmod{11}$.

4 Find the remainder of $13^{133} + 5$ on division by 19.

5 Determine whether $11^{204} + 1$ is exactly divisible by: a   13   b   17

6 Deduce by the Little Theorem that $17 \mid 13^{16n+2} + 1$ for all $n \in \mathbb{Z}^+$.

7 Deduce by the Little Theorem that $13 \mid 9^{12n+4} - 9$ for all $n \in \mathbb{Z}^+$.

8 Find the units digit of 7^{100} by the Little Theorem.

9 Let p be prime and $\gcd(a, p) = 1$. Use the Little Theorem to verify that $x \equiv a^{p-2}b \pmod{p}$ is a solution of the linear congruence $ax \equiv b \pmod{p}$.

   Hence solve the congruences $2x \equiv 1 \pmod{31}$, $6x \equiv 5 \pmod{11}$, $3x \equiv 17 \pmod{29}$.

10 Solve the linear congruences: a $7x \equiv 12 \pmod{17}$ b $4x \equiv 11 \pmod{19}$

11 Use the Little Theorem to prove that, if p is an odd prime then:

   a $\displaystyle\sum_{k=1}^{p-1} k^{p-1} \equiv -1 \pmod{p}$ b $\displaystyle\sum_{k=1}^{p-1} k^{p} \equiv 0 \pmod{p}$

12 Use the Little Theorem to find the last digit of the base 7 expansion of 3^{100}.

GRAPH THEORY

B.1   PRELIMINARY PROBLEMS INVOLVING GRAPH THEORY

The following problems provide a useful introduction to graph theory.

EXERCISE 11B.1

1   Can you draw the diagram on the right without taking your pen from the paper and without drawing over any line more than once?

   If you cannot, what is the minimum number of pen strokes that are required to draw the diagram?

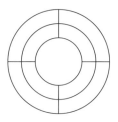

2   Can you redraw the diagram on the right so that none of the lines (redrawn as curves if necessary) joining the points intersect?

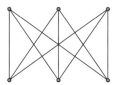

3   Starting with point A, can you visit each of the dots on the diagram alongside once and once only and get back to your starting point?

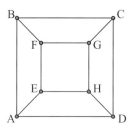

4   **a**   Suppose the diagram below represents an offshore oilfield. The dots represent the oil wells and the lines joining them represent pipelines that could be constructed to connect the wells. The number shown on each line is the cost (in millions of dollars) of constructing that pipeline.

   Each oil well must be connected to every other, but not necessarily directly. Which pipelines should be constructed to minimise the cost?

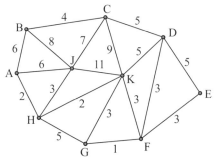

   b   Suppose the diagram above represents the walking trails in a national park. The numbers on the edges represent the suggested walk time in hours for that trail. If I want to walk from point A to point E in the shortest possible time, what route should I take?

B.2   TERMINOLOGY

A **graph** is a set of points (**vertices**), some or all of which are joined by a set of lines (**edges**).

If there is a maximum of one edge connecting any pair of vertices, then the graph is said to be **simple**. Hence all of the diagrams in the previous section were simple graphs.

If there is more than one edge connecting any pair of vertices directly, then the graph is said to be a **multigraph**.

Below are some more examples of simple graphs:

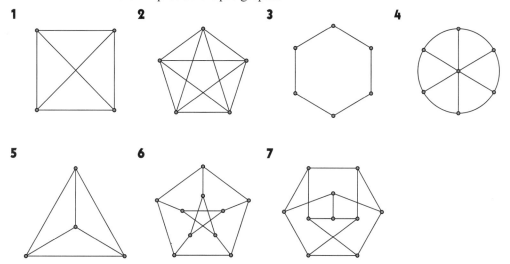

You should note the following features:

- Graph **1** has four vertices, since where the edges cross is not a vertex.

- Graphs **1**, **2**, and **5** are said to be **complete**, since each vertex is joined by an edge to every other vertex on the graph.

- Graph **2** is denoted K_5, the complete graph on 5 vertices. 4 edges are **incident** (meet) at each vertex, so each vertex is **adjacent** (joined) to four vertices. We say that the **degree of each vertex** in K_5 is four.

- Graph **3** is denoted C_6, the **circuit graph** on 6 vertices.

- Graph **4** is W_7, the **wheel graph** on 7 vertices It consists of a circuit of 6 vertices, plus a **hub** in the centre which is connected to every other vertex.

- Graph **5** is both W_3 and K_4.

- Graph **6** is known as the **Petersen Graph**. It is an example of a graph which is not complete, but in which all vertices have the same degree, in this case 3. We say that the graph is **regular** of **degree 3**, or **cubic**. Similarly, K_5 (graph **2**) is regular of degree four.

- Graphs **1** and **5** are in fact the same, just drawn differently. We say that they are **isomorphic** to each other. Graphs **6** and **7** are also isomorphic.

These are formal definitions of concepts you will meet in this section:

Graph	A set of vertices joined by a set of curves or lines called edges.
Simple Graph	A graph in which no vertex connects to itself and each pair of vertices is joined by a maximum of one edge.
Multigraph	A graph somewhere in which: • more than one edge is incident on the same two vertices, *and/or* • a vertex is connected to itself by an edge (loop).
Degree of a Vertex	The number of edges incident on that vertex.
Adjacent Vertices	Vertices that are joined to each other by an edge.
Incident Arc/Vertex	An arc which connects two adjacent vertices is said to be incident on each vertex.
Order of a Graph	The number of vertices in the graph.
Size of a Graph	The number of edges in the graph.
Loop	An edge that connects a vertex to itself in a multigraph.
Connected Graph	A graph in which every vertex can be reached from every other vertex by a sequence of edges.
Complete Graph	A graph in which every vertex is adjacent to every other vertex.
Subgraph	A graph made from a subset of the vertex set and a subset of the edge set of another graph.
Regular Graph	A graph in which every vertex has the same degree.
Graph Complement	The graph whose vertex set is the same as the given graph, but whose edge set is constructed by vertices adjacent if and only if they were not adjacent in the given graph.
Planar Graph	A graph which can be drawn on paper (shown on a plane) without any edges needing to cross.
Bipartite Graph	A graph whose vertices can be divided into two disjoint sets, with two vertices of the same set never sharing an edge, i.e., with no two vertices of the same set being adjacent.

Notation:

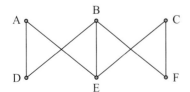

For the given graph G,

G is represented by $G = \{V, E\}$ where

$V = \{$A, B, C, D, E, F$\}$ is the **vertex set** and

$E = \{$AD, AE, BD, BE, BF, CE, CF$\}$ is the **edge set**.

Example 32

Consider the graph G shown:

a Define the graph in terms of its vertices and edges.

b Find the order and size of G.

c Comment on the nature of G.

d Find a graph which is isomorphic to G.

e Draw a subgraph of G.

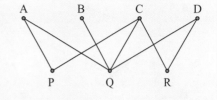

a The graph is represented by $G = \{V, E\}$ where
$V = \{$A, B, C, D, P, Q, R$\}$ and
$E = \{$AP, AQ, BQ, CP, CQ, CR, DQ, DR$\}$

b G has order $= 7$ {7 vertices}   and size $= 8$ {8 edges}.

c G is *simple* because no vertex joins directly to itself and each pair of vertices is joined by at most one edge.

It is also *connected* since all of the vertices can be reached from all of the others.

For example, A $\rightarrow$ R by the edge sequence of length 3: AQ, QD, DR.

The degrees of the vertices A, B, C, D, P, Q, R are 2, 1, 3, 2, 2, 4, 2 respectively. These are the numbers of edges incident on each vertex.

Since the degrees of all the vertices are not all the same, G is not regular.

However, G is *bipartite* with the two disjoint vertex sets $V_1 = \{$A, B, C, D$\}$ and $V_2 = \{$P, Q, R$\}$.

d G is also *planar* since it can be drawn without any of the edges crossing, as illustrated opposite.

This graph is isomorphic to that shown in the question.

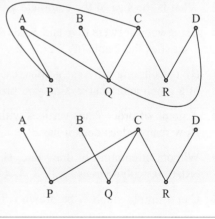

e A subgraph of G is shown opposite:

This subgraph is connected, but not all subgraphs of G are connected.

COMPLETE BIPARTITE GRAPHS

The graph shown opposite is a **complete bipartite graph**.

It has two disjoint vertex sets and each element in the first vertex set is adjacent to every vertex in the other vertex set.

This graph is denoted as $K_{4,3}$, since there are 4 vertices in one set and 3 in the other.

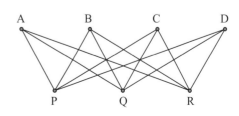

EXERCISE 11B.2

1   For each graph write down: **i**   its order   **ii**   its size   **iii**   the degrees of its vertices.

   a

   b

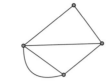

   c

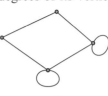

   d

   e

   f

2   Which of the graphs in **1** are   **i**   simple   **ii**   connected   **iii**   complete?

3   Draw:

   a   **i** $G = \{V, E\}$ where $V = \{A, B, C, D\}$ and $E = \{AB, BC, CD, AD, BD\}$

       ii $G = \{V, E\}$ where $V = \{P, Q, R, S, T\}$ and $E = \{PQ, PR, RS, PT\}$

      iii $G = \{V, E\}$ where $V = \{W, X, Y, Z\}$ and $E = \{XY, YZ, YZ, ZX, XX\}$

      iv a graph with 5 vertices, each joined to every other vertex by a single edge

       v a simple, connected graph with 4 vertices and 3 edges.

   b   Is there more than one possible answer to **a v**?

   c   Which of the graphs in **a** are   **(1)** simple   **(2)** connected   **(3)** complete?

4   What is the minimum number of edges a simple connected graph of order k can have?

5   What is the size of the complete graph of order p?

6   Using your answers to **4** and **5**, show that a simple connected graph of order n and size s satisfies the inequality $2n - 2 \leqslant 2s \leqslant n^2 - n$.

7   By considering different graphs, establish a formula connecting the sum of the degrees of a graph and its size. Can you prove your result?

8   A graph of order 7 has vertices with degrees 1, 2, 2, 3, 4, 5, 5.
   How many edges does it have?

9   Without attempting to draw one, show that it is impossible to have a simple graph of order six with degrees 1, 2, 3, 4, 4, 5.

10 Can a simple graph G be drawn with vertices of degrees   **a**   2, 3, 4, 4, 5

                                              b   1, 2, 3, 4, 4?

11 **a**   Given the degrees of the vertices of a graph G, is it possible to determine its order and size?

   b   Given the order and size of a graph G, is it possible to determine the degrees of its vertices?

12 Wherever possible, draw simple graphs with:

   a   no odd vertices   **b**   no even vertices

   c   exactly one vertex which is odd   **d**   exactly one vertex which is even

   e   exactly 2 odd vertices   **f**   exactly 2 even vertices.

13 If G is a graph of order p and size q, and is r-regular with $p > r$, express q in terms of p and r.

14 Give an example of a graph which is:

    a 0 regular and not complete   **b** 1 regular and not complete

    c 2 regular and not complete   **d** 3 regular and not complete

15 Draw the following graphs: **a** W_5 **b** $K_{3,3}$ **c** K_6.

16 How many edges have: **a** K_{10} **b** $K_{5,3}$ **c** W_8 **d** K_n **e** $K_{m,n}$?

17 Give an example (if it exists) of:

    a a bipartite graph that is regular of degree 3

    b a complete graph that is a wheel

    c a complete graph that is bipartite.

B.3 FUNDAMENTAL RESULTS OF GRAPH THEORY

From **Exercise 11B.2**, you will possibly have discovered some general results of graphs. In this secton we explore and prove some of these results.

The Handshaking Lemma:

For any graph G, the sum of the degrees of the vertices in G is twice the size of G.

Proof:

Each edge has two endpoints, and each endpoint contributes one to the degree of each vertex.

Hence the sum of the degrees of the vertices in G is twice the number of edges of G, i.e., it is twice the size of G.

Result:

Any graph G has an even number of vertices of odd degree. These are known as **odd vertices**.

Proof: (by contradiction)

Suppose the graph has an odd number of odd vertices.

Adding the degrees of all of the (odd and even) vertices gives a total which is odd.

However, by the handshaking lemma, the sum of the degrees must be twice the size of the graph, and hence even. This is a contradiction, so the initial supposition is false.

Before we can introduce the next result, we require a well-known principle of discrete mathematics, namely the **pigeonhole principle** of Dirichlet.

THE PIGEONHOLE PRINCIPLE

If we have n pigeons in m pigeonholes, then if $n > m$, there must be at least one hole containing more than one pigeon.

This principle as stated sounds trivial, yet it can be used to establish some surprising results that would be awkward to prove otherwise.

Example 33

Five points are placed anywhere in a square of side 2 m. Show that there must be two points whose distance apart is less than 1.5 m.

Divide the square into four smaller squares of side 1 m. By the Pigeonhole Principle, at least two of the five points must go into the same small square. The furthest distance apart between any two points in a square is the diagonal, which has length $\sqrt{2}$ m.

Therefore, there will two points whose distance apart is less than $\sqrt{2}$ m, and therefore less than 1.5 m.

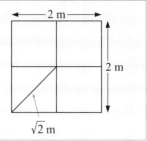

EXERCISE 11B.3.1

1   Show that in any group of 13 people there will be 2 or more people who are born in the same month.

2   Seven darts are thrown onto a circular dartboard of radius 10 cm. Assuming that all the darts land on the dartboard, show that there are two darts which are at most 10 cm apart.

3   17 points are randomly placed in an equilateral triangle of side 10 cm. Show that at least two of the points are at most 2.5 cm away from each other.

4   10 children attended a party and each child received at least one of 50 party prizes. Show that there were at least two children who received the same number of prizes.

5   Show that if nine of the first twelve positive integers are selected at random, the selection contains at least three pairs whose sum is 13.

Theorem:

In any *simple*, *connected* graph G, there are always at least two vertices of the same degree.

Proof:

Suppose that G has n vertices. Since it is both simple and connected, the minimum degree of a vertex is 1 and maximum degree of a vertex is $n - 1$.

So, as there are n vertices with $n - 1$ possible degrees, by the pigeonhole principle, there must be at least two vertices with the same degree.

GRAPH ISOMORPHISM

Isomorphism is an important concept in many areas of mathematics. You may have met it in other areas of the IB Higher Level Mathematics course, such as in Group Theory.

In **Section 11B.2**, we briefly introduced graph isomorphism when we compared the wheel graph W_3 with the complete graph K_4. We saw that these graphs have seemingly different representations on paper, as illustrated below, but they are in fact the same. Here they are again (and there are many other representations):

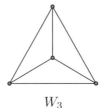

W_3

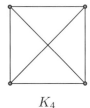

K_4

The concept of isomorphism allows us to know when two different graphs are, in fact, different or whether they are simply different representations of the same **isomorphic** graph.

Definition:

Two graphs G and H are said to be **isomorphic** if, for every vertex of G, there exists a unique corresponding vertex of H (and vice versa) such that adjacency of all vertices is preserved.

For those who have done the Set Theory option, we may refine the definition as follows:

Two graphs G and H are said to be **isomorphic** if there is a bijection $f : V(G) \to V(H)$ such that two vertices u and v of G are adjacent if and only if $f(u)$ and $f(v)$ are adjacent in H.

Notation: If G and H are isomorphic, we write: $G \cong H$.

Example 34

Consider the graphs below. Explain why no pair is isomorphic.

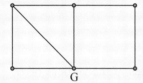 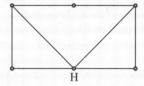 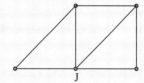

J has one less vertex than G and H, so it cannot be isomorphic to either of them.

Now both G and H have 6 vertices and 8 edges, and the degrees of their vertices are both, in descending order: 4, 3, 3, 2, 2, 2.

However, the two odd vertices in G are adjacent, whereas this is not the case in H.

Hence adjacency of vertices is *not* preserved, and the pair is not isomorphic.

Example 35

Show that the following graphs are isomorphic.

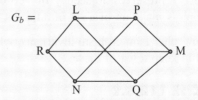

The graphs have the same number of vertices, and the vertices are all of the same degree (all degree 3 in this case).

We therefore attempt to redraw G_a so the graph looks the same as the graph of G_b, while preserving the adjacency of vertices.

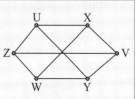

Check in the diagram alongside that every vertex is still adjacent to the same vertices as in the question. Now, we can see the correpondence of vertices:

$$U \leftrightarrow L, \quad V \leftrightarrow M, \quad W \leftrightarrow N, \quad X \leftrightarrow P, \quad Y \leftrightarrow Q, \quad Z \leftrightarrow R.$$

The graphs are therefore isomorphic.

Definition:

Isomorphism invariants are the properties of graphs that are preserved under an isomorphism.

They provide a checklist when trying to determine whether two graphs are isomorphic. If any of them fail, then the graphs in question are not isomorphic. However, even if the invariants all hold for two graphs, the graphs are *not guaranteed* to be isomorphic. We say that the isomorphism invariants are *necessary* conditions for isomorphism but that they are not *sufficient*.

Isomorphism invariants:

If two graphs, G and H are isomorphic, then:

1 The size of G is equal to the size of H.

2 The order of G is equal to the order of H.

3 The degrees of the vertices of G are exactly the degrees of the vertices of H.

4 The connectivity of G and H is preserved.

Proofs: (involve Set Theory)

1 The bijection f maps $u \to f(u)$ and $v \to f(v)$. If u and v are adjacent in G then $f(u)$ and $f(v)$ are adjacent in H. Hence edge (u, v) is mapped onto edge $(f(u), f(v))$.   This occurs for all edges, and so the size is preserved.

2 For every vertex of G, there exists a unique corresponding vertex of H, and vice vera. Hence the number of vertices (order) is preserved.

3 Suppose the degree of u is n, so there are n vertices adjacent to u. Since f preserves adjacency, the n vertices adjacent to u are mapped to n vertices adjacent to $f(u)$. Hence, the degree of $f(u)$ is n.

4 Now f preserves adjacency of vertices and thus edges. Therefore, since a connected graph is made up of a set of adjacent edge sequences, connectivity is preserved.

There are other isomorphism invariants, which you will meet in the coming work. You are advised to keep a list of these.

EXERCISE 11B.3.2

1 Will two graphs having the same number of vertices always be isomorphic? Justify your answer.

2 Will two graphs having the same number of edges always be isomorphic? Justify your answer.

3 Will two graphs having the same number of vertices of degree k for each $k \in \mathbb{Z}$ always be isomorphic? Justify your answer.

4   Are the pairs of graphs below isomorphic? If so, label the vertices and write down the isomorphism. If not, justify your answer.

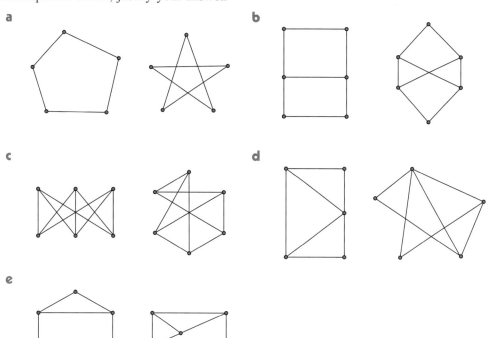

5   Are the following pairs of graphs isomorphic? Justify your answer.

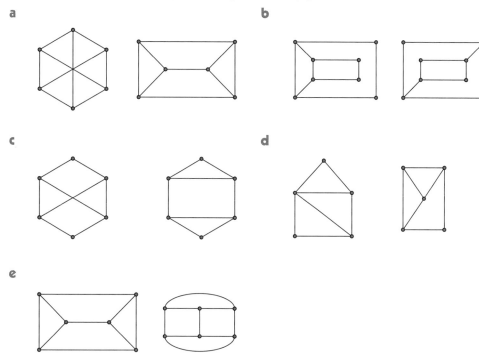

6 **a** Explain why the sum of the degrees of the vertices in any graph is always even.

  b Deduce a result concerning the number of odd vertices in a graph.

  c Show that in a group of nine people it is not possible for each to be friends with exactly five others.

7 Prove that a simple graph with $n > 1$ vertices always has at least two vertices of the same degree.

8 How many non-isomorphic connected simple graphs are there of:

  a order 2   **b** order 3   **c** order 4?

9 How many non-isomorphic simple graphs are there of:

  a order 2   **b** order 3   **c** order 4?

10 Prove the pigeonhole principle using proof by contradiction.

11 A simple graph isomorphic to its complement is said to be **self-complementary**.

  a Find all self-complementary graphs with 4 and 5 vertices.

  b Can you find a self-complementary graph with 3 vertices?

  c Find a self-complementary graph with 8 vertices.

  d Prove that if G is self-complementary, then G has either $4k$ or $4k + 1$ vertices, $k \in \mathbb{Z}$.

ISOMORPHISM AND MATRICES

We have already seen how graphs can be represented as a list of vertices and edges. They can also be represented as matrices. Matrix form is particularly important when using computers to solve more complicated graph theory problems, for example, dealing with the airline route map of a major airline.

In this section we look at matrix representations of graphs and multigraphs, and how these relate to the work we have done thus far.

Consider the graph G alongside:

$$G = \{V, E\}$$
$$\text{where } V = \{A, B, C, D\}$$
$$\text{and } E = \{AB, BC, CD, DA\}$$

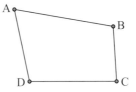

G can also be represented as a matrix:

$$
\begin{array}{c}
 \\
\textit{From}
\end{array}
\begin{array}{c}
 \\
\begin{array}{c|cccc}
 & A & B & C & D \\
\hline
A & 0 & 1 & 0 & 1 \\
B & 1 & 0 & 1 & 0 \\
C & 0 & 1 & 0 & 1 \\
D & 1 & 0 & 1 & 0
\end{array}
\end{array}
\quad \textit{or} \quad
\begin{bmatrix}
0 & 1 & 0 & 1 \\
1 & 0 & 1 & 0 \\
0 & 1 & 0 & 1 \\
1 & 0 & 1 & 0
\end{bmatrix}
$$

To (above the matrix)

Recall that vertices which are joined by edges are said to be **adjacent**. Hence the matrix is called the **adjacency matrix** $\mathbf{A} = (a_{ij})$ of the graph.

In general, we can represent a graph G with n vertices as an $n \times n$ adjacency matrix $\mathbf{A}(G)$ in which the i, jth entry is 1 if there is an edge between v_i and v_j, and 0 otherwise.

Note that adjacency matrices are always symmetric, since if i is adjacent to j then j is adjacent to i.

For example:

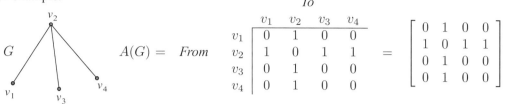

As each 1 in row i corresponds to an edge incident to vertex v_i,
the number of 1s in row i = the degree of v_i.

Hence, the total number of 1s in the adjacency matrix is $\displaystyle\sum_{i=1}^{n} \deg(v_i)$, which is twice the size of the graph.

EXERCISE 11B.3.3

1 Which of these adjacency matrices cannot represent undirected graphs?

a
$$\begin{bmatrix} 0 & 1 & 1 & 0 \\ 1 & 0 & 1 & 0 \\ 1 & 1 & 0 & 1 \\ 0 & 0 & 1 & 0 \end{bmatrix}$$

b
$$\begin{bmatrix} 0 & 1 & 0 & 1 & 0 \\ 1 & 0 & 0 & 1 & 1 \\ 0 & 0 & 0 & 0 & 1 \\ 1 & 1 & 0 & 0 & 0 \\ 0 & 0 & 0 & 0 & 0 \end{bmatrix}$$

c
$$\begin{bmatrix} 1 & 1 & 1 \\ 1 & 1 & 1 \\ 1 & 1 & 1 \end{bmatrix}$$

2 Consider the adjacency matrix $\mathbf{A} = \begin{bmatrix} 0 & 1 & 0 & 1 \\ 1 & 0 & 1 & 1 \\ 0 & 1 & 0 & 1 \\ 1 & 1 & 1 & 0 \end{bmatrix}$.

Draw the graph corresponding to $\mathbf{A}$. Verify that the total number of 1s in the matrix equals the sum of the degrees of the vertices.

3 Construct the graph for each adjacency matrix:

a
$$\begin{bmatrix} 0 & 1 & 1 & 0 & 1 \\ 1 & 0 & 1 & 1 & 1 \\ 1 & 1 & 0 & 1 & 0 \\ 0 & 1 & 1 & 0 & 0 \\ 1 & 1 & 0 & 0 & 0 \end{bmatrix}$$

b
$$\begin{bmatrix} 0 & 1 & 1 & 1 \\ 1 & 0 & 1 & 1 \\ 1 & 1 & 0 & 1 \\ 1 & 1 & 1 & 0 \end{bmatrix}$$

4 Construct adjacency matrices for each graph:

a G_1

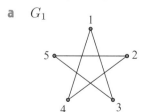

b G_2

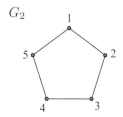

c G_3

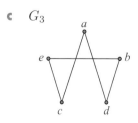

Relabel the vertices of G_3 above such that $a \to 1$, $b \to 3$, $c \to 5$, $d \to 2$, $e \to 4$. Are G_2 and G_3 isomorphic? Are all three graphs isomorphic?

5 Are the following pairs of graphs isomorphic? Justify your answer.

a

$$A(G_1) = \begin{bmatrix} 0 & 1 & 1 & 1 \\ 1 & 0 & 1 & 1 \\ 1 & 1 & 0 & 0 \\ 1 & 1 & 0 & 0 \end{bmatrix}$$

b

G_1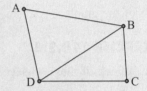

$$A(G_2) = \begin{bmatrix} 0 & 1 & 0 & 1 \\ 1 & 0 & 1 & 1 \\ 0 & 1 & 0 & 1 \\ 1 & 1 & 1 & 0 \end{bmatrix}$$

$$A(G_2) = \begin{bmatrix} 0 & 1 & 1 & 1 \\ 1 & 0 & 1 & 1 \\ 1 & 1 & 0 & 1 \\ 1 & 1 & 1 & 0 \end{bmatrix}$$

INVESTIGATION 4   FURTHER USE OF THE ADJACENCY MATRIX

1 Consider the graph alongside.
How many routes go from A to B via **one** other point?
What about from A to C and A to D?
How many routes start and finish at A?

2 Write down the graph's adjacency matrix **A** and use it to evaluate $\mathbf{A}^2$.

3 Interpret your results in **1** in terms of the entries of $\mathbf{A}^2$.
What do the entries on the main diagonal of matrix $\mathbf{A}^2$ represent for the vertices of the original graph?
What do you think the entries of $\mathbf{A}^3$ would represent?
What do you think the entries of $\mathbf{A}^4......\mathbf{A}^n$ would represent?

Theorem:

Let G be a graph with vertices $v_1, v_2, ..., v_n$ and adjacency matrix **A**. The number of different paths of length n from v_i to v_j equals the (i, j)th entry of $\mathbf{A}^n$.

Proof: (by induction on n)

For $n = 1$, the (i, j)th entry of **A** is the number of edges from v_i to v_j, and hence the number of paths from v_i to v_j of length 1.

Assume that the (i, j)th entry of $\mathbf{A}^k$ is the number of paths of length k from v_i to v_j.

Since $\mathbf{A}^{k+1} = \mathbf{A}^k \mathbf{A}$, the (i, j)th entry of $\mathbf{A}^{k+1}$ is $b_{i1}a_{1j} + b_{i2}a_{2j} + b_{i3}a_{3j} + ... + b_{in}a_{nj}$, where the a_{rj} are entries in the jth column of **A** and the b_{is} are entries in the ith row of $\mathbf{A}^k$ and represent the number of paths of length k from v_i to v_s.

However, a path of length $k + 1$ from v_i to v_j is made up of a path of length k from v_i to some intermediary vertex v_s, and an edge from v_s to v_j.

The number of such paths is the product of the number of paths of length k from v_i to v_s, namely b_{is}, and the number of edges from v_s to v_j, namely a_{sj}.

When these results are added for all possible intermediate vertices, the result is
$b_{i1}a_{1j} + b_{i2}a_{2j} + b_{i3}a_{3j} + ... + b_{in}a_{nj}$,   the (i, j)th entry of $\mathbf{A}^{k+1}$.

EXERCISE 11B.3.4

1   Represent the following graphs by their adjacency matrices:

   a K_4 **b** C_4 **c** W_4 **d** $K_{1,4}$ **e** $K_{2,3}$

2   Find the form of the adjacency matrices of the following graphs:

   a K_n **b** C_n **c** W_n **d** $K_{m,n}$

3   Find the number of paths of length n between two different vertices in K_4 if n is:

   a 2   **b** 3   **c** 4   **d** 5

4   Find the number of paths of length n between two adjacent vertices in $K_{3,3}$ if n is:

   a 2   **b** 3   **c** 4   **d** 5

5   Find the number of paths of length n between two non-adjacent vertices in $K_{3,3}$ if n is:

   a 2   **b** 3   **c** 4   **d** 5

6   **a** Write down the adjacency matrix $\mathbf{A}$ for K_3. Write down also the matrices $\mathbf{A}^2$, $\mathbf{A}^3$
        and $\mathbf{A}^4$.

   b Postulate a formula for $\mathbf{A}^n$.

7   What is the general form of the matrices $\mathbf{A}$, $\mathbf{A}^2$, $\mathbf{A}^3$, ... and $\mathbf{A}^n$ for K_m, the complete
   graph on m vertices?

8   **a** Write down the adjacency matrix $\mathbf{A}$ for $K_{3,2}$. Write down also the matrices $\mathbf{A}^2$,
        $\mathbf{A}^3$ and $\mathbf{A}^4$.

   b Postulate a formula for $\mathbf{A}^k$.

9   Repeat **8** for $K_{m,n}$.

ADJACENCY MATRICES FOR MULTIGRAPHS

Consider the multigraph G alongside. We
can represent G as an $n \times n$ adjacency matrix $\mathbf{A}(G)$ in which the (i, j)th entry is k if
there are k edges between v_i and v_j.

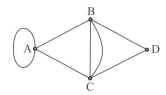

So, the matrix $\mathbf{A}$ for multigraph G is
$$\begin{bmatrix} 1 & 1 & 1 & 0 \\ 1 & 0 & 2 & 1 \\ 1 & 2 & 0 & 1 \\ 0 & 1 & 1 & 0 \end{bmatrix}.$$

Note that we have put the entry $a_{11} = 1$. So, we consider the loop as only one edge (even
though we can traverse it in two different directions). This has implications for the result that
"the sum of a row's entries is the degree of the vertex". In particular:

How does the convention about loops affect results about the powers of the adjacency matrix?
Can you alter your previous results on simple graphs to take notice of loops?

B.4   JOURNEYS ON GRAPHS AND THEIR IMPLICATIONS

Now that we know what a graph is, we begin to consider various ways of moving from vertex to vertex on a graph. For example, we may have to visit each vertex once and once only on our journey, disallow retracing our steps, or take account the time it takes to traverse a given set of edges.

As we do this, we consider the work of two of the founding mathematicians of Graph Theory, **Leonard Euler** and **William Hamilton**, and introduce the two classic problems their work eventually gave rise to.

INVESTIGATION 5   THE BRIDGES OF KÖNIGSBERG

 One of Euler's most famous contributions to mathematics concerned the town of Kaliningrad, or Königsberg as it was then known. The town is situated on the river Pregel in Germany, and has seven bridges linking two islands and the north and south banks of the river.

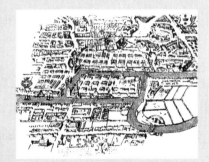

The question is: could a tour be made of the town, returning to the original point, that crosses all of the bridges once only? A simplified map of Kaliningrad is shown alongside. Euler answered this question - can you?

Apparently, such a circuit is not possible. However, it would be possible if either one bridge was removed or one was added. Which bridge would you remove? Where on the diagram would you add a bridge?

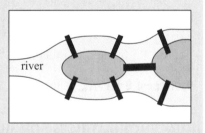

TERMINOLOGY

The Bridges of Königsberg question is closely related to children's puzzles in which a graph can or cannot be drawn without the pen leaving the paper. If such a drawing can be made, the graph is said to be **traversable**. Note that the start and end points need not be the same vertex in this case.

Which of these are traversable?

A **walk** is a finite sequence of steps $V_0 \rightarrow V_1 \rightarrow V_2 \rightarrow \ldots \ldots \rightarrow V_{n-1} \rightarrow V_n$ in which every two consecutive vertices are adjacent. We begin our walk at the **initial vertex** and end it at the **final vertex**. Its **length** is the number of steps or edges we walk along.

In the multigraph alongside, a walk of length 6 might be $V \to W \to Y \to Z \to Z \to Y \to X$.

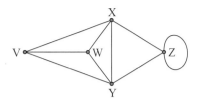

In a walk, any vertex may be visited any number of times and any edge may be used as often as one wishes. Thus, a walk is a very general concept.

> A **trail** is a walk where *all of the edges are distinct*. Vertices may be visited as often as one wishes, but once an edge has been used it may not be used again.
>
> A **path** is a trail where *all of the vertices are distinct* (with the possible exception of the end vertices).

For example, in the multigraph above,

$X \to V \to W \to Y \to Z \to X \to Y$ is a trail, and

$V \to W \to Y \to X$ and $W \to X \to V \to Y \to Z$ are paths.

A path or trail is said to be **closed** if the initial and final vertices are the same.

A closed trail is called a **circuit** and a closed path is called a **cycle**.

For example, in the multigraph above,

$V \to W \to Y \to X \to Z \to Y \to V$ is a circuit and

$V \to W \to Y \to X \to V$ and $W \to X \to Y \to W$ are cycles.

Note that $W \to X \to Y \to W$ and $X \to Y \to W \to X$ and $X \to W \to Y \to X$ all represent the same cycle, since they all contain the same set of edges.

> An **Eulerian Trail** is a trail which uses every edge exactly once. If such a trail exists, the graph is **traversable**.
>
> An **Eulerian Circuit** is an Eulerian trail which starts and ends at the same graph vertex.
>
> A connected graph G is **Eulerian** if it contains an **Eulerian circuit**.
>
> A connected graph G is **semi-Eulerian** if it contains an **Eulerian trail** but not an **Eulerian circuit**.

The Königsberg bridges problem attempts to find an Eulerian circuit that visits each vertex exactly once, rather like $V \to W \to Y \to X \to Z \to Y \to V$ in the multigraph above.

The symbolic representation of the Königsberg bridges problem is shown opposite. Notice that the degrees of the vertices are all odd. This is why no Eulerian circuit is possible.

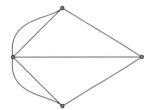

In fact, we can show that if a graph contains *any* vertices of odd degree, it cannot be Eulerian:

Proof:

For a graph to contain an Eulerian circuit, each vertex must be entered by an edge and left by another edge.

However, if there is an odd vertex, then at least one edge is unused from an odd vertex.

So, if there is an odd vertex, the graph cannot be Eulerian.

Euler was also able to prove the converse of this statement as well. We are hence able to determine the following results:

A closed graph is **Eulerian** if and only if all of its vertices are even.

A closed graph is **traversable** if and only if at most two of its vertices are odd.

We can also formalise the definition of a connected graph as:

A graph is **connected** if and only if there is a path between all pairs of vertices.

Theorem:

A graph is bipartite if and only if each circuit in the graph is of even length.

Theorem:

A simple connected graph on n vertices with m edges satisfies $n - 1 \leqslant m \leqslant \frac{1}{2}n(n-1)$

Corollary:

Any simple graph with n vertices and more than $\frac{1}{2}(n-1)(n-2)$ edges is connected.

EXERCISE 11B.4.1

1 Classify the following as Eulerian, traversable or neither:

   a   **b**    **c**

   d   **e**   **f**

2 Give an example of a graph of order 7 which is:

   a   Eulerian   **b**   traversable   **c**   neither

3 Decide whether the following graphs are Eulerian, traversable or neither:

   a K_5 **b** $K_{2,3}$ **c** W_n **d** C_m

4 For which values of:

   a n is K_n Eulerian   **b** m, n is $K_{m,n}$ Eulerian?

5 A *simple* graph G has five vertices, and each vertex has the same degree d.

   a   State the possible values of d.

   b   If G is connected, what are the possible values of d?

   c   If G is Eulerian, what are the possible values of d?

6 The **girth** of a graph is defined as the length of its shortest cycle.

What are the girths of:

   a K_9 **b** $K_{5,7}$ **c** the Petersen graph   ?

7 Consider the Bonnigskerb bridge problem opposite. Can a circular walk be performed?

Would either the addition or deletion of one bridge allow a circular walk to be performed?

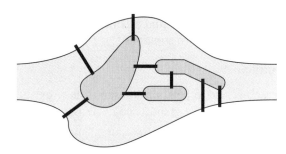

8 Show that it is possible to transform any connected graph G into an Eulerian graph by the addition of edges.

9 How many continuous pen strokes are needed to draw the diagram on the right, without repeating any line?

How is this problem related to Eulerian graphs?

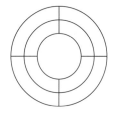

10 Suppose you have a job as a road cleaner and the diagram of the roads to be cleaned is shown opposite.

Is it possible to begin at A, clean every road exactly once, and return to A?

What about B?

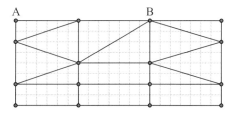

Now suppose that you have to begin and end your sweeping duties at A, so you will have to walk down some streets more than once. If the diagram is to scale and your walking speed never varies, what is the most efficient way of completing your task?

11 Prove that a graph is bipartite if and only if each circuit in the graph is of even length.

12 Prove that any simple graph with n vertices and more than $\frac{1}{2}(n-1)(n-2)$ edges is connected. A diagram may be useful.

HAMILTONIAN GRAPHS

William Rowan Hamilton invented a game known as **The Icosian Game**. It was sold for £25 by Hamilton and was marketed as "Round the World". It essentially required finding a closed trail on the dodecahedron.

A picture of the game can be found at:

   http://www.puzzlemuseum.com/month/picm02/200207icosian.htm

A **Schlegel** diagram is a graph whose edges do not cross, which is drawn to represent a 3-dimensional solid.

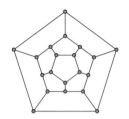

For example, a Schlegel diagram of the dodecahedron is shown opposite. Is it possible, starting and finishing at the same vertex, to follow the edges and visit every other vertex exactly once without lifting the pen?

You are being asked to find a **Hamiltonian cycle** of the dodecagon. There are, in fact, two solutions.

Definition:

A graph is said to be **Hamiltonian** if there exists a closed path (cycle) that passes through every vertex on the graph. The cycle is called a **Hamiltonian cycle**.

If a path exists that passes through every vertex on the graph exactly once and which is not closed, then the graph is said to be **semi-Hamiltonian**. The path is called a **Hamiltonian path**.

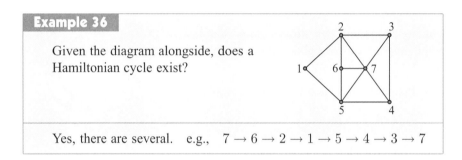

Notice in **Example 36** that only seven edges of the graph are used to form the Hamiltonian cycle. Remember that a Hamiltonian cycle visits all *vertices* of a graph exactly once, whereas an Eulerian circuit uses every *edge* exactly once.

While we can clearly state the condition required for a graph to be Eulerian, i.e., that all vertices have even degree, we cannot give a precise set of conditions for a graph to be Hamiltonian.

However, here are some important observations that have been made:

- If G is a graph of order n where $n > 2$ and if each vertex has degree $\geqslant \frac{1}{2}n$ then there exists a Hamiltonian cycle. (**Dirac**, 1952)

- If G is a simple graph of order n where $n \geqslant 3$ with at least $\frac{1}{2}(n-1)(n-2)+2$ edges, then there exists a Hamiltonian cycle.

- If G is a graph of order n where $n \geqslant 3$, and if degree (V) + degree (W) $\geqslant n$ for all non-adjacent vertices V and W, then there exists a Hamiltonian cycle. (**Ore**, 1960)

Note that while these are all *sufficient* conditions for the cycle, they are not *necessary*.

For example, in the graph alongside, all the vertices are degree 2, but it is Hamiltonian.

EXERCISE 11B.4.2

1 State whether the graphs are Hamiltonian or semi-Hamiltonian.

   a **i** K_5 **ii** $K_{2,3}$ **iii** W_6

   b **i**   **ii**   **iii**

       iv   **v**

2 Which of the graphs in **1** satisfy any of the three observations above about Hamiltonian graphs?

3 Give examples of graphs which are:

   a both Hamiltonian and Eulerian **b** Hamiltonian but not Eulerian

   c Eulerian but not Hamiltonian   **d** semi-Hamiltonian.

4 What are the conditions on m and n so that $K_{m,n}$ is Hamiltonian?

5 Prove K_n is Hamiltonian for all $n > 2$. How many Hamiltonian cycles does K_n have?

6 Show that the Groetsch graph shown alongside is Hamiltonian.

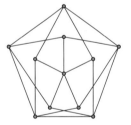

7 Prove that if G is a bipartite graph with an odd number of vertices, then G is not Hamiltonian.

   a Deduce that the graph alongside is not Hamiltonian.

   b Show that if n is odd, it is not possible for a knight to visit all of the squares on an $n \times n$ chessboard exactly once and return to its starting point.

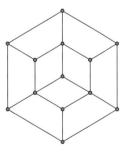

8 Can you find a Hamiltonian cycle in the Herschel graph alongside?

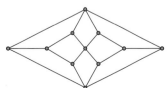

9 Find a solution to the Hamiltonian cycle for the dodecahedron. Trace it out on its Schlegel diagram.

B.5   PLANAR GRAPHS

Definition:

A graph G is planar if and only if there exists a graph H where $G \cong H$ such that H can be drawn on a plane without any edges that cross over each other.

H is said to be an **embedding** of the graph in the plane, or a **plane representation**.

The issue of planarity is important for the class of three dimensional solids known as **polyhedra**.

A **polyhedron** is a solid with flat or plane faces such as the cuboid alongside.

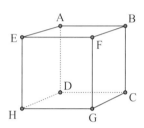

This is a two-dimensional perspective representation of a three-dimensional solid. It is also a graph. However, is it a *planar* graph?

The answer is yes, since the Schlegel diagram opposite shows the same structure as the cuboid, but with non-intersecting edges.

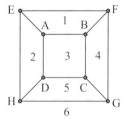

Note that the regions 1, 2, 3, 4, 5 and 6 (the infinite region) represent the faces of the cuboid.

Planar graphs can be represented by their vertices, edges and, unlike non-planar graphs, their regions.

EXERCISE 11B.5.1

1 Convert the given polyhedra into planar graphs:

a
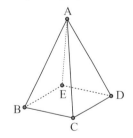

b
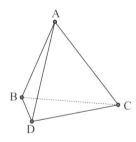

c
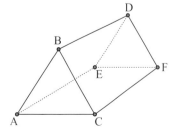

d
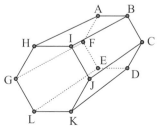

2 A famous problem based on planar graphs is that of connecting each of the three houses shown to each of the three services electricity, telephone and gas, with no pipes or cables crossing.

Can the problem be solved? Could the problem be solved if we drew the houses and services on the surface of a cylinder or sphere?

You should find that any connection of all the services to all three houses gives rise to a non-planar graph.

3 Where possible, convert these into planar graphs:

a **b** **c** **d**

INVESTIGATION 6   EULER'S FORMULA

If a planar graph is drawn on a piece of paper, we say the plane is divided into a number of regions, one of which is infinite.

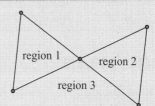

In this case there are:

5 vertices, 6 edges, 3 regions

Euler found a relationship which holds for any planar graph between its number of vertices, v, edges, e, and regions, r.

1 By considering some examples of planar graphs, suggest Euler's result.

Now, prove your result by induction, using the number of edges and the following steps:

  a Let your basic case be the graph K_2 (although K_1, the null graph, would do) and verify your result.

  b Now, add an edge to K_2 in as many different ways as you can. Note how this addition affects the number of vertices, and/or regions, but does not affect the formula. This will be the inductive step.

  c Perform the inductive step on an arbitrary graph of size k for which Euler's relation is assumed to hold. Hence complete your proof.

2 There is a similar relation for disconnected planar graphs.

Let n = number of separate parts of the graph. In the graph opposite, $n = 3$, $v = 8$, $e = 6$, and $r = 2$.

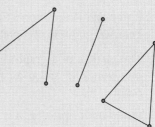

Modify the approach from **1** to determine a rule for this new situation. Prove your result by induction.

Euler's Formula:

A connected graph G is planar if and only if it satisfies Euler's formula $e + 2 = r + v$.

Consider again the "utilities" problem in **Exercise 11B.5.1** question **2**, which is equivalent to asking whether $K_{3,3}$ is planar. We can now use Euler's formula to prove it is not, and hence that the "utilities" problem is not possible.

Example 37

Prove that $K_{3,3}$ is not planar.

$K_{3,3}$ has 6 vertices and 9 edges.

$\therefore$ supposing it is planar, by Euler's formula it must have 5 regions.

Since $K_{3,3}$ is bipartite, none of the regions in its plane representation are triangles.

$\therefore$ each region has at least 4 edges, so if we count the edges around all 5 regions, we get at least $4 \times 5 = 20$.

However, we have counted every edge twice, since every edge is on the border of two regions. Hence if $K_{3,3}$ is planar, it must have at least 10 edges.

$\therefore$ since $K_{3,3}$ has only 9 edges, it is not planar.

EXERCISE 11B.5.2

1   Prove that K_5 is not planar by following these steps:
   a   Find the number of vertices and edges in K_5.
   b   Use Euler's relation to find the number of regions if we assume that K_5 is planar.
   c   Find a minimum number of edges necessary to make this many regions, and hence establish a contradiction.

2   Prove that a graph in which triangular regions are permitted is planar if and only if $e \leqslant 3v - 6$.

3   Prove that a bipartite graph can only be planar if $e \leqslant 2v - 4$.

Note: Consider the two inequalities $e \leqslant 2v - 4$ and $e \leqslant 3v - 6$ in **2** and **3**. They state that for a set number of vertices, there is an upper bound on edges before they have to start crossing each other.

4   Verify by substitution into the inequalities established in **2** and **3** that K_5 and $K_{3,3}$ are non-planar, but that K_4 and $K_{2,3}$ are planar.

5   Prove that if the shortest cycle in a graph is 5, $3e \leqslant 5v - 10$.   Hence deduce that the Petersen graph is non-planar.

6   The **girth** g of a graph is the length of its shortest cycle. Establish a general inequality involving e, v and g for planar graphs using a similar counting technique to the above proofs.

7   Using the inequality $e \leqslant 3v - 6$, prove that in a planar graph there exists at least one vertex of degree less than or equal to 5.

8 Use the formula in **7** to determine which complete graphs K_n are planar.

9 Draw a planar graph in which each vertex has degree 4.

10 Prove that all bipartite graphs of the form $K_{2,n}$ are planar.

11 For which values of $s,\ t > 1$ is the complete bipartite graph $K_{s,t}$ non-planar?

12 Prove that for a simple graph G with at least 11 vertices, G and its complement $\overline{G}$ cannot both be planar.

Hint: Consider the total number of edges in both G and $\overline{G}$ and then use the inequality.

The **platonic solids** are regular polyhedra whose faces are all the same shape. They can all be drawn as planar graphs. Click on the icon to obtain an investigation on platonic solids.

You can click on the second icon to obtain an investigation on soccer balls, or on the third icon to obtain extension material on **Homeomorphic** graphs and the **Theorem of Kuratowski**.

PLATONIC SOLIDS
INVESTIGATION

SOCCER BALLS
INVESTIGATION

HOMEOMORPHIC
GRAPHS

B.6 TREES AND ALGORITHMS

We now consider the class of connected graphs without cycles, known as **trees**. We extend our work to include **weighted graphs** and consider three algorithms for them: **Kruskal's**, **Prim's**, and **Dijkstra's**.

Definition:

A **tree** is a connected, simple graph with no circuits or cycles. We say it is **acyclic**.

Some examples of trees are shown below:

In a sense, a tree is the simplest possible connected graph. Every connected simple graph has a tree as a subgraph.

Definition:

A **spanning tree** is a connected subgraph with no cycles but which contains all the vertices of the original graph.

Theorem:

A graph G is connected if and only if it possesses a spanning tree.

Proof:

$(\Rightarrow)$ If G has a spanning tree T, then by definition, T is connected and contains all the vertices in G.
$\therefore$ since G contains all the edges in T, G is also connected.

($\Leftarrow$)   Suppose G is connected. Then
either G is a tree, in which case it is its own spanning tree,
or G contains cycles. In this case, we can keep deleting edges of G without
deleting vertices until it is impossible to continue without disconnecting G. At
this time, we are left with a spanning tree of G.

Note that the spanning tree of a graph need
not be unique.

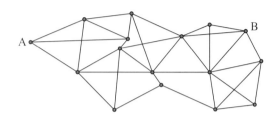

For example, one spanning tree of the tree
on the right is shown on the next page.

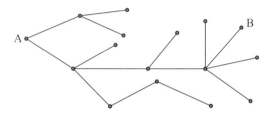

In the spanning tree:

- There are 16 vertices, so its order is 16.
- There are 15 edges, so its size is 15.
- There is one path only from A to B.
- If we delete any edge from the tree, then the graph is disconnected.
- If we add an edge without adding a vertex, then the graph has a circuit.

PROPERTIES OF TREES

The following properties of trees are all equivalent and may each used to establish if a given
graph is a tree.

1 T is a tree if and only if any two of its vertices are connected by exactly one path.

Proof:

($\Rightarrow$)   If T is a tree then it is connected. Hence there exists a simple path between
any two vertices.
However, suppose there is more than one simple path between two vertices.
Then *either* the two simple paths are disjoint, so we have a cycle,
or at some intervening vertex on the initially common simple path, the paths
become disjoint, and we also have a cycle.
$\therefore$ since T is acyclic, we have a contradiction, and there is a unique path
between any two vertices.

($\Leftarrow$)   If T is not a tree, then
either it is disconnected, in which case there are no paths between some vertices,
or it is cyclic, in which case there exist two simple paths between two vertices.
Hence if T is not a tree, not every two vertices of T are connected by exactly
one path.

2 T is a tree if and only if it is connected and the removal of any one edge results in
the graph becoming disconnected.

Proof:

($\Rightarrow$)   If T is a tree, then by property **1**, any edge is the unique path between the two
incident vertices. $\therefore$ removing this edge disconnects the graph.

$(\Leftarrow)$ If T is not a tree, then
either T is already disconnected,
or T is connected and contains a cycle. If this is true, then we can remove at least one edge without the graph becoming disconnected.

3   If T has order n, then it is a tree if and only if it contains no cycles and has $n - 1$ edges.

Proof:

$(\Rightarrow)$ If T is a tree of order n, then by definition it contains no cycles.
Now if T has order 2, then T is K_2, which indeed has only 1 edge.
Now suppose that all trees with k vertices have $k - 1$ edges.
Adding one vertex to the tree without the tree becoming disconnected requires us to add another edge.
Hence we form a tree with $k + 1$ vertices and k edges.
$\therefore$ by induction, a tree of order n has $n - 1$ edges.

$(\Leftarrow)$ Suppose G is a graph with n vertices, $n - 1$ edges and no cycles.
Since there are no cycles, there exists no more than one path between any two vertices.
Now if G is disconnected, it is made up of k disconnected subgraphs ($k > 1$), none of which cycle, i.e., it is made up of k disconnected trees.
But we already know that a tree with m vertices has $m - 1$ edges, so for k disconnected trees with a total of n vertices, the total number of edges is $n - k$.
Hence $k = 1$, which is a contradiction.
$\therefore$ G must be connected, and since is contains no cycles, it is a tree.

4   If T has order n, then it is a tree if and only if it is connected and has $n - 1$ edges.

Proof:

$(\Rightarrow)$ If T is a tree of order n, then by definition it contains no cycles.
Now if T has order 2, then T is K_2, which indeed has only 1 edge.
Now suppose that all trees with k vertices have $k - 1$ edges.
Adding one edge to the tree without making a cycle requires us to add another vertex.
Hence we form a tree with $k + 1$ vertices and k edges.
$\therefore$ by induction, a tree of order n has $n - 1$ edges.

$(\Leftarrow)$ Let G be a connected graph with n vertices, $n - 1$ edges.
If G is cyclic, then we can delete an edge from the graph to form a connected subgraph of G with the same number of vertices as G. We can continue this process r times ($r > 0$) until we obtain a tree T with n vertices and $n - 1 - r$ edges.
However, we know that a tree with n vertices has $n - 1$ edges, so $r = 0$.
This is a contradiction, so G must be acyclic.
$\therefore$ since G is connected, it is a tree.

5 T is a tree if it contains no cycles, but the addition of any new edge creates exactly one cycle.

Proof: If T is a tree, then by definition it is connected and contains no cycles.
Now if we add an edge between two existing vertices A and B, then there are

now exactly two paths from A to B. Hence there is now a single cycle which starts and finishes at A, and travels in either direction via B. The cycle through B is the same cycle since it contains the same set of edges.

Hence exactly one cycle is created.

EXERCISE 11B.6.1

1   Which of the graphs below are trees?

a  b  c d

2   Find all non-isomorphic trees of order 6.

3   Can a complete graph be a tree? Explain.

4   What is the sum of the degrees of the vertices of a tree of order n?

   a   A tree has two vertices of degree 4, one of degree 3 and one of degree 2. All others have degree 1. How many vertices does it have? Draw it.

   b   A tree has two vertices of degree 5, three of degree 3, two of degree 2, and the remainder have degree 1. How many vertices does it have? Draw it.

5   Which of these trees are isomorphic?

a  b  c

d 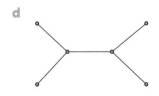 e 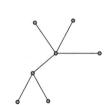 f

g h  i

6   Show that there is a tree with six vertices of order 1 and one of each with degrees 2, 3 and 5.

7   Which complete bipartite graphs $K_{m,n}$ are trees ?

8 Show that for $n > 2$, any tree on n vertices has at least two vertices of degree one, i.e., end vertices.

THE BREADTH FIRST SEARCH

There are two algorithms for finding a spanning tree on a graph in as efficient a way as possible. These are the **depth first search** and the **breadth first search**. However, here we will consider only the **breadth first search** algorithm:

From a given starting vector, we visit all adjacent vertices. Then for each of these vertices, we visit all the adjacent vertices except those to which we have already been, and so on until we have visited all vertices.

For example, for the graph alongside:

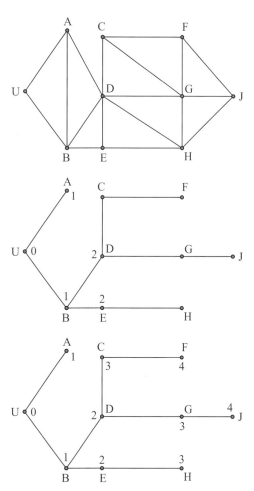

1 We choose a starting vertex, U. We label vertex U with 0, since it is 0 steps from itself.

2 We move to vertices adjacent to U, i.e., A and B. We label these 1, because they are both 1 step from U.

3 Next, we choose one of these two adjacent vertices (we will choose B for no particular reason) and move to the **unlabelled** vertices adjacent to B. These are D and E, and we label them both 2 because they are both two steps from U. We repeat this with the **unlabelled** vertices adjacent to A, but in this case there are none.
Note that by moving only to the unlabelled vertices we ensure that we do not form a circuit.

4 All unlabelled vertices adjacent to those labelled with a 2 are labelled 3 etc. as they are 3 steps from U and cannot be reached in less than 3 steps. This process is continued until all vertices have been reached. We end up with the spanning tree of the graph shown alongside.

Notes:

- This spanning tree is not unique, because we could choose a different start vertex, or different orders in which to visit the adjacent vertices,
  e.g., if we had chosen to consider A before B.
- Since a spanning tree exists if and only if the original graph is connected, this algorithm can be used to **test** whether or not a graph is connected. If the graph is not connected, we can never label all vertices.
- The BFS algorithm can tell you the minimum length (in terms of the number of edges on the path) from the starting point to any other vertex on the graph.

EXERCISE 11B.6.2

1 Starting at A, find spanning trees for these graphs:

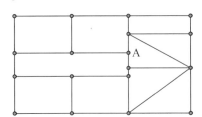

2 How many different spanning trees are there for C_n $(n \geqslant 3)$?   (Include isomorphisms.)

Extension:

3 Including isomorphisms, how many spanning trees do

    a K_2 **b** K_3 **c** K_4 **d** K_5 **e** K_6 have?

Hence postulate a formula for K_n.

Hint: Illustrate the different isomorphic forms the trees can take.

4 How many spanning trees do

    a $K_{1,1}$ **b** $K_{2,2}$ **c** $K_{3,3}$ **d** $K_{4,4}$ have?

 Include isomorphisms but assume the discrete sets of vertices are distinguishable.
Postulate a formula for $K_{n,n}$.

5 How many spanning trees does $K_{m,n}$ have?

WEIGHTED GRAPHS

Definition:

A **weighted graph** is one in which a numerical value (weight) is apportioned to each edge
of the graph.

An example of a weighted graph was considered in the road cleaner problem in **Exercise
11B.4.1**. In this problem, we considered an optimal route that depended on the length or
weight of each edge we travelled along.

We will consider two types of problems on weighted
graphs.
These correspond to the situations we considered in
the introductory exercise on Graph Theory, **Exercise
11B.1** question **4**. We considered two scenarios corresponding to the following weighted graph:

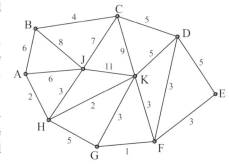

1 Suppose the diagram represents an offshore oilfield. The dots represent the oil wells and the
lines joining them represent pipelines that could
be constructed to connect the wells.
The number shown on each edge is the cost (in millions of dollars) of constructing that
pipeline. Each oil well must be connected to every other, but not necessarily directly.
Which pipelines should be constructed to minimise the cost?

This problem is concerned with finding the **minimum weight spanning tree** of the graph. Note that since the graph is connected, it has to have at least one spanning tree. There are two algorithms for finding the spanning tree of minimum weight: Kruskal's Algorithm and Prim's Algorithm.

2 Suppose the diagram represents the walking trails in a national park. The numbers on the edges represent the suggested walk time in hours for that trail. If I want to walk from point A to point E in the shortest possible time, what route should I take?

This question does not ask for the minimum weight spanning tree, but rather for the **minimum connector** (minimum weight path) between two given points. In this case we need to use a different method, known as Dijkstra's Algorithm.

In the exercise at the end of this section, we will solve these two problems by algorithmic means. We will therefore demonstrate the three algorithms using a different graph.

MINIMUM WEIGHT SPANNING TREES

The two different procedures for finding a minimum weight (or length) spanning tree are Kruskal's algorithm and Prim's algorithm. These are both termed "greedy algorithms" because we always take the best option at each stage regardless of the consequences.

KRUSKAL'S ALGORITHM

In **Kruskal's algorithm**, we grab edges one at a time, taking the edge of least weight at every stage while ensuring that no cycles are being formed. For a graph of order n, the minimum weight spanning tree is obtained after $n - 1$ successful choices of edge.

Step 1: Start with the shortest edge. If there are several, choose one at random.

Step 2: Choose the shortest edge remaining that does not complete a circuit with any of those already chosen. If there is more than one possible choice, pick one at random.

Step 3: Repeat *Step 2* until you have chosen $n - 1$ edges.

Example 38

Use Kruskal's algorithm to find the minimum length spanning tree of the graph below.

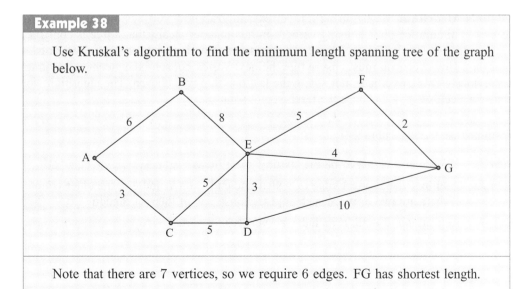

Note that there are 7 vertices, so we require 6 edges. FG has shortest length.

Edge	Length	Circuit	Edge List	Total Length
FG	2	No	FG	2
DE	3	No	FG, DE	5
AC	3	No	FG, DE, AC	8
EG	4	No	FG, DE, AC, EG	12
EF	5	Yes - reject	FG, DE, AC, EG	8
CE	5	No	FG, DE, AC, EG, CE	17
CD	5	Yes - reject	FG, DE, AC, EG, CE	17
AB	6	No	FG, DE, AC, EG, CE, AB	23

We have 6 edges, so we stop the algorithm.

The total minimum weight spanning tree has weight 23, and is shown below.

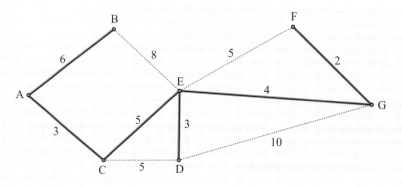

Note that in this case the minimum spanning tree is not unique. We could have chosen CD instead of CE.

PRIM'S ALGORITHM

In **Prim's Algorithm**, we begin with a vertex and grab new vertices one at a time along edges of minimum length. Choosing vertices in this manner means that a tree is constructed at each stage, so checks for cycles are not necessary. This is one advantage over Kruskal's Algorithm. However, you must ensure that the next vertex chosen is adjacent to any one of the previously chosen vertices, not solely the last one that was chosen. The algorithm works because at each stage, we choose the least weight solution.

We summarise the algorithm as follows:

Step 1:   Choose any vertex to be the starting point of your tree, which we label T.

Step 2:   Add to T the shortest edge of which one end is on T and one the other is not. If there are two or more such edges, choose one of them at random.

Step 3:   Repeat *Step 2* until T includes all vertices.

Example 39

Apply Prim's algorithm to find the minimum spanning tree of the graph in **Example 38**.

There are 7 vertices so we require 6 edges.
Let vertex C be the starting point.

Vertex Set	Adjacent Vertices	Edges Chosen	Length	Total Length
C	**A**, D, E	CA	3	3
C, **A**	**D**, E, B	CD	5	8
C, A, **D**	B, **E**, G	DE	3	11
C, A, D, **E**	B, F, **G**	EG	4	15
C, A, D, E, **G**	B, **F**	GF	2	17
C, A, D, E, G, **F**	**B**	AB	6	23

Just as in **Example 38**, we find the total minimum weight spanning tree has weight 23.
However, in this case we have found a different minimum weight spanning tree:

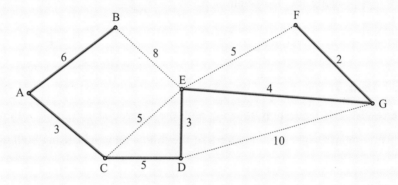

Note that at stage 2, we chose edge CD, this was not necessarily the only choice.
We could equally well have have chosen CE.

In order to find a minimum spanning tree for large graphs, the only practical option is to use a computer. We construct a **cost adjacency matrix C** for the graph in which each number represents the weight of an edge between two vertices, and a cross indicates that vertices are not adjacent. We can then apply a special form of the Prim algorithm.

For example:

This graph has the cost adjacency matrix shown alongside:

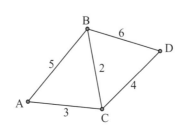

		To		
		A	B	C	D
From	A	X	5	3	X
	B	5	X	2	6
	C	3	2	X	4
	D	X	6	4	X

The rows are the vertices we are coming from and the columns are the vertices we are going to.

Suppose we decide to start the spanning tree at B, so we search the B row for the vertex which is closest. The shortest possible edge is BC, so we add C to our list of vertices. In order to avoid circuits forming, no further edges should end at B or C, so columns B and C are deleted from the table, as shown alongside:

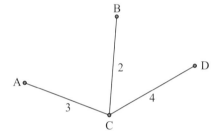

We can now build onto the tree from either B or C. We therefore select the edge of minimum length which is left in either the B or the C row. This is CA with length 3.

Deleting the A column, it is clear that the last link should be from CD, with length 4.

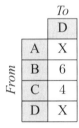

The resulting minimum weight spanning tree is shown alongside. Its weight is 9.

EXERCISE 11B.6.3

1 Solve **Exercise 11B.1** question **4a** using both the Kruskal and Prim algorithms.

2 Find the minimum weight spanning trees of the following graphs using both the Kruskal and Prim algorithms.

a

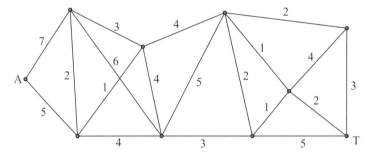

b

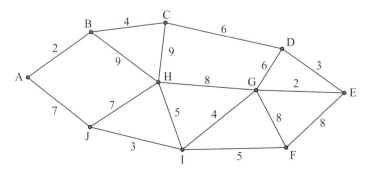

3 The table represents a complete weighted graph K_5.

    a How do we know it is a complete graph?

    b Find a minimum spanning tree for the graph. Use the matrix form of Prim's algorithm.

    c Draw the graph then use Kruskal's algorithm to find a minimum spanning tree.

To

From	A	B	C	D	E
A	X	10	8	7	10
B	10	X	5	4	9
C	8	5	X	7	10
D	7	4	7	X	8
E	10	9	10	8	X

4 Find a minimum weight spanning tree for the network represented by the table opposite:

To

From	A	B	C	D	E	F	G
A	X	X	30	X	X	50	45
B	X	X	70	35	40	X	X
C	30	70	X	50	X	X	20
D	X	35	50	X	10	X	15
E	X	40	X	10	X	15	X
F	50	X	X	X	15	X	10
G	45	X	20	15	X	10	X

THE MINIMUM CONNECTOR PROBLEM

Consider the shipping lanes between seven ports where the edge weights represent the estimated time in days between ports, as shown alongside. The problem is to find the quickest route from A to D.

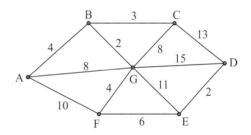

We can generally solve problems with small graphs such as this by inspection: the quickest time is 18 days using either $A \to B \to G \to F \to E \to D$

      or $A \to F \to E \to D$.

However, real life problems generally require much larger and more involved graphs that can only be sensibly handled using computers. Finding optimum paths through such graphs therefore requires an algorithm or set of rules that can be programmed into a computer.

Finding more efficient algorithms for this and other graph theory tasks is a very active area of research, for they are used in areas as diverse as cancer research and electrical engineering.

In this course, we find the minimum weight path between two given vertices on a weighted connected graph using Dijkstra's algorithm.

It is important for this algorithm to work that all weights on the graph are non-negative. This is generally physically realistic, since the cost, distance, or time, etc., of travelling along an edge cannot be negative.

DIJKSTRA'S ALGORITHM

Step 1:   Assign a value of 0 to the starting vertex. We draw a box around the vertex label and the 0 to show the label is permanent.

Step 2:   Consider all unboxed vertices adjacent to the latest boxed vertex. Label them with the minimum weight from the starting vertex via the set of boxed vertices.

Step 3:   Choose the least of *all* of the unboxed labels on the *whole* graph, and make it permanent by boxing it.

Step 4:   Repeat *steps 2* and *3* until the destination vertex has been boxed, then backtrack through the set of boxed vertices to find the shortest path through the graph.

In each stage we try to find the path of minimum weight from a given vertex to the starting vertex. We can therefore discard previously found shortest paths as we proceed, until we have obtained the path of minimum weight from the start to the finishing vertex.

We will now apply Dijkstra's algorithm to the example on the previous page:

Begin by labelling A with 0 and drawing a box around it. Label the adjacent vertices B, G and F with the weights of the edges.

The weight of edge AB is least, so we draw a box around B and its label.

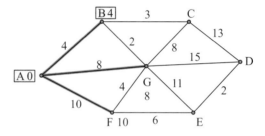

Next we consider moving from B to all adjacent vertices.   These are C, which has cumulative minimum weight 7, and G, which has cumulative minimum weight via B of 6. We therefore label C with 7 and replace the 8 next to G with a 6. This indicates that the minimum weight path from A to G is via B, and its weight is 6. We know it is the minimum because it is the least of the unboxed labels on the graph. Therefore, we put a box around the G and the 6.

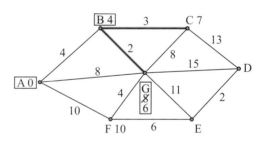

Now C is unboxed and adjacent to G, but $6 + 8 = 14 > 7$. We therefore do not update the label. We also label D with 21, E with 17, and F is labelled with 10. Notice that the minimum path of weight 10 from A to F is obtained by either $A \rightarrow B \rightarrow G \rightarrow F$ or $A \rightarrow F$ direct.

Of the new options, C is the least is therefore boxed.

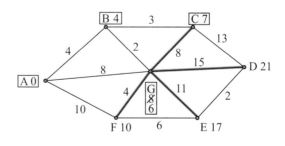

We now consider all unboxed vertices adjacent to C. We can update D from 21 to 20.

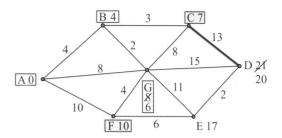

We choose the least of all of the unboxed labels on the whole graph, and this is the 10 corresponding to F. F is therefore the next vertex to be boxed.

We can now update E to 16, and box it because it now has the lowest unboxed label.

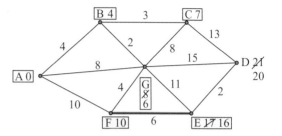

Finally, we update D to 18, and we are now sure that the lowest label is attached to the final destination. The algorithm stops, and its completed diagram is shown opposite:

To complete the route, we have to backtrack from D to A using the final boxed labels. We have 18 units (and no more) to use, so we have to retrace steps back through E and F. From F, we can either return directly to A, or return via G and B. We therefore have the two solutions, each of weight 18, that were found by inspection.

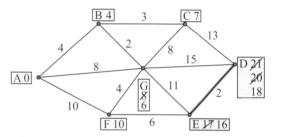

These are: $A \rightarrow B \rightarrow G \rightarrow F \rightarrow E \rightarrow D$
and $A \rightarrow F \rightarrow E \rightarrow D$.

Note two unusual features of this example that do not in occur in most problems:

- All vertices were considered. In general, the algorithm stops as soon as the destination vertex is boxed, irrespective of whether all other vertices have been considered. This is because a vertex is only boxed when we are sure it has the **minimum** cumulative weight.

- The minimum weight path from A to F was the same either via the intermediate vertices B and G or directly along the incident edge. This does not in general occur, but if it does, either path is equally valid.

EXERCISE 11B.6.4

1 Find the minimum connector from A to D for the networks below:

a

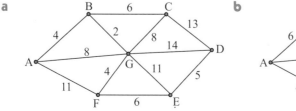

b

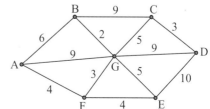

2   Find the shortest path from A to G on the graph below.

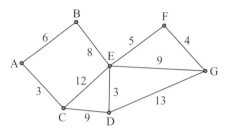

3   Solve **Exercise 11B.1** question **4b** using the Dijkstra algorithm.

4   Find the shortest path from A to G on the graph below.

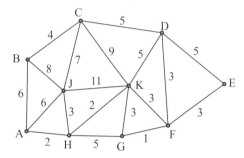

B.7   THE CHINESE POSTMAN PROBLEM

This problem was posed by Chinese mathematician **Kwan Mei-Ko**. It involves finding the minimum weight Eulerian circuit of a weighted connected graph, i.e., given a weighted connected graph, what is the minimum weight closed walk that covers each edge at least once?

Now if all the vertices of the graph have even degrees, the graph is Eulerian and there exists an Eulerian circuit that traverses every edge exactly once. The Chinese Postman Problem is therefore trivial in this case.

However, most graphs are not Eulerian and so some of the edges must be walked twice. The task is to minimise the total weight of the edges we double up on.

For non-Eulerian graphs, vertices with odd degrees exist in pairs (consider the Hand-Shake problem). We therefore need to walk twice over edges that are between pairs of odd vertices. We work out how to do this most efficiently either by inspection or by using of Dijkstra's algorithm: the edges identified by Dijkstra are the ones that should be traversed twice.

Example 40

Solve the Chinese Postman Problem for the weighted graph shown.

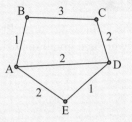

The graph is not Eulerian since the degrees of vertices A and D are odd.

We therefore need to walk twice between these vertices. We could do this by walking along the paths:

$$A \to B \to C \to D \quad \text{with weight} \quad 1 + 3 + 2 = 6$$
$$A \to D \quad \text{with weight} \quad 2$$
$$A \to E \to D \quad \text{with weight} \quad 2 + 1 = 3$$

The most efficient way is therefore to traverse the edge AD twice.

The minimum weight closed walk that covers every edge at least once has weight equal to the sum of the weights of the edges, plus 2, i.e., $11 + 2 = 13$.

Example 41

Use Dijkstra's algorithm to solve the Chinese Postman Problem for the weighted graph shown.

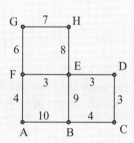

The graph is not Eulerian since the degrees of vertices B and F are odd.

We therefore need to walk twice between these vertices, and use Dijkstra's algorithm to do this in the most efficient way:

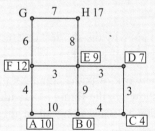

The most efficient way is therefore to traverse the route $B \to E \to F$ twice.

If there are more than two odd vertices, we need a counting procedure to identify the different possible pairings of vertices, and then apply Dijkstra's algorithm in each case to find the minimum route.

Example 42

Solve the Chinese Postman Problem for the weighted graph opposite.

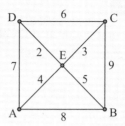

The graph is not Eulerian since the degrees of vertices A, B, C and D are odd.

There are six possible pairings of the odd vertices, and they go together in the following groups of two: AB and CD,   AC and BD,   AD and BC.

For every pair, we find the minimum weight connector between the vertices, either by inspection or using Dijkstra's algorithm. We can then choose the combination of pairs with the overall minimum weight.

Pairing	Minimum Weight Connector		Combination's Total
	Path	Weight	Minimum Weight
AB	$A \rightarrow B$	8	13
CD	$C \rightarrow E \rightarrow D$	5	
AC	$A \rightarrow E \rightarrow C$	7	14
BD	$B \rightarrow E \rightarrow D$	7	
AD	$A \rightarrow E \rightarrow D$	6	14
BC	$B \rightarrow E \rightarrow C$	8	

Hence the most efficient way is to construct an Eulerian circuit which travel both routes $A \rightarrow B$ and $C \rightarrow E \rightarrow D$ twice each.

EXERCISE 11B.7

1 A snowplough must clear snow by driving along all of the roads shown in the graph, starting and finishing at the garage A. All distances shown are in km.

Explain why the shortest distance the snowplough must travel is 24 km.

2 A network of paths connects four mountain tops as shown in the figure alongside. A keen rambler wishes to walk along all of the paths linking the peaks.

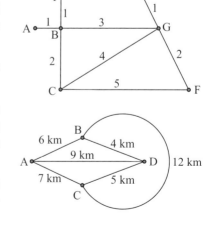

a Explain why the rambler will have to repeat some sections of the track. How many sections will have to be repeated?

b Considering all possible combinations of pairs, find the minimum distance that the rambler must travel to cover every section of track, starting and finishing at A. Suggest a possible route that achieves this minimum distance.

c After some careful thought, the rambler realises that because of the terrain, he would be better off considering the time required to walk the paths instead of the distances. The map with the times for each section of track is shown alongside. If the rambler wants to minimise the total time on route, what could his strategy be?

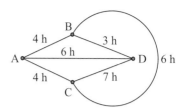

3 A roadsweeper based at A must clean all of the roads shown at least once. Explain why:

  a some the roads will have to be swept twice

  b the shortest distance the roadsweeper must travel is 63 units.

Find a route by which the roadsweeper can achieve this minimum.

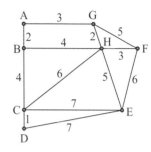

4

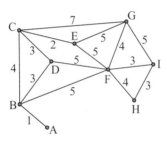

The graph opposite shows the roads in Postman Peter's mailing route. If the Post Office where Peter starts and finishes his round is at A, how should Peter minimise the distance he must walk?

5 A carnival procession wishes to march down each of the roads shown in the diagram given, in which all lengths are shown in kilometres.

  a List the three different ways in which the four odd vertices in the diagram can be paired.

  b Find the shortest distance that the procession has to travel if they are to start and finish at E.

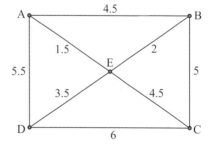

6

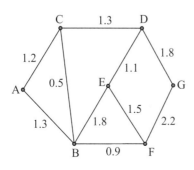

The graph opposite is a schematic drawing of an oil field in which the oil wells (the vertices) are connected by pipelines (the edges).

The cost of inspecting each edge (in tens of thousands of dollars) by means of a robotic device is displayed.

What is the least cost solution for completing the inspection, given that the robot once on a pipeline must inspect all of it?

B.8   THE TRAVELLING SALESMAN PROBLEM (TSP)

Recall that a Hamiltonian cycle is a cycle in which we visit each vertex of a connected graph exactly once. One of the great unsolved problems of pure mathemics is how to efficiently find the least weight Hamiltonian cycle of a weighted complete graph. This is known as the Travelling Salesman Problem (TSP).

In graphs with a small number of vertices and edges such as that alongside, it is possible to solve the TSP relatively quickly. However, as the size and order of a graph increases, the TSP rapidly becomes inefficient to solve even on a computer. There are $\frac{1}{2}(n-1)!$ distinct Hamiltonian cycles on K_n, so for large n we simply cannot test each one.

Evaluate $\frac{1}{2}(n-1)!$ for $n=20$ and $n=40$ to see why. Imagine the number of cases for $n=100$!!

There are two versions of the TSP, the **classical** version and the **practical** version.

In the **classical** TSP, we insist that each vertex must be visited exactly once.

However, in the **practical** version, we allow vertices to be used on more than one occasion. We therefore are not exactly finding the least weight Hamiltonian cycle of the graph, but something very similar. The problem is still very complex and inaccessible to algorithmic solution.

If the original graph itself is not Hamiltonian, it can be transformed to be so, and extended further to be a complete graph by adding extra edges. We are therefore able to transform the practical version of the TSP into the classical version by the addition of edges, provided the graph that is used obeys the triangle inequality. We will therefore only consider the classical version in this text.

For example, consider the graph on the left below. We can transform it into the graph on the right, thus converting it to the classical TSP.

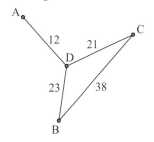
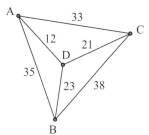

We can find all of the Hamiltonian cycles in the graph starting and finishing at A, and compare their total weights. These are:

ABCDA:	$35+38+21+12=106$		ACDBA:	$33+21+23+35=112$
ABDCA:	$35+23+21+33=112$		ADBCA:	$12+23+38+33=106$
ACBDA:	$33+38+23+12=106$		ADCBA:	$12+21+38+35=106$

Note that the three cycles on the right are simply those on the left in reverse order, so we can discard them as non-unique. We can see that the minimum solution to the TSP is 106 in this case, and the maximum is 112.

We now explore upper and lower bounds for what the minimum weight Hamiltonian cycle might be; these give us an indication of whether a cycle is reasonably close to the mimimum length and hence correct solution.

FINDING AN UPPER BOUND

Clearly, any solution to the problem is an upper bound for what the solution could be. So, we could find any Hamiltonian cycle.

Twice the length of the minimum spanning tree is an upper bound to the practical TSP, because it involves visiting each vertex then returning by the same path. It will thus serve as an upper bound to the classical problem provided the triangle inequality holds for the graph.

Examples:

1 In the example on the previous page, the minimum spanning tree is 56, so an upper bound for the solution to the TSP is 112. Note that twice the length of the minimum spanning tree must be greater than or equal to our largest solution, and in this rather simple case it is equal. It is an efficient way of finding a maximum bound because even if we cannot find the minimum spanning tree by inspection, we can use either Prim or Kruskal.

2 We can use Prim or Kruskal to find the two minimum spanning trees for the weighted graph based on K_5 shown opposite.

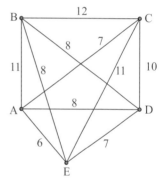

The minimum spanning trees have length 28, so the upper bound for the TSP is 56.

If we consider the minimum spanning tree on the right, the walk EACAEDBDE starts and finishes at the same point, and visits every vertex. Although we cannot use this route in the classical problem, it will still serve as an upper bound for it.

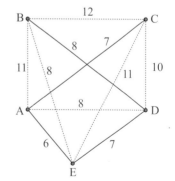

A more appropriate upper bound would complete a Hamiltonian cycle by simply adding the edge BC to the minimum spanning tree. This gives an upper bound of $28 + 12 = 40$ to the problem.

Therefore, although, this method of doubling the minimum spanning tree gives an upper bound, it can be much greater than the optimum solution.

By inspection, the optimum solution to the TSP is $A \to E \to B \to D \to C \to A$
which has length 39, which is barely less than the reduced upper bound. This
is therefore a better method of obtaining solutions that are closer to the optimum.
However, it cannot be modelled algorithmically.

FINDING A LOWER BOUND

The following method gives a lower bound to the TSP solution, but does not necessarily find
the solution itself:

Step 1:   Delete a vertex, together with all incident edges, from the original graph.

Step 2:   Find the minimum spanning tree for the remaining graph.

Step 3:   Add to the length of the minimum spanning tree the lengths of the two shortest
deleted edges.

For example, consider the same graph as before,
shown opposite.

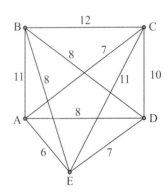

Suppose we delete vertex A and all its incident
edges. We then find the **two** minimum spanning
trees for the remaining subgraph. They are shown
below. Both have length 25.

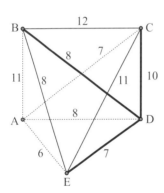
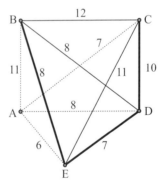

Now, we add the lengths of the two shortest deleted edges. In this case they have lengths 6
and 7. We therefore obtain the lower bound $25 + 6 + 7 = 38$.

Note that in this case it is not actually the solution to the TSP. It will only be the solution
to the TSP if there is a minimum length spanning tree with only two end vertices *and* if the
minimum lengths deleted are incident to these end vertices.

Notice also that if a different vertex is deleted, the lower bound will change. However, since
they are both valid lower bounds, we can take the largest one without fear that the solution
to the TSP is lower.

EXERCISE 11B.8

1 **a** Find a minimum spanning tree for the graph alongside based on K_4. Hence find an upper bound for the TSP.

  b Use a shortcut to find a better upper bound.

  c By deleting each vertex in turn, find a set of lower bounds.

  d Hence solve the TSP problem for this graph.

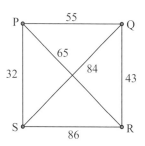

2

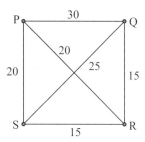

  a Find two minimum spanning trees for the graph alongside based on K_4.

  b Using one of these, find an upper bound for the TSP.

  c By deleting each vertex in turn, find a set of lower bounds.

  d Solve the TSP problem for this graph.

3 **a** Find a minimum spanning tree for the graph alongside based on K_5. Hence find an upper bound for the TSP.

  b Use a shortcut to find a better upper bound.

  c By deleting the vertices in turn, find a set of lower bounds.

  d Solve the TSP problem for this graph.

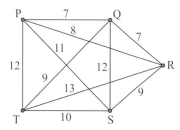

REVIEW SETS

REVIEW SET 11A

1 **a** Use the Euclidean algorithm to find the greatest divisor of 552 and 208.

  b Hence or otherwise, find two integers m and n such that $552m - 208n = 8$.

2 Using Euclid's algorithm, find integers x and y such that $17x + 31y = 1$.

3 Suppose $d = \gcd(378, 168)$. Use Euclid's algorithm to find d, and hence find one pair of integers x and y such that $d = 378x + 168y$.

4 Prove that $a \times b = \gcd(a, b) \times \operatorname{lcm}(a, b)$ for any positive integers a and b.

5 Show that the modular equation $22x \equiv 41 \pmod{17}$ has a unique solution. Find the solution.

6 Find the smallest positive integer n such that $n \equiv 3 \pmod{19}$ and $n \equiv 2 \pmod{11}$.

7 Solve: $14x + 17 \equiv 27 \pmod{6}$.

8   What is the units digit of 3^{2007} ?

9   Suppose N_k is the kth repunit, so $N_1 = 1$, $N_2 = 11$, $N_3 = 111$, etc.

If m, $n \in \mathbb{Z}^+$ are such that $m < n$ and $m \mid n$, deduce that $N_m \mid N_n$.

Hint: Note that N_m and N_n in expanded index form can be written as the sum of geometric progressions.

10   Let a and b be integers such that $\gcd(a, b) = 1$.   Find the possible values of:

    a $\gcd(a + b, a - b)$ **b** $\gcd(2a + b, a + 2b)$.

11   If a, $b \in \mathbb{Z}^+$, show that if $3 \mid (a^2 + b^2)$ then $3 \mid a$ and $3 \mid b$, but if $5 \mid (a^2 + b^2)$ then 5 need not necessarily divide either a or b.

12   If a and b are relatively prime, show that for any $c \in \mathbb{Z}^+$, $\gcd(a, bc) = \gcd(a, c)$.

13   **a**   Suppose we have a three-digit number of the form bba. If the sum of its digits is divisible by 12, show that the number itself is divisible by 12.

    b   Suppose we have a three-digit number of the form bab. If the number itself *and* the sum of its digits is divisible by k, show that the only possible values of k less than 10 are 3 and 9.

    c   Show that if any three-digit number is divisible by k *and* the sum of its digits is divisible by k, then the only possible values of k less than 10 are 3 and 9.

14   Solve: $57x \equiv 20 \pmod{13}$.

15   **a**   Given $n \not\equiv 0 \pmod{5}$, show that $n^2 \equiv \pm 1 \pmod{5}$
    b   Hence, prove that $n^5 + 5n^3 + 4n$ is divisible by 5 for all $n \in \mathbb{Z}^+$

REVIEW SET 11B

1   Show that if $\sqrt{6}$ can be written in the form $\sqrt{6} = \dfrac{a}{b}$ where a, $b \in \mathbb{Z}^+$ are both relatively prime, then a must be an even number.

Hence prove that $\sqrt{6}$ is irrational.

2   **a**   Let $n \in \mathbb{Z}^+$, $n \geqslant 2$, and let $m = (n + 1)! + 2$. Show that m is even and that $3 \mid (m + 1)$.

    b   Let $n \in \mathbb{Z}^+$, $n \geqslant 3$, and let $m = (n + 2)! + 2$. Show that m is even and that $3 \mid (m + 1)$ and $4 \mid (m + 2)$.

    c   Prove that there is a series of n consecutive numbers that are all composite.

3   Convert 7203842 (base 9) to base 3.

4   Determine, with reasons, the number of incongruent solutions to the equation $165x \equiv 105 \pmod{51}$.   Find the solutions.

5   Determine a divisibility test for 36, stating why it works.

Is 14 975 028 526 645 824 divisible by 36?

6   Use the Chinese Remainder Theorem to solve $19x \equiv 99 \pmod{260}$.

7 Prove that $3 \,|\, (a^3 + 5a)$ for all $a \in \mathbb{Z}^+$.

8 Given the recurrence relation $L_{k+2} = L_{k+1} + L_k$ with $L_1 = 1$ and $L_2 = 2$,

    a write down the first 10 terms of the sequence

    b determine $\sum\limits_{k=1}^{n} L_k$ for $n = 1, 2, 3, 4, 5,$ and postulate a closed form solution

       for $\sum\limits_{k=1}^{n} L_k$ in terms of other L_j.

    c Prove your result in **b** by induction.

9 Convert 144 (base 5) into: **a** binary   **b** octal.

10 Prove that if n^2 is divisible by 5 then so is n.

11 Prove or disprove that   if n^2 is divisible by 12, then so is n.

12 Prove that $n^2 - 1$ is either divisible by 4 or is of the form $4k + 3$.

13 Is $4^{35}(47) - 48$ divisible by 3?

14 Determine the truth or otherwise of the statement
$a^2 \equiv b^2 (\mathrm{mod}\, n) \;\Rightarrow\; a \equiv b(\mathrm{mod}\, n)$.
If the statement is false find a counter example.   Is the converse statement true?
Is the statement $a^2 \equiv b^2 (\mathrm{mod}\, n) \;\Rightarrow\; a \equiv b(\mathrm{mod}\, n)$ true when n is a prime number?
Is there any conclusion that can be drawn about a and b $(\mathrm{mod}\, n)$ given the statement
$a^2 \equiv b^2 (\mathrm{mod}\, n)$?

15 Given the statement $ab \equiv 0 \;(\mathrm{mod}\, n),$ what are the conditions on n that makes the conclusion "either $a = 0(\mathrm{mod}\, n)$ or $b \equiv 0(\mathrm{mod}\, n)$" a true statement.

16 Prove that for all $n \in \mathbb{Z}^+,$ $n^5 - 37n^3 + 36n$ is divisible by 4.

REVIEW SET 11C

1 For which values of m are the following graphs bipartite?
    a K_m **b** C_m **c** W_m

2 What are the numbers of edges and vertices in the following graphs?
    a K_m **b** C_m **c** W_m **d** $K_{m,\, n}$

3 Let G be a graph with v vertices and e edges. Let M be the maximum degree of the vertices and let m be the minimum degree of the vertices. Show that $m \leqslant \dfrac{2e}{v} \leqslant M$.

4 If the simple graph G has v vertices and e edges, how many edges does $\overline{G}$ have?

5 If G is a simple graph with 17 edges and its complement, $\overline{G}$, has 11 edges, how many vertices does G have?

6 Show that if G is a bipartite simple graph with v vertices and e edges then $e \leqslant \dfrac{v^2}{4}$.

7 Represent the following graphs by their adjacency matrices:

  a K_4 **b** $K_{1,4}$ **c** $K_{2,3}$

8 Find a self-complementary graph with:

  a   4 vertices   **b**   5 vertices.

9 How many paths are there of length n between two different vertices in K_4 for the cases where n is

  a   2   **b**   3   **c**   4?

10 How many paths are there of length n between two *adjacent* vertices in $K_{3,3}$ given that n is

  a   2   **b**   3   **c**   4?

11 For which values of m, n does $K_{m,n}$ have a Hamiltonian cycle?

12 Suppose that a connected planar simple graph with v vertices and e edges contains no circuits of length 4 or less. Show $e \leqslant \dfrac{5v - 10}{3}$.

13 A connected planar graph has 8 vertices each of degree 3 (is 3-regular or cubic). How many regions does it have?

14 How many regions does a 4-regular connected planar graph with 6 vertices have?

REVIEW SET 11D

1 Which of the following graphs are bipartite?

2 If G is a simple graph with at least two vertices, prove that G has two or more vertices of the same degree.

3 Classify the following graphs as

  i   Eulerian, transversable or neither

  ii Hamiltonian, semi-Hamiltonian or neither:

  a K_5 **b** $K_{2,3}$ **c**   **d**

4 A bipartite graph G has an odd number of vertices.
     Prove that it cannot be Hamiltonian.

5 Given two graphs G and H such that $G \cong H$, prove that the order of G equals the order of H and that the size of G equals the size of H.

   Show, by counterexample, that the converse of this statement is false.

6 Determine whether the graphs below are isomorphic.

A **B** 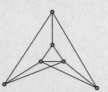 **C**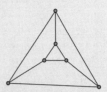

7 a Find all non-isomorphic simple connected graphs of order four.

   b Find all non-isomorphic simple graphs of order four.

8 Determine whether there exist simple graphs with 12 vertices and 28 edges in which

   a the degree of each vertex is either 3 or 4

   b the degree of each vertex is either 5 or 6.

9 Find the fewest vertices required to construct a simple connected graph with at least 500 edges.

10 Given that both a graph G and its complement $\overline{G}$ are trees, what is the order of G?

11 Given a simple cubic graph G is planar, find a relationship between the regions in G and its order. Verify that K_4 satisfies this relationship.

REVIEW SET 11E

1 Use the breadth first search starting at O to find a spanning tree for the graph alongside:

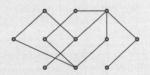

2 How many spanning trees does W_3 have? Include all isomorphisms.

3 Find a minimum weight spanning tree for the graph below using Kruskal's algorithm.

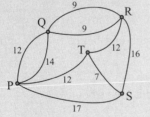

4 Use Prim's algorithm to find a minimum weight spanning tree for the graph below:

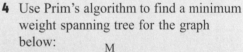

5 Find the minimum connector from X to Y in the graph alongside.

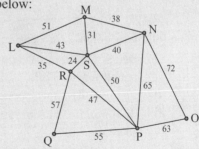
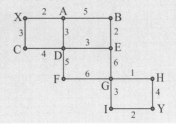

6 The network alongside shows the connecting roads between towns A and B. The weights on the edges represent distances in kilometres. Find the length of the shortest path from A to B.

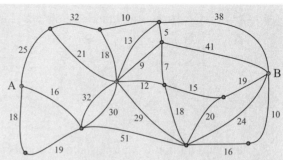

7 A sewage network graphed alongside needs to have all tunnels inspected. The weights on the edges are their lengths in metres.

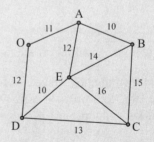

  a If there are entrances at each of the nodes, where should the inspection start and finish so that the minimum distance is covered?

  b State an inspection plan that covers each tunnel only once.

  c If the inspector must start and finish his inspection at A, which tunnel will be covered twice for him to travel the minimum distance?

  d What is the minimum distance that must be covered if the inspector starts and finishes at A?

8 For the graph alongside, solve the Chinese Postman Problem. Assume the postman starts and finishes at O.

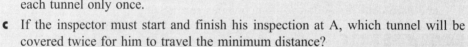

9 The following graphs represent Travelling Salesman Problems. In each case:

   i find a minimum spanning tree for the graph and hence find an upper bound for the TSP
   ii improve the upper bound by using a shortcut
   iii delete each vector in turn and hence find a lower bound
   iv solve the TSP.

a

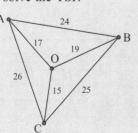

b

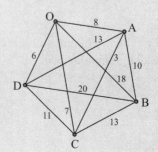

APPENDIX
Methods of proof

Greek mathematicians more than 2000 years ago were the first to realise that progress in mathematical thinking could be brought about by conscious formulation of the methods of **abstraction** and **proof**.

From a few examples one might notice a certain common quality and formulate a general idea. This is the process of **abstration**.

a	b	a^2	b^2
1	2	1	4
3	5	9	25
4	5	16	25
5	7	25	49
6	9	36	81

For example, by considering the given table of values one may abstract:

"If a and b are real numbers then $a < b$ implies that $a^2 < b^2$."

However, on observing that $-2 < 1$, but $(-2)^2 \not< 1^2$, one might change the abstraction to:

"If a and b are positive real numbers then $a < b$ implies $a^2 < b^2$.

Convinced that this abstraction is now correct one must now provide **proof** to remove any possibility of scepticism. This is done by providing a logical argument which leaves no doubt that the abstraction is indeed a truth. No flaws can be found in any step of the argument.

We have already examined in the Core HL text, proof by **the principle of mathematical induction**. Other methods of proof include:

DIRECT PROOF

In a **direct proof** we start with a known truth and by a succession of correct deductions finish with the required result.

Example 1:   Prove that   if $a, b \in \mathbb{R}$ then $a < b \implies a < \dfrac{a+b}{2}$

$$\textbf{Proof:} \quad a < b \quad \implies \quad \frac{a}{2} < \frac{b}{2} \qquad \{\text{as we are dividing by 2 which is} > 0\}$$

$$\implies \quad \frac{a}{2} + \frac{a}{2} < \frac{a}{2} + \frac{b}{2} \quad \{\text{adding } \frac{a}{2} \text{ to both sides}\}$$

$$\implies \quad a < \frac{a+b}{2}$$

PROOF BY CONTRADICTION (AN INDIRECT PROOF)

In **proof by contradiction** we deliberately assume the opposite to what we are trying to prove true. Then, by a series of correct steps we show that this is impossible and hence our assumption is false.

Consider **Example 1** again: **Proof (by contradiction):**

$$\text{For} \quad a < b, \quad \text{suppose that} \quad a \geqslant \frac{a+b}{2}$$

$$\implies \quad 2a \geqslant 2\left(\frac{a+b}{2}\right) \quad \{\text{multiplying both sides by 2}\}$$

$$\implies \quad 2a \geqslant a + b$$

$$\implies \quad a \geqslant b \qquad \{\text{subtracting } a \text{ from both sides}\}$$

$$\text{which is false}$$

Since the steps of the argument are correct, the supposition must be false and the alternative, $a < \dfrac{a+b}{2}$ must be true.

Example 2:   Prove that the solution of $3^x = 8$ is irrational.

Proof (by contradiction):

Suppose the solution of $3^x = 8$ is rational,   i.e., x is rational.

$\Rightarrow$ $x = \dfrac{p}{q}$ where $p, q \in \mathbb{Z}, \quad q \neq 0$

$\Rightarrow$ $3^{\frac{p}{q}} = 8$

$\Rightarrow$ $\left(3^{\frac{p}{q}}\right)^q = 8^q$

$\Rightarrow$ $3^p = 8^q$

which is impossible as 3^p is always odd and 8^q is always even.

Thus, the assumption is false and its opposite, x is irrational, must be true.

Example 3:   Prove that no positive integers x and y exist such that $x^2 - y^2 = 1$.

Proof (by contradiction):

Suppose $x, y \in \mathbb{Z}^+$ exists such that $x^2 - y^2 = 1$.

$\Rightarrow$ $(x+y)(x-y) = 1$

$\Rightarrow$ $\underbrace{x+y = 1 \quad \text{and} \quad x-y = 1}_{\text{case 1}}$ **or** $\underbrace{x+y = -1 \quad \text{and} \quad x-y = -1}_{\text{case 2}}$

$\Rightarrow$ $x = 1, \quad y = 0$ (from case 1)   **or** $x = -1, \quad y = 0$ (from case 2)

Both cases provide a contradiction of $x \geqslant 1$ and $y \geqslant 1$.

Thus, the supposition is false.   Hence, the opposite is true.

i.e.,   positive integers x and y do not exist such that $x^2 - y^2 = 1$.

Indirect proof often seems cleverly contrived, especially if no direct proof is forthcoming. It is perhaps more natural to seek a direct proof of an abstraction, but we should not overlook the alternative of an indirect proof such as proof by contradiction.

ERRORS IN PROOF

One must be careful not to make errors in algebra or reasoning. To illustrate the point, examine carefully the following examples.

Example 2 (again)

Invalid argument: $3^x = 8$

$\Rightarrow$ $\log 3^x = \log 8$

$\Rightarrow$ $x \log 3 = \log 8$

$\Rightarrow$ $x = \dfrac{\log 8}{\log 3}$ where both $\log 8$ and $\log 3$ are irrational.

$\Rightarrow$ x is irrational.

The last step is not valid. The argument that an irrational divided by an irrational is rational is not correct. For example, $\frac{\sqrt{2}}{\sqrt{2}} = 1$.

To disprove a statement we need supply only *one counter-example*.

Example 4:   Prove without decimalisation that $\sqrt{3} - 1 > \frac{1}{\sqrt{2}}$.

> Invalid argument: $\sqrt{3} - 1 > \frac{1}{\sqrt{2}}$
>
> $\Rightarrow$ $\left(\sqrt{3} - 1\right)^2 > \left(\frac{1}{\sqrt{2}}\right)^2$ {both sides are > 0, so we can square them}
>
> $\Rightarrow$ $4 - 2\sqrt{3} > \frac{1}{2}$
>
> $\Rightarrow$ $\frac{7}{2} > 2\sqrt{3}$
>
> $\Rightarrow$ $7 > 4\sqrt{3}$
>
> $\Rightarrow$ $7^2 > 48$ {squaring again}
>
> $\Rightarrow$ $49 > 48$

The error in this argument is that we are assuming that which we are trying to prove, and concluding that $49 > 48$,   which requires no proof.

However, we could establish the truth $\sqrt{3} - 1 > \frac{1}{\sqrt{2}}$ by either:

- reversing the steps of the above argument, or by
- using proof by contradiction   (supposing $\sqrt{3} - 1 \leqslant \frac{1}{\sqrt{2}}$).

Example 5:   Invalid proof that $0 = 1$:

> Suppose $a = 1$ $\Rightarrow$ $a^2 = a$
>
> $\Rightarrow$ $a^2 - 1 = a - 1$
>
> $\Rightarrow$ $(a + 1)(a - 1) = a - 1$
>
> $\Rightarrow$ $a + 1 = 1$ .... *
>
> $\Rightarrow$ $a = 0$
>
> So, $0 = 1$

The invalid step in the argument is at $*$ where we divide both sides by $a - 1$. As $a = 1$, $a - 1 = 0$.   So, we are dividing by 0 which is illegal.

USING PREVIOUS RESULTS

In Mathematics we build up, step-by-step, collections of important and useful results, each depending on previously proven statements.

Here is a trivial example.

Conjecture: The recurring decimal $0.\overline{9} = 0.999\,999\,99\,.......$ is exactly equal to 1.

Proof (by contradiction):

Suppose $0.\overline{9} < 1$

> then $0.\overline{9} < \dfrac{0.\overline{9} + 1}{2}$ {We proved earlier that $a < b \Rightarrow a < \dfrac{a+b}{2}$}
>
> $\Rightarrow$ $0.\overline{9} < \dfrac{1.\overline{9}}{2}$ $\left\{ \text{Ordinary division:}\quad \dfrac{2 \mid 1.99999999......}{0.99999999......} \right\}$
>
> $\Rightarrow$ $0.\overline{9} < 0.\overline{9}$ clearly a contradiction

Therefore the supposition is false, and so $0.\overline{9} \geqslant 1$ is true.

and of course, $0.\overline{9} > 1$ is ridiculous.   Thus $0.\overline{9} = 1$

EQUIVALENCE

Some abstractions with two statements A and B involve equivalence.

$A \Leftrightarrow B$ means $A \Rightarrow B$ and $B \Rightarrow A$

We say A *is equivalent to* B,   or A is true *if and only if* B is true.

The phrase "if and only if" is often written as "iff".

In order to prove an equivalence, we need to establish *both* of these implications, i.e., prove that $A \Rightarrow B$ *and*   that $B \Rightarrow A$.

$\qquad$ Notice: $x^2 = 9 \iff x = 3$ is a false statement.

$\qquad\qquad\qquad x = 3 \Rightarrow x^2 = 9$ is true

$\qquad\qquad$ but $x^2 = 9 \nRightarrow x = 3$ {as x may be -3}

Example 6:   Prove that $(n+2)^2 - n^2$ is a multiple of 8 $\Leftrightarrow$ n is odd.

$\qquad$ **Proof:** $(\Rightarrow)$ $(n+2)^2 - n^2$ is a multiple of 8,

$\qquad\qquad\qquad \Rightarrow n^2 + 4n + 4 - n^2 = 8A$ for some integer A

$\qquad\qquad\qquad \Rightarrow 4n + 4 = 8A$

$\qquad\qquad\qquad \Rightarrow n + 1 = 2A$

$\qquad\qquad\qquad \Rightarrow n = 2A - 1$

$\qquad\qquad\qquad \Rightarrow n$ is odd.

$\qquad\qquad$ $(\Leftarrow)$ n is odd,

$\qquad\qquad\qquad \Rightarrow n = 2A - 1$

$\qquad\qquad\qquad \Rightarrow n + 1 = 2A$ for some integer A

$\qquad\qquad\qquad \Rightarrow 4n + 4 = 8A$

$\qquad\qquad\qquad \Rightarrow (n^2 + 4n + 2) - n^2 = 8A$

$\qquad\qquad\qquad \Rightarrow (n-2)^2 - n^2$ is a multiple of 8.

In the above example the $(\Rightarrow)$ argument is clearly reversible to give the $(\Leftarrow)$ argument. However, this is not always evident or possible.

Example 7:   Prove that for all $x \in \mathbb{Z}^+$,

$\qquad\qquad x$ is not divisible by 3 $\Leftrightarrow$ $x^2 - 1$ is divisible by 3.

$\qquad$ **Proof:** $(\Rightarrow)$ x is not divisible by 3

$\qquad\qquad\qquad \Rightarrow$ either $x = 3k + 1$ or $x = 3k + 2$ for some $x \in \mathbb{Z}$

$\qquad\qquad\qquad \Rightarrow x^2 - 1 = 9k^2 + 6k$ or $9k^2 + 12k + 3$

$\qquad\qquad\qquad \Rightarrow x^2 - 1$ is divisible by 3

$\qquad\qquad$ $(\Leftarrow)$ $x^2 - 1$ is divisible by 3

$\qquad\qquad\qquad \Rightarrow 3 \mid x^2 - 1$

$\qquad\qquad\qquad \Rightarrow 3 \mid (x+1)(x-1)$

$\qquad\qquad\qquad \Rightarrow 3 \mid (x+1)$ or $3 \mid (x-1)$ {as 3 is a prime number}

$\qquad\qquad\qquad \Rightarrow 3 \nmid x$

$\qquad\qquad\qquad\qquad$ i.e., x is not divisible by 3

PROOF USING CONTRAPOSITIVE

To prove $A \Rightarrow B$, we could show that
$$\sim B \quad \Rightarrow \quad \sim A$$
$$\text{i.e.,} \quad \text{not } B \quad \Rightarrow \quad \text{not } A$$

For example, the statement

"If it is Jon's bicycle, then it is blue" is the same as
"If that bicycle is not blue, then it is not Jon's".

Example 8:   Prove that, "for $a, b \in R$, ab irrational $\Rightarrow$ either a or b is irrational."

> **Proof**   **(Using contrapositive):**
>
> If a and b are rational $\Rightarrow$ $a = \dfrac{p}{q}$ and $b = \dfrac{r}{s}$ where
>
> $$p, q, r, s \in \mathbb{Z}, \quad q \neq 0, \quad r \neq 0$$
>
> $$\Rightarrow \quad ab = \left(\frac{p}{q}\right)\left(\frac{r}{s}\right) = \frac{pr}{qs} \quad \text{where} \quad qs \neq 0$$
>
> $$\Rightarrow \quad ab \text{ is rational.}$$
>
> Thus ab irrational $\Rightarrow$ either a or b is irrational

Example 9:   Prove that   "If n is a positive integer of the form $3k + 2$, $k \geqslant 0$, $k \in \mathbb{Z}$, then n is not a perfect square."

> **Proof**   **(Using contrapositive):**
>
> If n is a perfect square then
> n has one of the forms $(3a)^2$, $(3a + 1)^2$ or $(3a + 2)^2$
> $\Rightarrow$ $n = 9a^2$, $9a^2 + 6a + 1$, $9a^2 + 12a + 4$
> $\Rightarrow$ $n = 3(3a^2)$, $3(3a^2 + 2a) + 1$ or $3(3a^2 + 4a + 1) + 1$
> $\Rightarrow$ n has form $3k$ or $3k + 1$ only, $k \in \mathbb{Z}$
> $\Rightarrow$ n does not have form $3k + 2$

Note: Excellent Websites exist on different methods of proof.

Try searching for   **Proof by Contradiction**

Proof by Contrapositive

if and only if proof

ANSWERS

EXERCISE 8A

1 a $\mu(3X - 2Y) = 0$ and $\sigma(3X - 2Y) \approx 2.26$
  b $P(3X - 2Y > 3) \approx 0.0920$

2 a $E(U) = 20$ and $\sigma(U) \approx 10.4$
  b $P(U < 0) \approx 0.0277$

3 $\mu \approx 54.6$ and $\sigma \approx 19.8$

4 $M \sim N(61, 11^2)$ and $C \sim N(48, 4^2)$
  $U = M_1 + M_2 + M_3 + M_4 + C_1 + C_2 + C_3$
  $U \sim N(338, 532)$
  $P(U > 440) \approx 0.0121$ if unsafe
  Assumption: The random variables $M_1, M_2, M_3, M_4,$
  $\qquad\qquad\quad$ C_1, C_2 and C_3 are independent.

5 $C \sim N(120, 7^2)$ and $M \sim N(28, 4.5^2)$
  $U = C + M$ and $U \sim (148, 69.25)$
  $P(U < 135.5) \approx 0.0665$ which is $> 1\%$.
  So, machine should be adjusted.

6 a $S \sim N(280, 4)$ and $L \sim N(575, 16)$
  $\quad$ Want $P(L < 2S)$ i.e., $P(L - 2S < 0)$
  $\quad$ If $U = L - 2S,$ $U \sim N(15, 32)$
  $\quad$ $P(L < 2S) \approx 0.004\,01$
  b Want $P(L < S_1 + S_2)$ i.e., $P(L - S_1 - S_2 < 0)$
  $\quad$ If $V = L - S_1 - S_2,$ $V \sim N(15, 24)$
  $\quad$ $P(L < S_1 + S_2) \approx 0.001\,10$

7 a Want $P(L > 5S)$ i.e., $P(L - 5S > 0)$
  $\quad$ If $U = L - 5S,$ $U \sim N(-15, 140)$
  $\quad$ $(L > 5S) \approx 0.102$
  b Want $P(L > S_1 + S_2 + S_3 + S_4 + S_5)$
  $\quad$ i.e., $P(L - S_1 - S_2 - S_3 - S_4 - S_5 > 0)$
  $\quad$ If $V = L - S_1 - S_2 - S_3 - S_4 - S_5$
  $\quad$ then $V \sim N(-15, 40)$
  $\quad$ $P(L > S_1 + S_2 + S_3 + S_4 + S_5) \approx 0.008\,85$

EXERCISE 8B.1

1 a X is distributed uniformly (discrete) and
  $\quad$ $P(X = x) = \frac{1}{6},$ $X \sim DU(6)$
  b $\mu = 17.5$ **c** $P(X < \mu) = \frac{1}{2}$ **d** $\sigma \approx 8.54$

2 $p \approx 0.300$ and $P(X = 2) \approx 0.318$

3 $X \sim B(7, 0.35)$ **a** 0.268 **b** 0.468 **c** 0.800
  d $5(0.35)^3(0.65)^4 \approx 0.0383$

4 Due to the very large number of pens, X (the number of
  reds selected) is approximately $\sim B(n, 0.2)$
  As $P(X \geqslant 1) = 0.9,$ $n \approx 10.3$
  $\therefore$ need to select 11 or more pens.
  We are assuming independence of each outcome.

5 a X = number of cells failing in one year
  $\quad$ $X \sim B(15, 0.7)$ $P(X = 15) \approx 0.004\,75$
  b ≈ 0.995
  c $P(\text{operates}) = 1 - (0.7)^n$
  $\quad$ Hence, we need to solve $1 - (0.7)^n \geqslant 0.98$
  $\quad$ $n \approx 10.97,$ so smallest number is 11

6 a X = number of letters addressed to AD
  $\quad$ $X \sim B(20, 0.7)$ $P(X \geqslant 11) \approx 0.952$
  b $X \sim B(70, 0.7)$ $\mu = np = 49$ letters
  $\quad$ $\sigma = \sqrt{npq} \approx 3.83$

7 a $P(P) = 0.605$ $P(IS \mid P) = \frac{0.175}{0.605} \approx 0.289$

b For **one parcel**, $P((IS \text{ or } IN) \mid S) \approx 0.417\,72$
  $\quad$ If X = number of standard parcels selected
  $\quad$ $X \sim B(2, 0.417\,72)$ and $P(X = 1) \approx 0.486$
  $\quad$ *Assumption:*   Independence.

8 X = score on the wheel $X \sim DU(50)$
  From page 31 of text for **a** and **b**.

  a $\mu = \dfrac{n+1}{2} = 25.5$ **b** $\sigma = \sqrt{\dfrac{n^2 - 1}{12}}$ $\therefore$ $\sigma \approx 14.4$
  c 0.14
  d Y = number of multiples of 7 obtained
  $\quad$ $Y \sim B(500, 0.14)$ 15% of 500 = 75
  $\quad$ $P(Y > 75) \approx 0.237$
  e $Y \sim B(500, 0.14)$ and $E(Y) = 70$
  $\quad$ Expect $1600
  f Lose if $20[(500 - Y) - 5Y] < 0$ i.e., $Y > 83\frac{1}{3}$
  $\quad$ and $P(Y > 83\frac{1}{3}) \approx 0.0435$

EXERCISE 8B.2

1 $X \sim Geo(0.25)$
  a ≈ 0.105 **b** ≈ 0.422 **c** 0.4375 **d** $E(X) = \dfrac{1}{p} = 4$
  On average it takes 4 trials to achieve a success if
  $X \sim Geo(0.25)$.

2 a mode = 1   (for all geometric distributions)
  b $\mu = E(X) = \frac{1}{0.33} \approx 3.03$
  c $\sigma^2 = \dfrac{q}{p^2} = \dfrac{0.67}{(0.33)^2} \approx 6.1524$ $\Rightarrow$ $\sigma \approx 2.48$

3 $X \sim Geo(0.29)$
  a $P(X = 4) \approx 0.104$ **b** $\mu \approx 3$ (nearest integer)
  c $Y \sim NB(3, 0.29)$
  $\quad$ $\therefore$ $P(Y = 7) = \binom{6}{2}(0.29)^3(0.71)^4 \approx 0.0930$
  d $\mu = \dfrac{r}{p} = \dfrac{3}{0.29} \approx 10.3$
  $\quad$ i.e.,   10 bowls (to the nearest integer)

4 $X \sim Geo(p)$ and $P(X = 3) = p(1-p)^2$
  $\Rightarrow$ $p(1-p)^2 = 0.023\,987$
  $\Rightarrow$ $p \approx 0.0253$ or 0.830 {gcalc}
  But $p > 0.5,$ so $p \approx 0.830$
  $P(X \geqslant 3) = 1 - P(X \leqslant 2) \approx 0.0289$

5 $X \sim Geo(0.05)$ $\mu = \dfrac{1}{p} = 20$
  i.e.,   expected number of throws is 20.

6 $X \sim NB(3, 0.35)$
  a $P(X = 4) = \binom{3}{2}(0.35)^3(0.65)^1 \approx 0.0836$
  b $P(\text{Eva beats Paul in a match})$
  $\quad = P(X = 3, 4, 5)$
  $\quad = \binom{4}{2}(0.35)^3(0.65)^2 + \binom{3}{2}(0.35)^3(0.65)^1$
  $\qquad + \binom{2}{2}(0.35)^3(0.65)^0$
  $\quad \approx 0.235$

7 $X \sim Geo(0.15)$
  a $P(\text{1st snow on Nov 15})$
  $\quad = P(X = 15)$
  $\quad \approx 0.0154$
  b $P(\text{snow falls on or before } n \text{ days})$
  $\quad = 1 - P(\text{snow does not fall in } n \text{ days})$
  $\quad = 1 - (0.85)^n$

So we need to solve $1 - (0.85)^n > 0.85$

i.e., $(0.85)^n < 0.15$

$$\Rightarrow \quad n > \frac{\log(0.15)}{\log(0.85)}$$

$\{\log(0.85) < 0\}$

$$\Rightarrow \quad n > 11.67....$$

So, we must book for Dec 12.

8 a Difference table

6	⑤	④	3	2	1	0
5	④	3	2	1	0	1
4	3	2	1	0	1	2
3	2	1	0	1	2	3
2	1	0	1	2	2	④
1	0	1	2	3	④	⑤
0	1	2	3	4	5	6

P(difference is no more than 3) $= \frac{30}{36} = \frac{5}{6}$

b $X \sim \text{Geo}\left(\frac{5}{6}\right)$

P(player 1 is first to start on 2nd roll)
$= \text{P}(X = 5)$
$\approx 0.000\,643$

c $\text{E}(X) = \dfrac{1}{p} = \frac{1}{\frac{5}{6}} = 1.2$ rolls

d $4 \times 1.2 = 4.8$ i.e.,   about 5 rolls.

EXERCISE 8B.3

1 $X \sim \text{Hyp}(5, 5, 12)$

a $\text{P}(X = 3) = \dfrac{\binom{5}{3}\binom{12-5}{2}}{\binom{12}{5}} \approx 0.265$

b $\text{P}(X = 5) = \dfrac{\binom{5}{5}\binom{7}{0}}{\binom{12}{5}} \approx 0.001\,26$

c $\text{P}(X \leqslant 2)$
$= \text{P}(X = 0, 1 \text{ or } 2)$
$= \dfrac{\binom{5}{0}\binom{7}{5}}{\binom{12}{5}} + \dfrac{\binom{5}{1}\binom{7}{4}}{\binom{12}{5}} + \dfrac{\binom{5}{2}\binom{7}{3}}{\binom{12}{5}} \approx 0.689$

d $\text{E}(X) = n\dfrac{M}{N} = 5 \times \frac{5}{12} \approx 2.08$

e $\text{Var}(X) = n\dfrac{M}{N}\left(1 - \dfrac{M}{N}\right)\left(\dfrac{N-n}{N-1}\right)$
$= 5 \times \frac{5}{12}\left(1 - \frac{5}{12}\right)\left(\frac{12-5}{12-1}\right)$
≈ 0.773

2 $X \sim \text{P}_0(\mu)$

a $\text{P}(X = 2) = \text{P}(X = 0) + 2\text{P}(X = 1)$
$$\Rightarrow \quad \frac{m^2 e^{-m}}{2!} = \frac{e^{-m}}{0!} + \frac{2me^{-m}}{1!}$$
$$\Rightarrow \quad m^2 = 2 + 4m$$
$$\Rightarrow \quad m^2 - 4m - 2 = 0$$
$$\Rightarrow \quad m = \frac{4 \pm \sqrt{16 - 4(1)(-2)}}{2}$$
$$\Rightarrow \quad m = 2 \pm \sqrt{6}$$
But $m > 0$ $\therefore$ $m \approx 4.45$
i.e., $\mu \approx 4.45$

b $\text{P}(1 \leqslant X \leqslant 5) = \text{P}(X \leqslant 5) - \text{P}(X = 0)$
$\approx 0.711\,53 - 0.011\,68$
≈ 0.700

3 $X \sim \text{Hyp}(4, 5, 24)$
a $\text{P}(X = 2) \approx 0.161$ **b** $\text{P}(X = 0) \approx 0.365$

4 $X \sim \text{P}_0(0.05)$ $\{$as $\dfrac{50 \text{ m}}{1000 \text{ m}} = 0.05\}$

a $\text{P}(X = 0) \approx 0.951$

b $\text{P}(X \leqslant 2) \approx 0.999\,98 \approx 1$

c $\text{P}(X \leqslant 1) \approx 0.9988$ which is > 0.995
Yes, the chain is considered safe.

5 a $X \sim \text{B}(255, 0.0375)$

b $\text{P}(X < 5) = \text{P}(X \leqslant 4) \approx 0.0362$
i.e., a 3.62% chance of more passengers than seats.

c P(empty seats)
$= \text{P}(X > 5)$
$= 1 - \text{P}(X \leqslant 5)$
≈ 0.918
i.e., a 91.8% chance of having empty seats.

d i $\mu(X) = np = 9.5625 \approx 9.56$

ii $\text{Var}(X) = np(1 - p) \approx 9.20$

iii As $\mu(X) \approx \text{Var}(X)$ we can approximate
by $X \sim \text{P}_0(9.5625)$ and
$\text{P}(X < 5) = \text{P}(X \leqslant 4) \approx 0.0387$

iv $\text{P}(X > 5) = 1 - \text{P}(X \leqslant 5) \approx 0.914$

e The approximation is not too bad if accurate answers
are not important. This is an example of being able
to approximate a binomial RV by a Poisson RV where
$n > 50$ and $p < 1$.

6 $X =$ number of rotten eggs $X \sim \text{Hyp}(2, 1, 12)$
a $\text{P}(X = 0) = \frac{5}{6}$

b P(buys first 5 cartons) $= \left(\frac{5}{6}\right)^5 \approx 0.402$

c $\text{E}(X) = n\dfrac{M}{N} = 2 \times \frac{1}{12} = \frac{1}{6}$
i.e., will reject 1 in 6 cartons.
Hence, on average, he will inspect 6 cartons to purchase
5 of them.

7 a $X =$ number of internal calls
$Y =$ number of external calls
$X \sim \text{P}_0\left(\frac{5}{4}\right)$ and $Y \sim \text{P}_0\left(\frac{10}{6}\right)$ $\{$for 5 min$\}$
Total number of calls received $= X + Y$
$\text{E}(X + Y) = \frac{5}{4} + \frac{10}{6} \approx 2.917$
$\text{Var}(X + Y) = \frac{5}{4} + \frac{10}{6} \approx 2.917$
$\therefore$ $X + Y \sim \text{P}_0(2.917)$
assuming X, Y are independent RVs
$\text{P}(X + Y = 3) \approx 0.224$

b As $\text{E}(X + Y) \approx 2.917$, the receptionist can expect
3 calls each 5 minutes.

c i $\text{P}(X + Y > 5) = 1 - \text{P}(X + Y \leqslant 5)$
≈ 0.0758

ii 5 calls in 20 mins $= \frac{5}{20} \times 7$ calls in 7 min
$= \frac{7}{4}$ calls in 7 min
10 calls in 30 min $= \frac{10}{30} \times 7$ calls in 7 min
$= \frac{7}{3}$ calls in 7 min
$\text{E}(X + Y) = \text{Var}(X + Y) = \frac{7}{4} + \frac{7}{3}$
≈ 4.0833
$\therefore$ $\text{P}(X + Y > 5) = 1 - \text{P}(X + Y \leqslant 5)$
≈ 0.228

8 X = number of faulty balls

a $X \sim \text{B}(8, 0.01)$

$P(X = x) = \binom{8}{x} (0.01)^x (0.99)^{8-x}$

where $x = 0, 1, 2, 3, ..., 8.$

b $P(X = 0) \approx 0.922\,745$ $P(X = 2) \approx 0.002\,636$
$P(X = 1) \approx 0.074\,565$ $P(X = 3) \approx 0.000\,053$
$P(X = 4 \text{ to } 8) \approx 0.000\,001$

Consider acceptance A

$P(A \mid X = 0) = 1$

$P(A \mid X = 1) = \dfrac{\binom{1}{0}\binom{7}{2}}{\binom{8}{2}} \approx 0.75$

$P(A \mid X = 2) = \dfrac{\binom{2}{0}\binom{6}{2}}{\binom{8}{2}} \approx 0.5357$

$P(A \mid X = 3) = \dfrac{\binom{3}{0}\binom{5}{2}}{\binom{8}{2}} \approx 0.357\,14$

$P(A \mid X = 4) = \dfrac{\binom{4}{0}\binom{4}{2}}{\binom{8}{2}} \approx 0.214\,29$

Now by Bayes' Theorem

$$P(A) = \sum_{x=0}^{8} P(A \mid X = x)\, P(X = x)$$

$$\approx 1 \times 0.922\,745 + 0.75 \times 0.074\,565$$
$$+ 0.5357 \times 0.002\,636 + ...$$

$$\approx 0.9801$$

$\therefore$ $P(\text{reject}) \approx 0.0199 \approx 2\%$

Hence, for each 1000 cartons the buyer would expect to reject 20 of them.

EXERCISE 8B.4

1 **A** $X \sim \text{P}_0(6)$, $P(X = 3) \approx 0.0892$

B $X \sim \text{P}_0(1)$, $P(X = 1) \approx 0.3679$

C $X \sim \text{P}_0(24)$, $P(X < 17) = P(X \leqslant 16) \approx 0.0563$
So, **B** is most likely to occur.

2 $X \sim \text{DU}(50)$ $\mu(X) = \dfrac{n+1}{2} = 25.5$

$\sigma(X) = \sqrt{\dfrac{n^2 - 1}{12}} \approx 14.4$

3 $X \sim \text{NB}(4, 0.47)$

a $P(X = 5) = \binom{4}{3}(0.47)^4(0.53)^1 \approx 0.103$

b $P(X = 7) = \binom{6}{3}(0.47)^4(0.53)^3 \approx 0.145$

c $P(\text{Redsox win})$
$= 1 - P[X = 4, 5, 6 \text{ or } 7]$
$= 1 - \binom{3}{3}(0.47)^4 - \binom{4}{3}(0.47)^4(0.53)^1$
$\quad - \binom{5}{3}(0.47)^4(0.53)^2 - \binom{6}{3}(0.47)^4(0.53)^3$
≈ 0.565

d $X \sim \text{NB}(4, 0.53)$

$E(X) = \dfrac{r}{p} = \dfrac{4}{0.53} \approx 7.55$ games

This is the average number of games it would take the Redsox to win without restriction, i.e., by playing as many as they need. However, in a World Series, no more than 7 games will be played (assuming no draws) to decide the winner.

4 **a** Let X be the number of attempts needed. Assuming attempts are independent and the probability of getting through remains constant, $X \sim \text{Geo}(0.62)$.

b $P(X \geqslant 3) = 1 - P(X \leqslant 2) \approx 0.1444$

c $\mu = \dfrac{1}{p} \approx 1.61$, $\sigma = \sqrt{\dfrac{1-p}{p^2}} \approx 0.994$

5 **a** $X \sim \text{Hyp}(5, 4, 52)$ and $X = 0, 1, 2, 3$ or 4

b $P(X = 2) = \dfrac{\binom{4}{2}\binom{48}{3}}{\binom{52}{5}} \approx 0.0399$

c **i** $Y \sim (30, 0.039\,93)$

ii $P(Y \geqslant 5) = 1 - P(Y \leqslant 4) \approx 0.006\,27$

iii $E(Y) = np \approx 30 \times 0.03993 \approx 1.20$
i.e.,   about once

iv $E(X) = n\dfrac{M}{N} = 5 \times \dfrac{4}{52} \approx 0.385$

6 **a** X = return from playing the game
$= 10$ cents, 20 cents, ..., \$100

b $E(X) = \sum x_i p_i$
$= (-14.9 - 14.8 - 14.7 - 14.6 - 14.5$
$\quad -14.4 - 14.3 + 0 + 15 + 85) \times \frac{1}{10}$
$= -0.22$
$\text{Var}(X) = \sum x_i^2 p_i - (-0.22)^2 \approx 894.2$

c If $X \sim \text{DU}(10)$, it assumes X has values 1, 2, 3, 4, ..., 10   which is not the case here.

d **i** For a game costing \$15 the expected loss is 22 cents. So, for a game costing
\$14.90, the expected loss is 12 cents,
\$14.80, the expected loss is 2 cents,
i.e., \$14.80

ii For each game $E(X) = -1.22$ dollars
$\therefore$ for 1000 games, expected return
$= \$1.22 \times 1000$
$= \$1220$

7 **a** $X \sim \text{Geo}\left(\frac{1}{8}\right)$

b *Assumptions:*
- each call is made with $\frac{1}{8}$ probability of success
- calls are independent of each other

c $E(X) = \dfrac{1}{p} = 8$ and $\sigma = \sqrt{\dfrac{1-p}{p^2}} \approx 7.48$

d $P(X < 5) = P(X \leqslant 4) \approx 0.414$

8 **a** T = dials wrong number in 75 calls
$T \sim \text{B}(75, 0.005)$, $T = 0, 1, 2, ..., 75$

b **i** $P(T = 0) \approx 0.687$

ii $P(T > 2) = 1 - P(T \leqslant 2) \approx 0.006\,46$

iii $E(T) = np = 0.375$
$\text{Var}(T) = np(1-p) \approx 0.373$

The mean and variance are almost the same which suggests that T can be approximated by a Poisson distribution.

c If $T \sim \text{P}_0(0.375)$ **i** $P(T = 0) \approx 0.687$

ii $P(T > 2) = 1 - P(T \leqslant 2) \approx 0.006\,65$

Both results are very close to those from the binomial distribution. This verifies the property that for large n and small p, the binomial distribution can be approximated by the Poisson distribution with the same mean,
i.e., $X \sim \text{P}_0(np)$.

EXERCISE 8B.5

1 $T \sim \mathrm{U}(-\pi, \pi)$ $\mu = \dfrac{a+b}{2} = \dfrac{-\pi + \pi}{2} = 0$

$\sigma = \sqrt{\dfrac{(b-a)^2}{12}} = \sqrt{\dfrac{4\pi^2}{12}} = \dfrac{\pi}{\sqrt{3}}$

2 **a** The best chance of getting a ticket is as soon as possible after release. As time goes by it gets increasingly difficult and very quickly almost impossible. X is a continuous RV.

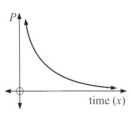

b median = 10

$\Rightarrow \displaystyle\int_0^{10} \lambda e^{-\lambda x}\, dx = 0.5$

$\Rightarrow \lambda \left[\dfrac{e^{-\lambda x}}{-\lambda}\right]_0^{10} = 0.5$

$\Rightarrow \left[-e^{-\lambda x}\right]_0^{10} = 0.5$

$\Rightarrow -e^{-10\lambda} + 1 = 0.5$

$\Rightarrow e^{-10\lambda} = 0.5 = \frac{1}{2}$

$\Rightarrow e^{10\lambda} = 2$

$\Rightarrow 10\lambda = \ln 2$

$\Rightarrow \lambda = \frac{\ln 2}{10} \approx 0.0693$

c P(Seat purchased after 3 days)
$= \mathrm{P}(X \geqslant 72)$
$= 1 - \mathrm{P}(X < 72)$
$= 1 - \displaystyle\int_0^{72} \lambda e^{-\lambda x}\, dx$
$= 1 - 0.069\,31 \displaystyle\int_0^{72} e^{-0.069\,31 x}\, dx$
$\approx 0.006\,80$

i.e., only a 0.68% chance of getting a ticket after 3 or more days.

d $\mathrm{E}(X) = \dfrac{1}{\lambda} \approx 14.4$ hours

i.e., the average time it takes to buy a ticket is about 14.4 hours.

3 $\qquad X \sim \mathrm{N}(\mu, \sigma^2)$

$\qquad \mathrm{P}(X > 13) = 0.4529$

$\qquad \therefore \quad \mathrm{P}(X \leqslant 13) = 0.5471$

$\therefore \ \mathrm{P}\left(\dfrac{X - \mu}{\sigma} \leqslant \dfrac{13 - \mu}{\sigma}\right) = 0.5471$

$\therefore \ \mathrm{P}\left(Z \leqslant \dfrac{13 - \mu}{\sigma}\right) = 0.5471$

$\therefore \ \dfrac{13 - \mu}{\sigma} = \mathrm{invNorm}(0.5471)$

$\qquad \mathrm{P}(X > 28) = 0.1573$

$\qquad \therefore \quad \mathrm{P}(X \leqslant 28) = 0.8427$

$\therefore \ \mathrm{P}\left(Z < \dfrac{28 - \mu}{\sigma}\right) = 0.8427$

$\therefore \ \dfrac{28 - \mu}{\sigma} = \mathrm{invNorm}(0.8427)$

$\therefore \ 13 - \mu \approx 0.1183\sigma$

$\therefore \ 28 - \mu \approx 1.0056\sigma$

Solving simultaneously $\mu \approx 11.0$ and $\sigma \approx 16.9$

4 **a** $\displaystyle\int_0^k (6 - 18x)\, dx = 1 \quad \Rightarrow \quad k = \frac{1}{3}$

b $\mu = \displaystyle\int_0^k x\, f(x)\, dx = \int_0^{\frac{1}{3}} (6x - 18x^2)\, dx$

$\Rightarrow \mu = \frac{1}{9}$ and $\sigma^2 = \displaystyle\int_0^k x^2 f(x)\, dx - \mu^2$

$\qquad\qquad\qquad = \displaystyle\int_0^{\frac{1}{3}} (6x^2 - 18x^3)\, dx - \left(\frac{1}{9}\right)^2$

$\qquad\qquad\qquad \approx 0.006\,172\,8....$

$\Rightarrow \mu = \frac{1}{9}, \quad \sigma \approx 0.0786$

5 **a** X is a discrete RV. In fact

  i $X \sim \mathrm{B}(180, 0.41)$

  ii $\mathrm{E}(X) = np = 73.8$ and
    $\mathrm{Var}(X) = np(1-p) \approx 43.5$

  iii $\mathrm{P}(X \geqslant 58) = 1 - \mathrm{P}(X \leqslant 57) \approx 0.994$

b As np and nq are both > 5, we can approximate to the normal distribution, i.e., $X \sim \mathrm{N}(73.8, 43.5)$

$\qquad \mathrm{P}(X \geqslant 58) \qquad \{X \text{ discrete}\}$

$\approx \mathrm{P}(X^* \geqslant 57.5) \qquad \{X \text{ continuous}\}$

≈ 0.993

6 **a** $X \sim \mathrm{P}_0(2.5)$,   a discrete RV
$Y = X_1 + X_2 + ... + X_{50}$ where the X_i are assumed to be independent.

$\therefore \ \mathrm{E}(Y) = 52 \times \mathrm{E}(X) = 130$
and $\mathrm{Var}(Y) = \mathrm{Var}(X_1) \times 50 = 130$ also.
So $Y \sim \mathrm{P}_0(130)$

b $\mathrm{P}(X > 2) = 1 - \mathrm{P}(X \leqslant 2) \approx 0.456$

c $\mathrm{P}(Y > 104) = 1 - \mathrm{P}(Y \leqslant 104) \approx 0.989$

d $\mathrm{E}(X) = \mathrm{Var}(X) = 2.5 \qquad \mathrm{E}(Y) = \mathrm{Var}(Y) = 130$

e Using normal approximations
$X \sim \mathrm{N}(2.5, 2.5)$ and $Y \sim \mathrm{N}(130, 130)$
So, $\mathrm{P}(X > 2) \approx \mathrm{P}(X^* > 2.5) = 0.500$
and $\mathrm{P}(Y > 104) \approx \mathrm{P}(Y^* \geqslant 104.5) \approx 0.987$

The approximation for X is poor, but is very good for Y. This is probably due to the fact that λ is not large enough for the X distribution.

Note: If $\lambda > 15$ we can approximate $X \sim \mathrm{P}_0(\lambda)$
$\qquad\qquad$ by $X \sim \mathrm{N}(\lambda, \lambda)$.

This theory is *not* a syllabus requirement.

7 X is a uniform continuous RV.

a $\displaystyle\int_1^k \frac{2}{5}\, dx = 1 \ \Rightarrow \ k = 3.5 \qquad$ So, $X \sim \mathrm{U}(1, 3.5)$.

b $\mathrm{P}(1.7 \leqslant X \leqslant 3.2) = 0.6$

c $\mathrm{E}(X) = 2.25, \quad \mathrm{Var}(X) = \dfrac{(b-a)^2}{12} \approx 0.521$

8 **a**

					$y = k$
	0.3	0.6		0.1	
	a	3		12 b	x

Now $(12 - 3)k = 0.6$

i.e., $9k = 0.6 = \frac{3}{5}$

$\therefore \ k = \frac{1}{15}$

$(3 - a)\frac{1}{15} = 0.3$ and $(b - 12)\frac{1}{15} = 0.1$

$\Rightarrow \ a = -1.5, \quad b = 13.5$

b pdf is $f(x) = \frac{1}{15}, \quad -1.5 \leqslant x \leqslant 13.5$

c $\mathrm{P}(5 < X < 9) = \frac{4}{15}$

d $F(x) = \displaystyle\int_{-1.5}^x f(x)\, dx = \left[\frac{1}{15}x\right]_{-1.5}^x$

$\therefore \quad F(x) = \begin{cases} \frac{1}{15}x + \frac{1}{10}, & -1.5 < x < 13.5 \\ 0, & \text{everywhere else} \end{cases}$

9 a $P(|T - 6| < 2.3) = P(-2.3 < T - 6 < 2.3)$
$= P(3.7 < T < 8.3)$
$\approx 0.2946 \quad \leftarrow p$

b $X \sim B(4, 9)$ where
$X = $ number of times $|T - 6| < 2.3$
$P(X = 2) = $ binomialpdf$(4, 0.2946, 2) \approx 0.259$

10 $f(x) = \lambda e^{-\lambda x}, \quad x \geqslant 0$
$\mu = E(x) = \int_0^\infty x f(x)\, dx = \int_0^\infty \lambda x e^{-\lambda x}\, dx$

We use integration by parts.

Let $\quad u = x \qquad v' = \lambda e^{-\lambda x}$
$\therefore \quad u' = 1 \qquad v = -e^{-\lambda x}$
$\therefore \quad \mu = [uv]_0^\infty - \int_0^\infty u'v\, dx$

$= \left[-xe^{-\lambda x}\right]_0^\infty - \int_0^\infty -e^{-\lambda x}\, dx$
$= (0 - 0) + \left[\frac{1}{-\lambda}e^{-\lambda x}\right]_0^\infty$
$= 0 + \frac{1}{\lambda}$
$= \frac{1}{\lambda}, \quad$ as required.

$\sigma^2 = E(X^2) - \{E(X)\}^2$
$= \int_0^\infty x^2 f(x)\, dx - \frac{1}{\lambda^2}$
$= \int_0^\infty \lambda x^2 e^{-\lambda x}\, dx - \frac{1}{\lambda^2}$

Integrating by parts again,

$\quad u = x^2 \qquad v' = \lambda e^{-\lambda x}$
$\quad u' = 2x \qquad v = -e^{-\lambda x}$

$= [uv]_0^\infty - \int_0^\infty u'v\, dx - \frac{1}{\lambda^2}$
$= \left[-x^2 e^{-\lambda x}\right]_0^\infty + \int_0^\infty 2xe^{-\lambda x}\, dx - \frac{1}{\lambda^2}$
$= (0 - 0) + 2\int_0^\infty xe^{-\lambda x}\, dx - \frac{1}{\lambda^2}$
$= 2\left(\frac{1}{\lambda^2}\right) - \frac{1}{\lambda^2}$
$= \frac{1}{\lambda^2}, \quad$ as required.

11 $f(x) = k, \quad$ on $a \leqslant x \leqslant b$

a On $0 \leqslant x \leqslant 1$, area $= k \times 1 = 1 \quad \Rightarrow \quad k = 1$
$\mu = \frac{a+b}{2} = \frac{1}{2}, \quad \sigma = \sqrt{\frac{(b-a)^2}{12}} = \frac{1}{\sqrt{12}}$

b On $2 \leqslant x \leqslant 6$, area $= k \times 4 = 1 \quad \Rightarrow \quad k = \frac{1}{4}$
$\mu = \frac{2+6}{2} = 4, \quad \sigma = \sqrt{\frac{4^2}{12}} = \frac{4}{\sqrt{12}}$

c On $0 \leqslant x \leqslant a$, area $= ka = 1 \quad \Rightarrow \quad k = \frac{1}{a}$
$\mu = \frac{0+a}{2} = \frac{a}{2}, \quad \sigma = \sqrt{\frac{a^2}{12}} = \frac{a}{\sqrt{12}}$

d On $m \leqslant x \leqslant n$, area $= k(n - m) = 1$
$\Rightarrow \quad k = \frac{1}{n - m}$
$\mu = \frac{m + n}{2}, \quad \sigma = \sqrt{\frac{(n-m)^2}{12}} = \frac{n - m}{\sqrt{12}}$

EXERCISE 8C.1

1 a, b

Poss. sample	$\bar{x}$	Poss. sample	$\bar{x}$
1, 1	1	3, 1	2
1, 2	1.5	3, 2	2.5
1, 3	2	3, 3	3
1, 4	2.5	3, 4	3.5
2, 1	1.5	4, 1	2.5
2, 2	2	4, 2	3
2, 3	2.5	4, 3	3.5
2, 4	3	4, 4	4

c

$\bar{x}$	1	1.5	2	2.5	3	3.5	4
Freq.	1	2	3	4	3	2	1
$P(\bar{x})$	$\frac{1}{16}$	$\frac{2}{16}$	$\frac{3}{16}$	$\frac{4}{16}$	$\frac{3}{16}$	$\frac{2}{16}$	$\frac{1}{16}$

d

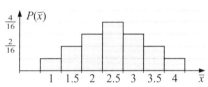

2 c

$\bar{x}$	1	$\frac{4}{3}$	$\frac{5}{3}$	2	$\frac{7}{3}$
Freq.	1	3	6	10	12
$P(\bar{x})$	$\frac{1}{64}$	$\frac{3}{64}$	$\frac{6}{64}$	$\frac{10}{64}$	$\frac{12}{64}$

$\bar{x}$	$\frac{8}{3}$	3	$\frac{10}{3}$	$\frac{11}{3}$	4
Freq.	12	10	6	3	1
$P(\bar{x})$	$\frac{12}{64}$	$\frac{10}{64}$	$\frac{6}{64}$	$\frac{3}{64}$	$\frac{1}{64}$

d

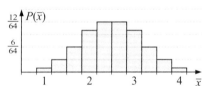

3 a

Poss. sample	$\bar{x}$	Poss. sample	$\bar{x}$
2, 2, 2, 2	2	3, 3, 2, 2	$\frac{10}{4}$
2, 2, 2, 3	$\frac{9}{4}$	3, 2, 3, 2	$\frac{10}{4}$
2, 2, 3, 2	$\frac{9}{4}$	3, 2, 2, 3	$\frac{10}{4}$
2, 3, 2, 2	$\frac{9}{4}$	2, 3, 3, 3	$\frac{11}{4}$
3, 2, 2, 2	$\frac{9}{4}$	3, 2, 3, 3	$\frac{11}{4}$
2, 2, 3, 3	$\frac{10}{4}$	3, 3, 2, 3	$\frac{11}{4}$
2, 3, 2, 3	$\frac{10}{4}$	3, 3, 3, 2	$\frac{11}{4}$
2, 3, 3, 2	$\frac{10}{4}$	3, 3, 3, 3	3

b

$\bar{x}$	2	$\frac{9}{4}$	$\frac{10}{4}$	$\frac{11}{4}$	3
Freq.	1	4	6	4	1
$P(\bar{x})$	$\frac{1}{16}$	$\frac{4}{16}$	$\frac{6}{16}$	$\frac{4}{16}$	$\frac{1}{16}$

4

$\bar{x}$	1	1.5	2	2.5	3	3.5
Freq.	1	2	3	4	5	6
$P(\bar{x})$	$\frac{1}{36}$	$\frac{2}{36}$	$\frac{3}{36}$	$\frac{4}{36}$	$\frac{5}{36}$	$\frac{6}{36}$

$\bar{x}$	4	4.5	5	5.5	6
Freq.	5	4	3	2	1
$P(\bar{x})$	$\frac{5}{36}$	$\frac{4}{36}$	$\frac{3}{36}$	$\frac{2}{36}$	$\frac{1}{36}$

EXERCISE 8C.2

1 $\mu = 64$, $\sigma = 10$ **a** $\mu_{\overline{X}} = 64$, $s_{\overline{X}} \approx 1.67$

2 a $\sigma = 24$ $s_{\overline{X}} = \dfrac{24}{\sqrt{n}}$ **b i** 12   **ii** 6   **iii** 3   **c** 36

d

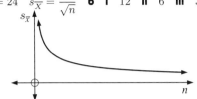

$s_{\overline{X}}$

n

As n gets larger, $s_{\overline{X}}$ gets smaller and approaches 0. Hence, for large n, $n \to$ population size, and the sampling error of the mean is effectively zero, i.e., when the sample is the population $\overline{x} = \mu$ without error.

3 a $E(\overline{X}) = 100$ **b** $s_{\overline{X}} = 2.5$
   c A normal distribution (as n is sufficiently large).

4 a $\mu = \frac{1}{2}$, $\sigma = \frac{1}{2}$

b

HHHH	HHHT	HHTT	TTTH	TTTT
	HHTH	HTHT	TTHT	
	HTHH	HTTH	THTT	
	THHH	TTHH	HTTT	
		THTH		
		THHT		

$\overline{X}_i$	0	$\frac{1}{4}$	$\frac{2}{4}$	$\frac{3}{4}$	1
p_i	$\frac{1}{16}$	$\frac{4}{16}$	$\frac{6}{16}$	$\frac{4}{16}$	$\frac{1}{16}$

c i mean$_{\overline{X}} = \frac{1}{2}$ **ii** $s_{\overline{X}} = \frac{1}{4}$
d mean$_{\overline{X}} = \mu$, $s_{\overline{X}} = 0.25$

5 a From the CLT, $\overline{X} \sim N(320\,000, \frac{80\,000^2}{25})$ for large n.
   $P(\overline{X} \geqslant 343\,000) \approx 0.0753$

b The answer may not be all that reliable as X is not normal. Hence, we treat the answer with great caution. Note that the result states that about 7.53% of all samples of size 25 will have an average value of at least $343\,000.

6 W = weight of adult males $W \sim N(73.5, 8.24^2)$

   If $n = 9$, $\overline{W} \sim N\left(73.5, \frac{8.24^2}{9}\right)$

   $P(\overline{W} \leqslant \frac{650}{9}) \approx 0.321$ or   32.1%

   If $n = 8$, $\overline{W} \sim N\left(73.5, \frac{8.24^2}{8}\right)$

   $P(\overline{W} \leqslant \frac{650}{8}) \approx 99.6\%$ which is $> 99.5\%$
   So, 8 is the max. recommended no. of adult males.

   Note: We do not have to have n large here as W is already distributed normally.

7 X = duration of pregnancy (in days)
   $X \sim N(267, 15^2)$

   a $P(274 < X < 281) \approx 0.145$ or   14.5%
   b We need to solve $P(X \leqslant a) = 0.8$
      $a = \text{invNorm}(0.8, 267, 15) \approx 279.6$
      i.e., longest 20% last 280 or more days.
   c $\overline{X} \sim N(267, \frac{15^2}{64})$ i.e., normal with mean 267 days and sd of $\frac{15}{8}$ days.
   d $P(\overline{X} \leqslant 260) \approx 0.000\,094\,5$ a very small chance.
   e As X is now not normally distributed we cannot use answers for **a** and **b**. As $n > 30$, answers **c** and **d** still give good approximations.

8 A = units of milk from Ayrshire cows
   J = units of milk from Jersey cows
   $A \sim N(49, 5.87^2)$, $J \sim N(44.8, 5.12)^2$
   a $P(A > 50) \approx 0.432$
   b Consider $D = J - A$
      $\mu_D = 44.8 - 49 = -4.2$ $\sigma_D^2 = \sigma_J^2 + \sigma_A^2 = 60.67$
      assuming J and A are independent RVs
      $D \sim N(-4.2, 60.67)$ and $P(D > 0) \approx 0.295$
   c $\overline{J} \sim N(44.8, \frac{5.12^2}{25})$ $P(\overline{J} > 46) \approx 0.121$
   d $\overline{J} \sim N(44.8, \frac{5.12^2}{25})$, $\overline{A} \sim N(49, \frac{5.87^2}{15})$
      Let $U = \overline{A} - \overline{J}$
      $\mu_U = 49 - 44.8 = 4.2$ $\sigma_U^2 = \frac{5.87^2}{15} + \frac{5.12^2}{25} \approx 3.3457$
      assuming $\overline{A}$ and $\overline{J}$ are independent $\overline{U} \sim N(4.2, 3.3457)$
      $P(U \geqslant 4) \approx 0.544$

EXERCISE 8C.3

1 $\overline{X} \sim N(40, \frac{4^2}{5})$ **a** ≈ 0.868 **b** ≈ 0.712 **c** ≈ 0.821

2 $\overline{X} \sim N(42.8, \frac{8.7^2}{60})$ {CL theorem}
   $P(\overline{X} < 45) \approx 0.975$

3 $\overline{X} \sim N(1067, \frac{61.7^2}{30})$ {CL theorem}
   $P(\overline{X} > 1050) \approx 0.934$

4 $\overline{X} \sim N(1183, \frac{88.6^2}{50})$ {CL theorem}
   $P(1150 < \overline{X} < 1200) \approx 0.908$

5 $\overline{X} \sim N(18, \frac{5.3^2}{37})$ {CL theorem}
   $P(17 < \overline{X} < 20) \approx 0.864$

6 a $X \sim N(382, 16.2^2)$ $P(X < 375) \approx 0.333$
   b $\overline{X} \sim N(382, \frac{16.2^2}{24})$ {CL theorem}
      $P(\overline{X} < 375) \approx 0.0171$

7 a $X \sim N(1067, 61.7^2)$ $P(X \geqslant 1060) \approx 0.545$
   b $\overline{X} \sim N(1067, \frac{61.7^2}{50})$ $P(\overline{X} \geqslant 1060) \approx 0.789$

8 $\overline{X} \sim N(\mu, \frac{1.27^2}{300})$ {CL theorem}
   $P\left(\left|\overline{X} - \mu\right| \geqslant 0.1\right)$
   $= 1 - P\left(\left|\overline{X} - \mu\right| < 0.1\right)$
   $= 1 - P(-0.1 < \overline{X} - \mu < 0.1)$
   $= 1 - P\left(\dfrac{-0.1}{\frac{1.27}{\sqrt{300}}} < \dfrac{\overline{X} - \mu}{\frac{1.27}{\sqrt{300}}} < \dfrac{0.1}{\frac{1.27}{\sqrt{300}}}\right)$
   $= 1 - P\left(\dfrac{-0.1}{\frac{1.27}{\sqrt{300}}} < Z < \dfrac{0.1}{\frac{1.27}{\sqrt{300}}}\right)$
   ≈ 0.173

9 Claim is $p = 0.04$, $n = 1000$
   As np, $n(1-p)$ are both $\geqslant 10$ we can assume
   $\widehat{p} \sim N(0.04, \frac{0.04 \times 0.96}{1000})$
   $P(\widehat{p} \geqslant 0.07) \approx 6.46 \times 10^{-7}$ with such a small probability we reject the claim.

10 $p = \frac{2}{7}$, $n = 100$ np and nq are both > 10
   $\therefore$ $\widehat{p} \sim N(\frac{2}{7}, \frac{\frac{2}{7} \times \frac{5}{7}}{100})$ i.e., $\widehat{p} \sim N(\frac{2}{7}, \frac{1}{490})$
   $P(\widehat{p} < \frac{29}{100}) \approx 0.538$

11 **a** $p = 0.85$ If n is large

$\widehat{p} \sim N\left(0.85, \dfrac{0.85 \times 0.15}{n}\right)$ i.e., $\widehat{p} \sim N(0.85, \frac{0.1275}{n})$

  b $np \geqslant 10$ and $nq \geqslant 10$
  $\Rightarrow$ $0.85n \geqslant 10$ and $0.15n \geqslant 10$
  $\Rightarrow$ $n \geqslant 11.76$ and $n \geqslant 66.67$
  $\Rightarrow$ $n \geqslant 67$

  c i $\widehat{p} \sim N(0.85, \frac{0.1275}{\sqrt{200}})$

   $P(\widehat{p} < 0.75) \approx 0.000\,037\,4$

   ii $P(0.75 < \widehat{p} < 0.87) \approx 0.786$

  d $n = 500$, $\widehat{p} = \frac{350}{500} = 0.7$, $p = 0.85$

   np and $nq \geqslant 10$ $\widehat{p} \sim N(0.85, \frac{0.1275}{500})$

   i $P(\widehat{p} \leqslant 0.7) \approx 0$ {gcalc}

   ii Under the given conditions, there is virtually no
      chance of this happening. This means either
      (1) it was a freak occurrence, possible but extremely
         unlikely   or
      (2) the population proportion was no longer 85%
         (probably $< 85\%$)   or
      (3) the sample was not taken from the area
         mentioned.

12 $\widehat{p} \sim N\left(\frac{2}{5}, \dfrac{\frac{2}{5} \times \frac{3}{5}}{400}\right)$ i.e., $N\left(\frac{2}{5}, 0.0006\right)$

  a $P\left(\widehat{p} > \frac{150}{400}\right) \approx 0.846$ **b** $P\left(\widehat{p} \geqslant \frac{150}{400}\right) \approx 0.846$

  c $P\left(\widehat{p} < \frac{175}{400}\right) \approx 0.937$

13 $n = 250$,   claim is $p = 0.9$

  $np = 225$, $nq = 25$ are both > 10

  a $\widehat{p} \sim N\left(0.9, \dfrac{0.9 \times 0.1}{250}\right)$ i.e., $\widehat{p} \sim N(0.9, 0.000\,36)$

   Assumptions:
   • the approximation to normal is satisfactory
   • the life of any tyre is independent of the life of any
     other tyre when selected at random.

  b $P\left(\widehat{p} \leqslant \frac{200}{250}\right) \approx 6.82 \times 10^{-8}$ i.e., virtually 0

  c Since this probability is so small there is doubt that the
     manufacturer's claim is correct.

EXERCISE 8D

1 **a** Z-distribution $25.6 < \mu < 32.2$ **b** $24.5 < \mu < 33.3$
  c It becomes wider.

2 When increasing the level of certainty we increase the interval width. We can estimate μ in a narrower interval but
   with less certainty.

3 Z-distribution
  a i $78.0 < \mu < 85.2$ **ii** $79.4 < \mu < 83.8$
  b The width decreases as n increases.

4 Z-distribution **a** $a \approx 2.576$ **b** $a \approx 1.282$
  c $a \approx 1.440$ **d** $a \approx 2.054$

5 Z-distribution
  a i $37.0 < \mu < 40.4$ **ii** $34.5 < \mu < 42.9$
  b As σ increases, the width increases.

6 Z-distribution **a** $\sigma \approx 2.083$ **b** $8.33 < \mu < 9.07$
  c For the normal distribution 99.7% of all scores lie within
     3 sds of the mean. Hence $\sigma \approx$ range $\div 6$
     (**Note:** Here we are not using an unbiased estimate of
        the population standard deviation, s_{n-1}.)

7 t-distribution $\overline{x} = 513.8$, $n = 75$, $s_n = 14.9$

  $s_{n-1} = \sqrt{\dfrac{n}{n-1}}s_n = \sqrt{\dfrac{75}{74}} \times 14.9 \approx 15.0$

  So 99% CI is $509.3 < \mu < 518.4$

8 t-distribution $\overline{x} = 38.2$, $n = 42$, $s_n = 4.7$

  $s_{n-1} = \sqrt{\dfrac{n}{n-1}}s_n \approx 4.757$

  90% CI is $37.0 < \mu < 39.4$

9 Z-distribution   **a** $\sigma \approx \dfrac{\text{range}}{6} \approx 250.5$

  b We need to look at $P(\left|\overline{X} - \mu\right| < 70) = 0.95$

   $\Rightarrow$ $P(-70 < \overline{X} - \mu < 70) = 0.95$

   $\Rightarrow$ $P\left(\dfrac{-70}{\frac{250.5}{\sqrt{n}}} < \dfrac{\overline{X} - \mu}{\frac{250.5}{\sqrt{n}}} < \dfrac{70}{\frac{250.5}{\sqrt{n}}}\right) = 0.95$

   $\Rightarrow$ $P(-0.2794\sqrt{n} < Z < 0.2794\sqrt{n}) = 0.95$
   $\Rightarrow$ $P(Z < 0.2794\sqrt{n}) = 0.975$
   $\Rightarrow$ $0.2794\sqrt{n} \approx 1.960$
   $\Rightarrow$ $n \approx 49.2$

  So, a sample size of about 50 will do.

  Note: We have used a Z-distribution even though we
  have approximated for σ. We have not used an unbiased
  estimate of σ. Hence our estimate for n is rough. As we
  do not know n, we cannot use the t-distribution.

10 Z-distribution, $\sigma = 17.8$
   The 98% CI is $\overline{x} - 2.326\frac{\sigma}{\sqrt{n}} < \mu < \overline{x} + 2.326\frac{\sigma}{\sqrt{n}}$

   $\Rightarrow$ $|\mu - \overline{x}| < 2.326\frac{\sigma}{\sqrt{n}}$
   $\Rightarrow$ $2.326\frac{\sigma}{\sqrt{n}} < 3$
   $\Rightarrow$ $\sqrt{n} > \dfrac{2.326 \times 17.8}{3}$
   $\Rightarrow$ $n > 190.46\,....$
  $\therefore$ should sample 191 packets.

11 Z-distribution, $\sigma^2 = 22.09$
   The 99% CI is $\overline{x} - 2.576\frac{\sigma}{\sqrt{n}} < \mu < \overline{x} + 2.576\frac{\sigma}{\sqrt{n}}$

   $\Rightarrow$ $|\mu - \overline{x}| < 2.576\frac{\sigma}{\sqrt{n}}$
   $\Rightarrow$ $\dfrac{2.576 \times \sqrt{22.09}}{\sqrt{n}} < 1.8$
   $\Rightarrow$ $\sqrt{n} > \dfrac{2.576 \times \sqrt{22.09}}{1.8}$
   $\Rightarrow$ $n > 45.24\,....$
  $\therefore$ should sample at least 46.

12 Z-distribution (large n) $\widehat{p} = \frac{1051}{2839} \approx 0.3702$

   95% CI is $\widehat{p} - 1.96\sqrt{\dfrac{\widehat{p}(1-\widehat{p})}{2839}} < p < \widehat{p} + 1.96\sqrt{\dfrac{\widehat{p}(1-\widehat{p})}{2839}}$

   $\Rightarrow$ $0.352 < p < 0.388$
   $\therefore$ $35.2\% < p < 38.8\%$

13 Z-distribution (large n) $\widehat{p} = \frac{281}{500}$, $X = 281$, $n = 500$
   99% CI for p is

   $\widehat{p} - 2.576\sqrt{\dfrac{\widehat{p}(1-\widehat{p})}{500}} < p < \widehat{p} + 2.576\sqrt{\dfrac{\widehat{p}(1-\widehat{p})}{500}}$

   $\Rightarrow$ $0.505 < p < 0.619$

  As the CI does not include $p = \frac{1}{2}$ we argue that we are
  99% confident that the coin is biased towards getting a head.

14 a $\widehat{p} = \frac{1822}{2587} \approx 0.7043 \approx 70.4\%$

b Z-distribution (large n)

99% CI for p is

$$\widehat{p} - 2.576\sqrt{\frac{\widehat{p}(1-\widehat{p})}{2587}} < p < \widehat{p} + 2.576\sqrt{\frac{\widehat{p}(1-\widehat{p})}{2587}}$$

i.e., $0.681 < p < 0.727$
i.e., $68.1\% < p < 72.7\%$

c Expect to get $\frac{1822}{2587} \times 5629 \approx 3965$ to be worse off,
$\therefore$ 1664 to be better off.

Weaknesses:
- We are using an estimate of p based on a smaller sample.
- We are using a 'point' estimate for p.
  There are many values in the CI we could have used.

15 Z-distribution   Large sample 80% CI for p is

$$\widehat{p} - 1.282\sqrt{\frac{\widehat{p}(1-\widehat{p})}{n}} < p < \widehat{p} + 1.282\sqrt{\frac{\widehat{p}(1-\widehat{p})}{n}}$$

16 a $\widehat{p} = \frac{70}{80} = \frac{7}{8}, \quad X = 70, \quad n = 80$
  Large n $\therefore$ Z-distribution

b 95% CI for p is $0.803 < p < 0.945$

c The 95% CI for p includes $p = 90\% = 0.9$. Hence, the evidence is not in contradiction of the manufacturer's claim.

17 $\widehat{p} = \frac{68}{187} \approx 0.3636, \quad X = 68, \quad n = 187$

A Z-distribution (as n is large)

A 95% CI for p is $0.295 < p < 0.433$
i.e., $29.5\% < p < 43.3\%$

As 40% is included in the 95% CI for p we do not reject the claim at a 95% level.

18 n is large, $\therefore$ Z-distribution

a $Z_\alpha \approx 1.960$
  Max. sampling error $= \pm 1.960\left(\frac{1}{2\sqrt{1500}}\right) \approx \pm 0.0253$
  $\approx \pm 2.53\%$

b $Z_\alpha \approx 2.576$
  Max. sampling error $= \pm 2.576\left(\frac{1}{2\sqrt{1500}}\right) \approx \pm 3.33\%$

19 Z-distribution as n is large. $Z_\alpha \approx 1.960$

a Max. sampling error $= \pm 1.96(\frac{1}{2\sqrt{500}}) \approx \pm 4.38\%$

b $\pm 3.10\%$ **c** $\pm 2.19\%$ **d** $\pm 1.55\%$
  Note: The sampling error decreases as the sample size increases.

20 a Z-distribution $\widehat{p}$ unknown, n large

$$Z_\alpha \approx 1.96 \quad \Rightarrow \quad 1.96\left(\frac{1}{2\sqrt{n}}\right) \approx 2\%$$
$$\Rightarrow \qquad \sqrt{n} \approx \frac{1.96}{2 \times 0.02}$$
$$\Rightarrow \qquad n \approx 2401$$

i.e.,   a sample size should be 2401.

b If the probability is raised to 0.99 $Z_\alpha \approx 2.576$

$$\Rightarrow \quad \sqrt{n} \approx \frac{2.576}{2 \times 0.02} \approx 4147.36$$
$$\Rightarrow \quad n \approx 4147.36 \quad \text{i.e., a sample size of 4148}$$

21 Z-distribution as n is large.

$\widehat{p} = \frac{2106}{2750} \approx 0.7658, \quad Z_\alpha \approx 1.645$

a SE $\approx \pm 1.645 \times \sqrt{\dfrac{\widehat{p}(1-\widehat{p})}{n}}$

$\approx \pm 1.645 \times \sqrt{\dfrac{0.7658 \times 0.2342}{2750}}$

$\approx \pm 1.33\%$

b $0.01328 \approx 1.96\sqrt{\dfrac{0.7658 \times 0.2342}{n}}$

$\Rightarrow \quad n \approx \left(\dfrac{1.96^2 \times 0.7658 \times 0.2342}{0.01328^2}\right)$

$\Rightarrow \quad n \approx 3907$ voters

22 Z-distribution, as n is large

a $\widehat{p} = \frac{43}{189} \approx 0.2275, \quad Z_\alpha \approx 1.96$

SI $\approx \pm 1.96\sqrt{\dfrac{\widehat{p}(1-\widehat{p})}{189}} \approx \pm 5.98$

b Using $\widehat{p} \approx 0.2275$

$1.96\sqrt{\dfrac{(0.2275)(0.7725)}{n}} \approx 0.03$

$\Rightarrow \quad n \approx \dfrac{1.96^2 \times 0.2275 \times 0.7725}{0.03^2}$

$\Rightarrow \quad n \approx 750.1$ i.e., a sample of 751

23 a $\widehat{p} = \frac{27}{300} = 0.09$ is an unbiased (point) estimate of fish caught with length below the legal limit.

b A 98% CI for p is

$$0.09 - 2.326\sqrt{\frac{\widehat{p}(1-\widehat{p})}{300}} < p < 0.09 + 2.326\sqrt{\frac{\widehat{p}(1-\widehat{p})}{300}}$$

i.e., $0.0516 < p < 0.1284$
i.e., $5.16\% < p < 12.84\%$

We are 98% confident that there are between 5.16% and 12.84% of all fish with length below the legal limit.

c This estimate is appropriate as
  (1) we are approximating p by $\widehat{p}$ in its calculation
  (2) as n is large (300) we are approximating a binomial RV with a normal RV and are not using a continuity correction.

d For a 98% CI, $Z_\alpha \approx 2.326$

So, $2.326\sqrt{\dfrac{(0.09)(0.91)}{n}} = 0.02 \quad \Rightarrow \quad n \approx 1108.1$

i.e., we need to randomly sample about 1100 fish in the region.

24 $\widehat{p} = \frac{43}{75} \approx 0.5733, \quad Z_\alpha \approx 1.96$

a 95% CI is $0.461 < p < 0.685$ i.e., $46.1\% < p < 68.$

b We need n when $1.96\sqrt{\dfrac{0.5733 \times 0.4267}{n}} = 0.025$

$\Rightarrow \quad n \approx 1503.6$

So, we need a sample of 1504 residents or about this number.

c • We estimate the true p by $\widehat{p}$.

    • As n is large we have approximated the binomial RV by a normal RV and not used a continuity correction.

d $\widehat{p}$ the estimate of p is the midpoint of the CI,

i.e., $\quad \widehat{p} = \dfrac{0.441 + 0.579}{2} = 0.51$

But $\quad \widehat{p} = \dfrac{X}{n} \quad \therefore \quad 0.51 = \dfrac{X}{200} \quad \Rightarrow \quad X = 102$

i.e., 102 voted in favour of the Euro.

EXERCISE 8E.1

1 a A Type I error involves rejecting a true null hypothesis.

b A Type II error involves accepting a false null hypothesis.

c The null hypothesis is a statement of *no difference*.

d The alternative hypothesis is a statement that there is a difference.

2 a i a Type I error **ii** a Type II error

b i a Type II error **ii** a Type I error

3 a The alternative hypothesis (H_1) would be that the person on trial is guilty.

b a Type I error **c** a Type II error

4 a A Type I error would result if X and Y are determined to have different effectiveness, when in fact they have the same.

b A Type II error would result if X and Y are determined to have the same effectiveness, when in fact they have different effectiveness.

5 a H_0: new globe has mean life 80 hours
$\quad H_1$: new globe has mean life > 80 hours

b H_0: new globe has mean life 80 hours
$\quad H_1$: new globe has mean life < 80 hours

6 H_0: new design has top speed of 26.3 knots
$\quad H_1$: new design has top speed > 26.3 knots

EXERCISE 8E.2

1 a $z_\alpha > 1.645$ **b** $z_\alpha < -1.645$
c $z_\alpha < -1.96$ or $z_\alpha > 1.96$

2 a $z_\alpha > 2.326$ **b** $z_\alpha < -2.326$
c $z_\alpha < -2.576$ or $z_\alpha > 2.576$

3 a H_0: $\mu = 80$ and H_1: $\mu > 80$
b Z-distribution with $\sigma = 12.9$
c $z \approx 3.398$ **d** rejection region $z > 2.326$
e Reject H_0 at a 1% level, accept $\mu > 80$.
$\quad$ P(type I error) $= 0.01$

4 a H_0: $\mu = \$13.45$ and H_1: $\mu < \$13.45$
b t-distribution with $s_{n-1} = \sqrt{\dfrac{388}{387}} \times \$0.25$
$$\approx 0.2503$$
c $t \approx -11.82$ **d** p-value, P($t < -11.82) \approx 0$
e Reject H_0 at a 2% level, i.e., accept the claim that the mean price has fallen. P(type I error) $= 0.02$

5 a Z-distribution, $\widehat{p} = \dfrac{123}{237} \approx 0.5190$ $z = 0.5846$
$\quad p$-value ≈ 0.279, $\therefore$ accept H_0: $p = 0.5$
$\quad$ Could be making a type II error.

b Z-distribution, $\widehat{p} = \dfrac{295}{382} \approx 0.7723$ $z \approx -1.356$
$\quad p$-value ≈ 0.1751, $\therefore$ accept H_0: $p = 0.85$
$\quad$ There is $\approx 17.5\%$ chance of getting this sample result if $p = 0.8$.
$\quad$ Could be making a Type II error.

6 Z-distribution, $\quad \widehat{p} = \dfrac{182}{400} = 0.455$

H_0: $p = 0.5$ and H_1: $p \neq 0.5$
p-value $\approx 0.071\,86$ which is > 0.05
So, accept H_0.

There is insufficient evidence at a 5% level to reject the hypothesis that the coin is unbiased. So, we accept that the coin is unbiased. Here we could be making a Type II error.

7 Z-distribution, with $\quad \widehat{p} = \dfrac{57}{231} \approx 0.2468$

H_0: $p = \frac{1}{6}$ and H_1: $p > \frac{1}{6}$
p-value $\approx 0.000\,545$ which is < 0.01
$\therefore$ we reject H_0, $\quad p = \frac{1}{6}$

There is sufficient evidence at a 1% level to reject the hypothesis that the dice are fair. So, we accept that the player has switched to leaded dice.
Here, P(type I error) $= 0.01$

8 Z-distribution, $\widehat{p} = \dfrac{45}{57} \approx 0.7895$

H_0: $p = 0.85$ and H_1: $p < 0.85$
p-value ≈ 0.1003 which is > 0.01
$\therefore$ we do not reject H_0.

There is insufficient evidence at a 1% level to reject the hypothesis that the dealer's claim is valid. Hence we accept the hypothesis that at least 85% of customers do recommend his boats. There is a risk of making a type II error. (In this question we could consider doing a 2-tailed test, i.e., test H_1: $p \neq 0.85$. Why?)

9 Z-distribution, $\widehat{p} = \dfrac{16}{389} \approx 0.041\,13$

H_0: $p = 0.05$ and H_1: $p < 0.05$
p-value ≈ 0.2111 which is > 0.02
So, we do not reject H_0.

There is insufficient evidence (at a 2% level) to reject the hypothesis that 5% of the apples have skin blemishes. We recommend that the purchaser does not buy them. This conclusion risks a type II error.

10 a $s_n = \$14\,268$, $\quad n = 113$, $\quad s_{n-1} \approx \$14\,331.55$ is an unbiased estimate of s_n.

b H_0: $\mu = \$95\,000$ and H_1: $\mu > \$95\,000$
c A t-distribution with $\nu = 112$ **d** $t \approx 0.9776$
e p-value ≈ 0.1652
f critical value is $\quad t_{0.02} \approx 2.078$
$\quad \therefore$ critical region is $\quad t > 2.078$

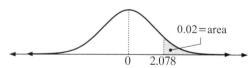

g As $t \approx 0.9776$ is < 2.078 we have insufficient evidence to reject H_0.
$\quad$ So, we reject the claim that $\mu > \$95\,000$

h If the assertion was incorrect, i.e., accepting H_0 when H_1 is correct, we are committing a type II error.

i The 99% CI for mean income is $]\,\$92\,785, \$99\,850\,[$ which confirms that there is not enough evidence to reject H_0 as this value, $\mu = 95\,000$ lies within the interval.
$\quad$ [Although $\alpha = 0.02$, we verify with a 99% CI as we have a 1-tailed test here.]

11 a H_0: $\mu = 250$, H_1: $\mu \neq 250$ (2-tailed)

t-distribution as σ^2 is unknown, $\nu = 59$

$s_n = 7.3$, so $s_{n-1} \approx 7.362$ $(n = 60)$ $t \approx -7.786$,

p-value $= P(t \leqslant -7.786) + P(t \geqslant 7.786)$
$\approx 1.26 \times 10^{-10}$

and as $p < 0.05$, we reject H_0.

P(type I error) $= 0.05$

There is sufficient evidence to reject H_0.

This suggests that $\mu \neq 250$. Since the sample mean was < 250 mg we surmise that the true population mean is smaller than 250 mg.

Note: The critical t-value is $t_{0.975} \approx 2$ $(\nu = 59)$. Hence the critical region is $t < -2$, $t > 2$ And, as $t^* \approx -7.786$, we reject H_0.

b As 95% CI for μ is $240.7 < \mu < 244.5$ which confirms the above as we are 95% confident that the true population mean is well below 250 mg.

Hence, we would reject H_0 in **a** and argue again that the mean is less than 250 mg.

12 Let X_1 represent the test score before coaching, X_2 represent the test score after coaching and let $U = X_2 - X_1$.

U-values are $5, -1, 0, 7, 0, -1, 3, 3, 4, -1, 1, -6$

$\overline{U} \approx 1.1667$, $s_{n-1} \approx 3.4597$

H_0: $\mu = 0$ (i.e., test scores have not improved)
H_1: $\mu > 0$

t-distribution, $\nu = 11$ $t^* \approx 1.168$

We reject H_0 if p-value < 0.05

p-value $= P(t > 1.168) \approx 0.1337$

The decision:

either As p-value > 0.05, we do not reject H_0.

or The rejection region is $t_{0.05} > 1.796$ and t^* does not lie in it. So, we reject H_0.

13 Z-distribution as σ is known $(\sigma^2 = 2.25)$.

$\overline{x} = 1001$, $\sigma = 1.5$

H_0: $\mu = 1000$ grams, H_1: $\mu > 1000$ grams

$z^* \approx 1.8856$ p-value $= P(z^* \geqslant 1.8856) \approx 0.02967$

The decision:

either As p-value > 0.01 we do not reject H_0.

or As $z_{0.01} \approx 2.326$, the critical region is $z \geqslant 2.326$. z^* lies outside this region, so we do not reject H_0.

Conclusion:

There is insufficient evidence to support the overfilling claim. This decision was made at a 1% level of significance. However, we could be making a type II error.

14 H_0: $\mu = 500$ mL and H_1: $\mu \neq 500$ mL

t-distribution as σ^2 is unknown. $t \sim T(9)$ $s_n = 1.2$ mL

$\therefore$ $s_{n-1} \approx 1.2649$ is an unbiased estimate of σ.

$t^* \approx -2.500$

p-value $= P(t \leqslant -2.5$ or $t \geqslant 2.5) \approx 0.0339$

and so we do not reject H_0 as p-value > 0.01

or critical t-value is $t_{0.005} \approx 3.250$.

So the critical region is $t < -3.250$ or $t > 3.250$.

As $t^* \approx -2.500$ does not lie in the CR we do not reject H_0.

Conclusion:

There is insufficient evidence to suggest that the sample mean is significantly different from the expected value at a 0.01 level. We risk making a type II error, i.e., accepting H_0 when it is false.

EXERCISE 8F

1 H_0: the results are independent of weather.

The expected values (frequencies) matrix is

$$\begin{bmatrix} 12\ (8.96) & 14\ (7.04) \\ 8\ (6.72) & 4\ (5.28) \\ 8\ (13.32) & 14\ (9.68) \end{bmatrix}$$ $\chi^2_{calc} \approx 6.341$ with $\nu = 2$.

p-value ≈ 0.0420

Hence, at a 1% level, we accept Juventus' results are independent of weather as $0.0420 > 0.01$.

At a 5% level, as $0.0420 < 0.05$ we conclude that Juventus' results depend on the weather.

2 H_0: results are independent of immunisation.

The EV(F) matrix is

$$\begin{bmatrix} 30\ (36.9) & 51\ (44.1) \\ 61\ (54.1) & 58\ (64.9) \end{bmatrix}$$ $\chi^2_{calc} \approx 3.932$ with $\nu = 1$

p-value ≈ 0.0474

So, at a 5% level we reject H_0, i.e., people who receive flu immunisation are less likely to suffer from colds.

P(type I error) $= 0.05$

Note: With Yates' correction, $\chi^2_{calc} \approx 3.4271$ with p-value ≈ 0.0641 and we would not reject H_0.

3

f_0	97	91	12
f_e	116	76	8

$\chi^2_{calc} = \sum \dfrac{(f_0 - f_e)^2}{f_e} \approx 8.0726$

p-value $= P[\chi^2 > 8.0726] \approx 0.0177$ with $\nu = 2$.

At a 1% level we do not reject H_0,

i.e., the Principal's results match those of the EA.

At a 5% level, we reject H_0 as $0.0177 < 0.05$,

i.e., the Principal's results contradict the EA's.

We could be making a type II error if $\alpha = 0.01$ and a type I error if $\alpha = 0.05$.

4 a $\overline{x} = \dfrac{\sum fx}{\sum f} = \dfrac{46}{52} \approx 0.88462$

b

	0	1	2	3	$\geqslant 4$
f_0	26	11	10	5	0
f_e	21.47	18.99	8.40	2.48	0.66

combine

f_0	26	11	15
f_e	21.47	18.99	11.54

$\chi^2_{calc} = \sum \dfrac{(f_0 - f_e)^2}{f_e} \approx 5.355$

with $\nu = 3 - 2 = 1$, as the mean was estimated.

p-value $= P\left(\chi^2_{calc} > 5.355\right) \approx 0.0207$ which is < 0.05

So, at a 5% level of significance we do not reject H_0, i.e., the Poisson model is not adequate for this data set. We are risking making a type I error with probability 0.05.

5 a $400 - 198 - 92 - 57 = 53$ fail both

b H_0: results in each subject are unrelated.

Matrix is $\begin{bmatrix} 198\ (185) & 92\ (105) \\ 57\ (70) & 53\ (40) \end{bmatrix}$

$\chi^2_{calc} \approx 9.3471$, $\nu = 1$, p-value ≈ 0.00223

Hence, at a 5% level we reject H_0,

i.e., performances in each subject are related.

Note: With Yates' continuity correction $\chi^2_{\text{calc}} \approx 8.6486$ and p-value $\approx 0.003\,27$ we come to the same conclusion.

6 a H_0: Of the six coins, five are fair and the other is a double tailed coin.

  H_1: All six coins are fair.

  Let X be the number of tails, then under H_0

  $P(X = x) = C^5_{x-1}(\frac{1}{2})^5$ for $x = 1, 2, 3, ..., 6$

f_0	13	47	91	85	31	8
f_e	8.6	43.0	85.9	85.9	43.0	8.6

  $\chi^2_{\text{calc}} \approx 6.326$, p-value ≈ 0.276, $\nu = 6 - 1 = 5$

  Hence, at a 5% level, we do not reject H_0, i.e., the observer's conclusion that one of the coins has two tails whilst the other five are fair is correct.

7 The null distribution is Geometric, i.e., if X is the number of tosses needed to get a head, then $X \sim \text{Geo}(0.5)$

  H_0: the coin is fair H_1: the coin is not fair

  $P(X = x) = (0.5)^x$ where $x = 1, 2, 3, ..., 8$.

f_0	46	20	12	8	5	3	4	2
f_e	50	25	12.5	6.25	3.13	1.56	0.78	0.39

combine

f_0	46	20	12	8	14
f_e	50	25	12.5	6.25	6.25

  $\chi^2_{\text{calc}} \approx 11.44$ $\nu = 5 - 1 = 4$

  p-value $= P\left(\chi^2_{\text{calc}} > 11.44\right) \approx 0.0220$

  Hence, for $\alpha = 0.05$, we reject H_0. That is, the geometric distribution does not adequately fit the data and we conclude that the coin is not fair.

8 H_0: alcohol consumption and tobacco usage are independent.

  The matrix is $\begin{bmatrix} 105 & 7 & 11 \\ 58 & 5 & 13 \\ 84 & 37 & 42 \\ 57 & 16 & 17 \end{bmatrix}$

  $\chi^2_{\text{calc}} \approx 42.25$, p-value $\approx 1.64 \times 10^{-7}$ $\nu = 3 \times 2 = 6$

  Hence, at a 5% level, we reject H_0.

  That is, alcohol consumption and tobacco usage are dependent.

  $P(\text{type I error}) = 0.05$

9 a $\int_0^1 (e - ke^x)dx = 1$

  $\Rightarrow \qquad [ex - ke^x]_0^1 = 1$

  $\Rightarrow \quad (e - ke) - (-k) = 1$

  $\Rightarrow \qquad e - ke + k = 1$

  $\Rightarrow \qquad k(1 - e) = 1 - e$

  $\Rightarrow \qquad\qquad k = 1$

  b $50\int_0^{0.2} (e - e^x)dx \approx 16.1$

  $50\int_{0.2}^{0.4} (e - e^x)dx \approx 13.7$

  $50\int_{0.4}^{0.6} (e - e^x)dx \approx 10.7$

  $50\int_{0.6}^{0.8} (e - e^x)dx \approx 7.0$

  $50\int_{0.8}^{1} (e - e^x)dx \approx 2.5$

f_0	18	11	10	6	5
f_e	16.1	13.7	10.7	7.0	2.5

combine as $2.5 < 5$

f_0	18	11	10	11
f_e	16.1	13.7	10.7	9.5

  $\chi^2_{\text{calc}} \approx 1.039$, $\nu = 4 - 1 = 3$

  and p-value $= P(\chi^2 \geqslant 1.039) \approx 0.792$

  Hence, at a 5% level, we do not reject H_0, i.e., H_0 described by the given pdf is an adequate model.

  Hence, we accept that battery lifetime is modelled by the continuous pdf given. We risk making a type II error here.

REVIEW SET 8A

1 $S \sim \text{N}(338, 3^2)$ $L \sim \text{N}(1010, 12^2)$

  a Let $U = L - (S_1 + S_2 + S_3)$ $E(U) = -4$,

  $\text{Var}(U) = 171$ $U \sim \text{N}(-4, 171)$, $P(U > 0) \approx 0.380$

  b Let $V = L - 3S$ $E(V) = -4$, $\text{Var}(V) = 225$

  $V \sim \text{N}(-4, 225)$, $P(V > 0) \approx 0.395$

2 a $\sum p_i = 1 \;\Rightarrow\; 5c = 1 \;\Rightarrow\; c = \frac{1}{5}$

  b $\mu(X) = \sum x_i p_i = 1$

  c $P(X > 1) = P(X = 3 \text{ or } 5) = \frac{2}{5}$

  d $\text{Var}(X) = \sum x_i^2 p_i - \mu^2 = 45\left(\frac{1}{5}\right) - 1^2 = 8$

3 a $X \sim \text{Geo}(0.35)$ **i** $P(X \leqslant 4) \approx 0.821$

  ii $E(X) = \dfrac{1}{p} \approx 2.86$ or 3 buses

  b $X \sim \text{NB}(3, 0.35)$

  i $P(X = 7) = \binom{6}{2}(0.35)^3(0.65)^4 \approx 0.115$

  ii $E(X) = \dfrac{r}{p} = \frac{3}{0.35} \approx 8.57$ i.e., approx. 9 buses

  iii $P(X \leqslant 5)$

  $= P(X = 3 \text{ or } 4 \text{ or } 5)$

  $= (0.35)^3 + \binom{3}{2}(0.35)^3(0.65) + \binom{4}{2}(0.35)^3(0.65)^2$

  ≈ 0.235

4 a $X \sim \text{Po}(14 \times \frac{3}{4})$ $P(X = 5) \approx 0.0293$

  b $X \sim \text{Po}(14 \times \frac{1}{2})$ $P(X < 7) = P(X \leqslant 6) \approx 0.450$

5 a $F \sim \text{Hyp}(2, 3, 12)$ and is discrete

  b

$F = f$	0	1	2
$P(F = f)$	0.545	0.409	0.045

  c i $P(\text{buy packet}) = 1 - P(\text{do not buy packet})$

  $= 1 - (0.045 + 0.409 \times \frac{2}{10})$

  ≈ 0.873

  ii F is now binomial

  i.e., $F \sim \text{B}(12, \frac{1}{4})$ and

  $P(\text{buy packet})$

  $= 1 - P(\text{do not buy packet})$

  $= 1 - \left\{P(F = 2) + P(F = 1) \times \frac{2}{10}\right\}$

  $= 1 - \left\{\binom{2}{2}\left(\frac{1}{4}\right)^2 + \binom{2}{1}\left(\frac{1}{4}\right)^1\left(\frac{3}{4}\right)^1 \times \frac{2}{10}\right\}$

  ≈ 0.863

6 a $\int_0^1 f(x)\,dx = 1$ and $\int_0^1 x\,f(x)\,dx = 0.7$

$\int_0^1 (ax^3 + bx^2)\,dx = 1 \;\Rightarrow\; \left[\dfrac{ax^4}{4} + \dfrac{bx^3}{3}\right]_0^1 = 1$

$\qquad\qquad\qquad\qquad\Rightarrow\; \dfrac{a}{4} + \dfrac{b}{3} = 1$

$\qquad\qquad\qquad\qquad\Rightarrow\; 3a + 4b = 12 \;\ldots\; (1)$

and $\int_0^1 (ax^4 + bx^3)\,dx = 0.7$

$\qquad\Rightarrow\; \left[\dfrac{ax^5}{5} + \dfrac{bx^4}{4}\right]_0^1 = 0.7$

$\qquad\Rightarrow\; \dfrac{a}{5} + \dfrac{b}{4} = \dfrac{7}{10}$

$\qquad\Rightarrow\; 4a + 5b = 14 \;\ldots\; (2)$

Solving (1) and (2) gives $a = -4, \quad b = 6$

So, $f(x) = 6x^2 - 4x^3, \quad 0 \leqslant x \leqslant 1$

b $P(X > 0.95) = \int_{0.95}^1 (6x^2 - 4x^3)\,dx \approx 0.0998$
$\qquad\qquad\qquad\qquad\qquad\qquad\quad \approx 9.98\%$

So, there is about a 10% chance that the provider will run out of petrol in any given week.

7 $n = 300$ which is large $\widehat{p} \sim N(p, \dfrac{pq}{n})$

$\Rightarrow\; \widehat{p} \sim N\!\left(0.12, \dfrac{0.12 \times 0.88}{300}\right)$

i.e., $\mu = 0.12, \quad \sigma = \sqrt{\dfrac{0.12 \times 0.88}{300}} \approx 0.018\,76$

a $P(\widehat{p} < 0.11) \approx 0.297$ **b** $P(\widehat{p} > 0.14) \approx 0.143$
c $P(0.11 < \widehat{p} < 0.14) \approx 0.560$

Note: With cc these are **a** ≈ 0.267 **b** ≈ 0.124 **c** ≈ 0.507

8 a $\overline{x} = 212.275, \quad s_n \approx 1.5164, \quad s_{n-1} \approx 1.5357$
b σ^2 is unknown, $X \sim t(39)$
95% CI for μ is $211.8 < \mu < 212.8$

9 a $n = 225$ is large, so we approximate

p by $\widehat{p} \sim N\!\left(0.93, \dfrac{0.93 \times 0.07}{225}\right)$

$\mu = 0.93, \quad \sigma \approx 0.017\,01$
$X = np = 225 \times 0.93 \approx 209$
(gcalc) gives $89.5\% < p < 96.2\%$
a direct calculation gives $89.7\% < p < 96.3\%$

b We are 95% confident that between 89.5% and 96.2% of all athletes believe that "all athletes should be tested for HIV".

10 $n = 420, \quad \dfrac{X}{n} = \dfrac{86}{420} \approx 0.2048$

As n is large, $\widehat{p} \sim N\!\left(0.2048, \dfrac{0.2048 \times 0.7952}{420}\right)$

$\mu \approx 0.2048$ and $\sigma \approx 0.0197$

a A 95% CI for p is $0.166 < p < 0.243$
b As $P(\text{getting a } 6) = \dfrac{1}{6} = 0.1666\ldots$ for a 'fair' coin,

and $\dfrac{1}{6}$ lies in the CI, there is no evidence to suggest that the die is unfair.

Note: We can be 90% sure that the die is unfair as the 90% CI for p is $0.172 < p < 0.237$ and $\dfrac{1}{6}$ does not lie in this CI.

11 a A type I error would result if it was determined that Quickchick is supplying underweight chickens when they are in fact not.

b A type II error would result if Quickchick is supplying underweight chickens when it is determined that they are not.

12 a $\overline{x} = 4.02$
b For Binomial, $\overline{x} \approx np \;\Rightarrow\; p \approx \dfrac{4.02}{6} \approx 0.670$
c

f_0	1	3	9	17	31	28	11
f_e	0.1	1.6	8.0	21.6	32.9	26.7	9.0

$C_0^6 (0.67)^0 (0.33)^6 \times 100$

combining
gives

f_0	13	17	31	28	11
f_e	9.7	21.6	32.9	26.7	9.0

$\chi^2_{\text{calc}} \approx 2.72$ with $\nu = 5 - 1 - 1 = 3$
{we had to estimate p}
p-value $= P(\chi^2 > 2.7198) \approx 0.437$
Hence, at a 10% level we do not reject H_0,
i.e.,   the binomial distribution is an adequate model.
So, we support the claim.

13 Let $X \sim N(100, 100)$
$\quad P(80.5 < X < 90.5) \times 2000 \approx 291$
$\quad P(90.5 < X < 100.5) \times 2000 \approx 698$
$\quad P(100.5 < X < 110.5) \times 2000 \approx 667$

f_0	10	45	287	641	725	250	40	2
f_e	3	48	291	698	667	253	38	2

combine   combine

f_0	55	287	641	725	250	42
f_e	51	291	698	667	253	40

$\chi^2_{\text{calc}} \approx 10.202$ with $\nu = 6 - 1 = 5$
p-value $= P(\chi^2_{\text{calc}} > 10.202) \approx 0.0697$
Hence, we do not reject H_0 at a 5% level, i.e., the normal distribution is an adequate model if $\mu = 100, \;\sigma = 10$.

14 a Observations are not independent as we have the same group of students. So, the difference between means is not appropriate.

Student	Pre-test	Post-test	Difference (d)
A	12	11	-1
B	13	14	1
C	11	16	5
D	14	13	-1
E	10	12	2
F	16	18	2
G	14	15	1
H	13	14	1
I	13	15	2
J	12	11	-1
			$\sum d = 11$

$\overline{d} = \dfrac{\sum d}{n} = \dfrac{11}{10} = 1.1$

$s_n^2 = \dfrac{\sum d^2}{n} - \overline{d}^{\,2} = \dfrac{43}{10} - 1.1^2 \approx 3.09$

$\therefore$ unbiased estimate of σ^2 is $s_{n-1}^2 = \dfrac{n}{n-1}s_n^2 \approx 3.4333\ldots$

So, the unbiased estimate of σ is $s_{n-1} \approx 1.8529$

As σ^2 was unknown we use a t-distribution $d \sim t(9)$

A 90% CI for d is $0.0259 < d < 2.1741$

b H_0: $\mu_d = 0$,   there is no improvement

H_1: $\mu_d > 0$,   there is an improvement

We will perform a 1-tailed t-test at a 5% level with 9 df. $d \sim t(9)$

$t \approx 1.877$ and p-value $\approx 0.0466 < 0.05$

So, we reject H_0.

REVIEW SET 8B

1 a $P(X = 6) = 1 - 0.3 - 0.2 - 0.2 = 0.3$

b $E(X) = \sum x_i p_i = 0.7$,   i.e.,   70 cents a game.

c If they charge 50 cents to play then on average they will lose 20 cents a game. If they charge \$1 to play then they would expect to gain 30 cents a game.

d $E(Y) = 0.1$,   i.e.,   10 cents a game.

e

5	0	4	8	11
2	-3	1	5	8
-3	-8	4	0	3
	-5	-1	3	6

X

$X \cap Y$	-8	-4	-3	0	1	3
P	0.15	0.10	0.09	0.16	0.06	0.15

$X \cap Y$	4	5	8	11
P	0.04	0.06	0.13	0.06

$E(X \cap Y) = \sum z_i p_i = 0.8$

i.e.,   80 cents per game (on average)

f Expected return

$= 500 \times \$0.30 + 500 \times \$0.90 + 1000 \times \$0.20 = \$800$

2 $X \sim B(1000, \frac{3}{5})$

a $\mu_X = E(X) = np = 600$

b $Var(X) = npq = 600 \times \frac{2}{5} = 240$ $\therefore$ $\sigma_X \approx 15.5$

3 $X \sim Geo\left(\frac{1}{6}\right)$.   Hence $\mu = \frac{1}{p} = 6$

So, on average it takes players 6 rolls to win 10 Euros. Pierre wants to profit 2 Euros per game. Hence he must charge 12 Euros over 6 rolls, i.e., 2 Euros per roll.

4 a $X \sim Hyp(10, 13, 100)$

b $P(X = x) = \dfrac{\binom{13}{x}\binom{87}{10-x}}{\binom{100}{10}}$, $(x = 0, 1, 2, 3, ..., 10)$

c $P(X \leqslant 2) = \dfrac{\binom{13}{0}\binom{87}{10} + \binom{13}{1}\binom{87}{9} + \binom{13}{2}\binom{87}{8}}{\binom{100}{10}}$

≈ 0.880

5 a $X \sim P_0(m)$ where m is the mean number of errors per page.

b $P(X = x) = \dfrac{m^x e^{-m}}{x!}$ $(x = 0, 1, 2, 3, ...)$

i $P(X = 0) = e^{-m} = q$ $(\ln q = -m)$

ii $P(X = 1) = me^{-m} = -q \ln q$

iii $P(X > 1) = 1 - P(X = 0) - P(X = 1)$

$= 1 - q + q \ln q$

c i

$Y = y$	10	1	-8
$P(Y = y)$	q	$-q \ln q$	$1 - q + q \ln q$

ii $E(Y) = \sum y_i p_i$

$= 10q - q \ln q - 8 + 8q - 8q \ln q$

$= 18q - 9q \ln q - 8$ dollars

iii We need to solve $18q - 9q \ln q - 8 = 0$

This is $q \approx 0.268$

6 a X = number who prefer right leg kick

$X \sim B(20, 0.75)$

i $P(X = 14) \approx 0.169$

ii $P(X \geqslant 15) = 1 - P(X \leqslant 14) \approx 0.617$

b $X \sim B(1050, 0.75)$

As $np > 10$ and $nq > 10$ we can approximate X by a normal variate $\mu = np = 787.5$

$\sigma = \sqrt{npq} = \sqrt{787.5 \times 0.25} \approx 14.03$

i $P(X = 0.7 \times 1050)$
$= P(X = 735)$
$\approx P(734.5 < X^* < 735.5)$
$\approx 0.000\,0260$

ii $P(X \geqslant 0.75 \times 1050)$
$= P(X \geqslant 787.5)$
$= 1 - P(X \leqslant 787)$
≈ 0.514

7 $X \sim N(\mu, 67^2)$

So $\overline{X} \sim N(\mu, \frac{67^2}{375})$ {CL Theorem}

$P(\,|\overline{X} - \mu| > 10)$

$= 1 - P(-10 < \overline{X} - \mu < 10)$

$= 1 - P\left(\dfrac{-10}{\frac{67}{\sqrt{375}}} < \dfrac{\overline{X} - \mu}{\frac{67}{\sqrt{375}}} < \dfrac{10}{\frac{67}{\sqrt{375}}}\right)$

$= 1 - P(-2.890 < Z < 2.890)$

$\approx 0.003\,85$

8 As $n = 173$ is large, $\widehat{p} \sim N(p, \frac{pq}{n})$

$\widehat{p} = \frac{56}{173} \approx 0.3237$

So,   a 90% CI for p is

$\widehat{p} - 1.645\sqrt{\dfrac{\widetilde{p}\,\widetilde{q}}{n}} < p < \widehat{p} + 1.645\sqrt{\dfrac{\widetilde{p}\,\widetilde{q}}{n}}$

i.e., $0.265 < p < 0.382$

i.e.,   the true percentage of deaths on Mars where drivers have high levels of alcohol/drugs is somewhere between 26.5% and 38.2% with 90% confidence.

9 $X = 32$, $n = 400$

a $\widehat{p} = \frac{32}{400} = 0.08$ (or 8%)

b A 95% CI for p is

$\widehat{p} - 1.96\sqrt{\dfrac{\widetilde{p}\,\widetilde{q}}{n}} < p < \widehat{p} + 1.96\sqrt{\dfrac{\widetilde{p}\,\widetilde{q}}{n}}$

i.e., $0.0534 < p < 0.1066$

c 95% of 150 = 142.5 or 143 such tests should contain p.

10 $n = 306 + 109 + 92 + 49 = 556$

f_0	306	109	92	49
f_e	312.75	104.25	104.25	34.75

e.g., $\dfrac{9}{16} \times 556$

H_0: numbers are in the ratio $9:3:3:1$
H_1: this is not true
$\chi^2_{\text{calc}} \approx 7.6451$ with $\nu = 4 - 1 = 3$
p-value $= P(\chi^2_{\text{calc}} \geqslant 7.6451) \approx 0.0539$
              which is > 0.05
Hence, there is not enough evidence to reject H_0 at a 5%
level, i.e., we accept the scientific theory.

11 H_0: location and type of tumour are independent
H_1: they are not

Under H_0 the matrix of observed frequencies (expected) is:

$$\begin{bmatrix} 21 \ (17.7) & 13 \ (14.1) & 2 \ (4.2) \\ 20 \ (14.3) & 7 \ (11.4) & 2 \ (3.38) \\ 18 \ (27.0) & 27 \ (21.5) & 10 \ (6.42) \end{bmatrix}$$

We note that the third column has 2 values of $f_e < 5$.
Hence we combine the 2nd and 3rd columns.

$$\begin{bmatrix} 21 \ (17.7) & 15 \ (18.3) \\ 20 \ (14.3) & 9 \ (14.8) \\ 18 \ (27.0) & 37 \ (27.9) \end{bmatrix}$$

$\chi^2_{\text{calc}} \approx 11.71$ with $\nu = 2$ and a p-value ≈ 0.00287
Hence at a 1% level we reject H_0 and conclude that there
is some dependence (association) between type and location
of the tumour. $P(\text{type I error}) = 0.01$

12 $X =$ volume of a bottle in mL $X \sim N(376, 1.84^2)$
$\overline{X} =$ average volume of each sample of 12
$\overline{X} \sim N\left(376, \dfrac{1.84^2}{12}\right)$

a $P(X < 373) \approx 0.0515$
i.e., about 5.15% will have a volume less than 373 mL
b $P(\overline{X} < 375) \approx 0.0299$
i.e., about 3% of all packs of 12 will have an average
contents less than 375 mL
c From **a** and **b** there is a smaller chance of picking a
12-pack that does not meet the rules than that for an
individual bottle.
Hence, would prefer method II.
d Let $X \sim N(\mu, 1.84^2)$
We want $P(\overline{X} < 375) = 0.01$

$\therefore$ $P\left(\dfrac{\overline{X} - \mu}{\frac{1.84}{\sqrt{12}}} < \dfrac{375 - \mu}{\frac{1.84}{\sqrt{12}}}\right) = 0.01$

i.e., $P\left(Z < \dfrac{375 - \mu}{\frac{1.84}{\sqrt{12}}}\right) = 0.01$

Thus $\dfrac{(375 - \mu)\sqrt{12}}{1.84} = \text{invNorm}(0.01)$

i.e., $375 - \mu \approx -1.235\,67$
$\therefore$ $\mu \approx 376.23....$
So, need to set it at $\mu = 377$ mL.

13 **a** $s_n^2 = \dfrac{\displaystyle\sum_{i=1}^{n}(x_i - \overline{x})^2}{n} = \dfrac{230}{15} \approx 15.33$

b $s_{n-1}^2 = \dfrac{n}{n-1}s_n^2 \approx 16.43$ is an unbiased estimate
of σ^2

c The 95% CI for μ is $124.94 < \mu < 129.05$
and $\overline{x}$ for this sample is the midpoint of the CI.

$\therefore$ $\overline{x} = \dfrac{124.94 + 129.05}{2} = 126.995$

As σ^2 is unknown (had to be estimated),
we have a t-distribution with $\nu = 15 - 1 = 14$
i.e., $t \sim T(14)$
A 95% CI is $124.75 < \mu < 129.24$

d The CI is $124.94 < \mu < 129.05$ taken from the sample.

$t^* = \dfrac{|\overline{x} - \mu|}{\frac{S_{n-1}}{\sqrt{n}}} = \dfrac{|126.995 - 129.05|}{\frac{\sqrt{16.43}}{\sqrt{15}}}$

$\Rightarrow$ $t^* \approx 1.9636$
$P(t < 1.9636) \approx 0.965\,12$

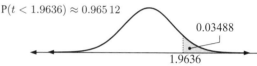

0.03488

1.9636

$\therefore$ confidence level $\approx 2 \times 0.034\,88 \approx 0.07$
i.e., a 7% CI

14 **a** Let $D = X_2 - X_1$ where
$X_2 =$ number of fish caught after course
$X_1 =$ number of fish caught before course
H_0: $\mu_D = 0$ and H_1: $\mu_D > 0$
(i.e.,   course has been effective)
D-values are: 12, 9, 18, -3, -9, 4, 0, 10, 4
$\overline{d} = 5$ and $s_{n-1} \approx 8.2614$

Test statistic is $t^* = \dfrac{\overline{d} - \mu}{\frac{s_{n-1}}{\sqrt{n}}} = \dfrac{5 - 0}{\frac{8.2614}{\sqrt{9}}}$

i.e., $t \approx 1.816$
p-value $= P(t > 1.815\,67) \approx 0.0535$

The decision:
• as p-value > 0.05 *or*
• as t^* does not lie in the rejection region
   $(t > 1.860$ from tables)   *then*   we do not reject
   H_0 and are subject to making a type II error
   i.e., accepting H_0 when it is in fact false.

Note: We do not have enough information to determine
the probability of making this type of error.

b A 90% confidence interval for the mean difference is

$$\left]\,\overline{d} - \dfrac{t^* s_{n-1}}{\sqrt{n}}, \ \ \overline{d} + \dfrac{t^* s_{n-1}}{\sqrt{n}}\,\right[$$

i.e., $\left]\,5 - \dfrac{1.860 \times 8.261}{\sqrt{9}}, \ \ 5 + \dfrac{1.860 \times 8.261}{\sqrt{9}}\,\right[$

i.e., $]-0.122, \ \ 10.122\,[$

Note: A gcalc gives $]-0.121, 10.121[$
As the null hypothesis value of $\mu_D = 0$ is within the
CI, then at a 5% level, this is consistent with the
acceptance of H_0.

EXERCISE 9A.1

1 **a** a, b, c Number of elements $= 3$.
  b $2, 3, 5, 7$ Number of elements $= 4$.
  c $3, 4, 5, 6, 7$ Number of elements $= 5$
  d no elements exist, i.e., number of elements $= 0$
  e $3, 4, \{3\}, \{4\}$ Number of elements $= 4$
  f $\varnothing$ Number of elements $= 1$. This is the set containing the symbol $\varnothing$.
  $\{\varnothing\}$ is not the empty set. $\{\}$ or $\varnothing$ is the empty set.

2 **a** As $\mathbb{Z}$ represents the set of all integers, the given set is finite.
  b infinite

3 **a** equal as repetitions are ignored
  b equal   (order of listing is not important)
  c equal as the solutions to $x^2 = 4$ are the same as the solutions to $|x| = 2$.
  d equal as both of these sets are empty sets
  e not equal as the first set does not contain $x = 2$ and $x = 5$.

EXERCISE 9A.2

1 **a** $P(A) = \{\varnothing, \{p\}, \{q\}, \{p, q\}\}$
  b $P(A) = \{\varnothing, \{1\}, \{2\}, \{3\}, \{1, 2\}, \{1, 3\}, \{2, 3\},$
       $\{1, 2, 3\}\}$
  c $P(A) = \{\varnothing, \{0\}\}$

2 **a** True, as the elements of A are also in B.
  b False as $0 \notin B$ **c** False as $9 \notin B$
  d False as $\sqrt{2} \in A$, but $\sqrt{2} \notin B$.

EXERCISE 9A.3

1 **a** $\{0, 1, 2, 3, 4, 5, 7\}$ **b** $\{7\}$ **c** $\varnothing$ **d** $\{1, 3, 7\}$
  e $\{1, 3, 7\}$ **f** $\{5, 6, 7, 8, 9\}$ **g** $\{6, 8, 9\}$
  h $\{6, 8, 9\}$

2 **a**    **b**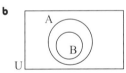

  c 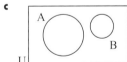   **d** not possible

  e    **f**

  g not possible

3 **a** Consider

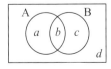

  where $n(A \cup B) = a + b + c$
          $n(A) = a + b$, etc.

c 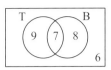   7 play both

EXERCISE 9A.4

1 **a** $\{o, n, u, a, c, e\}$ **b** $\{n, a\}$ **c** $\{c, j, g, t, e\}$
  d $\{c, o, j, u, g, t, e\}$ **e** $\{c, o, j, u, g, t, e\}$
  f $\{o, n, u, a\}$

2 **a** **i** 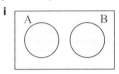   **ii**

  iii   **iv**

  b **i** 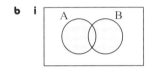   **ii**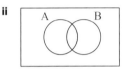

  iii 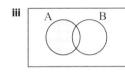   **iv**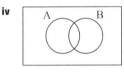

  c **i** 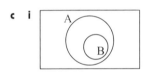   **ii**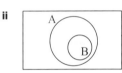

  iii 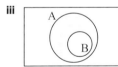   **iv**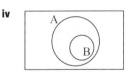

3 **a** 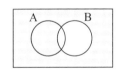   **b**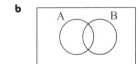

  c 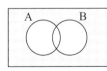   **d**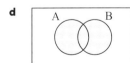

  e 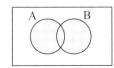   **f**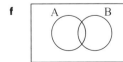

4 **a** **i** $\{2, 4\}$ **ii** $\varnothing$ **b** **i** $\{$irrational numbers$\}$ **ii** $\varnothing$
  c **i** $\{0, 1\}$ **ii** $\{4, 5\}$ **d** **i** $\{2, 3, 4\}$ **ii** $\{0, 1, 5\}$

5 a $\{b, c, d\}$ **b** $\{1, 2, 5\}$ **c** $\{1, 2, 3, 4, 5, 6\}$
   d $\{9, 11, 13\}$

EXERCISE 9B.1

1 a i $\{(1, 3), (1, 4), (1, 5), (2, 3), (2, 4), (2, 5)\}$
   ii $\{(3, 1), (3, 2), (4, 1), (4, 2), (5, 1), (5, 2)\}$
  b i $\{(a, a), (a, b)\}$ **ii** $\{(a, a), (b, a)\}$ **c i** $\varnothing$ **ii** $\varnothing$

2 a

b
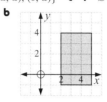

EXERCISE 9B.2

1 a domain $= \{0, 1, 2\}$ range $= \{2, 3, 5\}$
  b domain $= \{-3, -2, -1, 0, 1, 2, 3\}$
     range $= \{-3, -2\sqrt{2}, -\sqrt{5}, 0, \sqrt{5}, 2\sqrt{2}, 3\}$
  c domain $= \{x \mid x \in \mathbb{R}\}$
     range $= \{y \mid y \in \mathbb{R}, \ -1 \leqslant y \leqslant 1\}$

2 a $\{(2, 6), (2, 8), (3, 6), (4, 8), (5, 5)\}$
  b $\{(2, 5), (3, 6), (4, 7), (5, 8)\}$
  c $\{(2, 5), (2, 6), (2, 7), (2, 8), (3, 7), (3, 8)\}$

3 a i not reflexive **ii** not symmetric **iii** transitive
  b i not reflexive **ii** not symmetric **iii** transitive
  c i reflexive **ii** symmetric **iii** transitive
  d i reflexive **ii** symmetric **iii** transitive

4 a not reflexive **b** symmetric **c** not transitive

5 a i not reflexive **ii** symmetric **iii** not transitive
  b i reflexive **ii** not symmetric **iii** transitive
  c i reflexive **ii** symmetric **iii** transitive

EXERCISE 9B.3

1 a $a \equiv b \pmod{n} \ \Rightarrow \ a = b + k_1 n$ for some $k_1 \in \mathbb{Z}$
     Likewise
     $c \equiv d \pmod{n} \ \Rightarrow \ c = d + k_2 n$ for some $k_2 \in \mathbb{Z}$
     So $a + c = b + d + (k_1 + k_2)n$ where $k_1 + k_2 \in \mathbb{Z}$
     Thus, $a + c \equiv b + d \pmod{n}$
  b Likewise

2 $a = 1, \quad x = 1$ $a = 6, \quad x = 2$
    $a = 2, \quad x = 6$ $a = 7, \quad x = 8$
    $a = 3, \quad x = 4$ $a = 8, \quad x = 7$
    $a = 4, \quad x = 3$ $a = 9, \quad x = 5$
    $a = 5, \quad x = 9$ $a = 10, \quad x = 10$

3 b Every line in the plane will be in an equivalence class.
     For any given line the equivalence class will consist of
     all lines parallel to the given line.

4 a reflexive **b** not symmetric **c** not transitive

5 a $\{(a, a), (b, b), (c, c), (a, b), (b, c)\}$
  b $\{(a, b), (b, a), (a, c), (c, a)\}$ **c** $\{(a, b), (b, c), (a, c)\}$
  d $\{(a, a), (b, b), (c, c), (b, c), (c, b), (a, c), (c, a)\}$
  e $\{(a, a), (b, b), (c, c), (b, c), (c, a), (b, a)\}$
  f $\{(a, a), (b, b)\}$

Note: There are other possibilities for each of the above.

6 $(1, 1), (2, 2), (3, 3), (2, 1), (3, 2), (1, 3), (3, 1)$

8 R is an equivalence relation.

9 b Each point in $\mathbb{Z} \times \mathbb{Z}$ is related to all points above or
     below it. The equivalence classes are sets of points lying
     on vertical lines.

10 b Any point of $\mathbb{R} \times \mathbb{R} \setminus \{(0, 0)\}$ is related to all points on
     the line passing through the point and the origin. Each
     point is an element of exactly one equivalence class and
     consists of all points (excluding $(0, 0)$) lying on the line
     passing through O and the point.

11 b Any point of $\mathbb{R} \times \mathbb{R}$ is related to all points on the line
     through the point with gradient 3.
     Each point is an element of exactly one equivalence class
     containing all points which lie on the line through that
     point, with gradient 3.

EXERCISE 9C

1 a not a function **b** a function, not an injection
  c a function, an injection

2 a a function
     i not an injection **ii** a surjection **iii** not a bijection
  b a function **i** not an injection **ii** not a surjection
                    iii not a bijection
  c not a function
  d a function **i** not an injection **ii** not a surjection
                    iii not a bijection
  e a function
     i not an injection **ii** not a surjection **iii** a bijection

3 a both **b** surjection, but not an injection
  c surjection, but not an injection **d** both **e** both
  f injection, but not a surjection

4 a i 3 **ii** 0 **iii** 2 **iv** 1
  b i $\{(0, 2), (1, 0), (2, 1), (3, 3)\}$
    ii $\{(0, 2), (1, 3), (2, 0), (3, 1)\}$
    iii $\{(0, 1), (1, 3), (2, 2), (3, 0)\}$
    iv $\{(0, 1), (1, 3), (2, 2), (3, 0)\}$

5 a $[\ln(x + 1)]^2$ **b** $\ln(x^2 + 1)$ **c** $e^x - 1$ **d** $e^{\sqrt{x}} - 1$
  e $e^{\sqrt{x}} - 1$

EXERCISE 9D

1 a i 0 **ii** 2 **iii** -4 **iv** -6 **v** 0 **vi** 10 **vii** 10
  b i $x = -2$ **ii** $x = -1$

2 a not closed, e.g., $1 + i$ and $1 - i$ are in the set, but
     $(1 + i)(1 - i) = 2$ is not in the set
  b not closed, e.g., $2 + i$ and $1 + 2i$ are in the set, but
     $(2 + i)(1 + 2i) = 6i$ is not in the set
  c closed

3 a closed **b** closed
  c not closed, as for example $1 + 3 = 4$ is not an element
     of the set
  d closed The product of any two positive odds is always
     a positive odd. This is so as $2a - 1$, $2b - 1$ are odd if
     $a, b \in \mathbb{Z}^+$
     and $(2a - 1)(2b - 1) = 2(2ab - a - b) + 1$ which is
     odd as $2ab - b - b \in \mathbb{Z}$.
  e closed If $\dfrac{a}{b}, \ \dfrac{c}{d} \in \mathbb{Q}, \ a, b, c, d \in \mathbb{Z}, \ b \neq 0, \ d \neq 0,$
     then $\dfrac{a}{b} + \dfrac{c}{d} = \dfrac{ad + bc}{bd} \in \mathbb{Q}$, as $bd \neq 0$.
  f closed If $\dfrac{a}{b}, \ \dfrac{c}{d} \in \mathbb{Q}, \ a, b, c, d \in \mathbb{Z}, \ b \neq 0, \ d \neq 0,$
     then $\left(\dfrac{a}{b}\right)\left(\dfrac{c}{d}\right) = \dfrac{ac}{bd} \in \mathbb{Q}$, as $bd \neq 0$.

4

×₅	1	2	3	4
1	1	2	3	4
2	2	4	1	3
3	3	1	4	2
4	4	3	2	1

a $x = 3$
b $x = 2$
c $x = 3$
d $x = 4$

5 **a** If $a, b \in \mathbb{Q} \setminus \{1\}$, then a and b are rationals. Since $a + b$ and ab are rationals {$\mathbb{Q}$ is closed under $+, \times$}, also $a + b - ab \in \mathbb{Q}$ as $\mathbb{Q}$ is closed under $-$.

So it remains to show that
$$a - ab + b \neq 1 \quad \text{for } a \neq 1, \ b \neq 1$$
Now $a - 1 \neq 0$ and $b - 1 \neq 0$
$\therefore \ (a - 1)(b - 1) \neq 0$
$\Rightarrow \ ab - a - b + 1 \neq 0$
$\Rightarrow \ a - ab + b \neq 1$

b Show $(a \diamondsuit b) \diamondsuit c = a \diamondsuit (b \diamondsuit c)$ for all $a, b, c \in \mathbb{Q} \setminus \{1\}$

c Suppose $a \diamondsuit e = a$ for all $a \in \mathbb{Q} \setminus \{1\}$
$\Rightarrow \ a - ae + e = a$ for all $a \in \mathbb{Q} \setminus \{1\}$
$\Rightarrow \ e(1 - a) = 0$ for all $a \in \mathbb{Q} \setminus \{1\}$
$\Rightarrow \ e = 0$ as $a \neq 1$
Thus $a \diamondsuit 0 = a$ Also $0 \diamondsuit a = 0 - 0 + a = a$
Hence the identity is $e = 0$.

d Consider $a \diamondsuit x = e$
i.e., $a - ax + x = 0$
then $x(1 - a) = -a$ and so $x = \dfrac{a}{a - 1}$

Also $x \diamondsuit a = \dfrac{a}{a - 1} \diamondsuit a$

$= \dfrac{a}{a - 1} - \dfrac{a^2}{a - 1} + a$

$= \dfrac{a - a^2}{a - 1} + a$

$= -a \left(\dfrac{a - 1}{a - 1} \right) + a$

$= -a + a$ p.v. $a \neq 1$
$= 0$ as $a \neq 1$

Thus the inverse of $a \in \mathbb{Q} \setminus \{1\}$ is $\dfrac{a}{a - 1}$.

6 **a** 0 as $a + 0 = 0 + a = a$ for all $a \in \mathbb{R}$
b 1 as $a(1) = (1)a = a$ for all $a \in \mathbb{Z}$
c Consider $a * e = e * a = a$
then $e = a$ which is not unique and so e does not exist.
d Consider $a * e = e * a = a$
then $3ae = 3ea = a \Rightarrow e = \frac{1}{3}$
So, $\frac{1}{3}$ is the identity.

e Consider $a * e = e * a = a$
then $2a + ae + 2e = 2e + ea + 2a = a$
$\Rightarrow \ a + ae + 2e = 0$
$\Rightarrow \ e(a + 2) = -a$
$\Rightarrow \ e = \dfrac{-a}{a + 2}$ which is not unique and so e does not exist.

7 **a** The inverse of $a \in \mathbb{Q}$ is $-a \in \mathbb{Q}$
$\Rightarrow$ every element has an inverse in $\mathbb{Q}$.

b $0 \in \mathbb{Q}$ but 0 does not have an inverse under $\times$.

c No, for example 2 does not have an inverse under $\times$.
$2 \times x = 1$ where $x \in \mathbb{Z}^+$ is impossible.

d Suppose $a * e = e * a = a$ for all $a \in \mathbb{R}$
then $2ae = 2ea = a$ for all $a \in \mathbb{R}$
$\Rightarrow \ e = \frac{1}{2}$
If $a * x = e$, then $2ax = \frac{1}{2} \Rightarrow x = \dfrac{1}{4a}$
So $a = 0$ does not have an inverse.

8 **a** Show that
$$[(a, b) * (c, d)] * (g, h) = (a, b) * [(c, d) * (g, h)]$$
b Suppose $(a, b) * (e, f) = (a, b)$
and deduce that $e = 1$
Hence, deduce that $f = 0$
Check that $(1, 0) * (a, b) = (a, b)$ also.
So, $(1, 0)$ is the identity.

c $(0, 0)$ has no inverse as
$(a, b) * (0, 0) = (1, 0)$
$\Rightarrow \ (0, 0) = (1, 0)$ a contradiction

d $(a, b) * (c, d) = (ac - bd, ad + bc)$
$(c, d) * (a, b) = (ca - db, cb + da)$
and since $xy = yx$, $x + y = y + x$ for reals,
$*$ is commutative.

9 **a** **i** a is the identity
ii a has inverse a, b and c are inverses
iii $*$ is commutative (symmetry about the leading diagonal)
iv We need to check all 27 possibilities of $(x * y) * z$ and $x * (y * z)$ where $x, y, z \in \{a, b, c\}$. When this is done we find that $*$ is associative.

b **i** b is the identity
ii a has no inverse, b is its own inverse, c is its own inverse
iii $*$ is commutative (symmetry about the leading diagonal)
iv We need to check all 27 possibilities of $(x * y) * z$ and $x * (y * z)$ where $x, y, z \in \{a, b, c\}$. When this is done we find that $*$ is associative.

c **i** no identity exists
ii without an identity no inverses are possible
iii $*$ is commutative (symmetry about leading diagonal)
iv Not associative as, for example,
$(a * b) * c = c$ and
$a * (b * c) = a$
i.e., in general $(x * y) * z \neq x * (y * z)$
where $x, y, z \in \{a, b, c\}$.

d **i** b is the identity
ii a and c are inverses, b is its own inverse
iii $*$ is commutative (symmetry about leading diagonal)
iv Not associative as, for example,
$(a * c) * c = b * c = c$ and
$a * (c * c) = a * c = b$
i.e., $(a * c) * c \neq a * (c * c)$

e **i** no identity exists
ii without an identity no inverses can exist
iii $*$ is not commutative as there is no symmetry about the leading diagonal)
iv Not associative as, for example,
$(c * b) * a = a * a = b$ and
$c * (b * a) = c * a = c$
i.e., $(c * b) * a \neq c * (b * a)$

EXERCISE 9E.1

1 **a** An Abelian group with identity 1.
  b Not a group as each element does not have an inverse in the set.
  c An Abelian group with identity $3^0 = 1$.
  d An Abelian group with identity 1.
  e An Abelian group with identity 0.
  f Not a group as $0 \in S$ does not have a multiplicative inverse.
  g An Abelian group with identity $0 = 0 + 0i$
  h Not a group as $0 \in \mathbb{C}$ and 0 does not have a multiplicative inverse.
  i An Abelian group with identity $1 = 1 + 0i$.
  j Not a group as for example $\begin{bmatrix} 1 & 2 \\ 2 & 4 \end{bmatrix}$ does not have an inverse.

2 $\alpha = \frac{1}{2} + \frac{i\sqrt{3}}{2}, \quad \alpha^2 = -\frac{1}{2} + \frac{i\sqrt{3}}{2}, \quad \alpha^3 = -1,$
  $\alpha^4 = -\frac{1}{2} - \frac{i\sqrt{3}}{2}, \quad \alpha^5 = \frac{1}{2} - \frac{i\sqrt{3}}{2}, \quad \alpha^6 = 1$
  $S = \{1, \alpha, \alpha^2, \alpha^3, \alpha^4, \alpha^5\}$

The Cayley table is:

$\times$	1	α	α^2	α^3	α^4	α^5
1	1	α	α^2	α^3	α^4	α^5
α	α	α^2	α^3	α^4	α^5	1
α^2	α^2	α^3	α^4	α^5	1	α
α^3	α^3	α^4	α^5	1	α	α^2
α^4	α^4	α^5	1	α	α^2	α^3
α^5	α^5	1	α	α^2	α^3	α^4

Is an Abelian group.

Closure: When two elements are multiplied the result is also in S.

Associative: Multiplication of complex numbers is associative.

Identity: α and α^5 are inverses, α^2 and α^4 are inverses 1 and α^3 are their own inverses

Since $\times$ for complex numbers is commutative, we have an Abelian group.

EXERCISE 9E.2

1 $\{0, 1, 2\}$ under $+_3$
The identity is 0.

$+_3$	0	1	2
0	0	1	2
1	1	2	0
2	2	0	1

$\{0, 1, 2\}$ under $-_3$ would also have identity 0.

Possible tables are

$-_3$	0	1	2
0	0	1	2
1	1	0	2
2	2	1	0

$-_3$	0	2	1
0	0	1	2
2	2	0	1
1	1	2	0

Neither of these tables have the same structure as the first one. So, the groups are not isomorphic.

2 If $\alpha = -\frac{1}{2} + \frac{i\sqrt{3}}{2}, \quad \alpha^2 = -\frac{1}{2} - \frac{i\sqrt{3}}{2}, \quad \alpha^3 = 1$

$\{1, \alpha, \alpha^2\}$ under $\times$

$\times$	1	α	α^2
1	1	α	α^2
α	α	α^2	1
α^2	α^2	1	α

$\{1, 2, 4\}$ under $\times_7$

$\times_7$	1	2	4
1	1	2	4
2	2	4	1
4	4	1	2

So $1 \leftrightarrow 1$
  $\alpha \leftrightarrow 2$
  $\alpha^2 \leftrightarrow 4$

The tables are identical in structure
$\Rightarrow$ groups are isomorphic.

3 $\{0, 1, 2, 3, 4\}$
under $+_5$

$+_5$	0	1	2	3	4
0	0	1	2	3	4
1	1	2	3	4	0
2	2	3	4	0	1
3	3	4	0	1	2
4	4	0	1	2	3

$\{1, \alpha, \alpha^2, \alpha^3, \alpha^4\}$
under $\times$

$\times$	1	α	α^2	α^3	α^4
1	1	α	α^2	α^3	α^4
α	α	α^2	α^3	α^4	1
α^2	α^2	α^3	α^4	1	α
α^3	α^3	α^4	1	α	α^2
α^4	α^4	1	α	α^2	α^3

So, $0 \leftrightarrow 1, \quad 1 \leftrightarrow \alpha, \quad 2 \leftrightarrow \alpha^2, \quad 3 \leftrightarrow \alpha^3, \quad 4 \leftrightarrow \alpha^4$
The tables have identical structure
$\Rightarrow$ groups are isomorphic.

4 Letting the matrices be $\mathbf{M}_1, \mathbf{M}_2, \mathbf{M}_3$ and $\mathbf{M}_4$ respectively.
$\{\mathbf{M}_1, \mathbf{M}_2, \mathbf{M}_3, \mathbf{M}_4\}$
under $\times$ is

$\times$	$\mathbf{M}_1$	$\mathbf{M}_2$	$\mathbf{M}_3$	$\mathbf{M}_4$
$\mathbf{M}_1$	$\mathbf{M}_1$	$\mathbf{M}_2$	$\mathbf{M}_3$	$\mathbf{M}_4$
$\mathbf{M}_2$	$\mathbf{M}_2$	$\mathbf{M}_1$	$\mathbf{M}_4$	$\mathbf{M}_3$
$\mathbf{M}_3$	$\mathbf{M}_3$	$\mathbf{M}_4$	$\mathbf{M}_1$	$\mathbf{M}_2$
$\mathbf{M}_4$	$\mathbf{M}_4$	$\mathbf{M}_3$	$\mathbf{M}_2$	$\mathbf{M}_1$

$\{1, 3, 5, 7\}$
under $\times_8$ is

$\times_8$	1	3	5	7
1	1	3	5	7
3	3	1	7	5
5	5	7	1	3
7	7	5	3	1

$\mathbf{M}_1 \leftrightarrow 1$
$\mathbf{M}_2 \leftrightarrow 3$
$\mathbf{M}_3 \leftrightarrow 5$
$\mathbf{M}_4 \leftrightarrow 7$

The tables have identical structure
$\Rightarrow$ the groups are isomorphic.

5 $G = \{\mathbb{R}^+, \times\}$ is a group and $H = \{\mathbb{R}, +\}$ is a group
  • $f : x \mapsto \ln x$ is a bijection
  • $f(ab) = \ln(ab)$
    $= \ln a + \ln b$
    $= f(a) + f(b)$ for all $a, b \in G$

So, by definition, G and H are isomorphic.

EXERCISE 9E.3

1 **a** 2 **b** 2, 3 **c** 3, 5 **d** 2, 6, 7, 8

2 If $\alpha = -\frac{1}{2} + \frac{\sqrt{3}}{2}i, \quad \alpha^2 = -\frac{1}{2} - \frac{\sqrt{3}}{2}i, \quad \alpha^3 = 1$

$\begin{bmatrix} \alpha & 0 \\ 0 & -1 \end{bmatrix}^2 = \begin{bmatrix} \alpha^2 & 0 \\ 0 & 1 \end{bmatrix}$ and $\begin{bmatrix} \alpha & 0 \\ 0 & -1 \end{bmatrix}^3 = \begin{bmatrix} 1 & 0 \\ 0 & 1 \end{bmatrix}$

So, $G = \left\{ \begin{bmatrix} 1 & 0 \\ 0 & 1 \end{bmatrix}, \begin{bmatrix} \alpha & 0 \\ 0 & -1 \end{bmatrix}, \begin{bmatrix} \alpha^2 & 0 \\ 0 & 1 \end{bmatrix} \right\}$ under

matrix multiplication
is a cyclic group.

$\times$	$\mathbf{M}_1$	$\mathbf{M}_2$	$\mathbf{M}_3$
$\mathbf{M}_1$	$\mathbf{M}_1$	$\mathbf{M}_2$	$\mathbf{M}_3$
$\mathbf{M}_2$	$\mathbf{M}_2$	$\mathbf{M}_3$	$\mathbf{M}_1$
$\mathbf{M}_3$	$\mathbf{M}_3$	$\mathbf{M}_1$	$\mathbf{M}_2$

EXERCISE 9E.4

1 b no
   c $\{1\}, \{1, 5\}, \{1, 7\}, \{1, 11\}, \{1, 5, 7, 11\}$ under $\times_{12}$ are subgroups

3 b no **c i** a subgroup **ii** a subgroup

EXERCISE 9F.1

1 a $\begin{pmatrix} 1 & 2 & 3 & 4 \\ 3 & 4 & 2 & 1 \end{pmatrix}$ **b** $\begin{pmatrix} 1 & 2 & 3 & 4 \\ 4 & 1 & 2 & 3 \end{pmatrix}$

   c $\begin{pmatrix} 1 & 2 & 3 & 4 \\ 1 & 2 & 3 & 4 \end{pmatrix}$ **d** $\begin{pmatrix} 1 & 2 & 3 & 4 \\ 2 & 4 & 1 & 3 \end{pmatrix}$

2 a $\begin{pmatrix} 1 & 2 & 3 & 4 \\ 2 & 4 & 1 & 3 \end{pmatrix}$ **b** $\begin{pmatrix} 1 & 2 & 3 & 4 \\ 2 & 1 & 4 & 3 \end{pmatrix}$ **c** $\begin{pmatrix} 1 & 2 & 3 & 4 \\ 2 & 4 & 3 & 1 \end{pmatrix}$

4 a $p = \begin{pmatrix} 1 & 2 & 3 & 4 \\ 4 & 1 & 2 & 3 \end{pmatrix}$ **b** $p = \begin{pmatrix} 1 & 2 & 3 & 4 \\ 1 & 2 & 4 & 3 \end{pmatrix}$

5 a

	A	B	C	D
A	A	B	C	D
B	B	C	D	A
C	C	D	A	B
D	D	A	B	C

closed, identity **A**,
inverse of **A** is **A**
of **B** is **D**
of **C** is **C**
of **D** is **B**

Is isomorphic to $\{0, 1, 2, 3\}$ under $+_4$.

$+_4$	0	1	2	3
0	0	1	2	3
1	1	2	3	0
2	2	3	0	1
3	3	0	1	2

a known Abelian
group
{**Example 55**}

$\mathbf{B}^1 = \mathbf{B}, \quad \mathbf{B}^2 = \mathbf{C}, \quad \mathbf{B}^3 = \mathbf{CB} = \mathbf{D}, \quad \mathbf{B}^4 = \mathbf{DB} = \mathbf{A}$

So, is a cyclic group.

b

	A	B	C	D
A	A	B	C	D
B	B	A	D	C
C	C	D	A	B
D	D	C	B	A

is isomorphic to

$\times_8$	1	3	5	7
1	1	3	5	7
3	3	1	7	5
5	5	7	1	3
7	7	5	3	1

which is a group

So, is a group, but is not cyclic.

$\{1, 3, 5, 7\}$ under $\times_8$ is easily checked to be non-cyclic.

EXERCISE 9F.2

2 • Anti-clockwise rotation about the centre of the rectangle through $0°$.
   • Likewise but through $180°$.

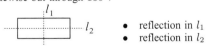

   • reflection in l_1
   • reflection in l_2

REVIEW SET 9A

1 a $\{a, b, c, d, e, f, g, h\}$ **b** $\{a, b, d, f\}$
   c $\{a, b, d, f, g, h\}$

2 $A \times B = \{(1, 2), (1, 4), (2, 2), (2, 4), (3, 2), (3, 4)\}$

6 $\{\varnothing, \{1\}, \{2\}, \{3\}, \{1, 2\}, \{1, 3\}, \{2, 3\}, \{1, 2, 3\}\}$
   a no **b** no

7 a No, e.g., $(1 * 2) * 1 = 3 * 1 = \frac{4}{9}$
   whereas $1 * (2 * 1) = 1 * \frac{3}{4} = \frac{7}{4}$
   i.e., $(1 * 2) * 1 \neq 1 * (2 * 1)$

b No, e.g., $(0 * 1) * 2 = 2 * 2 = 2^4$
   $0 * (1 * 2) = 0 * 8 = 2^8$
   i.e., $(0 * 1) * 2 \neq 0 * (1 * 2)$

   c Yes, $(a * b) * c$
   $= (a + b - 3ab) * c$
   $= a + b + c - 3ab - 3(a + b - 3ab)c$
   $= a + b + c - 3ab - 3ac - 3bc + 9abc$ .... (1)
   and likewise show $a * (b * c)$ is also equal to (1).

8 b Each integer belongs to exactly one equivalence class containing all integers which have the same remainder on division by 6 as that integer. These are the six equivalence classes [0], [1], [2], [3], [4] and [5].

9 b Each point (a, b) is an element of an equivalence class containing all points lying on a square, centre $(0, 0)$ with vertex at $(|a| + |b|, 0)$.
   $\{(0, 0)\}$ is an equivalence class with only 1 element.

10 b Each point (a, b) belongs to an equivalence class consisting of all points on the parabola $y = \dfrac{b}{a^2} x$, excluding $(0, 0)$ where $\dfrac{b}{a^2} > 0$.

11 Not correct as this does not show that $x \, R \, x$ for all $x \in S$. x may not be related to any other element in the set.

12

*	0	1	2	3	4	5
0	0	0	0	0	0	0
1	1	2	3	4	5	0
2	4	0	2	4	0	2
3	3	0	3	0	3	0
4	4	2	0	4	2	0
5	1	0	5	4	3	2

13 a i no **ii** yes **iii** does not exist **iv** not possible
   b i no **ii** no **iii** does not exist **iv** not possible
   c i no **ii** yes **iii** does not exist **iv** not possible
   d i no **ii** no **iii** does not exist **iv** not possible
   e i yes **ii** yes **iii** 0 **iv** $-\dfrac{a}{1 + 3a}, \ a \neq -\frac{1}{3}$
   f i no **ii** no **iii** does not exist **iv** not possible

14 a yes, $f^{-1}(x) = \sqrt[3]{x - 5}$ **b** yes, $f^{-1}(x) = e^x$
   c no **d** yes, $f^{-1}(x) = \frac{1}{2}x$ **e** no

15 a i $\begin{pmatrix} 1 & 2 & 3 & 4 \\ 2 & 1 & 4 & 3 \end{pmatrix}$ **ii** $\begin{pmatrix} 1 & 2 & 3 & 4 \\ 3 & 4 & 1 & 2 \end{pmatrix}$

   b i $\begin{pmatrix} 1 & 2 & 3 & 4 \\ 1 & 4 & 2 & 3 \end{pmatrix}$ **ii** $\begin{pmatrix} 1 & 2 & 3 & 4 \\ 3 & 1 & 2 & 4 \end{pmatrix}$ **c** $n = 3$

16 *Associativity* holds as 2×2 matrix multiplication is associative.
   Closure holds as the product of any 2×2 matrix is always a 2×2 matrix.
   $\begin{bmatrix} 1 & 0 \\ 0 & 1 \end{bmatrix} = \mathbf{I}$ is the *identity* matrix, $a = 0$.

   The *inverse* of $\begin{bmatrix} 1 & a \\ 0 & 1 \end{bmatrix}$ is $\begin{bmatrix} 1 & -a \\ 0 & 1 \end{bmatrix}$ for all $a \in \mathbb{Z}$.

   $\begin{bmatrix} 1 & a \\ 0 & 1 \end{bmatrix} \begin{bmatrix} 1 & b \\ 0 & 1 \end{bmatrix} = \begin{bmatrix} 1 & a + b \\ 0 & 1 \end{bmatrix} = \begin{bmatrix} 1 & b \\ 0 & 1 \end{bmatrix} \begin{bmatrix} 1 & a \\ 0 & 1 \end{bmatrix}$

   for all $a, b \in \mathbb{Z}$.
   $\Rightarrow$ *commutativity* holds

   Thus, M under matrix multiplication forms an Abelian group.

17 $S = \left\{ \begin{bmatrix} a & b \\ c & d \end{bmatrix} \mid a, b, c, d \in \mathbb{R}, \; ad - bc = 1 \right\}$

Associativity holds for 2×2 matrices under $\times$.
The product of two such matrices is another matrix where
$|\mathbf{AB}| = |\mathbf{A}| \, |\mathbf{B}| = 1 \times 1 = 1$.
$\Rightarrow$ *closure* under $\times$.

$\mathbf{I} = \begin{bmatrix} 1 & 0 \\ 0 & 1 \end{bmatrix}$ has $|\mathbf{I}| = 1$, is the *identity* under $\times$.

If $\mathbf{A} = \begin{bmatrix} a & b \\ c & d \end{bmatrix}$, $\mathbf{A}^{-1} = \begin{bmatrix} d & -b \\ -c & a \end{bmatrix} \in S$ is the

multiplication inverse as $|\mathbf{A}^{-1}| = ad - bc = |\mathbf{A}| = 1$.

Thus S under matrix multiplication forms a group.

19

$\times$	$\mathbf{M}_1$	$\mathbf{M}_2$	$\mathbf{M}_3$	$\mathbf{M}_4$
$\mathbf{M}_1$	$\mathbf{M}_1$	$\mathbf{M}_2$	$\mathbf{M}_3$	$\mathbf{M}_4$
$\mathbf{M}_2$	$\mathbf{M}_2$	$\mathbf{M}_3$	$\mathbf{M}_4$	$\mathbf{M}_1$
$\mathbf{M}_3$	$\mathbf{M}_3$	$\mathbf{M}_4$	$\mathbf{M}_1$	$\mathbf{M}_2$
$\mathbf{M}_4$	$\mathbf{M}_4$	$\mathbf{M}_1$	$\mathbf{M}_2$	$\mathbf{M}_3$

Show that this table is isomorphic to another known group.

20 a *Assoc.* holds for multiplication of all 3×3 matrices.

As

$\begin{bmatrix} 1 & k & 0 \\ 0 & 1 & 0 \\ 0 & 0 & 2^n \end{bmatrix} \begin{bmatrix} 1 & l & 0 \\ 0 & 1 & 0 \\ 0 & 0 & 2^m \end{bmatrix} = \begin{bmatrix} 1 & l+k & 0 \\ 0 & 1 & 0 \\ 0 & 0 & 2^{n+m} \end{bmatrix}$

S is *closed* under matrix multiplication.

$\begin{bmatrix} 1 & 0 & 0 \\ 0 & 1 & 0 \\ 0 & 0 & 1 \end{bmatrix}$ is the *identity* matrix and is in S $\{k = 0, \; n = 0\}$

$\begin{bmatrix} 1 & -k & 0 \\ 0 & 1 & 0 \\ 0 & 0 & 2^{-n} \end{bmatrix}$ is the multiplicative *inverse* of

$\begin{bmatrix} 1 & k & 0 \\ 0 & 1 & 0 \\ 0 & 0 & 2^n \end{bmatrix}$ and it lies in S.

So, $\{S, \times\}$ is a group.

b *Associativity* holds for all 3×3 matrix multiplication.

As $\begin{bmatrix} 1 & n & \frac{1}{2}n^2 \\ 0 & 1 & n \\ 0 & 0 & 1 \end{bmatrix} \begin{bmatrix} 1 & m & \frac{1}{2}m^2 \\ 0 & 1 & m \\ 0 & 0 & 1 \end{bmatrix}$

$= \begin{bmatrix} 1 & m+n & \frac{1}{2}m^2 + mn + \frac{1}{2}n^2 \\ 0 & 1 & m+n \\ 0 & 0 & 1 \end{bmatrix}$

$= \begin{bmatrix} 1 & m+n & \frac{1}{2}(m+n)^2 \\ 0 & 1 & m+n \\ 0 & 0 & 1 \end{bmatrix}$

S is *closed* under multiplication.

$\begin{bmatrix} 1 & 0 & 0 \\ 0 & 1 & 0 \\ 0 & 0 & 1 \end{bmatrix}$ where $n = 0$ is the *inverse* matrix

$\begin{bmatrix} 1 & -n & \frac{1}{2}n^2 \\ 0 & 1 & -n \\ 0 & 0 & 1 \end{bmatrix}$ is the *inverse* of $\begin{bmatrix} 1 & n & \frac{1}{2}n^2 \\ 0 & 1 & n \\ 0 & 0 & 1 \end{bmatrix}$

under matrix multiplication.

$\Rightarrow$ $\{S, \times\}$ is a group.

21

$\circ$	f_1	f_2	f_3	f_4
f_1	f_1	f_2	f_3	f_4
f_2	f_2	f_1	f_4	f_3
f_3	f_3	f_4	f_1	f_2
f_4	f_4	f_3	f_2	f_1

Show that this table is isomorphic to another known group.

22 b 1 has order 1, 3 has order 6, 5 has order 6, 9 has order 3, 11 has order 3, 13 has order 2
c yes

23 Produce a Cayley table and establish an isomorphism with a known group.

24 *Associativity* holds for multiplication of rationals.
$\left(\dfrac{2a_1 + 1}{2b_1 + 1} \right) \left(\dfrac{2a_2 + 1}{2b_2 + 1} \right) = \dfrac{2(a_1 a_2 + a_1 + a_2) + 1}{2(b_1 b_2 + b_1 + b_2) + 1}$
establishes closure $(a_1, b_1, a_2, b_2 \in \mathbb{Z})$.

$1 = \dfrac{2(0) + 1}{2(0) + 1}$ is the multiplicative *identity*.

The *inverse* of $\dfrac{2a + 1}{2b + 1}$ is $\dfrac{2b + 1}{2a + 1}$ and $\dfrac{2b + 1}{2a + 1} \in S$.

$\Rightarrow$ $\{S, \times\}$ is a group.

25 Associativity does not apply.

REVIEW SET 9B

1 a $\{3, 6\}$ **b** $\{0, 1, 5, 6, 9, 12\}$
c $\{0, 1, 3, 5, 7, 8, 9, 10, 11, 12, 13\}$
d $\{0, 1, 3, 5, 6, 8, 9, 10, 12\}$ **e** $\{1, 5, 8, 10\}$

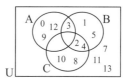

a

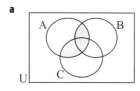

b

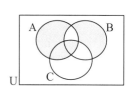

c

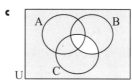

d

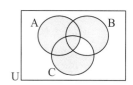

e

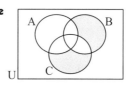

3 $\{\varnothing, \{1\}, \{2\}, \{1, 2\}\}$ **a** no **b** no
4 a $\{(0, 0), (1, 1), (2, 2), (3, 3), (4, 4), (5, 5), (0, 1), (1, 0),$
$(0, 2), (2, 0), (1, 2), (1, 3), (3, 1), (2, 3), (3, 2),$
$(2, 4), (4, 2), (3, 5), (5, 3), (4, 5), (5, 4)\}$

b **i** yes **ii** yes **iii** no

5 **b** Each point (a, b) belongs to an equivalence class consisting of all points on the circle, centre $(0, 0)$, radius $\sqrt{a^2 + b^2}$.

$\{(0, 0)\}$ is an equivalence class containing one element.

6 **b** Each point (a, b) belong to an equivalence class consisting of all points with integer coordinates lying in a horizontal line passing through (a, b).

7 **a** **i** injection **ii** surjection
b **i** not an injection **ii** not a surjection
c **i** not an injection **ii** a surjection
d **i** injection **ii** not a surjection

8 **a** 2 **b** 4 **c** 3

9

×	A	B	C	D
A	A	B	C	D
B	B	A	D	C
C	C	D	A	B
D	D	C	B	A

10 **b** 1 has order 1, 7 has order 2, **c** not cyclic
9 has order 2, 15 has order 2

11 Cayley table is

∘	f_1	f_2	f_3	f_4	f_5	f_6
f_1	f_1	f_2	f_3	f_4	f_5	f_6
f_2	f_2		f_1	f_3	f_4	f_5
f_3	f_3					
f_4	f_4	f_5	f_6	f_1	f_2	f_3
f_5	f_5					
f_6	f_6					

12 **b** no **c** m^3

13 **a** $(a, b) * (c, d) = (ac, bc + d)$
$\Rightarrow \quad [(a, b) * (c, d)] * (e, f)$
$= (ac, bc + d) * (e, f)$
$= (ace, bce + de + f)$
and $\quad (a, b) * [(c, d) * (e, f)]$
$= (a, b) * (ce, de + f)$
$= (ace, bce + de + f)$
$\therefore \quad *$ is associative

b $(1, 2) * (2, 3) = (2, 4 + 3) = (2, 7)$
$(2, 3) * (1, 2) = (2, 3 + 2) = (2, 5)$
$\therefore \quad *$ is not commutative

c If $(a, b) * (x, y) = (a, b)$ then
$(ax, bx + y) = (a, b)$
$\Rightarrow \quad x = 1, \quad y = 0$
also $(1, 0) * (a, b) = (a, (0)a + b) = (a, b)$
$\therefore$ identity is $(1, 0)$.

d Consider $(a, b) * (x, y) = (1, 0)$
$\Rightarrow \quad (ax, bx + y) = (1, 0)$
$\Rightarrow \quad x = \dfrac{1}{a}, \quad \dfrac{b}{a} + y = 0$
$y = -\dfrac{b}{a}$
Suggesting that $(\dfrac{1}{a}, -\dfrac{b}{a})$, $a \neq 0$ is the inverse of (a, b).
Check: $(\dfrac{1}{a}, -\dfrac{b}{a}) * (a, b) = (1, -b + b) = (1, 0)$ ✓

14

×	I	A	B
I	I	A	B
A	A	B	I
B	B	I	A

16 **a** $x = 3, 5$ or 6 **b** $x = 30$ **c** $x = 1, 3$ **d** $x = 2, 7$
17 **a** 3 **b** 2 **c** 2
18 $\{S, \times\}$ is a subgroup of G
19 **a** a group **b** not a group
20 **a** 1, 2 **b** 1, 2, 3, 4 **c** 1, 5
21 **b** no **c** **i** yes **ii** yes **d** **i** yes **ii** yes
25 **a** $x = 2$ **b** $x = 2, 4$
26 **a** **i** not associative **ii** commutative **iii** no identity
iv no inverses
b **i** associative **ii** commutative **iii** no identity
iv no inverses
c **i** not associative **ii** commutative **iii** no identity
iv no inverses
d **i** not associative **ii** commutative **iii** no identity
iv no inverses
e **i** not associative **ii** not commutative
iii no identity **iv** no inverses
f **i** not commutative **ii** commutative **iii** no identity
iv no inverses

27 Not groups: **a**, **b**, **c**, **f**, **g** Groups: **d**, **e**

28 **a** **i**

$\times_9$	1	2	4	5	7	8
1	1	2	4	5	7	8
2	2	4	8	1	5	7
4	4	8	7	2	1	5
5	5	1	2	7	8	4
7	7	5	1	8	4	2
8	8	7	5	4	2	1

b **i**

$\times_{16}$	1	5	9	13
1	1	5	9	13
5	5	9	13	1
9	9	13	1	5
13	13	1	5	9

c **i**

$\times_{20}$	1	9	11	19
1	1	9	11	19
9	9	1	19	11
11	11	19	1	9
19	19	11	9	1

d **i**

$\times_{20}$	1	3	7	9
1	1	3	7	9
3	3	9	1	7
7	7	1	9	3
9	9	7	3	1

e **i**

$\times_{20}$	1	9	13	17
1	1	9	13	17
9	9	1	17	13
13	13	17	9	1
17	17	13	1	9

b, **d** and **e** are isomorphic.

EXERCISE 10A.1

1 Use the definition $|a| = \begin{cases} a & \text{if } a \geqslant 0 \\ -a & \text{if } a < 0 \end{cases}$

2 Same hint as in **1**.

4 If $a < x < b$ and $a < y < b$ then $-b < -y < -a$
and so
$$a - b < x - y < b - a$$
$$\Rightarrow -(b - a) < x - y < b - a$$
$$\Rightarrow |x - y| < b - a$$

If two points lie in a particular interval on a number line, then the distance between them must be less than the width of the interval.

5 $|a - b| = |(a - c) + (c - b)|$
   $\leqslant |a - c| + |c - b|$ {triangle inequality}

6 $|x - a| < \dfrac{a}{2} \Rightarrow -\dfrac{a}{2} < x - a < \dfrac{a}{2}$ {since $a > 0$}
   $$\Rightarrow \frac{a}{2} < x < \frac{3a}{2}$$
   $$\Rightarrow x > \frac{a}{2}$$

7 $|(x + y) - (a + b)|$
   $= |(x - a) + (y - b)|$
   $\leqslant |x - a| + |y - b|$ {triangle inequality}
   $< \varepsilon + \varepsilon$
   i.e., $< 2\varepsilon$

8 Let $b = 1$ and $a = \varepsilon$, then by the AP there exists n
   such that $n\varepsilon > 1 \Rightarrow \dfrac{1}{n} < \varepsilon$.

9 Use Proof by Mathematical Induction.

10 Consider $A =]0, 1[$, a subset of $\mathbb{R}^+$.
   Suppose α is the least element of A.
   Then as $\alpha > 0$, $0 < \dfrac{\alpha}{2} < \alpha$ where $\dfrac{\alpha}{2} \in A$.
   We have a contradiction as α was the least element of A.

11 Suppose $r + x$ is rational.
   $$\Rightarrow r + x = \frac{a}{b}, \quad b \neq 0, \quad a, b \in \mathbb{Z}$$
   $$\Rightarrow x = \frac{a}{b} - r \text{ which } \in \mathbb{Q}, \text{ a contradiction}$$
   Similarly, suppose $rx = \dfrac{c}{d}, \quad d \neq 0, \quad c, d \in \mathbb{Z}$
   $$\Rightarrow x = \frac{c}{dr}, \text{ which } \in \mathbb{Q}, \text{ a contradiction.}$$

EXERCISE 10A.2

1 a 5 **b** 0 **c** 0 **d** $\frac{1}{2}\ln 2$ **e** $\frac{7}{4}$ **f** 1

2 a $\frac{1}{2}$ **b** $\frac{1}{2}$ **c** 1 **d** 1 **e** $\frac{1}{2}$ **f** 0 **g** ∞ **h** 0
   i 0 **j** $\ln\left(\frac{a}{b}\right)$

3 $\lim\limits_{x \to \frac{\pi}{2}^-} \dfrac{\tan x}{\sec x}$

   $= \lim\limits_{x \to \frac{\pi}{2}^-} \dfrac{\sec^2 x}{\sec x \tan x}$ {L'Hôpital's Rule}

   $= \lim\limits_{x \to \frac{\pi}{2}^-} \dfrac{\sec x}{\tan x}$

   $= \lim\limits_{x \to \frac{\pi}{2}^-} \dfrac{\sec x \tan x}{\sec^2 x}$ {L'Hôpital's Rule}

   $= \lim\limits_{x \to \frac{\pi}{2}^-} \dfrac{\tan x}{\sec x}$ which goes nowhere.

But, $\dfrac{\tan x}{\sec x} = \dfrac{\sin x}{\cos x} \div \dfrac{1}{\cos x} = \sin x$

$\Rightarrow \lim\limits_{x \to \frac{\pi}{2}^-} \dfrac{\tan x}{\sec x} = \lim\limits_{x \to \frac{\pi}{2}^-} \sin x = 1$

4 $\qquad x \ln\left(1 + \dfrac{1}{x}\right) = x \ln\left(\dfrac{1 + x}{x}\right)$

   $\qquad\qquad\qquad\qquad = \dfrac{\ln(1 + x) - \ln x}{x^{-1}}$

   $\Rightarrow \lim\limits_{x \to \infty} x \ln\left(1 + \dfrac{1}{x}\right) = \lim\limits_{x \to \infty} \dfrac{\dfrac{1}{1 + x} - \dfrac{1}{x}}{-\dfrac{1}{x^2}}$

   $\qquad\qquad\qquad\qquad\qquad$ {L'Hôpital's Rule}

   $\qquad\qquad\qquad\qquad = \lim\limits_{x \to \infty} \dfrac{\dfrac{-1}{x(1 + x)}}{-\dfrac{1}{x^2}}$

   $\qquad\qquad\qquad\qquad = \lim\limits_{x \to \infty} \dfrac{x}{1 + x}$

   $\qquad\qquad\qquad\qquad = \lim\limits_{x \to \infty} \dfrac{1}{1}$ {L'Hôpital's Rule}

   $\qquad\qquad\qquad\qquad = 1$

   Now $\left(1 + \dfrac{1}{x}\right)^x = e^{\ln(1 + \frac{1}{x})^x} = e^{x \ln(1 + \frac{1}{x})}$

   $\Rightarrow \lim\limits_{x \to \infty} \left(1 + \dfrac{1}{x}\right)^x = \lim\limits_{x \to \infty} e^{x \ln(1 + \frac{1}{x})} = e^1 = e$

5 Let $a \in \mathbb{Q}$ and $\{x_n\}$ be a sequence of irrational numbers that converges to a.
   Since $f(x_n) = 0$ for all $n \in \mathbb{Z}^+$, $\lim\limits_{n \to \infty} f(x_n) = 0$
   which is $\neq f(a) = 1$.
   So, $f(x)$ is discontinuous at all rational points.

EXERCISE 10A.3

1 a For $x \geqslant 1$, show that $0 < \dfrac{x}{2x^5 + 3x^2 + 1} < \dfrac{1}{2x^4}$
   and $\displaystyle\int_1^\infty \dfrac{1}{2x^4}\, dx = \frac{1}{6}$.
   As $\displaystyle\int_1^\infty \dfrac{1}{2x^4}\, dx$ converges, so does
   $\displaystyle\int_1^\infty \dfrac{1}{2x^5 + 3x^2 + 1}\, dx$.

b Converges

2 $\left|\dfrac{\sin x}{x^3}\right| \leqslant \dfrac{1}{x^3}$. Show that $\displaystyle\int_1^\infty \dfrac{1}{x^3}\, dx$ converges.
   Hence $\displaystyle\int_1^\infty \left|\dfrac{\sin x}{x^3}\right|\, dx$ and $\displaystyle\int_1^\infty \dfrac{\sin x}{x^3}\, dx$ converge.

3 a converges **b** converges **c** diverges **d** converges

4 Consider $p = 1$ first. Use integration by parts to show that the integral diverges.
   Consider $p < 1$. Use integration by parts to show that
   $$\int_e^\infty \frac{\ln x}{x^p}\, dx = \left[\frac{1}{p - 1} x^{1-p} \ln x\right]_e^\infty - \frac{1}{p - 1} \int_e^\infty \frac{1}{x^p}\, dx$$
   and hence show this diverges.

5 a $\displaystyle\int_0^\infty x^n e^{-x}\,dx = \begin{cases} 1 \text{ if } n=0 \\ 1 \text{ if } n=1 \\ 2 \text{ if } n=2 \\ 6 \text{ if } n=3 \end{cases}$

b As $1 = 0!,\ 1 = 1!,\ 2 = 2!,\ 6 = 3!$
we predict $\displaystyle\int_0^\infty x^n e^{-x}\,dx = n!$

6 a $\frac{\pi}{4a}$ **b** 2 **7** $\frac{\pi}{2} - \tan^{-1}(e^a)$ **9** 2 **10** $\tan^{-1}\left(\frac{1}{3}\right)$

EXERCISE 10A.4

1 a $\displaystyle\int_0^\infty \frac{1}{\sqrt{x+1}}\,dx \approx \sum_{i=0}^\infty \frac{1}{\sqrt{i+1}}$

b $\displaystyle\int_4^\infty e^{-x}\,dx \approx \sum_{i=4}^\infty e^{-i}$

2 a $\displaystyle\sum_{i=0}^\infty \frac{1}{i+2} \approx \int_0^\infty \frac{1}{x+2}\,dx$

b $\displaystyle\sum_{i=3}^\infty \frac{i+1}{i^2} \approx \int_3^\infty \frac{x+1}{x^2}\,dx$

3 a Show that $f'(x) < 0$ for all $x > 0$.

b Upper sum $= \displaystyle\sum_{i=0}^\infty e^{-i^2}$ Lower sum $= \displaystyle\sum_{i=0}^\infty e^{-(i+1)^2}$

c $\displaystyle\sum_{i=0}^\infty e^{-(i+1)^2} < \int_0^\infty e^{-x^2}\,dx < \sum_{i=0}^\infty e^{-i^2}$

4 a Show that $f'(x) < 0$ for all $x > 0$.

b Upper sum $= \displaystyle\sum_{i=1}^\infty \frac{1}{i^2}$ Lower sum $= \displaystyle\sum_{i=1}^\infty \frac{1}{(i+1)^2}$

c $\displaystyle\sum_{i=1}^\infty \frac{1}{(i+1)^2} < \int_1^\infty \frac{1}{x^2}\,dx < \sum_{i=1}^\infty \frac{1}{i^2}$

5 a Show that $f'(x) > 0$ for all $x > 0$.

b Upper sum $= \displaystyle\sum_{i=1}^\infty \frac{-1}{(i+1)^2}$ Lower sum $= \displaystyle\sum_{i=1}^\infty \frac{-1}{i^2}$

c $\displaystyle\sum_{i=1}^\infty \frac{-1}{i^2} < \int_1^\infty \frac{-1}{x^2}\,dx < \sum_{i=1}^\infty \frac{-1}{(i+1)^2}$

EXERCISE 10B.1

1 a 0 **b** 0 **c** $\frac{3}{5}$ **d** 1 **e** 0 **f** $\frac{16}{81}$

2 a converges to 0 **b** diverges to ∞ **c** converges to 1
d converges to 0 **e** converges to 0 **f** converges to 0

3 Show that $a_n = \frac{n+1}{2n}$. Hence $\displaystyle\lim_{n\to\infty} a_n = \frac{1}{2}$.

4 a As $n > 0,\ 1+n > 1 \ \Rightarrow\ 0 < \frac{1}{n+1} < 1$

So $\displaystyle\lim_{n\to\infty}\left(\frac{1}{n+1}\right)^n = 0$

b As $n > 0,\ 2+\frac{1}{n} > 2$ and $\left(2+\frac{1}{n}\right)^n > 2^n$

$\Rightarrow\ \displaystyle\lim_{n\to\infty}\left(2+\frac{1}{n}\right)^n > \lim_{n\to\infty} 2^n = \infty$

5 As $\displaystyle\lim_{n\to\infty} a_n = a$ and $\displaystyle\lim_{n\to\infty} b_n = b$,
for given $\varepsilon > 0$, there exists N such that

$|a_n - a| < \dfrac{\varepsilon}{2}$ and $|b_n - b| < \dfrac{\varepsilon}{2}$

for all $n \geqslant N$

But $|(a_n + b_n) - (a+b)|$
$= |(a_n - a) + (b_n - b)|$
$\leqslant |a_n - a| + |b_n - b|$
$< \dfrac{\varepsilon}{2} + \dfrac{\varepsilon}{2}$

i.e., $< \varepsilon$ for all $n \geqslant N$
$\Rightarrow \displaystyle\lim_{n\to\infty}(a_n + b_n) = a + b$

6 Show that $\left|\dfrac{3n+5}{7n-4} - \dfrac{3}{7}\right| < \dfrac{1}{|n-1|}$

If $\dfrac{1}{n-1} < \varepsilon,$ i.e., $n > \dfrac{1}{\varepsilon} + 1$

then $\left|\dfrac{3n+5}{7n-4} - \dfrac{3}{7}\right| < \varepsilon.$

So, for a given $\varepsilon > 0$, $\left|\dfrac{3n+5}{7n-4} - \dfrac{3}{7}\right| < \varepsilon$

for all $n \geqslant N > \dfrac{1}{\varepsilon} + 1.$

7 $\displaystyle\lim_{n\to\infty} \alpha a_n = \alpha \lim_{n\to\infty} a_n = \alpha a$
Likewise $\displaystyle\lim_{n\to\infty} \beta b_n = \beta b$

$\Rightarrow \displaystyle\lim_{n\to\infty}(\alpha a_n + \beta b_n) = \lim_{n\to\infty}\alpha a_n + \lim_{n\to\infty}\beta b_n$
$= \alpha a + \beta b$

Now set $\alpha = 1$ and $\beta = -1$ and the result follows.

EXERCISE 10B.2

1 a i Show that $u_{n+1} - u_n = \dfrac{25}{(3n+5)(3n+2)}$
> 0 for all $n \in \mathbb{Z}^+$

ii As u_n is increasing its lower bound is $u_1 = -1$.

Also $u_n = \dfrac{2n-7}{3n+2} = \dfrac{\frac{2}{3}(3n+2) - 8\frac{1}{3}}{3n+2}$

$\Rightarrow\ u_n = \dfrac{2}{3} - \dfrac{8\frac{1}{3}}{3n+2} < \dfrac{2}{3}$ for $n \in \mathbb{Z}^+$

$\Rightarrow\ -1 \leqslant u_n < \dfrac{2}{3}$
$\Rightarrow\ u_n$ is bounded

b i monotonic increasing, $\displaystyle\lim_{n\to\infty} a_n = 1$
ii monotonic increasing, $\displaystyle\lim_{n\to\infty} a_n = 1$
iii monotonic decreasing, $\displaystyle\lim_{n\to\infty} a_n = 0$

c First, note that $u_n > 0$ for all $n \in \mathbb{Z}^+$.

Since $\dfrac{u_{n+1}}{u_n} = \dfrac{2n+1}{2n+2} < 1,$

u_n is monotonic decreasing
$u_1 = \frac{1}{2}$ is therefore an upper bound
$\therefore$ since $0 < u_n < \frac{1}{2}$, $\{u_n\}$ is convergent

2 If we replace 2 with k, then you should find
$$\lim_{n \to \infty} u_n = \tfrac{1}{2} + \tfrac{1}{2}\sqrt{1 + 4k}.$$

3 Show that $\{x_n\}$ is monotonic increasing by using the Principle of Mathematical Induction.
Also use induction to prove that $x_n \leqslant 4$ for all $n \in \mathbb{Z}^+$
$$\lim_{n \to \infty} x_n = 4.$$

4 **a** $2, 1\tfrac{1}{2}, 1\tfrac{2}{3}$ **b** $u_n = 1 + \dfrac{1}{u_{n-1}}$ and $u_1 = 1$

  c From **a**, u_n is not monotonic.
  Explain why $1 \leqslant u_n \leqslant 2$ is true.

  d $L = \dfrac{\sqrt{5} + 1}{2}$

5 **a** $(1+x)^n = 1 + \binom{n}{1}x + \binom{n}{2}x^2 + \binom{n}{3}x^3 + \ldots\ldots + \binom{n}{n}x^n$

  b Replace $\binom{n}{1}$ by n, $\binom{n}{2}$ by $\dfrac{n(n-1)}{2!}$,

  $\binom{n}{3}$ by $\dfrac{n(n-1)(n-2)}{3!}$, ..., $\binom{n}{n}$ by $\dfrac{n!}{n!}$.

  c Show that $e_1 = 2$ and that $e_n > e_{n-1}$ for $n > 1$.
  d Show that $2 \leqslant e_n < 3$ to establish that e_n is bounded and hence convergent.

  e $\displaystyle\lim_{n \to \infty}\left(1 + \dfrac{1}{n}\right)^n = \lim_{n \to \infty}\left(\dfrac{n+1}{n}\right)^n = e$

  So, $\displaystyle\lim_{n \to \infty}\left(1 - \dfrac{1}{n}\right)^n = \lim_{n \to \infty}\left(\dfrac{n-1}{n}\right)^n$

  $\qquad\qquad = \displaystyle\lim_{m \to \infty}\left(\dfrac{m}{m+1}\right)^{m+1}$

  $\qquad\qquad$ {replacing $n-1$ by m}

  $\qquad\qquad = \dfrac{\displaystyle\lim_{m \to \infty}\left(\dfrac{m}{m+1}\right)}{\displaystyle\lim_{m \to \infty}\left(\dfrac{m+1}{m}\right)^m}$

  $\qquad\qquad = \dfrac{1}{e}$

  f $\dfrac{n!}{n^n} = \left(\dfrac{n-1}{n}\right)\left(\dfrac{n-2}{n}\right)\left(\dfrac{n-3}{n}\right)\ldots\ldots\left(\dfrac{1}{n}\right)$

  $\Rightarrow \dfrac{n!}{n^n} \leqslant \left(\dfrac{n-1}{n}\right)^{n-2}\left(\dfrac{1}{n}\right)$ {since $n \in \mathbb{Z}^+$}

  where $\displaystyle\lim_{n \to \infty}\left(\dfrac{n-1}{n}\right)^{n-2}$

  $\qquad = \displaystyle\lim_{n \to \infty}\left[\left(\dfrac{n-1}{n}\right)^n \times \left(\dfrac{n-1}{n}\right)^{-2}\right]$

  $\qquad = \dfrac{1}{e} \times 1^{-2}$

  $\qquad = \dfrac{1}{e}$

  $\Rightarrow 0 < \dfrac{n!}{n^n} < \left(\dfrac{n-1}{n}\right)^{n-2}\left(\dfrac{1}{n}\right) \to \dfrac{1}{e} \times 0$

  $\Rightarrow \displaystyle\lim_{n \to \infty}\dfrac{n!}{n^n} = 0$ {Squeeze theorem}

EXERCISE 10C.1

1 **a** $e > 2 \Rightarrow e^{2n} > 4^n \Rightarrow 0 < \dfrac{1}{e^{2n}} < \left(\dfrac{1}{4}\right)^n$

  where $\displaystyle\sum_{n=1}^{\infty}\left(\dfrac{1}{4}\right)^n$ is a convergent GP

  So, $\displaystyle\sum_{n=1}^{\infty}\dfrac{1}{e^{2n}}$ converges.   {Comparison test}

  b Show $\dfrac{n^2}{3n^2 + 9n + 6} \to \dfrac{1}{3}$ as $n \to \infty$

  So, by the Test for Divergence, $\displaystyle\sum_{n=1}^{\infty}\dfrac{n^2}{3n^2 + 9n + 6}$ diverges.

  c $0 < \dfrac{3^n + 2^n}{6^n} < \dfrac{3^n + 3^n}{6^n} = 2\left(\dfrac{3^n}{6^n}\right) = 2\left(\dfrac{1}{2}\right)^n$

  and $\displaystyle\sum_{n=1}^{\infty}2^{1-n}$ is a convergent GP.

  So, $\displaystyle\sum_{n=1}^{\infty}\dfrac{3^n + 2^n}{6^n}$ converges.   {Comparison test}

  d $\displaystyle\sum_{n=1}^{\infty}\left(\dfrac{1}{n} - \dfrac{1}{n^2}\right) = \sum_{n=2}^{\infty}\left(\dfrac{1}{n} - \dfrac{1}{n^2}\right)$

  $\qquad\qquad$ {as the first term was 0}

  Now $\dfrac{1}{n} - \dfrac{1}{n^2} = \dfrac{n-1}{n^2} \geqslant \dfrac{\frac{1}{2}n}{n^2}$ for $n \geqslant 2$

  $\Rightarrow \dfrac{1}{n} - \dfrac{1}{n^2} \geqslant \dfrac{1}{2n}$ for all $n \geqslant 2$.

  But $\displaystyle\sum_{n=2}^{\infty}\dfrac{1}{2n}$ diverges as $\displaystyle\sum_{n=2}^{\infty}\dfrac{1}{n}$ diverges

  $\Rightarrow \displaystyle\sum_{n=1}^{\infty}\left(\dfrac{1}{n} - \dfrac{1}{n^2}\right)$ diverges.   {Comparison test}

2 Let $a_n = \dfrac{2n^2 + 3n}{\sqrt{5 + n^7}}$ and $b_n = \dfrac{2}{\sqrt{n^3}} = \dfrac{2}{n^{\frac{3}{2}}}$.

  Show that $\dfrac{a_n}{b_n} \to 1$ as $n \to \infty$.

  As $\displaystyle\sum_{n=1}^{\infty}\dfrac{1}{n^{\frac{3}{2}}}$ converges   {p-series test}

  $\Rightarrow \displaystyle\sum_{n=1}^{\infty}\dfrac{2}{n^{\frac{3}{2}}}$ also converges

  $\Rightarrow \displaystyle\sum_{n=1}^{\infty}\dfrac{2n^2 + 3n}{\sqrt{5 + n^7}}$ converges   {Limit Comparison Test}

3 $\dfrac{1}{n^n} \leqslant \dfrac{1}{n^2}$ for all $n \in \mathbb{Z}^+$

where $\displaystyle\sum_{n=1}^{\infty} \dfrac{1}{n^2}$ converges {p-series test}

$\Rightarrow \displaystyle\sum_{n=1}^{\infty} \dfrac{1}{n^n}$ converges {Comparison test}

Also $\dfrac{1}{n!} = \dfrac{1}{n(n-1)(n-2)......(3)(2)(1)}$

$\Rightarrow \dfrac{1}{n!} \leqslant \dfrac{1}{2^{n-1}}$ for all $n \in \mathbb{Z}^+$

where $\displaystyle\sum_{n=1}^{\infty} \dfrac{1}{2^{n-1}}$ is a convergent GP

$\Rightarrow \displaystyle\sum_{n=1}^{\infty} \dfrac{1}{n!}$ converges {Comparison test}

4 **a** $\dfrac{1}{\sqrt{n(n+1)(n+2)}} < \dfrac{1}{\sqrt{n^3}} = \dfrac{1}{n^{\frac{3}{2}}}$

where $\displaystyle\sum_{n=1}^{\infty} \dfrac{1}{n^{\frac{3}{2}}}$ converges {p-series test}

$\Rightarrow \displaystyle\sum_{n=1}^{\infty} \dfrac{1}{\sqrt{n(n+1)(n+2)}}$ converges

{Comparison test}

b $\dfrac{1}{\sqrt[3]{n(n+1)(n-1)}} = \dfrac{1}{\sqrt[3]{n^3-n}} > \dfrac{1}{\sqrt[3]{n^3}}$

$\Rightarrow \dfrac{1}{\sqrt[3]{n(n+1)(n-1)}} > \dfrac{1}{n}$

where $\displaystyle\sum_{n=1}^{\infty} \dfrac{1}{n}$ diverges

$\Rightarrow \displaystyle\sum_{n=1}^{\infty} \dfrac{1}{\sqrt[3]{n(n+1)(n-1)}}$ also diverges

{Comparison test}

c $\dfrac{\sin^2 n}{n\sqrt{n}} \leqslant \dfrac{1}{n^{\frac{3}{2}}}$ where

$\displaystyle\sum_{n=1}^{\infty} \dfrac{1}{n^{\frac{3}{2}}}$ converges {p-series test}

$\Rightarrow \displaystyle\sum_{n=1}^{\infty} \dfrac{\sin^2 n}{n\sqrt{n}}$ converges {Comparison test}

d $\dfrac{\sqrt{n}}{n-1} > \dfrac{\sqrt{n}}{n} = \dfrac{1}{n^{\frac{1}{2}}}$

where $\displaystyle\sum_{n=2}^{\infty} \dfrac{1}{n^{\frac{1}{2}}}$ diverges {p-series test}

$\Rightarrow \displaystyle\sum_{n=2}^{\infty} \dfrac{\sqrt{n}}{n-1}$ also diverges

e $\dfrac{1+2^n}{1+3^n} < \dfrac{2^n+2^n}{3^n}$

So, $\dfrac{1+2^n}{1+3^n} < 2\left(\dfrac{2}{3}\right)^n$

where $2\displaystyle\sum_{n=1}^{\infty} \left(\dfrac{2}{3}\right)^n$ is a convergent GP

Hence $\displaystyle\sum_{n=1}^{\infty} \dfrac{1+2^n}{1+3^n}$ converges {Comparison test}

f As $n > \ln n$ for all n, $\dfrac{1}{\ln n} > \dfrac{1}{n}$.

But $\displaystyle\sum_{n=1}^{\infty} \dfrac{1}{n}$ diverges

so $\displaystyle\sum_{n=1}^{\infty} \dfrac{1}{\ln n}$ also diverges.   {Comparison test}

5 $\displaystyle\sum_{n=0}^{\infty} 2^n |\sin^n x| = \displaystyle\sum_{n=0}^{\infty} (2|\sin x|)^n$

and so is a GP which converges when

$|2\sin x| < 1$,   i.e.,   when $-\dfrac{1}{2} < \sin x < \dfrac{1}{2}$

$\Rightarrow \ 0 < x < \dfrac{\pi}{6}, \ \ \dfrac{5\pi}{6} < x < \dfrac{7\pi}{6}, \ \ \dfrac{11\pi}{6} < x < 2\pi$

6 $\displaystyle\sum_{n=2}^{\infty} \left(\dfrac{1}{1+c}\right)^n$ is a GP

$S_\infty = \dfrac{u_1}{1-r} \Rightarrow \dfrac{\left(\dfrac{1}{1+c}\right)^2}{1 - \dfrac{1}{1+c}} = 2$

which has solutions $c = \dfrac{-1 \pm \sqrt{3}}{2}$.

7 **a** Consider $f(x) = \dfrac{x}{x^2+1}$ for $x \geqslant 1$

$f'(x) = \dfrac{1-x^2}{(x^2+1)^2} < 0$ for $x \geqslant 1$

$\Rightarrow \ f(x)$ is decreasing for all $x \geqslant 1$

Since $x^2 \geqslant 1$, $x^2 + 1 \geqslant 2$,   and so $f(x)$ is positive for all $x \geqslant 1$.

Since $f(x)$ is continuous, positive, and decreasing, the Integral Test can be used.

Now $\displaystyle\int_1^{\infty} \dfrac{x}{x^2+1}\,dx$

$= \displaystyle\lim_{t\to\infty} \left\{ \int_1^t \tfrac{1}{2}\left(\dfrac{2x}{x^2+1}\right)dx \right\}$

$= \displaystyle\lim_{t\to\infty} \left\{ \tfrac{1}{2}\ln|t^2+1| - \tfrac{1}{2}\ln 2 \right\}$

$= \infty$

So, $\displaystyle\sum_{n=1}^{\infty} \dfrac{n}{n^2+1}$ diverges   {Integral test}

b Consider $f(x) = xe^{-x^2}$ where $x \geqslant 1$.
$f(x) > 0$ for all $x \geqslant 1$ and
$f'(x) = e^{-x^2}(1 - 2x^2) < 0$ for all $x \geqslant 1$.
Since $f(x)$ is continuous, positive, and decreasing, the Integral Test can be used.

Now $\int_1^\infty xe^{-x^2}\,dx$

$= \lim_{t \to \infty} \left\{ \int_1^t -\tfrac{1}{2}e^{-x^2}(-2x)\,dx \right\}$

$= \lim_{t \to \infty} \left\{ -\tfrac{1}{2}e^{-t^2} - \left(-\tfrac{1}{2}e^{-1} \right) \right\}$

$= \tfrac{1}{2}e^{-1}$ i.e., is convergent

$\Rightarrow \sum_{n=1}^\infty ne^{-n^2}$ is convergent.

c Consider $f(x) = \dfrac{\ln x}{x}$ for $x \geqslant 1$
$f(x) > 0$ for all $x \geqslant 1$
$f'(x) = \dfrac{1 - \ln x}{x^2}$

$\therefore\quad f'(x) < 0$ when $1 - \ln x < 0$
   i.e., $\ln x > 1$
   i.e., $x > e$
   i.e., for all $x \geqslant 3$

Hence $f(x)$ is decreasing for all $x \geqslant 3$.
Since $f(x)$ is continuous, positive, and decreasing, the Integral Test can be used.

$\int_1^\infty \dfrac{\ln x}{x}\,dx = \lim_{t \to \infty} \left[\tfrac{1}{2}(\ln x)^2 \right]_1^t = \infty$

So, $\sum_{n=1}^\infty \dfrac{\ln n}{n}$ diverges.

d Consider $f(x) = \dfrac{1}{x \ln x}$
$f(x) > 0$ for all $x \geqslant 2$
$f'(x) = \dfrac{-(\ln x + 1)}{(x \ln x)^2}$

$\therefore\quad f'(x) < 0$ when $\ln x + 1 > 0$
       i.e., $\ln x > -1$
       i.e., $x > e^{-1}$
       i.e., $x \geqslant 1$

Hence $f(x)$ is decreasing for all $x \geqslant 2$.
Since $f(x)$ is continuous, positive, and decreasing, the Integral Test can be used.

$\int_2^\infty \dfrac{1}{x \ln x}\,dx = \lim_{t \to \infty} \left[\ln(\ln x) \right]_2^t = \infty$

So, $\sum_{n=2}^\infty \dfrac{1}{n \ln n}$ diverges.

8 Let $f(x) = \dfrac{1}{1 + x^2}$,   so $f(x) > 0$ for all $x \geqslant 1$.

$f'(x) = \dfrac{-2x}{(1 + x^2)^2} < 0$ for all $x \geqslant 1$

$\Rightarrow\quad f(x)$ is decreasing for all $x \geqslant 1$
By the Integral test,

$\int_1^\infty \dfrac{1}{1 + x^2}\,dx < \sum_{n=1}^\infty \dfrac{1}{n^2 + 1} < a_1 + \int_1^\infty \dfrac{1}{1 + x^2}\,dx$

where $a_1 = f(1) = \tfrac{1}{2}$.
Complete the argument.

9 If $p = 1$, we showed in **7d** that $\sum_{n=2}^\infty \dfrac{1}{n \ln n}$ diverges.

If $p < 1$, then since $n \geqslant 2$, $n^p \ln n < n \ln n$.

So, $\dfrac{1}{n^p \ln n} > \dfrac{1}{n \ln n}$

$\Rightarrow \sum_{n=2}^\infty \dfrac{1}{n^p \ln n}$ diverges if $p < 1$ {Comparison test}

and so diverges for $p \leqslant 1$.

For $n > 3$, $\dfrac{1}{n^p \ln n} < \dfrac{1}{n^p}$.

Now $\sum_{n=2}^\infty \dfrac{1}{n^p}$ converges for $p > 1$. {p-test}

So $\sum_{n=2}^\infty \dfrac{1}{n^p \ln n}$ converges for $p > 1$.
   {Comparison test}

10 a $\displaystyle\int_{13}^\infty \dfrac{1}{5x^2}\,dx < R_{12} < \int_{12}^\infty \dfrac{1}{5x^2}\,dx$

where $\displaystyle\int_{13}^\infty \dfrac{1}{5x^2}\,dx = \lim_{t \to \infty} \left[\dfrac{-1}{5x} \right]_{13}^\infty$

$= \tfrac{1}{65}$

and $\displaystyle\int_{12}^\infty \dfrac{1}{5x^2}\,dx = \lim_{t \to \infty} \left[\dfrac{-1}{5x} \right]_{12}^\infty$

$= \tfrac{1}{60}$

So, $\tfrac{1}{65} < R_{12} < \tfrac{1}{60}$

b $R_k < \displaystyle\int_k^\infty \dfrac{1}{x^4}\,dx$

$\Rightarrow\quad R_k < \lim_{t \to \infty} \left[\dfrac{-1}{3x^3} \right]_k^t$

$\Rightarrow\quad R_k < \dfrac{1}{3k^3}$

So, we require $\dfrac{1}{3k^3} < 5 \times 10^{-7}$
   i.e., $k^3 > 666\,666\tfrac{2}{3}$
   $\Rightarrow\quad k > 87.358....$
   $\Rightarrow\quad k \geqslant 88$

11 $\displaystyle\sum_{n=1}^{\infty} a_n$ is convergent $\Rightarrow$ $\displaystyle\lim_{n\to\infty} a_n = 0$

$\Rightarrow$ $\displaystyle\lim_{n\to\infty} \frac{1}{a_n} = \infty$

$\Rightarrow$ $\displaystyle\sum_{n=1}^{\infty} \frac{1}{a_n}$ diverges {Test of Divergence}

12 $S_1 = 0$ so $a_1 = 0$

Also, $a_n = S_n - S_{n-1}$

$\Rightarrow$ $a_n = \dfrac{n-1}{n+1} - \dfrac{n-2}{n} = \dfrac{2}{n(n+1)}$

$\displaystyle\sum_{n=1}^{\infty} a_n = \lim_{n\to\infty} S_n = 1$

13 a $S_1 = \frac{1}{2}$, $S_2 = \frac{5}{6}$, $S_3 = \frac{23}{24}$, $S_4 = \frac{119}{120}$, $S_5 = \frac{719}{720}$

Conjecture: $S_n = \dfrac{(n+1)! - 1}{(n+1)!} = 1 - \dfrac{1}{(n+1)!}$

c $\displaystyle\sum_{n=1}^{\infty} \frac{n}{(n+1)!} = \lim_{n\to\infty} S_n = 1$

14 a $S_{16} > 1 + \frac{4}{2}$ **b** $S_{2^m} > 1 + \dfrac{m}{2}$

c $\displaystyle\lim_{m\to\infty} \left(1 + \frac{m}{2}\right) = \infty$

so $\displaystyle\lim_{m\to\infty} S_{2^m} = \infty$ {Comparison test}

Now for every $m \in \mathbb{Z}^+$, there exists $n \in \mathbb{Z}^+$ such that $2^m \leqslant n \leqslant 2^{m+1}$

$\Rightarrow$ $S_{2^m} \leqslant S_n \leqslant S_{2^{m+1}} + 1$ and as $S_{2^m} \to \infty$ then $S_n \to \infty$ as $n \to \infty$. {Squeeze}

EXERCISE 10C.2

1 a If $\dfrac{1}{r(r+2)} = \dfrac{A}{r} + \dfrac{B}{r+2}$ show that $A = \frac{1}{2}$ and $B = -\frac{1}{2}$.

$\therefore$ $\displaystyle\sum_{r=1}^{n} \frac{1}{r(r+2)} = \frac{1}{2}\sum_{r=1}^{n} \left(\frac{1}{r} - \frac{1}{r+2}\right)$

$\qquad = \frac{1}{2}\left(\frac{1}{1} - \frac{1}{3}\right.$
$\qquad\quad + \frac{1}{2} - \frac{1}{4}$
$\qquad\quad + \frac{1}{3} - \frac{1}{5}$
$\qquad\quad + \frac{1}{4} - \frac{1}{6}$
$\qquad\qquad \vdots$
$\qquad\quad + \frac{1}{n-2} - \frac{1}{n}$
$\qquad\quad + \frac{1}{n-1} - \frac{1}{n+1}$
$\qquad\quad + \left.\frac{1}{n} - \frac{1}{n+2}\right)$

$\qquad = \frac{1}{2}\left(\frac{3}{2} - \frac{1}{n+1} - \frac{1}{n+2}\right)$

$\therefore$ $\displaystyle\sum_{r=1}^{\infty} \frac{1}{r(r+2)} = \frac{1}{2} \times \frac{3}{2} = \frac{3}{4}$

$\left\{\text{as } n \to \infty, \ \dfrac{1}{n+1} \text{ and } \dfrac{1}{n+2} \to 0\right\}$

b If $\dfrac{1}{r(r+1)(r+2)} = \dfrac{A}{r} + \dfrac{B}{r+1} + \dfrac{C}{r+2}$

show that $A = \frac{1}{2}$, $B = -1$, $C = \frac{1}{2}$

Then show that

$\displaystyle\sum_{r=1}^{n} \frac{1}{r(r+1)(r+2)} = \frac{1}{4} - \frac{1}{2(n+1)} + \frac{1}{2(n+2)}$

Hence show $\displaystyle\sum_{r=1}^{\infty} \frac{1}{r(r+1)(r+2)} = \frac{1}{4}$

2 a Start with RHS of equation and use the recurrence relationship to simplify it to become equal to the LHS.

b Use **a** and then write down the series of differences.

After cancellation you should obtain a limit of $\dfrac{1}{f_1 f_2}$ which is 1.

3 $\displaystyle\sum_{r=1}^{n} \left(\sqrt{r+1} - \sqrt{r}\right)$ after cancellation becomes $\sqrt{n+1} - 1$

$\Rightarrow$ $\displaystyle\sum_{r=1}^{\infty} \left(\sqrt{r+1} - \sqrt{r}\right) = \lim_{n\to\infty} \left(\sqrt{n+1} - 1\right)$
$\qquad\qquad\qquad\qquad\qquad\quad = \infty$

4 $\displaystyle\sum_{n=1}^{\infty} \left(\sin\left(\frac{1}{n}\right) - \sin\left(\frac{1}{n+1}\right)\right)$

$= \sin 1 - \sin(\frac{1}{2})$
$\ \ + \sin(\frac{1}{2}) - \sin(\frac{1}{3})$
$\ \ + \sin(\frac{1}{3}) - \sin(\frac{1}{4})$
$\ \ + \ ......$

$= \sin 1$

5 If $\dfrac{1}{(x+n)(x+n-1)} = \dfrac{A}{x+n} + \dfrac{B}{x+n-1}$

show that $A = -1$ and $B = 1$.

Note that the expression is undefined whenever $x = -n$ or $-n+1$.

Then show that $\displaystyle\sum_{n=1}^{\infty} \frac{1}{(x+n)(x+n-1)} = \frac{1}{x}$

which is valid provided $x \neq 0$.

So, the series converges if $x \neq 0, -1, -2, ...$

6 $\displaystyle\sum_{n=1}^{\infty} \frac{1-n}{n^2} = \sum_{n=1}^{\infty} \frac{1}{n^2} - \sum_{n=1}^{\infty} \frac{1}{n}$

which diverges as $\displaystyle\sum_{n=1}^{\infty} \frac{1}{n^2}$ converges and $\displaystyle\sum_{n=1}^{\infty} \frac{1}{n}$ diverges.

$\displaystyle\sum_{n=1}^{\infty} \frac{1}{n} - \sum_{n=1}^{\infty} \frac{1-n}{n^2} = 2\sum_{n=1}^{\infty} \frac{1}{n} - \sum_{n=1}^{\infty} \frac{1}{n^2}$

which diverges as $\displaystyle\sum_{n=1}^{\infty} \frac{1}{n}$ diverges and $\displaystyle\sum_{n=1}^{\infty} \frac{1}{n^2}$ converges.

$\displaystyle\sum_{n=1}^{\infty} \frac{1}{n} - \sum_{n=1}^{\infty} \frac{n-1}{n^2} = \sum_{n=1}^{\infty} \frac{1}{n^2}$ which converges

7 a This series is $\displaystyle\sum_{n=2}^{\infty} \frac{(-1)^n}{\ln n}$

If $f(x) = \dfrac{1}{\ln x}$, $f'(x) = \dfrac{-1}{x[\ln x]^2} < 0$ for all $x \geqslant 2$

$\therefore$ $f(x)$ is decreasing for all $x \geqslant 2$ and $\displaystyle\lim_{n\to\infty} \frac{1}{\ln n} = 0$

So, $\displaystyle\sum_{n=2}^{\infty} \frac{(-1)^n}{\ln n}$ is a converging alternating series.

b Show $\displaystyle\lim_{n\to\infty} \frac{\sqrt{n}}{n + 4} = 0$

If $f(x) = \dfrac{\sqrt{x}}{x + 4}$ then $f'(x) = \dfrac{4 - x}{2\sqrt{x}(x + 4)^2}$

$\therefore$ $f'(x) < 0$ for all $x > 4$

$\Rightarrow$ $f(x)$ is decreasing for $x > 4$

$\Rightarrow$ $\displaystyle\sum_{n=1}^{\infty} \frac{(-1)^{n+1}\sqrt{n}}{n + 4}$ converges

c $\displaystyle\lim_{n\to\infty} \frac{n!}{n^n} = 0 \ \Rightarrow \ \lim_{n\to\infty} \frac{n^n}{n!} = \infty$

So, by the Test for Divergence $\displaystyle\sum_{n=1}^{\infty} \frac{(-1)^n n^n}{n!}$ diverges.

d $\displaystyle\lim_{n\to\infty} \sin\left(\frac{\pi}{n}\right) = 0$

If $f(x) = \sin\left(\dfrac{\pi}{x}\right)$ then $f'(x) = \cos\left(\dfrac{\pi}{x}\right) \times \dfrac{-\pi}{x^2}$

$\therefore$ $f'(x) < 0$ for all $x \geqslant 2$

$\Rightarrow$ $f(x)$ is decreasing for all $x \geqslant 2$

So, $\displaystyle\sum_{n=1}^{\infty} (-1)^n \sin\left(\frac{\pi}{x}\right)$ is a converging alternating series.

e $\displaystyle\lim_{n\to\infty} \frac{1}{(\ln n)^{\frac{1}{3}}} = 0$

Let $f(x) = \dfrac{1}{(\ln x)^{\frac{1}{3}}} = [\ln x]^{-\frac{1}{3}}$

$\therefore$ $f'(x) = -\frac{1}{3}[\ln x]^{-\frac{4}{3}} \times \dfrac{1}{x} = \dfrac{-1}{3x[\ln x]^{\frac{4}{3}}}$

$\therefore$ $f'(x) < 0$ for all $x \geqslant 2$

$\Rightarrow$ $f(x)$ is decreasing for all $x \geqslant 2$

So, $\displaystyle\sum_{n=2}^{\infty} \frac{(-1)^{n-1}}{\sqrt[3]{\ln n}}$ converges.

f $\displaystyle\sum_{n=1}^{\infty} \frac{\sin\left(\frac{n\pi}{2}\right)}{n!} = \frac{1}{1!} - \frac{1}{3!} + \frac{1}{5!} - \frac{1}{7!} + \dots.$

$= \displaystyle\sum_{n=1}^{\infty} \frac{(-1)^{n-1}}{(2n - 1)!}$ where $\displaystyle\lim_{n\to\infty} \frac{1}{(2n - 1)!} = 0$

Now $\left\{\dfrac{1}{(2n - 1)!}\right\}$ is a decreasing sequence.

So, the series converges.

g $\displaystyle\lim_{n\to\infty} \frac{1}{2^n n!} = 0$

and $\dfrac{1}{2^{n+1}(n + 1)!} < \dfrac{1}{2^n n!}$ for all $n \geqslant 1$

$\therefore$ $\left\{\dfrac{1}{2^n n!}\right\}$ is a decreasing sequence.

So, the series converges.

h $\displaystyle\lim_{n\to\infty} \frac{n^2}{n^3 + 1} = 0$

Let $f(x) = \dfrac{x^2}{x^3 + 1} \ \Rightarrow \ f'(x) = \dfrac{x(2 - x^3)}{(x^3 + 1)^2}$

For $x \geqslant 2$, $f'(x) < 0$

Thus $\left\{\dfrac{n^2}{n^3 + 1}\right\}$ is decreasing for all $n \geqslant 2$.

Hence, $\displaystyle\sum_{n=1}^{\infty} (-1)^{n+1} \frac{n^2}{n^3 + 1}$ converges.

8 a $S_4 = 0.625$ **b** 0.8415 **c** 0.6065

9 $S_1 = 1$ $S_5 \approx 0.904\,412$ $S_9 \approx 0.902\,116\,5$
    $S_2 = 0.875$ $S_6 \approx 0.899\,782\,4$ $S_{10} \approx 0.901\,116\,5$
    $S_3 = 0.912\,037$ $S_7 \approx 0.902\,697\,9$
    $S_4 \approx 0.896\,412$ $S_8 \approx 0.900\,744\,7$

An estimate of the error is $11^{-3} = 7.51 \times 10^{-4}$

11 a $\dfrac{a_{n+1}}{a_n} = -\dfrac{3}{n + 1}$

and so $\displaystyle\lim_{n\to\infty} \left|\frac{a_{n+1}}{a_n}\right| = 0$

Hence $\displaystyle\sum_{n=1}^{\infty} \frac{(-3)^n}{n!}$ is absolutely convergent.

b $\dfrac{a_{n+1}}{a_n} = -\dfrac{2(n^2 + 1)}{n^2 + 2n + 2} = -\dfrac{2 + \frac{2}{n^2}}{1 + \frac{2}{n} + \frac{2}{n^2}}$

and so $\displaystyle\lim_{n\to\infty} \left|\frac{a_{n+1}}{a_n}\right| = 2$

So, $\displaystyle\sum_{n=1}^{\infty} \frac{(-1)^n 2^n}{n^2 + 1}$ is divergent

c $\dfrac{\arctan n}{n^3} \leqslant \dfrac{\frac{\pi}{2}}{n^3}$ for all $n \geqslant 1$

Now $\displaystyle\sum_{n=1}^{\infty} \frac{1}{n^3}$ converges {p-series test}

$\Rightarrow$ $\dfrac{\pi}{2} \displaystyle\sum_{n=1}^{\infty} \frac{1}{n^3}$ converges

$\Rightarrow$ $\displaystyle\sum_{n=1}^{\infty} \frac{(-1)^n \arctan n}{n^3}$ is absolutely convergent.

d $\left|\dfrac{1-3n}{3+4n}\right| = \left|\dfrac{3n-1}{3+4n}\right| < \dfrac{3n}{4n}$ for all $n \geqslant 1$

$\Rightarrow \quad \left|\dfrac{1-3n}{3+4n}\right| < \tfrac{3}{4}$ for all $n \geqslant 1$

Thus $\left|\dfrac{1-3n}{3+4n}\right|^n < \left(\tfrac{3}{4}\right)^n$

and $\displaystyle\sum_{n=1}^{\infty} \left(\tfrac{3}{4}\right)^n$ is a converging GP

By the Comparison test, $\displaystyle\sum_{n=1}^{\infty} \left(\dfrac{1-3n}{3+4n}\right)^n$
is absolutely convergent.

12 a If $a_n = \dfrac{x^n}{n!}$ then $\left|\dfrac{a_{n+1}}{a_n}\right| = \left|\dfrac{x}{n+1}\right|$

Since $\displaystyle\lim_{n\to\infty} \left|\dfrac{a_{n+1}}{a_n}\right| = 0$,

$\displaystyle\sum_{n=1}^{\infty} \dfrac{x^n}{n!}$ converges for all $x \in \mathbb{R}$.

b By the converse of the Test for Divergence, as

$\displaystyle\sum_{n=1}^{\infty} \dfrac{x^n}{n!}$ converges, $\displaystyle\lim_{n\to\infty} \dfrac{x^n}{n!} = 0$

13 a By **12a**, $\displaystyle\sum_{n=0}^{\infty} \dfrac{10^n}{n!}$ converges.

b For $n > 1$, $\dfrac{1}{\sqrt{n \times n}} > \dfrac{1}{\sqrt{n(n+1)}} > \dfrac{1}{\sqrt{n(n+2)+1}}$

i.e., $\dfrac{1}{n} > \dfrac{1}{\sqrt{n(n+1)}} > \dfrac{1}{n+1}$

where $\displaystyle\sum_{n=1}^{\infty} \dfrac{1}{n}$ and $\displaystyle\sum_{n=1}^{\infty} \dfrac{1}{n+1}$ are divergent

$\Rightarrow \displaystyle\sum_{n=1}^{\infty} \dfrac{1}{\sqrt{n(n+1)}}$ diverges   {Squeeze}

c $\displaystyle\lim_{n\to\infty} \dfrac{2n}{8n-5} = \tfrac{1}{4}$ So, $\displaystyle\sum_{n=1}^{\infty} \dfrac{2n}{8n-5}$ diverges.

d $\left|\dfrac{\cos\left(\tfrac{n}{2}\right)}{n^2+4n}\right| \leqslant \dfrac{1}{n^2}$ for $n \geqslant 1$

where $\displaystyle\sum_{n=1}^{\infty} \dfrac{1}{n^2}$ converges

$\Rightarrow \displaystyle\sum_{n=1}^{\infty} \dfrac{\cos\left(\tfrac{n}{2}\right)}{n^2+4n}$ converges.

e $\dfrac{n^3+1}{n^4-1} > \dfrac{n^3+1}{n^4}$ for all $n \geqslant 1$

So $\dfrac{n^3+1}{n^4-1} > \dfrac{1}{n} + \dfrac{1}{n^4}$

where $\displaystyle\sum_{n=1}^{\infty} \dfrac{1}{n}$ diverges and $\displaystyle\sum_{n=1}^{\infty} \dfrac{1}{n^4}$ converges

$\therefore \displaystyle\sum_{n=1}^{\infty} \dfrac{n^3+1}{n^4-1}$ diverges.

f $\left|\dfrac{a_{n+1}}{a_n}\right| = \left|\dfrac{n+1}{3n+5}\right|$ which $\to \tfrac{1}{3}$ as $n \to \infty$

So, $\displaystyle\sum_{n=0}^{\infty} a_n$ absolutely converges   {Ratio test}

14 If $a_n = \dfrac{1}{n^2}$, $\dfrac{a_{n+1}}{a_n} = \dfrac{n^2}{(n+1)^2}$

So, $\displaystyle\lim_{n\to\infty} \left|\dfrac{a_{n+1}}{a_n}\right| = 1$ Inconclusive.

If $a_n = \dfrac{1}{n}$, $\dfrac{a_{n+1}}{a_n} = \dfrac{n}{n+1}$

So, $\displaystyle\lim_{n\to\infty} \left|\dfrac{a_{n+1}}{a_n}\right| = 1$ Inconclusive.

EXERCISE 10C.3

1 a $\left|\dfrac{a_{n+1}}{a_n}\right| = \left|\dfrac{x}{n+1}\right| \quad \Rightarrow \quad \displaystyle\lim_{n\to\infty} \left|\dfrac{a_{n+1}}{a_n}\right| = 0$

So, radius of convergence is ∞ and the interval of convergence is $\mathbb{R}$.

b $\left|\dfrac{a_{n+1}}{a_n}\right| = \left|\left(\dfrac{n+1}{n}\right)5x\right| \Rightarrow \displaystyle\lim_{n\to\infty} \left|\dfrac{a_{n+1}}{a_n}\right| = |5x|$

So, $\displaystyle\sum_{n=0}^{\infty} a_n$ is absolutely convergent if $|5x| < 1$,

i.e., $-\tfrac{1}{5} < x < \tfrac{1}{5}$

When $x = \tfrac{1}{5}$, $\displaystyle\sum_{n=1}^{\infty} a_n = \sum_{n=1}^{\infty} n$ which diverges.

When $x = -\tfrac{1}{5}$, $\displaystyle\sum_{n=1}^{\infty} a_n = \sum_{n=1}^{\infty} (-1)^n n$ which diverges.

Hence the radius of convergence is $\tfrac{1}{5}$ and the interval of convergence is $\left]-\tfrac{1}{5}, \tfrac{1}{5}\right[$.

c $\left|\dfrac{a_{n+1}}{a_n}\right| = \left|\left(\dfrac{n+1}{n+2}\right)^2 3x\right| \Rightarrow \displaystyle\lim_{n\to\infty} \left|\dfrac{a_{n+1}}{a_n}\right| = |3x|$

So, $\displaystyle\sum_{n=0}^{\infty} a_n$ is absolutely convergent if $|3x| < 1$,

i.e., $-\tfrac{1}{3} < x < \tfrac{1}{3}$

When $x = -\tfrac{1}{3}$, $\displaystyle\sum_{n=0}^{\infty} a_n = \sum_{n=0}^{\infty} \dfrac{(-1)^n}{(n+1)^2}$ which

converges by the Alternating Series Test.

When $x = \tfrac{1}{3}$, $\displaystyle\sum_{n=0}^{\infty} a_n = \sum_{n=0}^{\infty} \dfrac{1}{(n+1)^2}$ which

converges by comparison with $\displaystyle\sum_{n=1}^{\infty} \dfrac{1}{n^2}$.

Hence, the radius of convergence is $\tfrac{1}{3}$ and the interval of convergence is $\left[-\tfrac{1}{3}, \tfrac{1}{3}\right]$.

d $\left|\dfrac{a_{n+1}}{a_n}\right| = \left|\dfrac{x^2}{(2n+1)(2n)}\right| \Rightarrow \lim\limits_{n\to\infty}\left|\dfrac{a_{n+1}}{a_n}\right| = 0$

So, radius of convergence is ∞, and the interval of convergence is $\mathbb{R}$.

e $\left|\dfrac{a_{n+1}}{a_n}\right| = \left|\dfrac{n\ln n}{(n+1)\ln(n+1)}(2x+3)\right|$

and $\lim\limits_{n\to\infty}\left|\dfrac{a_{n+1}}{a_n}\right| = |2x+3|$

So, $\sum\limits_{n=2}^{\infty}$ is absolutely convergent for $|2x+3| < 1$,

i.e., $-1 < 2x+3 < 1$ i.e., $-2 < x < -1$

When $x = -1$, we have $\sum\limits_{n=2}^{\infty}\dfrac{(-1)^n}{n\ln n}$

Show that this is a converging alternating series.

When $x = -2$, we have $\sum\limits_{n=2}^{\infty}\dfrac{1}{n\ln n}$ which is divergent

by the integral test.

So, the radius of convergence is $\frac{1}{2}$ and the interval of convergence is $-2 < x \leqslant -1$ i.e., $\,]-2, -1]$.

2 $a_n = \dfrac{(2)(4)(6)\ \dots\dots\ (2n)x^n}{(1)(3)(5)\ \dots\dots\ (2n-1)}$

$\therefore\ \left|\dfrac{a_{n+1}}{a_n}\right| = \left|\dfrac{2n+2}{2n+1}x\right| \to |x|$ as $n \to \infty$

So, $\sum\limits_{n=1}^{\infty} a_n$ is abs. convgt. for $|x| < 1$ i.e., $-1 < x < 1$

When $x = 1$, $a_n = \dfrac{(2)(4)(6)\ \dots\dots\ (2n)}{(1)(3)(5)\ \dots\dots\ (2n-1)}$ which is > 1

for all $n \in \mathbb{Z}^+$.

So, $\lim\limits_{n\to\infty} a_n \neq 0$

Thus $\sum\limits_{n=1}^{\infty} a_n$ and $\sum\limits_{n=1}^{\infty}(-1)^n a_n$ diverge {Test of Div.}

The radius of convergence is 1.
The interval of convergence is $\,]-1, 1[$.

3 $\begin{aligned} f(x) &= 1 + x^2 + x^4 + x^6 + \dots\dots \\ &\quad + 2x(1 + x^2 + x^4 + x^6 + \dots\dots) \end{aligned}$

$= \dfrac{1}{1-x^2} + 2x\left(\dfrac{1}{1-x^2}\right)$ for $|\,| < 1$

{sum of an infinite GP}

i.e., $f(x) = \dfrac{1+2x}{1-x^2}$ and the interval of conv. is $\,]-1, 1[$.

4 $\sum\limits_{n=0}^{\infty} c_n x^n$ converges provided $|x| < R$.

Letting $x = y^2$, $\sum\limits_{n=0}^{\infty} c_n y^{2n}$ converges

provided $\left|y^2\right| < R$ i.e., $|y| < \sqrt{R}$.

$\therefore$ the radius of convergence of $\sum\limits_{n=0}^{\infty} c_n x^{2n}$ is $\sqrt{R}$.

5 If $\sum\limits_{n=0}^{\infty} c_n x^n$ and $\sum\limits_{n=0}^{\infty} d_n x^n$ are convergent

then $\sum\limits_{n=0}^{\infty} c_n x^n + \sum\limits_{n=0}^{\infty} d_n x^n = \sum\limits_{n=0}^{\infty}(c_n + d_n)x^n$.

Hence $\sum\limits_{n=0}^{\infty}(c_n + d_n)x^n$ is convergent

only if $\sum\limits_{n=0}^{\infty} c_n x^n$ and $\sum\limits_{n=0}^{\infty} d_n x^n$ are convergent.

This occurs when $|x| > 2$, so the radius of conv. is 2.

6 For the first power series

$\lim\limits_{n\to\infty}\left|\dfrac{a_{n+1}}{a_n}\right| = \lim\limits_{n\to\infty}\left|\dfrac{n^2}{(n+1)^2}\left(\tfrac{1}{3}\right)x\right| = \left|\dfrac{x}{3}\right|$

and is convergent for $\left|\dfrac{x}{3}\right| < 1$ i.e., $|x| < 3$

$\therefore$ its radius of convergence is 3.

At $x = 3$, $\sum\limits_{n=1}^{\infty} a_n = \sum\limits_{n=1}^{\infty}\dfrac{1}{n^2}$ which is convergent

At $x = -3$, $\sum\limits_{n=1}^{\infty} a_n = \sum\limits_{n=1}^{\infty}\dfrac{(-1)^n}{n^2}$ which converges (absolutely)

$\therefore$ the interval of convergence is $[-3, 3]$.

For the second power series

$\lim\limits_{n\to\infty}\left|\dfrac{a_{n+1}}{a_n}\right| = \lim\limits_{n\to\infty}\left|\dfrac{n}{n+1}\left(\tfrac{1}{3}\right)x\right| = \left|\dfrac{x}{3}\right|$

and is convergent for $|x| < 3$

$\therefore$ its radius of convergence is also 3.

At $x = 3$, $\sum\limits_{n=1}^{\infty} a_n = \tfrac{1}{3}\sum\limits_{n=1}^{\infty}\dfrac{1}{n}$ which diverges

At $x = -3$, $\sum\limits_{n=1}^{\infty} a_n = \tfrac{1}{3}\sum\limits_{n=1}^{\infty}\dfrac{(-1)^{n-1}}{n}$ which converges (conditionally)

$\therefore$ its interval of convergence is $[-3, 3[$.

7 $\dfrac{d}{dx}\left(\sum\limits_{n=1}^{\infty}\dfrac{x^n}{n!}\right) = \sum\limits_{n=1}^{\infty}\dfrac{d}{dx}\left(\dfrac{x^n}{n!}\right) = \sum\limits_{n=1}^{\infty}\dfrac{x^{n-1}}{(n-1)!}$

which converges for all $x \in \mathbb{R}$. {see **1 a**}

$\displaystyle\int_0^x\left(\sum\limits_{n=0}^{\infty}\dfrac{t^n}{n!}\right)dt = \sum\limits_{n=0}^{\infty}\left(\int_0^x\dfrac{t^n}{n!}\,dt\right)$

$= \sum\limits_{n=0}^{\infty}\left[\dfrac{t^{n+1}}{(n+1)!}\right]_0^x$

$= \sum\limits_{n=0}^{\infty}\dfrac{x^{n+1}}{(n+1)!}$

which converges for all $x \in \mathbb{R}$ {Ratio Test}

EXERCISE 10D

1 $\ln(1+x)$

$= x - \dfrac{x^2}{2} + \dfrac{x^3}{3} - \dfrac{x^4}{4} + \ldots\ldots + (-1)^{n-1}\dfrac{x^n}{n} + R_n(x:0)$

Interval of convergence $\,]-1, 1[\,$.

$R_n(x: 0) = f^{(n+1)}(c)\dfrac{(x-0)^{n+1}}{(n+1)!}$

$= \dfrac{(n-1)!(-1)^{n-1}}{(1+c)^n}\dfrac{x^{n+1}}{(n+1)!}$

$= \dfrac{(-1)^{n-1}}{(1+c)^n(n+1)n}x^{n+1}$

$\to 0 \quad \text{for} \quad |x| < 1, \quad c > 0$

2 $(1+x)^p$

$= 1 + px + \dfrac{p(p-1)}{2!}x^2 + \dfrac{p(p-1)(p-2)}{3!}x^3 + \ldots\ldots$

$\ldots\ldots + \dfrac{p(p-1)(p-2)\ldots\ldots(p-n+1)}{n!}x^n + R_n(x:0)$

$R_n(x:0)$

$= \left[\dfrac{p(p-1)(p-2)\ldots\ldots(p-n)(1+c)^{p-n-1}}{(n+1)!}\right]x^{n+1}$

$= a_n$

$\left|\dfrac{a_{n+1}}{a_n}\right| = \left|\dfrac{p-n-1}{n+2}\right|\left|\dfrac{x}{1+c}\right|$

$\therefore \quad \lim_{n\to\infty}\left|\dfrac{a_{n+1}}{a_n}\right| = \left|\dfrac{x}{1+c}\right|$

For $c > 0$, $\lim_{n\to\infty}\left|\dfrac{a_{n+1}}{a_n}\right| < 1$ for $|x| < 1$

So, the radius of convergence is 1.

$(1+x^2)^{-1}$ is obtained by replacing x by x^2 and p by -1.

Notice that the coefficient of x^n when $p = -1$ is

$\dfrac{(-1)(-2)(-3)\ldots\ldots(-n)}{n!} = (-1)^n$

So, $(1+x^2)^{-1} = 1 - x^2 + x^4 - x^6 + x^8 - \ldots\ldots$
$+ (-1)^n x^{2n} + R_n(x^2:0)$

3   If $f(x) = \ln x$, $f^{(n)}(x) = \dfrac{(-1)^{n-1}(n-1)!}{x^n}$

$\Rightarrow f^{(n)}(2) = \dfrac{(-1)^{n-1}(n-1)!}{2^n}$

So, $\ln n$

$= f(2) + \dfrac{f'(2)(x-2)}{2!} + \dfrac{f''(2)(x-2)^2}{3!} + \ldots\ldots$

$\ldots\ldots + \dfrac{f^{(n)}(2)(x-2)^n}{n!} + R_n(x:2)$

$= \ln 2 + \dfrac{1}{2}\dfrac{(x-2)}{1!} - \dfrac{1!}{2^2}\dfrac{(x-2)^2}{2!} + \dfrac{2!}{2^3}\dfrac{(x-2)^3}{3!} - \ldots\ldots$

$= \ln 2 + \tfrac{1}{2}(x-2)^1 - \tfrac{1}{8}(x-2)^2 + \tfrac{1}{24}(x-2)^3 - \ldots\ldots$

$\ldots\ldots + \dfrac{(-1)^{n-1}}{n2^n}(x-2)^n + R_n(x:2)$

$\lim_{n\to\infty}\left|\dfrac{a_{n+1}}{a_n}\right| = \lim_{n\to\infty}\left|\dfrac{n}{n+1}\left(\dfrac{x-2}{2}\right)\right| = \left|\dfrac{x-2}{2}\right|$

and we have convergence for $\left|\dfrac{x-2}{2}\right| < 1$ i.e., $|x-2| < 2$

$\Rightarrow$ radius of convergence is 2.

4 a $\sin x = x - \dfrac{x^3}{3!} + \dfrac{x^5}{5!} - \ldots + \dfrac{(-1)^n x^{2n+1}}{(2n+1)!} + \ldots$

and converges for all $x \in \mathbb{R}$

So, $x\sin x = x^2 - \dfrac{x^4}{3!} + \dfrac{x^6}{5!} - \ldots + \dfrac{(-1)^n x^{2n+2}}{(2n+1)!} + \ldots$

and converges for all $x \in \mathbb{R}$

b $e^x = 1 + x + \dfrac{x^2}{2!} + \dfrac{x^3}{3!} + \dfrac{x^4}{4!} + \ldots + \dfrac{x^n}{n!} + \ldots$

and converges for all $x \in \mathbb{R}$

So, $e^{-x^2} = 1 - x^2 + \dfrac{x^4}{2!} - \dfrac{x^6}{3!} + \ldots + \dfrac{(-1)^n x^{2n}}{n!} + \ldots$

and converges for all $x \in \mathbb{R}$. {Ratio test}

c $\cos x = 1 - \dfrac{x^2}{2!} + \dfrac{x^4}{4!} - \dfrac{x^6}{6!} + \ldots + \dfrac{(-1)^n x^{2n}}{(2n)!} + \ldots$

So, $\cos(x^3)$

$= 1 - \dfrac{x^6}{2!} + \dfrac{x^{12}}{4!} - \dfrac{x^{18}}{6!} + \ldots + \dfrac{(-1)^n x^{6n}}{(2n)!} + \ldots$

which converges for all $x \in \mathbb{R}$ as

$\lim_{n\to\infty}\left|\dfrac{a_{n+1}}{a_n}\right| = \lim_{n\to\infty}\left|\dfrac{x^{6n+6}}{(2n+2)!}\dfrac{(2n)!}{x^{6n}}\right|$

$= \lim_{n\to\infty}\left|\dfrac{x^6}{(2n+1)(2n+2)}\right|$

$= 0$

5 $\sin x = x - \dfrac{x^3}{3!} + \dfrac{x^5}{5!} + R_5(x)$

where $R_5(x) = \dfrac{f^{(6)}(c)x^6}{6!} = \dfrac{-\sin c \times x^6}{6!}$

where $c \in]-0.3, 0.3[$

On this interval, $f^{(6)}(c)$ is maximum when $c = 0.3$.

$\therefore$ maximum error $\approx \dfrac{(0.3)^6}{720} \times \sin 0.3 \approx 2.992 \times 10^{-7}$

6 $3° = \dfrac{\pi}{60}$ radians. So, $\sin 3° = \sin\left(\dfrac{\pi}{60}\right)$

$\sin 3° \approx \dfrac{\pi}{60} - \dfrac{\left(\frac{\pi}{60}\right)^3}{3!} + \dfrac{\left(\frac{\pi}{60}\right)^5}{5!} - \ldots\ldots$

$\approx 0.052\,359\,9 - 0.000\,023\,9 + 3.3 \times 10^{-9}$

$\approx 0.052\,34$

7 $e^x = 1 + x + \dfrac{x^2}{2!} + \dfrac{x^3}{3!} + \dfrac{x^4}{4!} + \ldots\ldots$

So, $e^{-x^2} = 1 - x^2 + \dfrac{x^4}{2!} - \dfrac{x^6}{3!} + \dfrac{x^8}{4!} - \ldots\ldots$

$\therefore \int_0^1 e^{-x^2}\,dx$

$\approx \left[x - \dfrac{x^3}{3} + \dfrac{x^5}{10} - \dfrac{x^7}{42} + \dfrac{x^9}{216} - \dfrac{x^{11}}{1320} + \dfrac{x^{13}}{9360}\right]_0^1$

≈ 0.747 (to 3 d.p.)

8 $e^{x^2} = 1 + x^2 + \dfrac{x^4}{2!} + \dfrac{x^6}{3!} + \dfrac{x^8}{4!} + \ldots\ldots$

So, $\displaystyle\int_0^1 e^{x^2}\, dx$

$\approx \left[x + \dfrac{x^3}{3} + \dfrac{x^5}{10} + \dfrac{x^7}{42} + \dfrac{x^9}{216} + \dfrac{x^{11}}{1320} + \dfrac{x^{13}}{9360} \right]_0^1 \approx 1.463$

9 From question **2**, $(1+x^2)^{-1}$
$= 1 - x^2 + x^4 - x^6 + x^8 - \ldots\ldots + (-1)^n x^{2n} + \ldots\ldots$
Integrating both sides with respect to x gives

$\arctan x = x - \dfrac{x^3}{3} + \dfrac{x^5}{5} - \dfrac{x^7}{7} + \dfrac{x^9}{9} - \ldots\ldots$

$\qquad\qquad + \dfrac{(-1)^n x^{2n+1}}{2n+1} + \ldots\ldots$

10 $2^x = e^{x \ln 2}$

$\therefore\ 2^x = 1 + x\ln 2 + \dfrac{(x\ln 2)^2}{2!} + \dfrac{(x\ln 2)^3}{3!} + \ldots\ldots$

$\qquad\qquad + \dfrac{(x\ln 2)^n}{n!} + \ldots\ldots$

Since the interval for convergence for e^x is $\mathbb{R}$ then $\mathbb{R}$ is the interval of convergence for 2^x.

11 From question **2**,
$(1+x)^{-1} = 1 - x + x^2 - x^3 + x^4 - x^5 + \ldots\ldots$
So, $(1+x^3)^{-1} = 1 - x^3 + x^6 - x^9 + x^{12} - x^{15} + \ldots\ldots$
and

$\displaystyle\int_0^{\frac13} \dfrac{1}{1+x^3}\, dx \approx \left[x - \dfrac{x^4}{4} + \dfrac{x^7}{7} - \dfrac{x^{10}}{10} + \dfrac{x^{13}}{13} - \ldots\ldots \right]_0^{\frac13}$

$\qquad\qquad \approx 0.3303$

12 From question **1**,

$\ln(1+x) = x - \dfrac{x^2}{2} + \dfrac{x^3}{3} - \dfrac{x^4}{4} + \ldots\ldots$

$\therefore\ \ln(1-x) = -x - \dfrac{x^2}{2} - \dfrac{x^3}{3} - \dfrac{x^4}{4} - \ldots\ldots$

But $\ln\left(\dfrac{1+x}{1-x}\right) = \ln(1+x) - \ln(1-x)$

$\therefore\ \ln\left(\dfrac{1+x}{1-x}\right) = 2x + \dfrac{2x^3}{3} + \dfrac{2x^5}{5} + \dfrac{2x^7}{7} + \ldots\ldots$

If $\dfrac{1+x}{1-x} = 2$, then $x = \frac13$

$\therefore\ \ln 2 \approx 2\left(\frac13\right) + \frac23\left(\frac13\right)^3 + \frac25\left(\frac13\right)^5$

i.e., $\ln 2 \approx 0.693\ \left(\text{or } \frac{842}{1215}\right)$

13 $e^x = 1 + x + \dfrac{x^2}{2!} + \dfrac{x^3}{3!} + \dfrac{x^4}{4!} + \dfrac{x^5}{5!} + \ldots\ldots$

$e^{-1} = 1 - 1 + \dfrac{1}{2!} - \dfrac{1}{3!} + \dfrac{1}{4!} - \dfrac{1}{5!} + \ldots\ldots$

$\qquad = \displaystyle\sum_{n=0}^{\infty} \dfrac{(-1)^n}{n!}\quad$ where $\displaystyle\lim_{n\to\infty} \dfrac{1}{n!} = 0$

and $\dfrac{1}{n!}$ is a positive decreasing sequence.

So, $|S - S_n| \leqslant b_{n+1}$
{Alternating Series Est. Theorem}
$\Rightarrow\ |S - S_{10}| \leqslant b_{11} = \frac{1}{10!} < 5 \times 10^{-7}$
and $S_{10} \approx 0.367\,879$

14 $e^x = 1 + x + \dfrac{x^2}{2!} + \dfrac{x^3}{3!} + \dfrac{x^4}{4!} + \ldots\ldots$

$\qquad > 1 + x\quad$ for all $x > 0$

So, $e^x \geqslant 1 + x$ is true as required

Thus $(1+u_1)(1+u_2)\ldots\ldots(1+u_n)$

$\qquad \leqslant e^{u_1} e^{u_2} \ldots\ldots e^{u_n}$

$\qquad \leqslant e^{u_1 + u_2 + \ldots\ldots + u_n}$

$\left\{ \displaystyle\prod_{k=1}^{n} (1+u_k) \right\}$ is increasing as $1 + u_i \geqslant 1$
$\qquad\qquad\qquad$ for $i = 1, 2, 3, \ldots\ldots, k$

and $\displaystyle\sum_{k=1}^{n} u_k \geqslant 0$

If $\displaystyle\sum_{k=1}^{n} u_k$ converges then $e^{\sum_{k=1}^{n} u_k}$ is an upper

bound for $\{a_n\}$. Hence $\displaystyle\prod_{k=1}^{n} (1+u_k)$ converges
{Monotonic convergence theorem}

15 a The roots of $\dfrac{\sin x}{x}$ are the solutions of $\dfrac{\sin x}{x} = 0$
$\qquad$ i.e., $\sin x = 0$ but $x \neq 0$
$\qquad$ These are $x = k\pi,\ k \in \mathbb{Z},\ k \neq 0$

b $\sin x = x - \dfrac{x^3}{3!} + \dfrac{x^5}{5!} - \dfrac{x^7}{7!} + \ldots + \dfrac{(-1)^n x^{2n-1}}{(2n-1)!} + \ldots$

$\therefore\ \dfrac{\sin x}{x}$

$= 1 - \dfrac{x^2}{3!} + \dfrac{x^4}{5!} - \dfrac{x^6}{7!} + \ldots + \dfrac{(-1)^n x^{2n-2}}{(2n-1)!} + \ldots$

where $\displaystyle\lim_{n\to\infty} \left| \dfrac{a_{n+1}}{a_n} \right| = \lim_{n\to\infty} \left| \dfrac{x^2}{(2n+1)2n} \right| = 0$

Interval of convergence is $\mathbb{R}$.

c The zeros of $\left(1 - \dfrac{x}{\pi}\right)\left(1 + \dfrac{x}{\pi}\right)\left(1 - \dfrac{x}{2\pi}\right)\left(1 + \dfrac{x}{2\pi}\right)$

are $\pm\pi,\ \pm 2\pi,\ \pm 3\pi,\ \ldots\ldots$

d Multiplying in pairs

$\left(1 - \dfrac{x}{\pi}\right)\left(1 + \dfrac{x}{\pi}\right) = 1 - \dfrac{x^2}{\pi^2}$

$\left(1 - \dfrac{x}{2\pi}\right)\left(1 + \dfrac{x}{2\pi}\right) = 1 - \dfrac{x^2}{4\pi^2}$

$\vdots$

etc.

From **a** and **c**, $\dfrac{\sin x}{x}$ and the product

$\left(1 - \dfrac{x}{\pi}\right)\left(1 + \dfrac{x}{\pi}\right)\left(1 - \dfrac{x}{2\pi}\right)\left(1 + \dfrac{x}{2\pi}\right)\ldots\ldots$

have the same zeros, supporting Euler's claim.

i.e., $\dfrac{\sin x}{x} = \left(1 - \dfrac{x^2}{\pi^2}\right)\left(1 - \dfrac{x^2}{4\pi^2}\right)\left(1 - \dfrac{x^2}{9\pi^2}\right)$

e The coefficient of x^2 in $\dfrac{\sin x}{x}$ is $-\dfrac{1}{3!}$

and the coefficient of x^2 in the product expansion

is $\left(-\dfrac{1}{\pi^2}\right)\left[1+\dfrac{1}{2^2}+\dfrac{1}{3^2}+\ldots\ldots\right]$

Thus $1+\dfrac{1}{2^2}+\dfrac{1}{3^2}+\ldots\ldots=\dfrac{\pi^2}{3!}=\dfrac{\pi^2}{6}$

f $\displaystyle\sum_{r=1}^{\infty}\dfrac{1}{(2r)^2}=\tfrac14\sum_{r=1}^{\infty}\dfrac{1}{r^2}=\dfrac{\pi^2}{24}$

$\Rightarrow\displaystyle\sum_{r=1}^{\infty}\dfrac{1}{(2r-1)^2}=\dfrac{\pi^2}{6}-\dfrac{\pi^2}{24}=\dfrac{\pi^2}{8}$

EXERCISE 10E.1

1

		x			
	-2	-1	0	1	2
-2	0.70	0.35	0	-0.35	-0.70
-1	0.35	0.17	0	-0.17	-0.35
y $\quad 0$	0	0	0	0	0
1	-0.35	-0.17	0	0.17	0.35
2	-0.70	-0.35	0	0.35	0.70

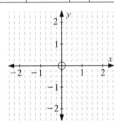

2 a

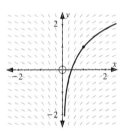

b

3

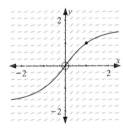

4

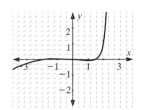

$\dfrac{dy}{dx}$ is undefined when $y=5x-10$

$\dfrac{dy}{dx}$ is 0 when $x^2+4y^2=1$

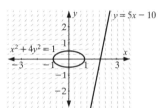

5 $\begin{cases} x_{n+1}=x_n+h \\ y_{n+1}=y_n+hf(x_n,y_n) \end{cases}$ where $h=0.2$

and $f(x_n,y_n)=1+2x_n-3y_n$

$\Rightarrow\ y_{n+1}=y_n+0.2(1+2x_n-3y_n)$
$\qquad\qquad=0.2+0.4x_n+0.4y_n$

$x_0=0$	$y_0=1$
$x_1=0.2$	$y_1=0.6$
$x_2=0.4$	$y_2=0.52$
$x_3=0.6$	$y_3=0.568$
$x_4=0.8$	$y_4=0.6672$
$x_5=1$	$y_5=0.786\,88$

So, $y(1)\approx y_5\approx 0.787$

6 $\begin{cases} x_{n+1}=x_n+0.1 \\ y_{n+1}=y_n+0.1\,(\sin(x_n+y_n)) \end{cases}$

$x_0=0$	$y_0\approx 0.5$
$x_1=0.1$	$y_1\approx 0.547\,94$
$x_2=0.2$	$y_2\approx 0.608\,30$
$x_3=0.3$	$y_3\approx 0.680\,61$
$x_4=0.4$	$y_4\approx 0.763\,69$
$x_5=0.5$	$y_5\approx 0.855\,52$

So, $y(0.5)\approx y_5\approx 0.856$

EXERCISE 10E.2

1 Solve all of these by separation of variables.

a $y=3+\ln 2-\ln|2-x|$ **b** $y=\arcsin\left[\tfrac32(x^2-1)\right]$

c $y=\ln\left(\sqrt[4]{|2x^2+4x+1|}(e^2+3)-3\right)$

d $y=3e^x\left|\dfrac{x-1}{x+1}\right|$ **e** $y=\arctan(\ln|x|)$

2 a $\dfrac{dT}{dt}=k(T-R)$, $\quad k$ a constant

b Solve $\dfrac{dT}{dt}=k(T-18)$ to obtain $T=Ae^{kt}+18$

Use $T(0)=82$ to find $A=64$
and $T(6)=50$ to find $e^k=\left(\tfrac12\right)^{\frac16}$

So, $T=64\left(\tfrac12\right)^{\frac{t}{6}}+18$

Show that when $T=26$, $\quad t=18$
and when $T=20$, $\quad t=30$

So, it would take $30-18=12$ min.

3

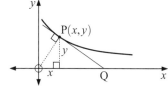

gradient of OP is $\dfrac{y}{x}$

$\Rightarrow$ gradient of PQ $= -\dfrac{x}{y}$

Solve $\dfrac{dy}{dx} = -\dfrac{x}{y}$ to obtain

$$\dfrac{y^2}{2} = \dfrac{-x^2}{2} + c$$

Given $(1, 2)$ lies on the curve, show that $c = 2\tfrac{1}{2}$

Hence, $y^2 = 5 - x^2$.

4

 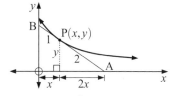

Slope of AB $= \dfrac{dy}{dx} = -\dfrac{y}{2x}$

Solve this to obtain $\ln|y| = -\tfrac{1}{2}\ln|x| + c$

Use the point $(1, 1)$ to show $c = 0$

Hence show $y = \dfrac{1}{\sqrt{x}}$.

5 a $\dfrac{dm}{dt} \propto m$ i.e., $\dfrac{dm}{dt} = -km$, k a constant > 0

{the negative sign is there because the mass is decreasing}

Solving gives $m = Ae^{-kt}$

When $t = 0$, $m = m_0$ $\Rightarrow$ $A = m_0$

So, $m = m_0 e^{-kt}$

b   When $t = 30$, $m = \tfrac{4}{5}m_0$

Use this to obtain $e^{-k} = (0.8)^{\frac{1}{30}}$

So, $m = m_0(0.8)^{\frac{t}{30}}$

$m = \tfrac{1}{2}m_0$ when $t \approx 93.2$ days

6 If $y = vx$, $\dfrac{dy}{dx} = \dfrac{dv}{dx}x + v$

a

$$\dfrac{dy}{dx} = \dfrac{x - y}{x}$$ becomes

$$\dfrac{dv}{dx}x + v = \dfrac{x - vx}{x}$$

Simplify to get $\dfrac{1}{1 - 2v}\dfrac{dv}{dx} = \dfrac{1}{x}$

then solve to get $1 - 2v = \dfrac{A}{x^2}$

i.e., $1 - \dfrac{2y}{x} = \dfrac{A}{x^2}$

i.e., $x^2 - 2xy = A$ (A a constant)

b $\arctan\left(\dfrac{y}{x}\right) - \tfrac{1}{2}\ln(x^2 + y^2) = c$ (c a constant)

c $x^2 + y^2 = Ax$, A a constant

7 a   Let $y = vx$, $\therefore$ $\dfrac{dy}{dx} = \dfrac{dv}{dx}x + v$

$\Rightarrow$ $x\dfrac{dv}{dx} + v = v + f(v)g(x)$

$\Rightarrow$ $x\dfrac{dv}{dx} = f(v)g(x)$

$\Rightarrow$ $\dfrac{1}{f(v)}\dfrac{dv}{dx} = \dfrac{g(x)}{x}$ i.e.,   is separable

b   For $x\dfrac{dv}{dx} = y + e^{\frac{y}{x}}$

we let $y = vx$

and hence show that $e^{-v}\dfrac{dv}{dx} = x^{-2}$

Solve to show $v = \ln\left(\dfrac{x}{1 - cx}\right)$

$\Rightarrow$ $y = x\ln\left(\dfrac{x}{1 - cx}\right)$

8 a $y = 3 + ce^{-4x}$ **b** $y = -\tfrac{1}{2}e^x + \left(\dfrac{2}{e^3} + \dfrac{1}{2e^2}\right)e^{3x}$

c $y = x - 1 + \tfrac{1}{2}e^x + \left(e - \dfrac{e^2}{2}\right)e^{-x}$

d $y = \sin x + \dfrac{\cos x}{x} + \dfrac{c}{x}$

9 Show that $\dfrac{dy}{dx} + \left(1 + \dfrac{1}{x}\right)y = 1 - x$

The IF is $e^{\int\left(1 + \frac{1}{x}\right)dx} = e^{x + \ln x} = e^x e^{\ln x} = xe^x$

$\therefore$ $xe^x\dfrac{dy}{dx} + (x + 1)e^x y = e^x x(1 - x)$

$\therefore$ $\dfrac{d}{dx}(xe^x y) = xe^x - x^2 e^x$

$\Rightarrow$ $xye^x = \int(xe^x - x^2 e^x)\,dx$

Using integration by parts

$$xye^x = e^x\left(-x^2 + 3x - 3\right) + c$$

$\Rightarrow$ $y = -x + 3 - \dfrac{3}{x} + \dfrac{c}{xe^x}$

10 a i $\mathcal{L}\{e^{ax}\} = \displaystyle\int_0^\infty e^{-sx}e^{ax}\,dx$

$= \displaystyle\int_0^\infty e^{(a-s)x}\,dx$

$= \left[\dfrac{1}{a - s}e^{(a-s)x}\right]_0^\infty$

$= -\dfrac{1}{a - s}e^0$ {since $s > a$}

$= \dfrac{1}{s - a}$

ii
$$\mathcal{L}\{x\} = \int_0^\infty e^{-sx} x\, dx$$
$$= \left[-\frac{x}{s}e^{-sx}\right]_0^\infty - \int_0^\infty \left(-\frac{1}{s}e^{-sx}\right) dx$$
{Integration by Parts}
$$= 0 + 0 + \frac{1}{s}\int_0^\infty e^{-sx}\, dx \quad \{\text{since } s > 0\}$$
$$= \frac{1}{s}\left[-\frac{1}{s}e^{-sx}\right]_0^\infty$$
$$= \frac{-1}{s^2}(0 - 1)$$
$$= \frac{1}{s^2}$$

iii
$$\mathcal{L}\{\sin ax\} = \int_0^\infty e^{-sx}\sin ax\, dx$$
Now $\int_0^\infty e^{-sx}\sin ax\, dx$
$$= \left[-\frac{1}{s}e^{-sx}\sin ax\right]_0^\infty - \int_0^\infty \left(-\frac{a}{s}e^{-sx}\cos ax\right) dx$$
{Integration by Parts}
$$= 0 - 0 + \frac{a}{s}\int_0^\infty e^{-sx}\cos ax\, dx$$
$$= \frac{a}{s}\left(\left[-\frac{e^{-sx}}{s}\cos ax\right]_0^\infty - \int_0^\infty \left(\frac{a}{s}e^{-sx}\sin ax\right) dx\right)$$
{Integration by Parts}
$$= \frac{a}{s}\left(0 - \left(-\frac{1}{-s}\right) - \frac{a}{s}\int_0^\infty e^{-sx}\sin ax\, dx\right)$$
$$= \frac{a}{s^2} - \frac{a^2}{s^2}\int_0^\infty e^{-sx}\sin ax\, dx$$
$$\therefore \quad \mathcal{L}\{\sin ax\} = \frac{a}{s^2} - \frac{a^2}{s^2}\mathcal{L}\{\sin ax\}$$
$$\therefore \quad \left(1 + \frac{a^2}{s^2}\right)\mathcal{L}\{\sin ax\} = \frac{a}{s^2}$$
$$\therefore \quad \frac{s^2 + a^2}{s^2}\mathcal{L}\{\sin ax\} = \frac{a}{s^2}$$
$$\therefore \quad \mathcal{L}\{\sin ax\} = \frac{a}{s^2 + a^2}$$

b i $\quad \mathcal{L}\{f'(x)\}$
$$= \int_0^\infty e^{-sx}\,(f'(x))\, dx$$
$$= \left[e^{-sx}f(x)\right]_0^\infty - \int_0^\infty \left(-se^{-sx}f(x)\right) dx$$
{Integration by Parts}
$$= 0 - f(0) + s\int_0^\infty \left(e^{-sx}f(x)\right) dx$$
$$= -f(0) + s\mathcal{L}\{f(x)\}$$
$$= s\mathcal{L}\{f(x)\} - f(0)$$

ii $\quad \mathcal{L}\{f''(x)\}$
$$= \int_0^\infty e^{-sx}\,(f''(x))\, dx$$
$$= \left[e^{-sx}f'(x)\right]_0^\infty - \int_0^\infty \left(-se^{-sx}f'(x)\right) dx$$
{Integration by Parts}
$$= 0 - f'(0) + s\int_0^\infty \left(e^{-sx}f'(x)\right) dx$$
$$= -f'(0) + s\mathcal{L}\{f'(x)\}$$
$$= -f'(0) + s\left(s\mathcal{L}\{f(x)\} - f(0)\right)$$
$$= s^2\mathcal{L}\{f(x)\} - sf(0) - f'(0)$$

iii Starting with $f''(x) + f(x) = x$, take the Laplace Transform of both sides.
$$\mathcal{L}\{f''(x) + f(x)\} = \mathcal{L}\{x\}$$
$$\therefore \quad \mathcal{L}\{f''(x)\} + \mathcal{L}\{f(x)\} = \frac{1}{s^2} \quad \{\textbf{a ii}\}$$
$$\therefore \quad s^2\mathcal{L}\{f(x)\} - sf(0) - f'(0) + \mathcal{L}\{f(x)\} = \frac{1}{s^2} \quad \{\textbf{b ii}\}$$
$$\therefore \quad \mathcal{L}\{f(x)\}(s^2 + 1) = \frac{1}{s^2} + s \times 0 + 2$$
$$\therefore \mathcal{L}\{f(x)\} = \frac{\frac{1}{s^2} + 2}{s^2 + 1} = \frac{2s^2 + 1}{s^2(s^2 + 1)}$$
$$= \frac{1}{s^2} + \frac{1}{s^2 + 1} \quad \{\text{using partial fractions}\}$$
$$= \mathcal{L}\{x\} + \mathcal{L}\{\sin x\}$$
$$\therefore \quad \text{Using } \textbf{a i} \text{ and } \textbf{ii}, \quad f(x) = x + \sin x$$

Check: If $f(x) = x + \sin x$
$$f'(x) = 1 + \cos x \quad \text{and} \quad f''(x) = -\sin x$$
$$\therefore \quad f''(x) + f(x) = x + \sin x - \sin x = x \quad \checkmark$$
Also, $f(0) = 0 + \sin 0 = 0 \quad \checkmark$
and $f'(0) = 1 + \cos 0 = 2 \quad \checkmark$

REVIEW SET 10A

2 1

3 a $-\frac{2}{7}$ **b** does not converge **c** 0 **d** diverges **e** 0 **f** $-\frac{1}{9}$
g $\frac{\sqrt{6}}{3}$ **h** $-\frac{1}{2}$ **i** 3 **j** $\frac{\pi}{2}$ **k** 0 **l** 0 **m** 0 **n** -1

REVIEW SET 10B

2 diverges when $x = 1$, converges (to $-\ln 2$) when $x = -1$

4 $\frac{1}{4}$, $\sum_{r=1}^\infty \frac{1}{r(r+1)(r+2)} = .25$

6 converges for $x \in [2, 4]$. Radius is 1.

7 diverges **8** diverges **10** diverges

11 If $a_n \in \mathbb{R}$ then $\sum_{n=0}^\infty a_n^2$ and $\sum_{n=0}^\infty \left(a_n - \frac{1}{n}\right)^2$ are not necessarily convergent.
For example, if $a_n = \frac{(-1)^n}{\sqrt{n}}$ then $\sum_{n=1}^\infty a_n$ converges.
However, $\sum_{n=1}^\infty a_n^2 = \sum_{n=1}^\infty \frac{1}{n}$ and
$$\sum_{n=1}^\infty \left(a_n - \frac{1}{n}\right)^2 = \sum_{n=1}^\infty \left(\frac{1}{n} - \frac{(-1)^n}{n\sqrt{n}} + \frac{1}{n^2}\right) \text{ both diverge.}$$

12 converges for $x < \frac{1}{2}$ **13 b** $b_{11} = \dfrac{1}{\ln 10} \approx 0.4343$

14 diverges as $\displaystyle\lim_{n\to\infty} \left(\dfrac{n}{n+5}\right)^n = \dfrac{1}{\displaystyle\lim_{n\to\infty}\left(1+\frac{5}{n}\right)^n} = \dfrac{1}{e^5}$

15 a $\dfrac{1}{x} + \dfrac{-1}{x+1}$

REVIEW SET 10C

1 $(x-1) + (x-1)^2 + \frac{1}{2}(x-1)^3$ **2** 0.310 **4** 1.350

6 If $-1 < x < 1$, then $1 - x + x^2 - x^3 + ... = \dfrac{1}{x+1}$

Integrating with respect to x,

$f(x) = \ln(1+x) = x - \frac{x^2}{2} + \frac{x^3}{3} - \frac{x^4}{4} + ...$

REVIEW SET 10D

1 $a = 2$, $b = -1$

2 a $\dfrac{dy}{dx} = \dfrac{2x - y}{x}$ **b** $\dfrac{dy}{dx} = -\frac{1}{2}y\tan x$

3

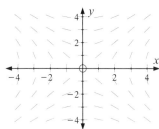

4 $y \approx 1.009$ **5** $y = 2(x-1)e^{x-2}$ **6** $y = \dfrac{-1}{x^2 - x + c}$

7 $y^2 = 3x^2 + 2x - 1$ **8** $y = \dfrac{x^8 - 1}{x^3}$

9 a $\dfrac{dV}{dt} = k\sqrt{h}$ **b** $\dfrac{dh}{dt} = \dfrac{k}{4}\sqrt{h}$ **c** 20 min

REVIEW SET 10E

1 For equation **a**, $\dfrac{dy}{dx} = 1$ at $(0, 0)$. Hence **a** is **B**.

For equation **b**, $\dfrac{dy}{dx} = 0$ at $(2, 2)$.

Hence **b** is **C** and **c** is **A**.

2

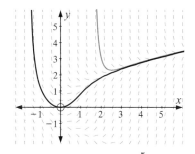

3 $y^2 + 2x^2\ln|x| + cx^2$ **4** $y = \dfrac{5}{\sqrt{x}}$

5 $\dfrac{dy}{dx} = \dfrac{y - 3x^2y^3}{x}$, $y = \sqrt{\dfrac{2x^2}{3x^4 - 40}}$

6 a $y = 2x\sqrt{x} - 4x$

b $y = \dfrac{-\cos^2 x}{2\sin x}$ or $y = -\frac{1}{2}\cot x \cos x$

7 a $P \approx \dfrac{400}{1 + \frac{123}{77}e^{-\frac{1}{5}t}}$ people **b** ≈ 387 people

c yes, 400

8 a Since the line from P is parallel to the x-axis, we can mark in the new angle α as shown {corresponding angles}

Hence $\theta = 2\alpha$ {exterior angle theorem}

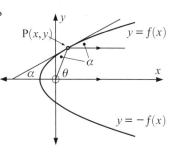

b Consider the triangle the tangent makes with the x- and y-axes.

$\text{slope} = \dfrac{\text{rise}}{\text{run}} = \tan\alpha$

$\therefore \dfrac{dy}{dx} = \tan\alpha$

c Now $\tan\theta = \tan 2\alpha$ {using **a**}

$= \dfrac{2\tan\alpha}{1 - \tan^2\alpha}$ {using the identity}

$\therefore \tan\theta(1 - \tan^2\alpha) = 2\tan\alpha$

$\therefore \tan\theta\tan^2\alpha + 2\tan\alpha - \tan\theta = 0$

$\therefore \tan\alpha = \dfrac{-2 \pm \sqrt{4 + 4\tan^2\theta}}{2\tan\theta}$

$= \dfrac{-1 \pm \sqrt{1 + \tan^2\theta}}{\tan\theta}$

But $\tan\theta > 0$ and $\tan\alpha > 0$,

so $\tan\alpha = \dfrac{-1 + \sqrt{1 + \tan^2\theta}}{\tan\theta}$

$\therefore$ since $\tan\theta = \dfrac{y}{x}$, $\tan\alpha = \dfrac{-1 + \sqrt{1 + \dfrac{y^2}{x^2}}}{\dfrac{y}{x}}$

$\therefore \dfrac{dy}{dx} = \dfrac{\sqrt{x^2 + y^2} - x}{y}$

d If we let $r^2 = x^2 + y^2$, then $y^2 = r^2 - x^2$

and $2r\dfrac{dr}{dx} = 2x + 2y\dfrac{dy}{dx}$

$\therefore y\dfrac{dy}{dx} = r\dfrac{dr}{dx} - x$ ...... (1)

But $\dfrac{dy}{dx} = \dfrac{\sqrt{x^2 + y^2} - x}{y}$

so $y\dfrac{dy}{dx} = \sqrt{x^2 + y^2} - x = r - x$ ...... (2)

$\therefore r\dfrac{dr}{dx} - x = r - x$ {from (1) and (2)}

$\therefore \dfrac{dr}{dx} = 1$ which has solution $r = x + c$

$\therefore r^2 = (x + c)^2$

$\therefore x^2 + y^2 = x^2 + 2cx + c^2$

$\therefore y^2 = c^2 + 2cx$ for some constant c.

e $y = f(x)$ is parabolic, since x is a quadratic in y.

EXERCISE 11A.1

1 It is false. For example if $n = 4$, $2^4 - 1 = 15 = 3 \times 5$ i.e., composite.

2 $2^p - 1$ (p a prime) will not always be a prime. For example, $p = 11$, $2^{11} - 1 = 2047 = 23 \times 89$.

3 **a** 32, 33, 34, 35, 36   **b** 90, 91, 92, 93, 94, 95

4 Impossible, as for example LHS is divisible by 3 whereas RHS is not divisible by 3.

5 **a** Factors of any integer appear in pairs. For example, factors of 12 are 1, 12 and 2, 6 and 3, 4. However, for a perfect square, one of the factor pairs is a repeat.

For example, factors of 16 are 1, 16 and 2, 8 and 4, 4. So we have at least one factor pair and one other factor (4 in the above example), which is an odd number of factors.

b Any positive integer $\geqslant 2$ can be written as a product of prime factors in index form. That is,

$$N = p_1{}^{a_1} p_2{}^{a_2} p_3{}^{a_3} \ldots\ldots p_k{}^{a_k}$$

$\therefore$ $N^2 = p_1{}^{2a_1} p_2{}^{2a_2} \ldots\ldots p_k{}^{2a_k}$

$\therefore$ the number of factors is
$$2a_1 + 2a_2 + 2a_3 + \ldots\ldots + 2a_k$$
$$= 2(a_1 + a_2 + a_3 + \ldots\ldots + a_k)$$
which is even

6 The number ends in 24 and so is divisible by 4.

(Any number ending in 24 has form $100n + 24$ where $n \in \mathbb{Z}^+$ and $100n + 24 = 4(25n + 6)$ where $25n + 6 \in \mathbb{Z}^+$.)

Also the sum of the number's digits is 63 where 63 is divisible by 9 and so the original number is divisible by 9.

So, the number is divisible by $4 \times 9 = 36$.

7 If $2x + 4y = 62$ then $x + 2y = 31$.

So, if $y = t$, $t \in \mathbb{Z}$ then $x = 31 - 2t$.

Hence, there are infinitely many solutions of the form $x = 31 - 2t$, $y = t$, $t \in \mathbb{Z}$.

If $t = 15$, $x = 1$, $y = 15$ is one solution.

8 Yes, even though the strings of composites between them seem to get larger.

Proof: Suppose the number of primes is finite and so there exists a largest prime, p say.

Suppose that the product of all primes less than or equal to p is N,

i.e., $N = 2 \times 3 \times 5 \times 7 \times 11 \times \ldots\ldots \times p$.

Now $N + 1$ is certainly $> p$.

If $N+1$ is a prime, then p is not the largest prime number.

If $N+1$ is composite, then it must contain at least one prime factor greater than p. This is because $N + 1$ when divided by primes less than or equal to p leaves a remainder of 1.

A contradiction in both cases. So, the number of primes is infinite.

9 Suppose $\sqrt{2}$ is rational,

i.e., $\sqrt{2} = \dfrac{p}{q}$ where $p, q \in \mathbb{Z}^+$ and p and q have no common factors.

$\therefore$ $2 = \dfrac{p^2}{q^2}$ which implies that $p^2 = 2q^2$

This is a contradiction as LHS has an even number of factors and RHS has an odd number of factors.

{We proved in **5b** that "A perfect square always has an even number of prime factors".}

10 $5041 = 71^2$ and so is not prime.

EXERCISE 11A.2.1

In questions **1** and **2** the 'induction step' only is shown.

1 **a**
$$3^{k+1} - 7(k + 1)$$
$$= 3 \times 3^k - 7k - 7$$
$$> 3(7k) - 7k - 7$$
i.e., $> 14k - 7$
i.e., $> 7(2k - 1)$
i.e., > 35 {as $k \geqslant 3$}
i.e., > 0

b
$$(k + 1)^{k+1} - (k + 1)!$$
$$= (k + 1)(k + 1)^k - (k + 1)k!$$
$$> (k + 1)k^k - (k + 1)k!$$
$$> (k + 1)\left[k^k - k!\right]$$
$$> 3 \times 0$$
i.e., > 0

c
$$(k + 1)! - 3^{k+1}$$
$$= (k + 1)k! - 3(3^k)$$
$$> (k + 1)3^k - 3(3^k)$$
$$> 3^k(k + 1 - 3)$$
$$> 3^k(k - 2)$$
i.e., > 0 as $k \geqslant 6$

2 **a**
$$(n + 1)^3 - 4(n + 1)$$
$$= n^3 + 3n^2 + 3n + 1 - 4n - 4$$
$$= (n^3 - 4n) + (3n^2 + 3n - 3)$$
$$= 3A + 3(n^2 + n - 1)$$
$$3(A + n^2 + n - 1) \quad \text{where}$$
$$A + n^2 + n - 1 \in \mathbb{Z}^+$$
etc.

b
$$5^{[k+1]+1} + 2(3^{k+1}) + 1$$
$$= 5(5^{k+1}) + 6(3^k) + 1$$
$$= 5\left[8A - 2(3^k) - 1\right] + 6(3^k) + 1$$
$$= 40A - 4(3^k) - 4$$
$$= 4(10A - [3^k + 1])$$
where 3^k is always odd
and so $3^k + 1$ is always even.
$$= 4(10A - 2B)$$
$$= 8(5A - B) \quad \text{where} \quad 5A - B \in \mathbb{Z}^+$$
etc.

c
$$8^{[k+1]+2} + 9^{2[k+1]+1}$$
$$= 8(8^{k+2}) + 81(9^{2k+1})$$
$$= 8(8^{k+2}) + 81(73A - 8^{k+2})$$
$$= 81(73A) - 73(8^{k+2})$$
$$= 73(81A - 8^{k+2})$$
where $81A - 8^{k+2} \in \mathbb{Z}$
etc.

3 **a** The nth repunit
$$= 1 + 10 + 10^2 + 10^3 + \ldots\ldots + 10^{n-1} \quad \text{which is a}$$
geometric series with $u_1 = 1$ and $r = 10$
$$= \frac{1(10^n - 1)}{10 - 1} \quad \text{or} \quad \frac{10^n - 1}{9}$$

b The first repunit is 1 which by definition is neither prime nor composite. So, the statement is false.

c Ali's statement is true.

Use if $\sim B \Rightarrow \sim A$ then $A \Rightarrow B$.

So we need to prove that "If a repunit does not have a prime number of digits then the repunit is not prime".

i.e., "If a repunit has a composite number of digits then the repunit is composite".

Proof:

If the nth repunit is such that $n = ab$, then

$$n = \underbrace{1111......1}_{a \text{ of these}} \underbrace{1111......1}_{a \text{ of these}} .... \underbrace{1111......1}_{a \text{ of these}}$$
$$\underbrace{\hspace{6cm}}_{b \text{ lots of } a}$$

$$= (1111......1)\left[1 + 10^a + 10^{2a} + ... + 10^{(b-1)a}\right]$$

or $\left(\dfrac{10^a - 1}{9}\right)\left(\dfrac{(10^a)^b - 1}{10^a - 1}\right)$

both forms of which are composite.

d The third repunit, $111 = 3 \times 37$ contradicts the statement.

EXERCISE 11A.2.2

1 Induction step only

$$\begin{aligned}
a_{k+1} &= a_k + a_{k-1} \\
&\leqslant \left(\tfrac{5}{3}\right)^k + \left(\tfrac{5}{3}\right)^{k-1} \\
&\leqslant \left(\tfrac{5}{3}\right)^{k+1}\left(\tfrac{3}{5} + \tfrac{9}{25}\right) \\
&\leqslant \left(\tfrac{5}{3}\right)^{k+1}\left(\tfrac{15}{25} + \tfrac{9}{25}\right) \\
&\leqslant \left(\tfrac{5}{3}\right)^{k+1}\left(\tfrac{24}{25}\right) \\
&\leqslant \left(\tfrac{5}{3}\right)^{k+1}, \quad \text{etc}
\end{aligned}$$

2 As b_1 and b_2 are odd and twice an odd is even, then $b_n = \text{even} + \text{odd} = \text{odd}$.

3 If $S_n = \sum\limits_{k=1}^{n} f_k$ then

$$\begin{aligned}
S_1 &= 1 \\
S_2 &= 2 \\
S_3 &= 4 \\
S_4 &= 7 \quad \text{and} \quad S_n = f_{n+2} - 1 \\
S_5 &= 12 \quad \{\text{by observation}\} \\
S_6 &= 20 \\
S_7 &= 33
\end{aligned}$$

Inductive step only

$$\begin{aligned}
S_{k+1} &= S_k + f_{k+1} \\
&= f_{k+2} - 1 + f_{k+1} \\
&= (f_{k+2} + f_{k+1}) - 1 \\
&= f_{k+3} - 1 \\
&= f_{[k+1]+2} - 1
\end{aligned}$$

4 Prove $f_n > \left(\tfrac{3}{2}\right)^{n-2}$, $n \geqslant 3$ first by induction.

Then prove $f_n < 2^{n-2}$, $n \geqslant 3$ by induction.

Likewise for the challenge where $n \geqslant 1$.

5
$$f_n = f_{n+2} - f_{n+1}$$

$$\begin{aligned}
\Rightarrow \quad \sum_{k=1}^{n} f_k &= \quad f_3 - f_2 \\
&\quad + f_4 - f_3 \\
&\quad + f_5 - f_4 \\
&\qquad \vdots \\
&\quad + f_{n+2} - f_{n+1} \\
&= f_{n+2} - f_2 \\
&= f_{n+2} - 1 \quad \text{(QED)}
\end{aligned}$$

6 Let $\sum\limits_{k=1}^{n} f_{2k-1} = S_n$ say, then

$$\begin{aligned}
S_1 &= f_1 = 1 = f_2 \\
S_2 &= f_1 + f_3 = 1 + 2 = 3 = f_4 \\
S_3 &= f_1 + f_3 + f_5 = 1 + 2 + 5 = 8 = f_6 \\
S_4 &= f_1 + f_3 + f_5 + f_7 = 1 + 2 + 5 + 13 = 21 = f_8
\end{aligned}$$

It appears that $S_n = f_{2n}$ for all $n \geqslant 1$.

Our postulate is then,

$$\sum_{k=1}^{n} f_{2k-1} = f_{2n} \quad \text{for all} \quad n \geqslant 1.$$

Induction step only (on r):

$$\begin{aligned}
\sum_{k=1}^{r+1} f_{2k-1} &= \sum_{k=1}^{r} f_{2k-1} + f_{2r+1} \\
&= f_{2r} + f_{2r+1} \\
&= f_{2r+2} \\
&= f_{2[r+1]} \quad \text{etc.}
\end{aligned}$$

7 Let $\sum\limits_{k=1}^{n} (f_k)^2 = S_n$ say, then

$$\begin{aligned}
S_1 &= (f_1)^2 = 1 = 1 \times 1 \\
S_2 &= (f_1)^2 + (f_2)^2 = 1 + 1 = 2 = 1 \times 2 \\
S_3 &= (f_1)^2 + (f_2)^2 + (f_3)^2 = 2 + 2^2 = 6 = 2 \times 3 \\
S_4 &= (f_1)^2 + (f_2)^2 + (f_3)^2 + (f_4)^2 = 6 + 9 = 15 = 3 \times 5 \\
S_5 &= 15 + 25 = 40 = 5 \times 8
\end{aligned}$$

It appears that $S_n = f_n f_{n+1}$ for all $n \geqslant 1$.

Our postulate is then,

$$\sum_{k=1}^{n} (f_k)^2 = f_n f_{n+1} \quad \text{for all} \quad n \geqslant 1.$$

Induction step only (on r):

$$\begin{aligned}
\sum_{k=1}^{r+1} (f_{k+1})^2 &= \sum_{k=1}^{r} (f_{k+1})^2 + (f_{r+1})^2 \\
&= f_r f_{r+1} + (f_{r+1})^2 \\
&= f_{r+1}(f_r + f_{r+1}) \\
&= f_{r+1} f_{r+2} \quad \text{etc.}
\end{aligned}$$

8   Induction step only

$$f_{k+2}f_k - (f_{k+1})^2$$
$$= (f_{k+1} + f_k)f_k - (f_{k+1})^2$$
$$= f_{k+1}f_k + (f_k)^2 - (f_{k+1})^2$$
$$= f_{k+1}f_k + f_{k+1}f_{k-1} - (-1)^k - (f_{k+1})^2$$
$$= f_{k+1}(f_k + f_{k-1} - f_{k+1}) + (-1)^{k+1}$$
$$= f_{k+1}(f_{k+1} - f_{k+1}) + (-1)^{k+1}$$
$$= (-1)^{k+1}$$

9   Let $S_n = \sum_{k=1}^{n} f_{2k}$

$\therefore$ $S_1 = f_2 = 1 = f_3 - 1$
$S_2 = f_2 + f_4 = 1 + 3 = 4 = f_5 - 1$
$S_3 = f_2 + f_4 + f_6 = 4 + 8 = 12 = f_7 - 1$
$S_4 = f_2 + f_4 + f_6 + f_8 = 12 + 21 = 33 = f_9 - 1$

So, we postulate that $\sum_{k=1}^{n} f_{2k} = f_{2n+1} - 1$

Induction step only (on r)

$$\sum_{k=1}^{r+1} f_{2k} = \sum_{k=1}^{r} f_{2k} + f_{2r+2}$$
$$= f_{2r+1} - 1 + f_{2r+2}$$
$$= f_{2r+3} - 1$$
$$= f_{2[r+1]+1} - 1$$
$$\text{etc.}$$

10   Let $S_n = \sum_{k=1}^{2n-1} f_k f_{k+1}$

$\therefore$ $S_1 = f_1 f_2 = 1 \times 1 = 1 = 1^2$
$S_2 = f_1 f_2 + f_2 f_3 + f_3 f_4 = 1 + 2 + 6 = 9 = 3^2$
$S_3 = f_1 f_2 + f_2 f_3 + f_3 f_4 + f_4 f_5 + f_5 f_6$
$\qquad = 9 + 15 + 40$
$\qquad = 64$
$\qquad = 8^2$

i.e., $S_1 = (f_2)^2,\ \ S_2 = (f_4)^2,\ \ S_3 = (f_6)^2,\ \ \ldots\ldots$

So we postulate that $\sum_{k=1}^{2n-1} f_k f_{k+1} = (f_{2n})^2$

Induction step only (on r)

$$\sum_{k=1}^{2r+1} f_k f_{k+1} = \sum_{k=1}^{2r-1} f_k f_{k+1} + f_{2r} f_{2r+1} + f_{2r+1} f_{2r+2}$$
$$= (f_{2r})^2 + f_{2r} f_{2r+1} + f_{2r+1}(f_{2r} + f_{2r+1})$$
$$= (f_{2r})^2 + 2 f_{2r} f_{2r+1} + (f_{2r+1})^2$$
$$= (f_{2r} + f_{2r+1})^2$$
$$= (f_{2r+2})^2 \quad \text{etc.}$$

11 $\mathbf{F} = \begin{bmatrix} 1 & 1 \\ 1 & 0 \end{bmatrix}$

$\mathbf{F}^2 = \begin{bmatrix} 1 & 1 \\ 1 & 0 \end{bmatrix}\begin{bmatrix} 1 & 1 \\ 1 & 0 \end{bmatrix} = \begin{bmatrix} 2 & 1 \\ 1 & 1 \end{bmatrix}$

$\mathbf{F}^3 = \begin{bmatrix} 2 & 1 \\ 1 & 1 \end{bmatrix}\begin{bmatrix} 1 & 1 \\ 1 & 0 \end{bmatrix} = \begin{bmatrix} 3 & 2 \\ 2 & 1 \end{bmatrix}$

$\mathbf{F}^4 = \begin{bmatrix} 3 & 2 \\ 2 & 1 \end{bmatrix}\begin{bmatrix} 1 & 1 \\ 1 & 0 \end{bmatrix} = \begin{bmatrix} 5 & 3 \\ 3 & 2 \end{bmatrix}$

$\mathbf{F}^5 = \begin{bmatrix} 5 & 3 \\ 3 & 2 \end{bmatrix}\begin{bmatrix} 1 & 1 \\ 1 & 0 \end{bmatrix} = \begin{bmatrix} 8 & 5 \\ 5 & 3 \end{bmatrix}$

So, we postulate that

$\mathbf{F}^n = \begin{bmatrix} f_{n+1} & f_n \\ f_n & f_{n-1} \end{bmatrix}$ where f_n is the nth Fibonacci number

Now prove this by induction on n.

Since $|\mathbf{F}^n| = |\mathbf{F}|^n$ {determinant property}

$$\begin{vmatrix} f_{n+1} & f_n \\ f_n & f_{n-1} \end{vmatrix} = \begin{vmatrix} 1 & 1 \\ 1 & 0 \end{vmatrix}^n$$

$\therefore$ $f_{n+1}f_{n-1} - (f_n)^2 = (-1)^n$

12 $(f_n)^2 - (f_{n-1})^2 + (-1)^n$
$= (f_n + f_{n-1})(f_n - f_{n-1}) + (-1)^n$
$= f_{n+1}(f_n - f_{n-1}) + (-1)^n$
$= f_n f_{n+1} - f_{n+1}f_{n-1} + (-1)^n$
$= f_n f_{n+1} - \left[(f_n)^2 + (-1)^n\right] + (-1)^n$ {from **8**}
$= f_n f_{n+1} - (f_n)^2 - (-1)^n + (-1)^n$
$= f_n(f_{n+1} - f_n)$
$= f_n f_{n-1}$ (QED)

gcd (LHS)   = gcd (RHS)
$\qquad\qquad$ = gcd of each term
$\qquad\qquad$ = 1   {from $(-1)^n$}

EXERCISE 11A.3.1

1 a $d \mid n \Rightarrow\ \ n = kd,\ \ k \in \mathbb{Z}$
$\qquad\qquad \Rightarrow\ \ an = kad,\ \ k \in \mathbb{Z}$
$\qquad\qquad \Rightarrow\ \ ad \mid an$

b $d \mid n$ and $d \mid m$
$\Rightarrow\ \ n = k_1 d$ and $m = k_2 d,\ \ k_1 k_2 \in \mathbb{Z}$
$\Rightarrow\ \ an + bm = k_1 ad + k_2 bd$
$\qquad\qquad\qquad = d(k_1 a + k_2 b)$
$\qquad\qquad\qquad\ $ where $k_1 a + k_2 b \in \mathbb{Z}$
$\Rightarrow\ \ d \mid an + bm$

c $d \mid n \Rightarrow\ \ n = kd,\ \ k \in \mathbb{Z}^+$
but $k \geqslant 1 \Rightarrow\ \ kd \geqslant d$
$\qquad\qquad\qquad \Rightarrow\ \ n \geqslant d$
$\qquad\qquad\qquad \Rightarrow\ \ d \leqslant n$

2   Let d be a common divisor of a and $a+1$,
i.e., $d \mid a$ and $d \mid a+1$
$\Rightarrow\ \ d \mid (a+1) - a$
{$d \mid n$ and $d \mid m \Rightarrow\ \ d \mid an + bm$ property}
$\Rightarrow\ \ d \mid 1$

3 a   We observe that $2 \mid 14m + 20n$
$\qquad \Rightarrow\ \ 2 \mid 101$ which is false.
Hence, the impossibility.

b $14m + 21n = 100$
But $7 \mid 14m + 21n$ and $7 \nmid 100$
Hence, the impossibility.

4 $a \mid b$ and $a \mid c$
$\Rightarrow\ \ b = k_1 a$ and $c = k_2 a,\ \ k_1 k_2 \in \mathbb{Z}$
$\Rightarrow\ \ b \pm c = k_1 a \pm k_2 a = (k_1 \pm k_2)a$ where $k_1 \pm k_2 \in \mathbb{Z}$
$\Rightarrow\ \ a \mid b \pm c$

EXERCISE 11A.3.2

1 a (only) $66 = 3(22) + 0$ i.e., $r = 0 \Rightarrow 3 \mid 66$

2 a (only) $100 = 17(5) + 15$
  $\Rightarrow$ quotient is 5, remainder is 15

5 No

6 Example: $4 \mid 2 \times 6$, but $4 \nmid 2$ and $4 \nmid 6$
  So, b and c have to contain factors whose product is a.

7 $p \mid q$ where $p, q \in \mathbb{Z}^+ \Rightarrow q = pk$ where $k \in \mathbb{Z}^+$
  But $k \geqslant 1 \Rightarrow pk \geqslant p$.
  So, $q \geqslant p$ i.e., $p \leqslant q$.

8 $p \mid q \Rightarrow q = ap, \quad a \in \mathbb{Z}$
  $\Rightarrow q^k = a^k p^k, \quad a^k \in \mathbb{Z}$
  $\Rightarrow p^k \mid q^k$

9 If all integers are not odd then at least one is even
  $\Rightarrow$ product is even.
  {odd $\times$ even $= (2a+1)2b$ which is even
  even $\times$ even $= 2a \times 2b$ which is even}

  Using the contrapositive:
  If product is *not* even $\Rightarrow$ all integers are odd
  i.e., product is odd $\Rightarrow$ all integers are odd.

10 a Any integer n takes the form $3a, 3a+1, 3a+2$
  where $a \in \mathbb{Z}$
  $\Rightarrow n^2 = (3a)^2, \quad (3a+1)^2 \text{ or } (3a+2)^2$
  $\Rightarrow n^2 = 3(3a^2), \quad 3(3a^2+2a)+1$
  or $3(3a^2+4a+1)+1$
  $\Rightarrow n^2 = 3k \text{ or } 3k+1, \quad k \in \mathbb{Z}$

b Any integer is odd or even
  $\Rightarrow n = 2k+1 \text{ or } n = 2k, \quad k \in \mathbb{Z}$
  $\Rightarrow n^2 = 4k^2 + 4k + 1 \text{ or } 4k^2$
  $\Rightarrow n^2 = 4(k^2+k)+1 \text{ or } 4k^2$
  $\Rightarrow n^2$ has form $4q$ or $4q+1, \quad q \in \mathbb{Z}$

c $1234567 = 4(308641) + 3$
  which is of the form $4q+3, \quad q \in \mathbb{Z}$
  $\Rightarrow 1234567$ is not a perfect square

EXERCISE 11A.3.3

1 To prove: $5 \mid a \Leftrightarrow 5 \mid a^2$

  $(\Rightarrow)$ If $5 \mid a$ then $a = 5q, \quad q \in \mathbb{Z}$
  $\Rightarrow a^2 = 25q^2$
  $\Rightarrow a^2 = 5(5q^2), \quad 5q^2 \in \mathbb{Z}$
  $\Rightarrow 5 \mid a^2$

  $(\Leftarrow)$ Using contrapositive (i.e., $5 \nmid a \Rightarrow 5 \nmid a^2$)
  If $5 \nmid a$ then $a = 5k+1, \quad 5k+2$
  $5k+3$ or $5k+4$

  $\Rightarrow a^2 = \begin{cases} 25k^2 + 10k + 1 \\ 25k^2 + 20k + 4 \\ 25k^2 + 30k + 9 \\ 25k^2 + 40k + 16 \end{cases}$

  $\Rightarrow a^2 = \begin{cases} 5(5k^2+2k)+1 \\ 5(5k^2+4k+1)-1 \\ 5(5k^2+6k+2)-1 \\ 5(5k^2+8k+3)+1 \end{cases}$

  $\Rightarrow a^2 = 5b \pm 1, \quad b \in \mathbb{Z}$
  $\Rightarrow 5 \nmid a^2$

  So, as $5 \nmid a \Rightarrow 5 \nmid a^2$ then $5 \mid a^2 \Rightarrow 5 \mid a$.

2 $3 \mid a^2 \Leftrightarrow 9 \mid a^2$
  $(\Rightarrow)$ $3 \mid a^2 \Rightarrow 3 \mid a$ {Example **9**}
  $\Rightarrow a = 3k, \quad k \in \mathbb{Z}$
  $\Rightarrow a^2 = 9k^2$
  $\Rightarrow 9 \mid a^2$
  $(\Leftarrow)$ $9 \mid a^2 \Rightarrow a^2 = 9k, \quad k \in \mathbb{Z}$
  $\Rightarrow a^2 = 3(3k)$
  $\Rightarrow 3 \mid a^2$

3 a $n = 2, \quad n - 2 = 0 \Rightarrow (n+3)(n-2) = 0$
b If $n = -3, \quad n + 3 = 0$
  So $(n+3)(n-2) = 0$ which $\not\Rightarrow n = 2$
  i.e., converse is false.

4 a False **b** True **c** False **d** True **e** False
  f False **g** False

5 a As $8p + 7 = 8p + 4 + 3$
  $= 4(2p+1) + 3$
  $= 4q + 3, \quad q \in \mathbb{Z}$

b $11 = 4(2) + 3$ has form $4q+3$
  but does not have form $8p + 7, \quad p \in \mathbb{Z}$.

6 a Every integer n has form $3a, 3a+1$ or $3a+2$
  $\therefore n^3 = 27a^3$
  or $27a^3 + 27a^2 + 9a + 1$
  or $27a^3 + 54a^2 + 36a + 8, \quad a \in \mathbb{Z}$
  $\therefore n^3 = 9(3a^3)$
  or $9(3a^3 + 3a^2 + a) + 1$
  or $9(3a^3 + 6a^2 + 4a + 1) - 1, \quad a \in \mathbb{Z}$
  $\therefore n^3$ has form $9k, 9k+1$ or $9k-1$

b Likewise, using $n = 5a, 5a+1, 5a+2, 5a+3$ or $5a+4$.

7 Suppose $3k^2 - 1 = n^2, \quad n \in \mathbb{Z}$
  $\therefore 3k^2 - 1 = (3a)^2 \text{ or } (3a+1)^2 \text{ or } (3a+2)^2$
  $\therefore 3k^2 = 9a^2 + 1$
  or $9a^2 + 6a + 2$
  or $9a^2 + 12a + 5$
  all of which are impossible as the LHS is divisible by 3,
  whereas the RHS is not divisible by 3.

8 n could be of the form $6a, 6a+1, 6a+2, 6a+3,$
  $6a+4$ or $6a+5$.
  Show for each case $\dfrac{n(n+1)(2n+1)}{6}$ is an integer.
  Alternatively
  $1^2 + 2^2 + 3^2 + \ldots + n^2 = \dfrac{n(n+1)(2n+1)}{6}$ is a well
  known formula and the LHS is the sum of integers.

9 The nth repunit is $1 + 10 + 10^2 + 10^3 + \ldots + 10^{n-1}$.
  Now $10^2, 10^3, 10^4, \ldots, 10^{n-1}$ are all divisible by 4
  $\Rightarrow$ the nth repunit has form $11 + 4k_1$
  $= 4(k_1 + 2) + 3$
  $= 4k + 3$

  However, we proved in **Exercise 11A.3.2** Question **10 b**
  that all perfect squares have form $4k$ or $4k+1$.
  Hence, the impossibility.

10 All integers a have form $7n$, $7n \pm 1$, $7n \pm 2$ or $7n \pm 3$

$\Rightarrow \quad a^2 = (7n)^2 = 7(7n^2) = 7k$

or $\quad (7n \pm 1)^2 = 49n^2 \pm 14n + 1 = 7k + 1$

or $\quad (7n \pm 2)^2 = 49n^2 \pm 28n + 4 = 7k + 4$

or $\quad (7n \pm 3)^2 = 49n^2 \pm 42n + 9 = 7k + 2$

and $\quad a^3 = (7n)^3 = 7(49n^3) = 7k$

or $\quad (7n \pm 1)^3 = 343n^3 \pm 147n^2 + 21n \pm 1$

$\qquad\qquad\quad = 7k \pm 1 \quad$ form

or $\quad (7n \pm 2)^3 = 343n^3 \pm 294n^2 + 84n \pm 8$

$\qquad\qquad\quad = 7k \pm 1 \quad$ form

or $\quad (7n \pm 3)^3 = 343n^3 \pm 441n^2 + 189n \pm 27$

$\qquad\qquad\quad = 7k \pm 6$

From both, it takes either the form $7k$ or $7k + 1$.

11 a $n = 2a$ or $2a + 1$, $a \in \mathbb{Z}$

i.e., either even or odd

$\Rightarrow \quad 7n^3 + 5n$

$= 7(2a)^3 + 5(2a)$ or $7(2a + 1)^3 + 5(2a + 1)$

$\Rightarrow \quad 7n^3 + 5n$

$= 56a^3 + 10a$ or $56a^3 + 84a^2 + 52a + 12$

both of which are even

b $n = 3a$, $3a + 1$ or $3a - 1$

$\Rightarrow \quad n(7n^2 + 5) = 3a(63a^2 + 5)$

or $\quad n(7n^2 + 5) = (3a + 1)(63a^2 + 42a + 12)$

or $\quad n(7n^2 + 5) = (3a - 1)(63a^2 - 42a + 12)$

and in each case one of the two factors is divisible by 3

$\therefore \quad n(7n^2 + 5)$ is of the form $3k$

c From **a** $n(7n^2 + 5)$ is divisible by 2

From **b** $n(7n^2 + 5)$ is divisible by 3

$\therefore \quad n(7n^2 + 5)$ is divisible by $2 \times 3 = 6$.

12 $a^3 - a = a(a^2 - 1) = a(a + 1)(a - 1)$

but a has form $3k$, $3k + 1$ or $3k - 1$

$\therefore \quad a^3 - a = 3k(3k + 1)(3k - 1)$

or $(3k + 1)(3k + 2)(3k)$

or $(3k - 1)(3k)(3k - 2)$

and in each case a factor of 3 exists

$\Rightarrow \quad 3 \mid a^3 - a$

13 a Let $4k_1 + 1$ and $4k_2 + 1$ be two such integers

$\therefore \quad (4k_1 + 1)(4k_2 + 1)$

$= 16k_1 k_2 + 4k_1 + 4k_2 + 1$

$= 4(4k_1 k_2 + k_1 + k_2) + 1$

which is also of the form $4k + 1$, $k \in \mathbb{Z}$

b Let $4k_1 + 3$ and $4k_2 + 3$ be two such integers

$\therefore \quad (4k_1 + 3)(4k_2 + 3)$

$= 16k_1 k_2 + 12k_1 + 12k_2 + 9$

$= 4(4k_1 k_2 + 3k_1 + 3k_2 + 2) + 1$

which is of the form $4p + 1$, $p \in \mathbb{Z}$

c The square of an odd number has form $4k + 1$, $k \in \mathbb{Z}$.

14 The square of an odd number has form $4p + 1$, $p \in \mathbb{Z}$ (Question **13c**)

i.e., $a^2 = 4p + 1$

$\Rightarrow \quad a^4 = (4p + 1)^2 = 16p^2 + 16p + 1$

$\Rightarrow \quad a^4 = 16(p^2 + p) + 1$

which is of the form $16k + 1$, $k \in \mathbb{Z}$

15 The induction step only.

If P_k is true, $(k - 1)(k)(k + 1) = 6A$, $A \in \mathbb{Z}$

Now $\quad k(k + 1)(k + 2)$

$= (k - 1)(k)(k + 1) + 3k(k + 1)$

$= 6A + 3(2B)$

$= 6(A + B) \quad$ where $\quad A + B \in \mathbb{Z}$

etc.

Note: $k(k + 1)$ is the product of consecutive integers, one of which must be even.

$\therefore \quad k(k + 1)$ is even.

or directly by the DA,

any integer n has form $6a$, $6a + 1$, $6a + 2$, $6a + 3$, $6a + 4$ or $6a + 5$ etc.

16 $n^5 - n = n(n^4 - 1)$

$= n(n^2 + 1)(n^2 - 1)$

$= n(n - 1)(n + 1)(n^2 + 1)$

where n has form $5a$, $5a + 1$, $5a + 2$, $5a + 3$ or $5a + 4$

So, $n^5 - n = 5a(5a - 1)(5a + 1)(25a^2 + 1)$

or $(5a + 1)(5a)(5a + 2)(25a^2 + 10a + 2)$

or $(5a + 2)(5a + 1)(5a + 3)(25a^2 + 20a + 5)$

or $(5a + 3)(5a + 2)(5a + 4)(25a^2 + 30a + 10)$

or $(5a + 4)(5a + 3)(5a + 5)(25a^2 + 40a + 17)$

and in each case one of the factors is divisible by 5.

etc.

17 Let the integers be $(n - 1)$, n and $(n + 1)$

$\therefore \quad$ sum of cubes

$= (n - 1)^3 + n^3 + (n + 1)^3$

$= n^3 - 3n^2 + 3n - 1 + n^3 + n^3 + 3n^2 + 3n + 1$

$= 2n^3 + 6n$

$= 2n(n^2 + 3)$

then use induction on n for $n \geqslant 1$, $n \in \mathbb{Z}$

then use the DA.

Which proof is better? Why?

EXERCISE 11A.3.4

1 $1\,001\,111\,101_2$

$= 2^9 + 2^6 + 2^5 + 2^4 + 2^3 + 2^2 + 2^0$

$= 637$ in base 10

2 $201\,021\,102_3$

$= 2 \times 3^8 + 1 \times 3^6 + 2 \times 3^4 + 1 \times 3^3 + 1 \times 3^2 + 2$

$= 14\,051_{10}$

3 a $110\,212_3$ **b** 2322_8 **c** $22\,462_7$ **4** $10\,300\,112_5$

5 $21\,331_4$ **6** 1175_8 **7 a** $21\,242_9$ **b** $5\,426\,128\,226_9$

9 $101\,110\,011\,101\,010\,111\,100\,011_2$

10 $110\,111\,011\,011\,000\,110_2$

11 $20\,100\,220\,111\,202\,102\,122_3$

13 $\frac{5}{7} = 0.\overline{714285}$ or $0.\dot{7}1428\dot{5}$

EXERCISE 11A.4.1

1 a No, as 9 is not a multiple of $\gcd(24, 18) = 6$

b $\gcd(2, 3) = 1$ and 67 is a multiple of 1

$\therefore \quad$ yes and infinitely many solutions exist.

c $\gcd(57, 95) = 19$ and 19 is a multiple of 19

$\therefore \quad$ yes and infinitely many solutions exist.

d $\gcd(1035, 585) = 45$ and 90 is a multiple of 45

$\therefore \quad$ yes and infinitely many solutions exist.

e gcd $(45, 81) = 9$ and 108 is a multiple of 9
 $\therefore$ yes and infinitely many solutions exist.

2 b $x = 2, \; y = 21$ **c** $x = -3, \; y = 2$
 d $x = -5, \; y = 9$ **e** $x = 6, \; y = 2$

3 b $x = 2 + 3t, \; y = 21 - 2t, \; t \in \mathbb{Z}$
 c $x = -3 + 5t, \; y = 2 - 3t, \; t \in \mathbb{Z}$
 d $x = -5 + 13t, \; y = 9 - 23t, \; t \in \mathbb{Z}$
 e $x = 6 + 9t, \; y = 2 + 5t, \; t \in \mathbb{Z}$

EXERCISE 11A.4.2

1 a $a \mid b \Rightarrow \quad b = ka, \quad k \in \mathbb{Z}$
 $\Rightarrow \quad bc = kac$
 $\Rightarrow \quad a \mid bc$

 b $a \mid b$ and $a \mid c \Rightarrow \; b = k_1 a$ and $c = k_2 a, \; k_1, k_2 \in \mathbb{Z}$
 $\Rightarrow \quad bc = k_1 k_2 a^2$
 $\Rightarrow \quad a^2 \mid bc$

 c $a \mid b$ and $c \mid d \Rightarrow \; b = k_1 a$ and $d = k_2 c, \; k_1, k_2 \in \mathbb{Z}$
 $\Rightarrow \quad bd = k_1 k_2 ac$
 $\Rightarrow \quad ac \mid bd$

 d $a \mid b \Rightarrow \quad b = ka, \quad k \in \mathbb{Z}$
 $\Rightarrow \quad b^n = k^n a^n$
 $\Rightarrow \quad a^n \mid b^n \quad$ as $\quad k^n \in \mathbb{Z}$
 Converse is true.

2 k must have form $3a, \; 3a + 1$ or $3a + 2$.

k	$k + 2$	$k + 4$
$3a$	$3a + 2$	$3a + 4$
$3a + 1$	$3a + 3$	$3a + 5$
$3a + 2$	$3a + 4$	$3a + 6$

 Each time one of $k, \; k + 2$ or $k + 4$ is divisible by 3.

3 The statement is false.
 For example, $8 \mid (13 + 3)$, but $8 \nmid 13$ and $5 \nmid 3$.

4 a i

n	$n + 1$	$n + 2$
$3a$	$3a + 1$	$3a + 2$
$3a + 1$	$3a + 2$	$3a + 3$
$3a + 2$	$3a + 3$	$3a + 4$

 Each time one of the factors is divisible by 3
 $\Rightarrow \; n(n + 1)(n + 2)$ is divisible by 3.

 ii In any set of 3 consecutive integers, at least one of them is even, i.e., divisible by 2. So, from **i** the product of 3 consecutive integers is divisible by $3 \times 2 = 6$.

 iii In any set of 4 consecutive integers, two of them are even. So, the product is divisible by 4.

 iv In any four consecutive integers, one of them must be divisible by 2 and one must be divisible by 4. Since one of them must be divisible by 3, the product is divisible by $2 \times 4 \times 3 = 24$.

5 As $k \in \mathbb{Z}$, k must have form $3a, \; 3a + 1$ or $3a + 2$.
 If $k = 3a,$ $k(k^2 + 8)$ is divisible by 3.
 If $k = 3a + 1,$ $k(k^2 + 8)$
 $= (3a + 1)(9a^2 + 6a + 9)$
 $= 3(3a + 1)(3a^2 + 2a + 3)$
 which is divisible by 3.
 If $k = 3a + 2,$ $k(k^2 + 8)$
 $= (3a + 2)(9a^2 + 12a + 12)$
 $= 3(3a + 2)(3a^2 + 4a + 4)$
 which is divisible by 3.

So, in all cases, $k(k^2 + 8)$ is divisible by 3
i.e., $3 \mid k(k^2 + 8)$.

6 a $1 \times 2 \times 3 \times 4 + 1 = 25 = 5^2$
 $2 \times 3 \times 4 \times 5 + 1 = 121 = 11^2$
 $3 \times 4 \times 5 \times 6 + 1 = 361 = 19^2$

 b $(n - 1)n(n + 1)(n + 2) + 1$
 $= (n^2 + 2n)(n^2 - 1) + 1$
 $= n^4 + 2n^3 - n^2 - 2n + 1$
 $= (n^2 + n - 1)^2, \quad$ a perfect square

7 a Let gcd $(a, a + n) = d$
 $\Rightarrow \quad d \mid a$ and $d \mid a + n$
 $\Rightarrow \quad d \mid (a + n) - a \quad$ {linearity}
 $\Rightarrow \quad d \mid n$
 i.e., gcd $(a, a + n) \mid n$

 b If $n = 1,$ gcd $(a, a + 1) \mid 1$
 $\therefore \quad$ gcd $(a, a + 1) = 1$

8 only a   gcd $(3k + 1, 13k + 4)$
 $= $ gcd $(3k + 1, 13(3k + 1) - 3(13k + 4)) \quad$ {linearity}
 $= $ gcd $(3k + 1, 1)$
 $= 1$

9 a Let $d = $ gcd $(4a - 3b, 8a - 5b)$
 $= $ gcd $(4a - 3b, 8a - 5b - 2(4a - 3b))$
 $= $ gcd $(4a - 3b, b)$
 $= $ gcd $(4a - 3b + 3b, b)$
 $= $ gcd $(4a, b) \quad \therefore \; d \mid 4a$ and $d \mid b$
 Now $d \mid b$ but d does not necessarily divide a.

 b If $b = -1, \; d = $ gcd $(4a + 3, 8a + 5)$
 $\Rightarrow \quad d \mid -1 \Rightarrow \; d = 1 \quad$ {as $d > 0$}
 $\Rightarrow \quad$ gcd $(4a + 3, 8a + 5) = 1$

10 a gcd $(a, b) = 1$
 $\Rightarrow \quad \exists \; x, y \in \mathbb{Z} \quad$ such that $ax + by = 1$
 But $c \mid a \Rightarrow \; a = kc$
 $\therefore \quad kcx + by = 1$
 $\Rightarrow \quad$ gcd $(c, b) = 1$

 b gcd $(a, b) = 1$
 $\Rightarrow \quad \exists \; x, y \in \mathbb{Z} \quad$ such that $ax + by = 1 \; \ldots\ldots \; (1)$
 $\Rightarrow \quad a^2 x^2 + 2abxy + b^2 y^2 = 1$
 $\Rightarrow \quad a^2 x^2 + b[2axy + by^2] = 1$
 and $[ax^2 + 2bxy]a + b^2 y^2 = 1$
 $\Rightarrow \quad$ gcd $(a^2, b) = 1$ and gcd $(a, b^2) = 1 \quad$ (QED)

 Thus $a^2 p_1 + b p_2 = 1 \; \ldots\ldots \; (2)$
  and $a q_1 + b^2 q_2 = 1 \; \ldots\ldots \; (3)$
  where $p_1, \; p_2, \; q_1, \; q_2 \in \mathbb{Z}$
 Now $ab(ax + by) = ab \quad$ {from (1)}
 From (2), $a^3 p_1 + abp_2 = a$
 $\Rightarrow \quad a^3 p_1 + (a^2 bx + ab^2 y)p_2 = a$
 $\Rightarrow \quad a = a^3 p_1 + a^2 \alpha + b^2 \beta$
 and in (3)
  $(a^3 p_1 + a^2 \alpha + b^2 \beta)q_1 + b^2 q_2 = 1$
 $\Rightarrow \quad a^2(ap_1 q_1 + \alpha q_1) + b^2(\beta q_1 + q_2) = 1$
 $\Rightarrow \quad$ gcd $(a^2, b^2) = 1$

11 **a** $2^k - 1 = (2-1)(2^{k-1} + 2^{k-2} + 2^{k-3} + \ldots\ldots + 2 + 1)$
{using the given identity}

$\therefore \quad 2^k - 1 = \underbrace{1111\ldots\ldots 1}_{k \text{ of them}}$ in base 2

If $d \mid n \Rightarrow \quad d$th repunit (base z) $\mid n$th repunit (base 2)
$\Rightarrow \quad 2^d - 1 \mid 2^n - 1$

b $5 \mid 35 \quad \Rightarrow \quad 2^5 - 1 \mid 2^{35} - 1$
$\Rightarrow \quad 31 \mid 2^{35} - 1$
$7 \mid 35 \quad \Rightarrow \quad 2^7 - 1 \mid 2^{35} - 1$
$\Rightarrow \quad 127 \mid 2^{35} - 1$
$\therefore \quad 2^{35} - 1$ is divisible by both 31 and 127.

12 **a** $\gcd(3k + 2, 5k + 3)$
$= \gcd(3k + 2, 5(3k + 2) - 3(5k + 3))$ {linearity}
$= \gcd(3k + 2, 1)$
$= 1$
$\Rightarrow \quad 3k + 2, \quad 5k + 3$ are relatively prime.

b $\gcd(5k + 3, 11k + 7)$
$= \gcd(5k + 3, 5(11k + 7) - 11(5k + 3))$ {linearity}
$= \gcd(5k + 3, 2)$ where $5k + 3$ is always odd
$= 1$
$\Rightarrow \quad 5k + 3, \quad 11k + 7$ are relatively prime.

EXERCISE 11A.4.3

1 **a** $\gcd = 11, \quad r = 5, \quad s = -26$
b $\gcd = 6, \quad r = 132, \quad s = -535$
c $\gcd = 793, \quad r = 0, \quad s = 1$
d $\gcd = 115, \quad r = 2, \quad s = -3$
e $\gcd = 1, \quad r = 13, \quad s = -21$
f $\gcd(f_{n+1}, f_n) = \gcd(f_{n+1} - f_n, f_n)$ {linearity}
$= \gcd(f_{n-1}, f_n)$
$= \gcd(f_n, f_{n-1})$
$\vdots$
$= \gcd(f_2, f_1)$ {by induction}
$= \gcd(1, 1)$
$= 1$

2 $\gcd(f_8, f_4) = \gcd(21, 3) = 3$
$\gcd(f_{12}, f_8) = \gcd(144, 21) = 3$
$\vdots$ etc.
suggests $\gcd(f_{4(n+1)}, f_{4n})$ could be 3.
Then prove this statement.

3 $\gcd(f_{10}, f_5) = \gcd(55, 5) = 5$
$\gcd(f_{15}, f_{10}) = \gcd(610, 55) = 5$
$\vdots$ etc.
suggests $\gcd(f_{5(n+1)}, f_{5n}) = 5$.
Then prove this statement.

EXERCISE 11A.4.4

1 First find the gcd. Then use $\text{lcm} = \dfrac{ab}{\gcd}$

a $\gcd = 1, \quad \text{lcm} = 32\,461$
b $\gcd = 1, \quad \text{lcm} = 475\,728$
c $\gcd = 6, \quad \text{lcm} = 6\,300\,402$
d $\gcd = 1, \quad \text{lcm} = 299\,307$

EXERCISE 11A.5

1 **a** No solutions exist
b $x = 445 + 14t, \quad y = -805 - 33t, \quad t \in \mathbb{Z}$
c No solutions exist
d $x = -15 + 7t, \quad y = 20 - 9t, \quad t \in \mathbb{Z}$
e $x = -3 + 4t, \quad y = 18 - 23t, \quad t \in \mathbb{Z}$
f $x = 176 - 35t, \quad y = -1111 + 221t, \quad t \in \mathbb{Z}$

2 **a** $x = 1, \quad y = 6$ **b**

x	16	9	2
y	2	20	38

c No positive solutions
d Infinitely many positive solutions of the form
$x = -242 + 57t, \quad y = -671 + 158t, \quad t \in \mathbb{Z}, \quad t \geqslant 5$.

3 $7 \mid x$ and $11 \mid y \Rightarrow x = 7a, \; y = 11b, \; a, b \in \mathbb{Z}$
So $7a + 11b = 100$.
General solution is
$a = -300 + 11t, \quad b = 200 - 7t, \quad t \in \mathbb{Z}$.
$a > 0, \quad b > 0, \quad \Rightarrow \quad t = 28$
So, $a = 8, \quad b = 4$ and $100 = 56 + 44$.

4 Show $m + w + c = 20$ ...... (1)
$5m + 4w + 2c = 62$ ...... (2)
and deduce that $3m + 2w = 42$
which has one solution $m = 14, \quad w = 0$
$\Rightarrow \quad m = 14 + 2t, \quad w = -3t, \quad t \in \mathbb{Z}$
So, $c = 6 + t$ {using (1)}
Putting $m > 0, \quad w > 0, \quad c > 0$ gives
$t = -1, -2, -3, -4, -5$
So solutions are:

m	12	10	8	6	4
w	3	6	9	12	15
c	5	4	3	2	1

5 Show that $c + r + f = 100$
$5c + r + \dfrac{f}{20} = 100$
leads to $19f = 80c$ and $99c + 19r = 1900$
One solution is $c = 0, \quad r = 100$
$\Rightarrow \quad c = 0 + 19t, \quad r = 100 - 99t$
But $c \geqslant 1$ and $r \geqslant 1$. Hence, $t = 1$.
Thus $c = 19, \quad r = 1, \quad f = 80$
i.e., buys 19 cats, 1 rabbit, 80 fish.

6 Smith travels for 6 hours. Jones travels for 2 hours.

7 Show $a + b + c = 100$ and
$35a + \dfrac{40b}{3} + 5c = 1000$
Hence, show that $18a + 5b = 300$.
One solution is $a = 0, \quad b = 60$.
General solution is
$a = 0 + 5t, \quad b = 60 - 18t, \quad t \in \mathbb{Z}$.
But $a > 0, \quad b > 0 \quad \therefore \quad t > 0$ and $t < 3\frac{1}{3}$
$\Rightarrow \quad t = 1, 2, 3$.

t	1	2	3
a	5	10	15
b	42	24	6
c	53	66	79

are the 3 possible solutions

EXERCISE 11A.6.1

1 a n has form $p_1^{a_1} \, p_2^{a_2} \, p_3^{a_3} \, ... \, p_k^{a_k}$

If all powers are even then

$a_1 = 2b_1, \quad a_2 = 2b_2, \quad ......, \quad a_k = 2b_k \quad$ where $b_i \in \mathbb{Z}$

$\Leftrightarrow \quad n = p_1^{2b_1} \, p_2^{2b_2} \, p_3^{2b_3} \, ... \, p_k^{2b_k}$

$\Leftrightarrow \quad n = (p_1^{b_1} \, p_2^{b_2} \, p_3^{b_3} \, ... \, p_k^{b_k})^2$

$\Leftrightarrow \quad n$ is a perfect square.

b The factors of any integer appear as factor pairs and in the case of a perfect square only we get a repeated pair. For example, the factors of 16 are   1, 16   2, 8 $\underbrace{4, 4}_{\text{repeat}}$

∴ the factors of a perfect square number $2p + 1$ are {p pairs plus 1}   i.e.,   an odd number of factors.

2 Suppose $\sqrt{2}$ is rational,

i.e., $\sqrt{2} = \dfrac{p}{q}, \quad p, q \in \mathbb{Z}, \ \gcd(p, q) = 1$

$\Rightarrow \quad p^2 = 2q^2$

By **1 b**, p^2 has an odd number of factors.

$\Rightarrow \quad 2q^2$ has an odd number of factors.

$\Rightarrow \quad q^2$ has an even number of factors.

a contradiction to the result of **1 b**.

Thus, the supposition is false and so $\sqrt{2}$ is irrational.

EXERCISE 11A.6.2

1 a $143 = 11 \times 13,$ so   143 is not a prime

b $221 = 13 \times 17,$ so   221 is not a prime

c 199 is a prime

d 223 is a prime

2 Any even number e, is a multiple of 2,

i.e., $e = 2k, \quad k \in \mathbb{Z}$

$\Rightarrow \quad e$ is prime $\Leftrightarrow \quad k = 1$

{otherwise e has 2 factors}

3 a $1 + a + a^2 + ... + a^{n-1} = \dfrac{1(a^n - 1)}{a - 1}$

{as is the sum of a geometric series}

$\Rightarrow \quad a^n - 1 = (a - 1)(1 + a + a^2 + ... + a^{n-1})$

and if a^{n-1} is a prime then $a - 1 = 1$ i.e., $a = 2$ {otherwise it has two factors}

b No, as for example, $2^4 - 1 = 15 = 3 \times 5$

i.e., $2^4 - 1$ is a composite.

c Let $n = kl$ where $k \geqslant 2$

∴ $2^n - 1 = 2^{kl} - 1$

$= (2^k)^l - 1$

$= (2^k - 1)[(2^k)^{l-1} + (2^k)^{l-2} + ... + 1]$

Now as $k \geqslant 2, \quad 2^k - 1 \geqslant 3$

$\Rightarrow \quad 2^n - 1$ is composite, so the claim is true.

d No, for example $2^{11} - 1 = 2047 = 23 \times 89$ which is composite.

4 $111 = 3 \times 37, \quad 1111 = 11 \times 101, \quad 11\,111 = 41 \times 271$

$\Rightarrow$ none of them is prime.

5 $p \mid q \quad \Rightarrow \quad q = kp$

which is composite unless $k = 1$

$\Rightarrow \quad q = p$

6 a $9555 = 3 \times 5 \times 7^2 \times 13$

b $989 = 23 \times 43$

c $9999 = 3^2 \times 11 \times 101$

d $111\,111 = 3 \times 7 \times 11 \times 13 \times 37$

7 a primes   **b**   the product of two primes

8 a The primes which divide 50!

are the prime factors of   1, 2, 3, 4, ..., 50

These are: 2, 3, 5, 7, 11, 13, 17, 19, 23, 29, 31, 37, 41, 43 and 47.

b There are many factors of 2 and fewer factors of 5 and as 2s and 5s are needed to create 0s, the number of zeros equals the number of 5s.

This is 12.   {as 25 and 50 provide two 5s each.}

So 50! ends in 12 zeros (in expanded form).

c

$$
\begin{array}{rcl}
1 &\to& 25 \qquad 6 \\
26 &\to& 50 \qquad 6 \\
51 &\to& 75 \qquad 6 \\
&\vdots& \\
276 &\to& 300 \qquad 6 \\
&& \qquad\quad \overline{72} \\
301 &\to& 310 \qquad 2 \\
&& \qquad\quad \overline{74}
\end{array}
$$

i.e., $n = 310, 311, 312, 313, 314$

9 a If $a = p_1^{a_1} \, p_2^{a_2} \, p_3^{a_3} \, ... \, p_k^{a_k}$

then $a^n = p_1^{na_1} \, p_2^{na_2} \, p_3^{na_3} \, ... \, p_k^{na_k}$

So, if $p \mid a^n$ then p is one of the p_i and so $p^n \mid a^n$.

b If $a = p_1^{a_1} \, p_2^{a_2} \, ... \, p_k^{a_k}$ then

$a^2 = p_1^{2a_1} \, p_2^{2a_2} \, ... \, p_k^{2a_k}$.

So, if $p \mid a^2$ then p is one of the p_i

$\Rightarrow \quad p \mid a$.

Similar argument for **c**.

10 a All integers have form $4k, \ 4k + 1, \ 4k + 2$ or $4k + 3$ where $4k$ and $4k + 2$ are composites as they are even

$\Rightarrow$ all odd primes have either the form $4k + 1$ or $4k + 3$.

b Suppose that there are a finite number of primes of the form $4k + 3$ and these are $p_1, p_2, p_3, ... \, p_n$ where

$p_1 < p_2 < p_3 < ...... < p_n$.

Let $N = 4(p_1 \, p_2 \, p_3 \, ... \, p_n) + 3$.

Notice that N has the form $4k + 3, \ k \in \mathbb{Z}$

If N is a prime number, then p_n is not the largest prime of the form $4k + 3$.

If N is composite, then it must contain prime factors of the form $4k + 1$ or $4k + 3$.

But N cannot contain only prime factors of the form $4k + 1$ since the product of any such numbers is not of the form $4k + 3$.

This is shown by: $(4k_1 + 1)(4k_2 + 1)$

$= 4(4k_1 k_2 + k_1 + k_2) + 1$

Hence, N must contain a prime factor of the form $4k + 3$.

Since $p_1, p_2, p_3, ..., p_n$ are not factors of N there exists a prime factor of the form $4k + 3$ which is greater than p_n. A contradiction!

EXERCISE 11A.7.1

1 **a** $15 - 1 = 14 = 2 \times 7$
    $\Rightarrow$ $1, 15$ are congruent (mod 7)
  b No, as $8 - (-1) = 9$ and $7 \nmid 9$.
  c No, as $99 - 2 = 97$ and $7 \nmid 97$.
  d $699 - (-1) = 700$ and $7 \mid 700$
    $\Rightarrow$ $-1, 699$ are congruent (mod 7)

2 **a** $29 - 7 = 22$ and 22 has factors 1, 2, 11, 22
    $\Rightarrow$ $m = 2, 11$ or 22
  b $100 - 1 = 99$ $\Rightarrow$ $m = 3, 9, 11, 33$ or 99
  c $53 - 0 = 53$ $\Rightarrow$ $m = 53$
  d $61 - 1 = 60$
    $\Rightarrow$ $m = 2, 3, 4, 5, 6, 10, 12, 15, 20, 30$ or 60

3 **a** 13 (mod 20)   **b** 33 mod (42)
  c 0 (mod 12)   **d** 4 mod (10)

4 **a** 2 (mod 7)   **b** 6 mod (7)
  c 2 (mod 7)   **d** 6 mod (7)

5 **a** 12 (mod 37)   **b** 9 mod (13)
  c 3 (mod 11)

6 **a** $53^{103} + 103^{53}$ (mod 39)
    $\equiv 14^{103} + (-14)^{53}$ (mod 39)
    $\equiv 14^{103} - 14^{53}$ (mod 39)
    $\equiv 14^{53}[14^{50} - 1]$ (mod 39)
    $\equiv 14^{53}[(14^2)^{25} - 1$ (mod 39)
    $\equiv 14^{53}[1^{25} - 1]$ (mod 39)
    $= 0$ (mod 39) $\therefore$ $53^{103} + 103^{53}$ is divisible by 39.
  b $333^{111} + 111^{333}$ (mod 7)
    $\equiv 4^{111} + (-1)^{333}$ (mod 7)
    $\equiv 2^{222} - 1$ (mod 7)
    $\equiv (2^3)^{74} - 1$ (mod 7)
    $\equiv 1^{74} - 1$ (mod 7)
    $\equiv 0$ (mod 7) $\therefore$ $333^{111} + 111^{333}$ is divisible by 7

7 **a** **i** 1 (mod 11) **ii** 1 (mod 13) **iii** 1 (mod 19)
    iv 1 (mod 17)
    Postulate: $a^{n-1} \equiv 1$ (mod n)
  b **i** 4 mod (12) **ii** 7 (mod 9)
    Neither agree with the postulate.
  c $13^4 \equiv 1$ (mod 5) agrees.
    New Postulate: $a^{p-1} \equiv 1$ (mod p), p a prime

8 **a** **i** $2! \equiv 2$ (mod 3)   **ii** $4! \equiv 4$ (mod 5)
    iii $10! \equiv 10$ (mod 11) **iv** $6! \equiv 6$ (mod 7)
    Postulate: $(n+1)! \equiv n + 1$ (mod n)
  b **i** $3! \equiv 2$ (mod 4)
    ii $5! \equiv 0$ (mod 6)   Do not agree with postulate.
  c $12! \equiv 12$ (mod 13) agrees.
    New postulate: $(p+1)! \equiv p + 1$ (mod p), p a prime.

9 **a** $5^{2n} + 3 \times 2^{5n-2}$ (mod 7)
    $= (5^2)^n + 3 \times 2^{5(n-1)+3}$ (mod 7)
    $\equiv 4^n + 3 \times 4^{n-1} \times 1$ (mod 7)
    $\equiv 4^{n-1}(4 + 3)$ (mod 7)
    $\equiv 0$ (mod 7)
    $\therefore$ $5^{2n} + 3 \times 2^{5n-2}$ is divisible by 7 for all $n \in \mathbb{Z}^+$

  b $3^{n+2} + 4^{2n+1}$ (mod 13)
    $= 3^{n+2} + (4^2)^n \times 4$ (mod 13)
    $\equiv 3^{n+2} + 3^n \times 4$ (mod 13)
    $\equiv 3^n(3^2 + 4)$ (mod 13)
    $\equiv 3^n(13)$ (mod 13)
    $\equiv 0$ (mod 13)
    $\therefore$ $3^{n+2} + 4^{2n+1}$ is divisible by 13 for all $n \in \mathbb{Z}^+$
  c $5^{n+2} + 2^{5n+1}$ (mod 27)
    $= 5^{n+2} + (2^5)^n \times 2$ (mod 27)
    $\equiv 5^{n+2} + 5^n \times 2$ (mod 27)
    $\equiv 5^n(5^2 + 2)$ (mod 27)
    $\equiv 5^n(27)$ (mod 27)
    $\equiv 0$ (mod 27)
    $\therefore$ $5^{n+2} + 2^{5n+1}$ is divisible by 27 for all $n \in \mathbb{Z}^+$

10 Let $n = 2k$, $k \in \mathbb{Z}$
    $\Rightarrow$ $n^2 = 4k^2$
    $\Rightarrow$ $n^2 \equiv 0$ (mod 4)
  Let $n = 2k + 1$, $k \in \mathbb{Z}$
    $\Rightarrow$ $n^2 = 4k^2 + 4k + 1$
    $\Rightarrow$ $n^2 = 4(k^2 + k) + 1$
    $\Rightarrow$ $n^2 \equiv 1$ (mod 4)

11 Any integer n must have form $3k$, $3k + 1$ or $3k + 2$
    i.e., $n \equiv 0, 1$ or 2 (mod 3)
    $\therefore$ $n^2 \equiv 0, 1$ or 1 (mod 3)
    i.e., $n^2 \equiv 0$ or 1 (mod 3)

12 If n is an integer then
    $n \equiv 0, 1, 2, 3, 4, 5, 6, 7$ or 8 (mod 9)
    $\therefore$ $n^3 \equiv 0, 1, 8, 0, 1, 8, 0, 1$ or 8 (mod 9)
    i.e., $n^3 \equiv 0, 1$ or 8 (mod 9)

13 Let any odd integer $n = 2k + 1$
    $\Rightarrow$ $n^2 = (2k + 1)^2 = 4k^2 + 4k + 1$
    $\Rightarrow$ $n^2 = 4k(k + 1) + 1$
  But $k(k + 1)$ is the product of two consecutive integers,
  one of which must be even.
    $\Rightarrow$ $n^2 = 4(2a) + 1$, $a \in \mathbb{Z}$
    $\Rightarrow$ $n^2 = 8a + 1$
    $\Rightarrow$ $n^2 \equiv 1$ (mod 8)
  If n is even, $n^2 \equiv 0$ (mod 8) or 4 (mod 8).

14 If $a \equiv b$ (mod c)   then
    $a = b + kc$ for $k \in \mathbb{Z}$
    $\therefore$ gcd (a, c)
    $= $ gcd $(b + kc, c)$
    $= $ gcd $(b + kc - kc, c)$ {linearity}
    $= $ gcd (b, c)
  This is a restatement of the Euclidean algorithm.

15 If $x^2 \equiv 1$ (mod 3)
  then $x^2 - 1 = 3k$, $k \in \mathbb{Z}$
    $\Rightarrow$ $(x + 1)(x - 1) = 3k$, $k \in \mathbb{Z}$
    $\Rightarrow$ $3 \mid x + 1$ or $3 \mid x - 1$
    $\Rightarrow$ $x + 1 = 3a$ or $x - 1 = 3b$, $a, b \in \mathbb{Z}$
    $\Rightarrow$ $x = -1 + 3a$ or $x = 1 + 3b$
    $\Rightarrow$ $x \equiv \pm 1$ (mod 3)

If $x^2 \equiv 4 \pmod 7$

then $x^2 - 4 = 7k, \quad k \in \mathbb{Z}$

$\Rightarrow \quad (x+2)(x-2) = 7k, \quad k \in \mathbb{Z}$

$\Rightarrow \quad 7 \mid x + 2 \quad \text{or} \quad 7 \mid x - 2$

$\Rightarrow \quad x + 2 = 7a \quad \text{or} \quad x - 2 = 7b \quad \text{where} \quad a, b \in \mathbb{Z}$

$\Rightarrow \quad x \equiv \pm 2 \pmod 7$

If $x^2 \equiv a^2 \pmod p$ where p is prime, by similar argument to the above $x \equiv \pm a \pmod p$.

16 $\displaystyle\sum_{k=1}^{n} k = 1 + 2 + 3 + 4 + \ldots\ldots + n$

$= \dfrac{n(n+1)}{2}$

$= n\left(\dfrac{n+1}{2}\right) \quad \text{where} \quad \dfrac{n+1}{2} \in \mathbb{Z} \quad \text{as } n \text{ is odd}$

$\therefore \quad \displaystyle\sum_{k=1}^{n} k \equiv 0 \pmod n$

If k is even, $\quad 1 + 2 = 3 \pmod 2 \quad \equiv 1 \pmod 2$

$1 + 2 + 3 + 4 = 10 \pmod 4 \equiv 2 \pmod 4$

$1 + 2 + 3 + 4 + 5 + 6 = 21 \pmod 6 \equiv 3 \pmod 6$

Suggests $\quad \displaystyle\sum_{k=1}^{n} k \equiv \dfrac{n}{2} \pmod n, \quad n \text{ even}$

Proof:

$1 + 2 + 3 + \ldots\ldots + n = \dfrac{n(n+1)}{2}$

$\therefore \quad 1 + 2 + 3 + \ldots\ldots + n = \dfrac{n}{2}(n+1)$

and $\therefore \quad 1 + 2 + 3 + \ldots\ldots + n \pmod n \equiv \dfrac{n}{2}(1) \pmod n$

$\equiv \dfrac{n}{2} \pmod n$

17 $\displaystyle\sum_{k=1}^{n-1} k^3 = 1^3 + 2^3 + 3^3 + \ldots\ldots + (n-1)^3$

$= \dfrac{(n-1)^2 n^2}{4} \quad$ {a well known formula}

Now consider $\quad n = 4m + r \quad$ for $\quad r = 0, 1, 2, 3$

If $\quad r = 0, \quad n = 4m \quad$ and

$\dfrac{(n-1)^2 n^2}{4}$

$= \dfrac{(4m-1)^2 16m^2}{4}$

$= 4m^2(4m-1)^2 \quad$ which is divisible by 4

If $\quad r = 1, \quad n = 4m + 1 \quad$ and

$\dfrac{(n-1)^2 n^2}{4}$

$= \dfrac{(4m)^2 (4m+1)^2}{4}$

$= 4m^2(4m-1)^2 \quad$ which is divisible by 4

If $\quad r = 2, \quad n = 4m + 2 \quad$ and

$\dfrac{(n-1)^2 n^2}{4}$

$= \dfrac{(4m+1)^2 4(2m+1)^2}{4}$

$= (4m+1)^2(2m+1)^2 \quad$ which is not divisible by 4

If $\quad r = 3, \quad n = 4m + 3 \quad$ and

$\dfrac{(n-1)^2 n^2}{4}$

$= \dfrac{(4m+2)^2(4m+3)^2}{4}$

$= (2m+1)^2(4m+3)^2 \quad$ which is not divisible by 4

Thus $\quad \displaystyle\sum_{k=1}^{n-1} k^3 \equiv 0 \pmod n \quad$ when

n has form $\quad 4m \quad$ or $\quad 4m + 1, \quad m \in \mathbb{Z}, \quad m \geqslant 1$

18 On experimenting we postulate

$\displaystyle\sum_{k=1}^{p} k^2 \equiv 0 \pmod p \quad$ for all primes $\quad p \geqslant 5$.

19 a Induction step only

If P_k is true, $\quad 3^k - 1 - 2k = 4a, \quad$ say.

Now $\quad 3^{k+1} - 1 - 2(k+1)$

$= 3(3^k) - 1 - 2k - 2$

$= 3(1 + 2k + 4a) - 1 - 2k - 2$

$= 3 + 6k + 12a - 3 - 2k$

$= 4k + 12a$

$= 4(k + 3a)$

$\equiv 0 \pmod 4$

etc.

Also for second part

If P_k is true, $\quad 4^k - 1 - 3k = 9a, \quad$ say.

Now $\quad 4^{k+1} - 1 - 3(k+1)$

$= 4(9a + 1 + 3k) - 1 - 3k - 3$

$= 36a + 4 + 12k - 3k - 4$

$= 36a + 9k$

$= 9(4a + k)$

$\equiv 0 \pmod 9$

etc.

b Yes,

If P_k is true, $\quad 5^k - 1 - 4k = 16a, \quad$ say.

Now $\quad 5^{k+1} - 1 - 4(k+1)$

$= 5(5^k) - 1 - 4k - 4$

$= 5[16a + 1 + 4k] - 5 - 4k$

$= 80a + 5 + 20k - 5 - 4k$

$= 80a + 16k$

$= 16(5a + k)$

$\equiv 0 \pmod{16}$

20 $2^{11} - 1 = (2^4)^2 \times 2^3 - 1$

$\equiv (-7)^2(8) - 1 \pmod{23}$

$\equiv 7 \times 56 - 1 \pmod{23}$

$\equiv 7 \times 10 - 1 \pmod{23}$

$\equiv 69 \pmod{23}$

$\equiv 0 \pmod{23}$

$\therefore \quad 2^{11} - 1 \quad$ is divisible by 23.

EXERCISE 11A.7.2

1 a $x = 5$ **b** $x = 10$ **c** $x = 2, 6, 10$

d $x = 5, 16, 27, 38, 49, 60, 71, 82, 93$

e $x = 15, 35$ **f** $x = 3$ **g** $x = 6, 15, 24$

h $x = 1, 4, 7, 10, 13, 16, 19$

2 a True **b** True **c** True **d** True **e** True
f True **g** True **h** False **i** True **j** True

EXERCISE 11A.8.1

1 $x \equiv 59$ (mod 77)   **2** $x \equiv 206$ (mod 210)

3 23 is the smallest positive number. All other numbers have form $23 + 105k$, $k \in \mathbb{Z}^+$

4 a $x \equiv 23$ (mod 30) **b** $x \equiv 6$ (mod 210)
c $x \equiv 52$ (mod 105)

EXERCISE 11A.8.2

1 a $x \equiv 59$ (mod 77) **b** $x \equiv 206$ (mod 210)
c $x \equiv 6$ (mod 210)

2 $x \equiv 99$ (mode 210)

3 All integers of the form $2 + 12k$, $k \in \mathbb{Z}$.

4 All integers of the form $72 + 105k$, $k \in \mathbb{Z}$.

5 The smallest integer is 28. All solutions have the form $28 + 60k$, $k \in \mathbb{Z}$.

6 119 sweets   **7** 3930 coins

8 $x = 3 + 7t$, $y = -1 - 4t$, $t \in \mathbb{Z}$

9 a $x = 5 + 8t$, $y = -3 - 11t$, $t \in \mathbb{Z}$
b $x = 4 + 5t$, $y = -3 - 7t$ $k \in \mathbb{Z}$

10 62 is the smallest integer > 2

11 $x \equiv 653, 1423, 2193$ (mod 2310)

EXERCISE 11A.9.1

1 a 1, 1, 2, 7, 0
b divisible by 11 only

Divisor	2	3	5	9
Remainder	1	1	2	7

2 e i 2^8 **ii** 2^{10} **iii** 2^1

3 a n^2 (mod 10) $\equiv$ 0, 1, 4, 9, 5, 6
b They are not perfect squares as their last digits are not 0, 1, 4, 5, 6 or 9.

4 No as $\sum_{r=1}^{3} = 1! + 2! + 3!$
$= 1 + 2 + 6$
$= 9$ is a perfect square

5 a 2^3 **b** 2^2 **c** 2^1 **d** 2^4

6 a $k = 3n$ for all $n \in \mathbb{Z}^+$ **b** $k = 9n$ for all $n \in \mathbb{Z}^+$
c $k = 2n$ for all $n \in \mathbb{Z}^+$

7 a i 2^0 **ii** Yes **b i** 2^3 **ii** No **c i** 2^2 **iii** No

8 a i 3^1 **ii** Yes **iii** No **b i** 3^1 **ii** Yes **iii** No
c i 3^2 **ii** Yes **iii** Yes

EXERCISE 11A.9.2

1 6994 is not, 6993 is

5 a i An integer is divisible by 25 if the number which is its last 2 digits is divisible by 25.
iii An integer is divisible by 125 if the number which is its last 3 digits is divisible by 125.
b i 5^3 **ii** 5^1 **iii** 5^9

6 a An integer is divisible by 6 if it is divisible by both 2 and 3.
b An integer is divisible by 12 if it is divisible by both 3 and 4.
c, d likewise

7 a No **b** No **c** No

8 a Yes, No, No **b** Yes, No, Yes **c** No, No, No
d Yes, Yes, No **e** Yes, Yes, Yes **f** No, No, No

EXERCISE 11A.10.1

1 a 1 (mod 13) **b** 2 (mod 7) **c** 9 (mod 17)
d 9 (mod 13)

EXERCISE 11A.10.2

1 a $x \equiv 4$ (mod 7) **b** $x \equiv 2$ (mod 13)
c $x \equiv 5$ (mod 11) **d** $x \equiv 5$ (mod 17)

EXERCISE 11A.10.3

4 15 **5 a** No **b** No

6 $13^{16} \equiv 1$ (mod 17) {FLT}
$\Rightarrow$ $13^{16n} \equiv 1^n$ (mod 17)
$\Rightarrow$ $13^{16n+2} \equiv 169$ (mod 17)
$\Rightarrow$ $13^{16n+2} + 1 \equiv 170$ (mod 17)
$\equiv 0$ (mod 17)
$\Rightarrow$ $7 \mid 13^{16n+2} + 1$ for all $n \in \mathbb{Z}^+$

7 likewise to **6** **8** 1 **9** $x \equiv 4201$ (mod 9889)

10 $x \equiv 264$ (mod 323) **12** 4

EXERCISE 11B.1

1 No. 4 pen strokes. **2** No **3** Yes

4 a minimum cost $26 million, several different answers. e.g.
b AHKFE, length 10 hours

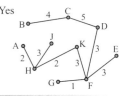

EXERCISE 11B.2

1 a i 4 **ii** 4 **iii** 2, 2, 2, 2
b i 4 **ii** 6 **iii** 2, 3, 3, 4
c i 4 **ii** 6 **iii** 2, 2, 3, 3
d i 2 **ii** 1 **iii** 1, 1
e i 5 **ii** 4 **iii** 1, 1, 2, 2, 2
f i 6 **ii** 15 **iii** 5, 5, 5, 5, 5, 5

2 i a, d, e, f **ii** a, b, c, d, f **iii** d, f

3 Note: These are examples only

a i **ii**

iii 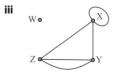 **iv**

v

b yes,

c **(1)** i, ii, iv, v **(2)** i, ii, iv, v **(3)** iv

4 $s \geqslant k-1$ edges **5** $s = \dfrac{p(p-1)}{2}$

6 Using **4** and **5**, a simple connected graph satisfies

$$n-1 \leqslant s \leqslant \dfrac{n(n-1)}{2}.$$

$$\therefore \quad 2n-2 \leqslant 2s \leqslant n^2 - n \text{ as required}$$

7 Every edge has 2 ends, so if there are n edges, the total number of edge ends is $2n$. Hence the sum of the degrees is $2n$.

8 11 edges

9 The sum of the degrees is 19, which is odd.

10 a No. For a graph of order n to be simple, no vertex can have degree more that $n-1$. Here, the order is 5 so we cannot have a vertex of degree 5.

b No. Since there are two vertices with degree 4, then if the graph is simple there are two vertices with edges leading to every other vertex. Hence the minimum degree of any other vertex is 2. This is not the case, however, so the graph cannot be simple.

11 a Yes. The order is the number of degrees. The size is the sum of the degrees, all divided by 2.

b No. For example, if a graph has order 4 and size 3, it could be one of several graphs: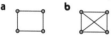

12 **Note:** These are examples only.

a   **b**   **c** Impossible, as the sum of the degrees of the graph must be even.

d   **e** **f**

13 $q = \dfrac{pr}{2}$

14 **Note:** These are examples only.

a **b** **c** **d**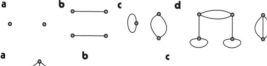

15 a   **b**   **c**

16 a 45 **b** 15 **c** 14 **d** $\dfrac{n(n-1)}{2}$ **e** mn

17 a $K_{4,4}$ **b** $W_3 (= K_4)$ **c** K_2

EXERCISE 11B.3.1

1 There are 12 months in a year, so by the Pigeonhole Principle there will be at least one month (pigeonhole) which is the birth month of two or more people (pigeons).

2 Divide the dartboard into 6 equal sectors. The maximum distance between any two points in a sector is 10 cm. Since there are 7 darts, at least two must be in the same sector (Pigeonhole Principle). Hence there are two darts which are at most 10 cm apart.

3 Divide the equilateral triangle into 16 identical triangles as shown. The length of each side of the small triangles is 2.5 cm.

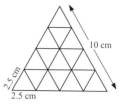

If there are 17 points, then at least two must be in the same triangle (Pigeonhole Principle). Hence, there are at least two points which are at most 2.5 cm apart.

4 Suppose they each receive a different number of prizes. Since each child receives at least one prize, the smallest number of prizes there can be is $1+2+3+4+5+6+7+8+9+10 = 55$. But there are only 50 prizes. Hence, at least two children must receive the same number.

5 The pairs of numbers 1 & 12, 2 & 11, 3 & 10, 4 & 9, 5 & 8, 6 & 7 all add up to 13. Consider the three numbers which are *not* selected. These can come from at least 3 of the pairs. Hence, there are at least 3 pairs for which both numbers are selected.

EXERCISE 11B.3.2

1 No. e.g.,   each have 4 vertices.

2 No. e.g.,   each have 3 edges.

3 No. We have the same size and order, and the degrees of the vertices of one match the degrees of the vertices of the other. However, the connectivity of the graphs is not necessarily preserved. e.g., and

4 a Yes

b No. The degrees of the vertices do not match.
c No. The first graph is bipartite while the second is not.
d Yes.
 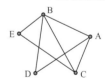

e No. The degrees of the vertices do not match.

5 a No. The graphs have the same size and order, and same degrees on the vertices. However, the connectivity is not preserved, since the graph on the left is bipartite but the graph on the right is not.

  is bipartite since every blue connects only to reds, and every red connects only to blues.

b No, as the connectivity is not preserved. The graph on the left has nodes of degree 2 being adjacent, whereas the graph on the right does not.

c No. The graph on the left is bipartite but the graph on the right is not.

is bipartite since every blue connects only to reds, and every red connects only to blues.

d Yes **e** Yes

6 a Each edge has two ends, and each end contributes one to the degrees of the vertices.

b The number of vertices of odd degree must be even.

c Let *"is a friend of"* be represented by an edge of a graph where the people are nodes. There are nine people, and if they are all friends with exactly five others, there would be an odd number of vertices of odd degree.

7 Suppose there are n vertices, each of different degree. For the graph to be simple, the highest degree that any vertex can be is $n - 1$. Hence the degrees must be 0, 1, 2, 3, ... $n - 1$.

However, this is a contradiction because if a simple graph has a vertex with degree $n - 1$ then it must be connected, yet we also have a vertex with degree 0.

∴ there are at most $n - 1$ different degrees, and so at least two vertices have the same degree. (Pigeonhole Principle)

8 a 1 **b** 2

c 6

9 a 2

b 4

c 11

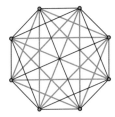

10 We have m pigeonholes containing n pigeons, where $n > m$. If none of the holes contain more than one pigeon, then there can be at most $m \times 1 = m$ pigeons.

Since $n > m$, this supposition is false. Hence, at least one hole contains more than one pigeon.

11 a With 4 vertices:

With 5 vertices:

b No. If there are 3 vertices, there are 3 possible edges. Hence, the complement of a graph with 3 vertices cannot have the same number of edges as the original graph.

c This is one of many answers:

d Consider a complete graph with n vertices. It has size $\dfrac{n(n-1)}{2}$. Now to create a self-complementary graph with n vertices, both the graph and its complement must have the same number of vertices.

Hence, $\dfrac{n(n-1)}{2}$ must be even.

i.e., $\dfrac{n(n-1)}{2} = 2t$, for some integer t

$\Rightarrow$ $n(n-1) = 4t$, $t \in \mathbb{Z}$.

Now if n is odd, then $n - 1$ is even, and vice versa.

$\Rightarrow$ whichever one is even must be a multiple of 4

$\Rightarrow$ either $n = 4k$ or $n - 1 = 4k$ for some integer k

$\Rightarrow$ G has either $4k$ or $4k + 1$ vertices, $k \in \mathbb{Z}$.

EXERCISE 11B.3.3

1 a can **b** cannot as it is not symmetric **c** can

2 There are 10 1s in the matrix.

Sum of degrees
$= 2 + 3 + 2 + 3$
$= 10$

3 a  **b**

4 a
$$\begin{bmatrix} 0 & 0 & 1 & 1 & 0 \\ 0 & 0 & 0 & 1 & 1 \\ 1 & 0 & 0 & 0 & 1 \\ 1 & 1 & 0 & 0 & 0 \\ 0 & 1 & 1 & 0 & 0 \end{bmatrix}$$
b
$$\begin{bmatrix} 0 & 1 & 0 & 0 & 1 \\ 1 & 0 & 1 & 0 & 0 \\ 0 & 1 & 0 & 1 & 0 \\ 0 & 0 & 1 & 0 & 1 \\ 1 & 0 & 0 & 1 & 0 \end{bmatrix}$$

c
$$\begin{bmatrix} 0 & 0 & 1 & 1 & 0 \\ 0 & 0 & 0 & 1 & 1 \\ 1 & 0 & 0 & 0 & 1 \\ 1 & 1 & 0 & 0 & 0 \\ 0 & 1 & 1 & 0 & 0 \end{bmatrix}$$
All 3 graphs are isomorphic

5 a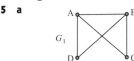

The graphs are the same; only their labels are changed.
$\Rightarrow$ they are isomorphic

b Yes. In both graphs, every vertex is adjacent to every other vertex.

EXERCISE 11B.3.4

1 a
$$\begin{bmatrix} 0 & 1 & 1 & 1 \\ 1 & 0 & 1 & 1 \\ 1 & 1 & 0 & 1 \\ 1 & 1 & 1 & 0 \end{bmatrix}$$
b
$$\begin{bmatrix} 0 & 1 & 0 & 1 \\ 1 & 0 & 1 & 0 \\ 0 & 1 & 0 & 1 \\ 1 & 0 & 1 & 0 \end{bmatrix}$$

c
$$\begin{bmatrix} 0 & 1 & 1 & 1 & 1 \\ 1 & 0 & 1 & 0 & 1 \\ 1 & 1 & 0 & 1 & 0 \\ 1 & 0 & 1 & 0 & 1 \\ 1 & 1 & 0 & 1 & 0 \end{bmatrix}$$
d
$$\begin{bmatrix} 0 & 1 & 1 & 1 & 1 \\ 1 & 0 & 0 & 0 & 0 \\ 1 & 0 & 0 & 0 & 0 \\ 1 & 0 & 0 & 0 & 0 \\ 1 & 0 & 0 & 0 & 0 \end{bmatrix}$$

e
$$\begin{bmatrix} 0 & 0 & 1 & 1 & 1 \\ 0 & 0 & 1 & 1 & 1 \\ 1 & 1 & 0 & 0 & 0 \\ 1 & 1 & 0 & 0 & 0 \\ 1 & 1 & 0 & 0 & 0 \end{bmatrix}$$

2 a
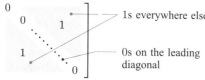

1s everywhere else

0s on the leading diagonal

b
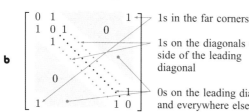

1s in the far corners

1s on the diagonals either side of the leading diagonal

0s on the leading diagonal and everywhere else

c
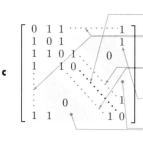

0s on the leading diagonal

1s everywhere else in the first row and column

1s on the diagonals either side of the leading diagonal

1s in the far corners of the remainder

0s everywhere else

d
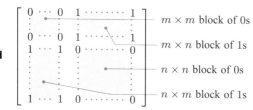

$m \times m$ block of 0s

$m \times n$ block of 1s

$n \times n$ block of 0s

$n \times m$ block of 1s

3 Find $\mathbf{A}$ for K_4, and then find $\mathbf{A}^2$, $\mathbf{A}^3$, $\mathbf{A}^4$, $\mathbf{A}^5$.
a 2 **b** 7 **c** 20 **d** 61

4 Find $\mathbf{A}$ for $K_{3,3}$, and then find $\mathbf{A}^2$, $\mathbf{A}^3$, $\mathbf{A}^4$, $\mathbf{A}^5$. Remember that the adjacent vertices are shown by the 1s in $\mathbf{A}$.
a 0 **b** 9 **c** 0 **d** 81

5 a 3 **b** 0 **c** 27 **d** 0

6 a
$$\mathbf{A} = \begin{bmatrix} 0 & 1 & 1 \\ 1 & 0 & 1 \\ 1 & 1 & 0 \end{bmatrix}, \quad \mathbf{A}^2 = \begin{bmatrix} 2 & 1 & 1 \\ 1 & 2 & 1 \\ 1 & 1 & 2 \end{bmatrix},$$

$$\mathbf{A}^3 = \begin{bmatrix} 2 & 3 & 3 \\ 3 & 2 & 3 \\ 3 & 3 & 2 \end{bmatrix}, \quad \mathbf{A}^4 = \begin{bmatrix} 6 & 5 & 5 \\ 5 & 6 & 5 \\ 5 & 5 & 6 \end{bmatrix}$$

b We can develop a recurrence relationship:

If $\mathbf{A}^{n-1} = \begin{bmatrix} a & b & b \\ b & a & b \\ b & b & a \end{bmatrix}$ then $\mathbf{A}^n = \begin{bmatrix} 2b & a+b & a+b \\ a+b & 2b & a+b \\ a+b & a+b & 2b \end{bmatrix}$

This can be written in the general form $\mathbf{A}^n = \begin{bmatrix} c & d & d \\ d & c & d \\ d & d & c \end{bmatrix}$

where $c = \frac{2}{3}[2^n - (-1)^n] = (-1)^{n-1} \sum_{i=0}^{n-2} (-2)^{i+1}$

and $d = \frac{1}{3}[2^n - (-1)^n] = (-1)^{n-1} \sum_{i=0}^{n-1} (-2)^i$

7 $\mathbf{A} = \begin{bmatrix} 0 & & & 1 \\ & 0 & \ddots & \\ & \ddots & & \\ 1 & & & 0 \end{bmatrix}$, $\mathbf{A}^2 = \begin{bmatrix} m & & & (m-1) \\ & m & \ddots & \\ & \ddots & & \\ & & & m \end{bmatrix}$

$\mathbf{A}^3 = \begin{bmatrix} m(m-1) & & & (m+(m-1)^2) \\ & m(m-1) & \ddots & \\ & \ddots & & \\ (m+(m-1)^2) & & & m(m-1) \end{bmatrix}$

The recurrence relationship is:

If $\mathbf{A}^{n-1} = \begin{bmatrix} a & & & b \\ & a & \ddots & \\ & \ddots & & \\ b & & & a \end{bmatrix}$ then $\mathbf{A}^n = \begin{bmatrix} bm & & & \\ & bm & \ddots & \\ & \ddots & & \\ & & & bm \end{bmatrix}$

$(a + b(m-1))$

This can be written in the general form $\mathbf{A}^n = \begin{bmatrix} c & & & d \\ & c & \ddots & \\ & \ddots & & \\ d & & & c \end{bmatrix}$

where $c = (-1)^{n-1} \sum_{i=0}^{n-2} (1-m)^{i+1}$

and $d = (-1)^{n-1} \sum_{i=0}^{n-1} (1-m)^i$

8 a $\mathbf{A} = \begin{bmatrix} 0 & 0 & 0 & 1 & 1 \\ 0 & 0 & 0 & 1 & 1 \\ 0 & 0 & 0 & 1 & 1 \\ 1 & 1 & 1 & 0 & 0 \\ 1 & 1 & 1 & 0 & 0 \end{bmatrix}$, $\mathbf{A}^2 = \begin{bmatrix} 2 & 2 & 2 & 0 & 0 \\ 2 & 2 & 2 & 0 & 0 \\ 2 & 2 & 2 & 0 & 0 \\ 0 & 0 & 0 & 3 & 3 \\ 0 & 0 & 0 & 3 & 3 \end{bmatrix}$

$\mathbf{A}^3 = \begin{bmatrix} 0 & 0 & 0 & 6 & 6 \\ 0 & 0 & 0 & 6 & 6 \\ 0 & 0 & 0 & 6 & 6 \\ 6 & 6 & 6 & 0 & 0 \\ 6 & 6 & 6 & 0 & 0 \end{bmatrix}$, $\mathbf{A}^4 = \begin{bmatrix} 12 & 12 & 12 & 0 & 0 \\ 12 & 12 & 12 & 0 & 0 \\ 12 & 12 & 12 & 0 & 0 \\ 0 & 0 & 0 & 18 & 18 \\ 0 & 0 & 0 & 18 & 18 \end{bmatrix}$

b For odd k, $\mathbf{A}^k = \begin{bmatrix} 0 & 0 & 0 & & \\ 0 & 0 & 0 & & 6^{\frac{k-1}{2}} \\ 0 & 0 & 0 & & \\ & 6^{\frac{k-1}{2}} & & 0 & 0 \\ & & & 0 & 0 \end{bmatrix}$

For even k, $\mathbf{A}^k = \begin{bmatrix} & & & 0 & 0 \\ 2^{\frac{k}{2}} \times 3^{\frac{k}{2}-1} & & & 0 & 0 \\ & & & 0 & 0 \\ 0 & 0 & 0 & & \\ 0 & 0 & 0 & & 2^{\frac{k}{2}-1} \times 3^{\frac{k}{2}} \end{bmatrix}$

9 a $\mathbf{A} = \begin{bmatrix} \underset{m \times m}{0} & \underset{m \times n}{1} \\ \underset{n \times m}{1} & \underset{n \times n}{0} \end{bmatrix}$, $\mathbf{A}^2 = \begin{bmatrix} \underset{m \times m}{n} & \underset{m \times n}{0} \\ \underset{n \times m}{0} & \underset{n \times n}{m} \end{bmatrix}$

$\mathbf{A}^3 = \begin{bmatrix} \underset{m \times m}{0} & \underset{m \times n}{mn} \\ \underset{n \times m}{mn} & \underset{n \times n}{0} \end{bmatrix}$, $\mathbf{A}^4 = \begin{bmatrix} \underset{m \times m}{mn^2} & \underset{m \times n}{0} \\ \underset{n \times m}{0} & \underset{n \times n}{m^2n} \end{bmatrix}$

b For odd k,

$\mathbf{A}^k = \begin{bmatrix} 0 & (mn)^{\frac{k-1}{2}} \\ (mn)^{\frac{k-1}{2}} & 0 \end{bmatrix}$

For even k,

$\mathbf{A}^k = \begin{bmatrix} m^{\frac{k}{2}-1} \times n^{\frac{k}{2}} & 0 \\ 0 & m^{\frac{k}{2}} \times n^{\frac{k}{2}-1} \end{bmatrix}$

EXERCISE 11B.4.1

1 a traversable   **b** traversable   **c** neither
   d neither   **e** traversable   **f** neither

2 Note: These are examples only.

a   **b**

c

3 a Eulerian   **b** traversable   **c** neither
   d Eulerian   (for $m \geqslant 3$)

4 a Eulerian for n odd, traversable for $n = 2$, otherwise
      neither.
   b Eulerian if m and n are both even, traversable if m or
      n is 2 and the other is odd, otherwise neither.

5 a 0, 2 or 4   **b** 2 or 4   **c** 2 or 4

6 a 3   **b** 4   **c** 5

7 No.   Yes - either   or
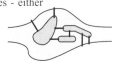 

8 For any graph G, the sum of the degrees of the vertices is
   even.
   $\Rightarrow$ there must be an even number of vertices of odd degree
   We can add an edge between any pair of vertices with odd
   degree, thus reducing the number of vertices with odd degree
   by 2. We repeat until all vertices have even degree.
   At this time the graph is Eulerian.

9 Only graphs which are Eulerian (no vertices with odd degree)
   or traversable (two vertices with odd degree) may be drawn
   with a single pen stroke without repeating an edge.
   Since there are 8 vertices with odd degree present, it takes
   $\frac{8}{2} = 4$ pen strokes.

10 There are 4 odd vertices, so that
   we cannot clear every road exactly
   once no matter where we start.

   The most efficient method is to
   repeat the roads shown:
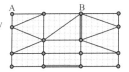

11 ($\Rightarrow$) Suppose the graph is bipartite, so there are two disjoint
   edge sets A and B. Suppose we are at a particular vertex
   in set A. In order to form a circuit back to this vertex,
   we must move to set B then back to set A, and repeat
   this a certain number of times. Each trip from set A to
   set B and back adds 2 to the length of the circuit.
   Hence, the circuit must have even length.

   ($\Leftarrow$) Suppose the graph contains only even length circuits.
   If we choose any vertex $v \in V(G)$, then we can define
   sets of vertices:
   Set A is the set of vertices with paths of odd length
   to v.
   Set B is the set of vertices with paths of even length
   to v.
   Now if any vertex w belongs to both sets A and B, then
   there must exist an odd length circuit in the graph. This
   is a contradiction, so A and B are disjoint sets. Since
   this is true for all vertices v, the graph is bipartite.

EXERCISE 11B.4.2

1 a i Hamiltonian   **ii** semi-Hamiltonian
      iii Hamiltonian
   b i semi-Hamiltonian   **ii** Hamiltonian
      iii semi-Hamiltonian   **iv** semi-Hamiltonian
      v Hamiltonian

2 K_5 and W_4 (**b ii**) satisfy the first observation.
   K_5, W_6 and W_4 (**b ii**) satisfy the second observation.
   K_5, and W_4 (**b ii**) satisfy the third observation.

3 Note: These are examples only.
   a C_n for all $n > 2$ **b** W_n for all $n > 2$
   c    **d** $K_{2,3}$

4 m and n must both be even.

5 K_n has n vertices, each with degree $n - 1$.
   From the observation of Dirac, a Hamiltonian cycle exists if
   $n - 1 \geqslant \frac{1}{2}n$, i.e., if $n \geqslant 2$
   However, from Dirac we must have $n > 2$.
   So, K_n contains a Hamiltonian cycle for all $n > 2$.

6
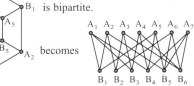

7 From **Exercise 11B.4.1,** question **11**, a graph is bipartite
   if and only if each of its circuits is of even length.
   $\Rightarrow$ if a bipartite graph has an odd number of vertices, it
      cannot contain a circuit visiting *every* vertex.
   $\Rightarrow$ G cannot be Hamiltonian.

a   If we label each vertex either A
           or B, we can show that the graph
           is bipartite.

becomes

   Since there are 13 vertices, which is an odd number, the
   graph is not Hamiltonian.

b If each square on a chessboard is represented by a vertex,
   and vertices are adjacent if a knight can move between
   them, then the resulting graph is bipartite. The white
   squares and the black squares form the two disjoint sets.
   If n is odd then $n \times n$ is also odd. Hence no Hamiltonian
   cycle exists. **Note:** If n is even, a Hamiltonian cycle still
   does not necessarily exist!

8 This graph is bipartite with 6 vertices in one edge set and 5 in
   the other. Since the total is odd, the graph is not Hamiltonian.

9
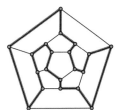

EXERCISE 11B.5.1

1 a

b

c

d

2 No, the problem cannot be solved on any surface.

3 a

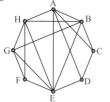 becomes

b non-planar

c

d non-planar

EXERCISE 11B.5.2

1 a 5 vertices, 10 edges

b Using $e + 2 = r + v$, we would need $r = 7$ regions.

c Each region of K_5 can be represented using a triangle.
$\Rightarrow$ each region has at least 3 edges.
Now $3 \times 7 = 21$, but since every edge is a border for two regions, we have counted every edge twice.
As $\frac{21}{2} = 10\frac{1}{2}$, we need at least 11 edges. But we only have 10 edges, so we have a contradiction and K_5 cannot be planar.

2 When we count over regions, each edge is counted twice.
Hence, $2e \geqslant 3r$, i.e., $r \leqslant \frac{2}{3}e$
Now for a planar graph, $e + 2 = v + r$
$\therefore\quad e + 2 \leqslant v + \frac{2}{3}e$
$\therefore\quad \frac{1}{3}e \leqslant v - 2$
$\therefore\quad e \leqslant 3v - 6$

3 Since the graph is bipartite, each region has a minimum of 4 edges. When we count over the regions, each edge is counted twice. Hence, $2e \geqslant 4r$, i.e., $r \leqslant \frac{1}{2}e$
Now for a planar graph, $e + 2 = v + r$
$\Rightarrow\quad e + 2 \leqslant v + \frac{1}{2}e$
$\therefore\quad \frac{1}{2}e \leqslant v - 2$
$e \leqslant 2v - 4$

Note: $e \leqslant 2v - 4$ is a necessary but not a sufficient condition for a bipartite graph to be planar.

e.g.,

   is bipartite but not planar. However, it has $e = 12$ and $v = 9$, so $e \leqslant 2v - 4$ is satisfied.

5 If the shortest cycle has length 5, then each region has at least 5 edges.
Hence, $2e \geqslant 5r$,   i.e., $r \leqslant \frac{2}{5}e$
Using $e + 2 = v + r$,
$\Rightarrow\quad e + 2 \leqslant v + \frac{2}{5}e$
$\therefore\quad \frac{3}{5}e \leqslant v - 2$
$\therefore\quad 3e \leqslant 5v - 10$

6 If the girth is g, then each region has at least g edges.
Hence, $2e \geqslant gr$,   i.e., $r \leqslant \dfrac{2}{g}e$
Using $e + 2 = v + r$,
$\Rightarrow\quad e + 2 \leqslant v + \dfrac{2}{g}e$
$\therefore\quad (1 - \dfrac{2}{g})e \leqslant v - 2$
$\therefore\quad (g - 2)e \leqslant gv - 2g$

7 The sum of the degrees of the edges is twice the number of edges.
Hence, if each of the v vertices has degree at least 6, then $2e \geqslant 6v$, i.e., $e \geqslant 3v$
This contradicts the requirement that $e \leqslant 3v - 6$.
So, there must be at least one vertex of degree less than or equal to 5.

8 K_n has n vertices and $\dfrac{n(n-1)}{2}$ edges
Since $e \leqslant 3v - 6$ {question **2**}
$\Rightarrow\quad \dfrac{n(n-1)}{2} \leqslant 3n - 6$
$\therefore\quad n^2 - n \leqslant 6n - 12$
$\therefore\quad n^2 - 7n + 12 \leqslant 0$
$\therefore\quad (n - 4)(n - 3) \leqslant 0$
$\therefore\quad 3 \leqslant n \leqslant 4$
Hence, K_3 and K_4 are the only complete planar graphs.

9

10 Consider the complete bipartite graph $K_{2,n}$.
This graph has $v = n + 2$ vertices, $e = 2n$ edges, and since every region is bounded by 4 edges, $r = \dfrac{e}{2} = n$
So, $r + v = n + (n + 2)$
$= 2n + 2$
$= e + 2$
i.e.,   Euler's formula is satisfied $\Rightarrow$ $K_{2,n}$ is planar.

11 The complete bipartite graph $K_{s,t}$ has $v = s + t$ vertices, $e = st$ edges, and since every region is bounded by 4 edges, $r = \dfrac{e}{2} = \dfrac{st}{2}$
So, $r + v = \dfrac{st}{2} + s + t$
and $e + 2 = st + 2$

∴   Euler's formula is satisfied when

$$\frac{st}{2} + s + t = st + 2$$

i.e., $st + 2s + 2t = 2st + 4$

i.e., $st - 2s - 2t + 4 = 0$

i.e., $(s-2)(t-2) = 0$

i.e., $s = 2$ or $t = 2$

i.e., $K_{s,t}$ is non-planar if both s and t are greater than 2.

12 Suppose G is a simple graph with v vertices and E edges.
Together, G and $\overline{G}$ have the same number of edges as K_v,
so $\overline{G}$ has v vertices and $\frac{v(v-1)}{2} - E$ edges

Assuming G is planar, $E \leqslant 3v - 6$ ...... (1)

Now if $\overline{G}$ is also planar, then

$$\frac{v(v-1)}{2} - E \leqslant 3v - 6$$

$$\therefore \quad v(v-1) \leqslant 2(3v - 6 + E)$$

$$\therefore \quad v^2 - v \leqslant 6v - 12 + 2(3v - 6)$$

$$\therefore \quad v^2 - v \leqslant 12v - 24$$

$$\therefore \quad v^2 - 13v + 24 \leqslant 0$$

Solving $v^2 - 13v + 24 = 0$ gives $v \approx 2.23$ or 10.8

∴ $\overline{G}$ is not planar if $v \geqslant 11$

∴   if G has at least 11 vertices, G and $\overline{G}$ cannot both
be planar.

EXERCISE 11B.6.1

1 **a** yes **b** no **c** yes **d** no

2

3 Only K_2 is a tree. K_n where $n > 2$ contains at least one cycle.

4 $2(n-1)$

a 11 vertices.
One example is

b 18 vertices.
One example is

5 **a** and **b**, **c** and **e**   **6** One example is

7 The complete bipartite graph $K_{m,n}$ has mn edges.
But a tree of order k has $k - 1$ edges.

$$\therefore \quad mn = m + n - 1$$

$$\therefore \quad m(n-1) = n - 1$$

$$\therefore \quad (n-1)(m-1) = 0$$

$$\therefore \quad n = 1 \text{ or } m = 1$$

Hence $K_{m,n}$ is a tree if either m or n is 1.

8 In a tree, no vertex can have a degree 0.
Now if every vertex has degree 2, the sum of the degrees is $2n$.
But a tree with n nodes has $n - 1$ edges and so the sum of the degrees is $2n - 2$, i.e., less than $2n$.
∴ at least 2 vertices have degree one.

EXERCISE 11B.6.2

1 These are examples only.

a

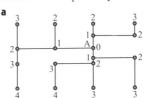

b

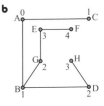

2 n

3, 4, 5 Click on the icon to find full solutions to these questions.

SOLUTIONS

EXERCISE 11B.6.3

1 There are other (minor) variations.

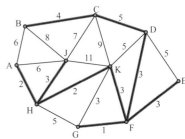

Minimum $26 million.

2 **a**

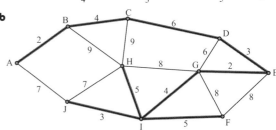

b

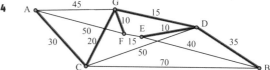

3 **a** There is a weight for every edge from every node to every other node.

b, c

4

A variation is EF instead of DG.

EXERCISE 11B.6.4

1 a

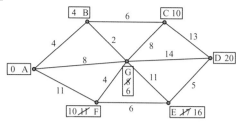

A → B → G → D,   weight 20

b

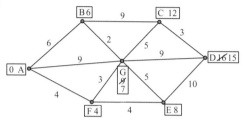

A → F → G → C → D,   weight 15

2

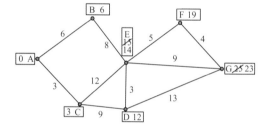

A → B → E → G   or   A → B → E → F → G,
both weight 23

3

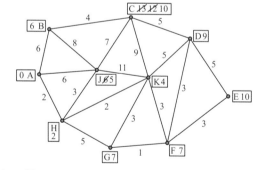

A → H → K → F → E,   10 hours

4

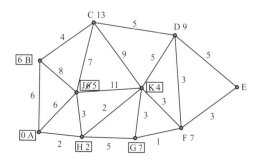

A → H → G   or   A → H → K → G,   both weight 7

EXERCISE 11B.7

1   Vertices A and C have odd degrees.
⇒ not Eulerian, and we have to travel between A and C twice.
The sum of the lengths of all the roads is 21 km and the
shortest path from A to C is 3 km.
So, the shortest distance the snowplough must travel is 24 km.

2 a   A, B, C and D have odd degrees. Since the graph is
complete, exactly two sections must be repeated.

b   Repeating AB and CD is $6 + 5 = 11$ km
Repeating AC and BD is $7 + 4 = 11$ km
Repeating AD and BC is $9 + 12 = 21$ km

The sum of the lengths of the paths is 43 km.
⇒ the shortest distance to be travelled is 54 km,
repeating either AB and CD   or   AC and BD.

An example route is:
A → B → C → A → D → C → D → B → A

c   Repeating AB and CD is $4 + 7 = 11$ hours
Repeating AC and BD is $4 + 3 = 7$ hours
Repeating AD and BC is $6 + 6 = 12$ hours

The sum of the times of the paths is 30 hours.
⇒ the shortest total time is 37 hours,
repeating AC and BD.

An example route is:
A → C → B → D → C → A → D → B → A

3 a   Vertices B, F, G and H have odd degrees.

b   Repeating BF and GH has smallest distance
$7 + 2 = 9$ units
Repeating BG and FH has smallest distance
$5 + 3 = 8$ units
Repeating BH and FG has smallest distance
$4 + 5 = 9$ units

The sum of the distances of all the roads is 55 units.
⇒ the shortest distance to be travelled is $55 + 8$
$= 63$ units, travelling BG and FH twice.
A possible route is:
A → B → C → D → E → C → H → E → F →
H → B → A → G → F → H → G → A

4   The vertices with odd degrees are A, D, E and I.
Repeating AD and EI has smallest distance
$4 + 8 = 12$ units
Repeating AE and DI has smallest distance
$7 + 8 = 15$ units
Repeating AI and DE has smallest distance
$9 + 5 = 14$ units
⇒ Peter should repeat AD (via B) and EI (via F)
An example route is:
A → B → C → D → B → D → F → E → C → G →
E → F → G → I → H → F → I → F → B → A

5 a   AB and CD,   AC and BD,   AD and BC.

b   Repeating AB and CD has smallest distance
$3.5 + 6 = 9.5$ km
Repeating AC and BD has smallest distance
$6 + 5.5 = 11.5$ km
Repeating AD and BC has smallest distance
$5 + 5 = 10$ km

The sum of the distances of all the roads is 32.5 km.
⇒ the shortest distance to be travelled is $32.5 + 9.5$
$= 42$ km, travelling AB (via E) and CD twice.

An example route is:
E → A → B → E → A → D → C → B → E →
D → C → E

6 a The vertices with odd degrees are C, D, E and F.

b Repeating CD and EF has smallest cost
$1.3 + 1.5 = 2.8$ thousand dollars
Repeating CE and DF has smallest cost
$2.3 + 2.6 = 4.9$ thousand dollars
Repeating CF and DE has smallest cost
$1.4 + 1.1 = 2.5$ thousand dollars

The sum of the costs for all routes is 13.6 thousand \$s.
$\Rightarrow$ the lowest cost solution is to travel CF (via B) and
DE twice, and this costs $\$13\,600 + \$2500 = \$16\,100$

An example route is:
$A \rightarrow B \rightarrow F \rightarrow G \rightarrow D \rightarrow E \rightarrow F \rightarrow B \rightarrow E \rightarrow$
$D \rightarrow C \rightarrow B \rightarrow C \rightarrow A$

EXERCISE 11B.8

1 a

minimum spanning tree
has weight 130
$\Rightarrow$ upper bound is 260.

b Shortcut SPQR then straight back to S.
Length is $130 + 86 = 216 \Rightarrow$ new upper bound is 216.

c Deleting S, min. spanning tree has length
$55 + 43 = 98$
Adding the shortest deleted edges gives
$98 + 32 + 84 = 214$

Deleting R, min. spanning tree has length
$55 + 32 = 87$
Adding the shortest deleted edges gives
$87 + 43 + 65 = 195$

Deleting Q, min. spanning tree has length
$32 + 65 = 97$
Adding the shortest deleted edges gives
$97 + 55 + 43 = 195$

Deleting P, min. spanning tree has length
$43 + 84 = 127$
Adding the shortest deleted edges gives
$127 + 32 + 55 = 214$
$\Rightarrow$ lower bound is 214.

d Shortest path SPQRS has length 216.

2 a

Both minimum spanning trees have length 50
$\Rightarrow$ upper bound is 100.

b Shortcut QRSP then straight back to Q.
Length is $50 + 30 = 80 \Rightarrow$ new upper bound is 80.

c

Vertex deleted	MST length	Shortest deleted edges	Total
P	30	$20 + 20$	70
S	35	$15 + 20$	70
R	45	$15 + 15$	75
Q	35	$15 + 25$	75

$\Rightarrow$ lower bound is 75.

d Shortest paths QRSPQ or QRPSQ have length 80.

3 a
P ──7── Q
Minimum spanning tree
has length 32.
$\Rightarrow$ upper bound is 64.

b Shortcut PQTSRQP.
Length is $32 + 10 + 7 = 49 \Rightarrow$ new upper bound is 49.

c

Vertex deleted	MST length	Shortest deleted edges	Total
P	25	$7 + 8$	40
Q	27	$7 + 7$	41
R	26	$7 + 8$	41
S	23	$9 + 10$	42
T	23	$9 + 10$	42

$\Rightarrow$ lower bound is 42.

d Shortest paths PQTSRP has length 43.

REVIEW SET 11A

1 a 8 **b** $m = -3,\ n = 8$

2 $x = 11 + 31t,\ y = -6 - 17t,\ t \in \mathbb{Z}$

3 $d = 42,\ x = 1,\ y = -2$ **5** $x \equiv 15 (\mathrm{mod}\,17)$

6 $n \equiv 79 (\mathrm{mod}\,209)$ **7** $x \equiv 2 (\mathrm{mod}\,6)$ or $5 (\mathrm{mod}\,6)$ **8** 7

9 $m \mid n \Rightarrow n = km$ for some $k \in \mathbb{Z}$

Now $\dfrac{N_n}{N_m} = \left(\dfrac{10^n - 1}{9}\right)\left(\dfrac{9}{10^m - 1}\right)$

$= \dfrac{10^{mk} - 1}{10^m - 1}$

$= \dfrac{a^k - 1}{a - 1},$ for $a = 10^m$

$= 1 + a + a^2 + a^3 + \ldots\ldots + a^{k-1}$

$= A,$ an integer

$\Rightarrow N_n = A\,N_m,\ A \in \mathbb{Z}$

$\Rightarrow N_m \mid N_n$

10 a 1 or 2 **b** 1 or 3

11 If $a, b \in \mathbb{Z}^+$ then $a, b \equiv 0, 1, 2 (\mathrm{mod}\,3)$.
Possibilities are:

a	b	a^2	b^2	$a^2 + b^2$
0	0	0	0	0
1	1	1	1	2
2	2	1	1	2

So, if $a^2 + b^2 \equiv 0\,(\mathrm{mod}\,3)$
then $a \equiv 0\,(\mathrm{mod}\,3)$ and $b \equiv 0\,(\mathrm{mod}\,3)$
$\Rightarrow 3 \mid a$ and $3 \mid b$

Now consider $a = 1,\ b = 2$
$\Rightarrow a^2 + b^2 = 5$
$\Rightarrow 5 \mid a^2 + b^2$
but $5 \nmid a$ and $5 \nmid b$

13 a only
'bba' is $100b + 10b + a = 110b + a$
But $2b + a = 12k,\ k \in \mathbb{Z}$
$\Rightarrow$ 'bba' $= 12k + 108b = 12(k + 9b)$
where $k + 9b \in \mathbb{Z}$
$\Rightarrow$ 'bba' is divisible by 12

15 a If $n \not\equiv 0 \,(\text{mod} \, 5)$ then
$$n \equiv 1, \, 2, \, 3, \, 4 \,(\text{mod} \, 5)$$
$$\Rightarrow \ n^2 \equiv 1, \, 4, \, 4, \, 1 \,(\text{mod} \, 5)$$
$$\Rightarrow \ n^2 \equiv 1, \, 4 \,(\text{mod} \, 5)$$
$$\Rightarrow \ n^2 \equiv \pm 1 \,(\text{mod} \, 5)$$

b From **a**
$$n^4 \equiv 1 \,(\text{mod} \, 5)$$
Now $n^5 + 5n^3 + 4n$
$$= n(n^4 + 5n^2 + 4)$$
$$= n(n^2 + 1)(n^2 + 4)$$
If $n^2 \equiv 1 \,(\text{mod} \, 5)$, $n^2 + 4 \equiv 0 \,(\text{mod} \, 5)$
If $n^2 \equiv -1 \,(\text{mod} \, 5)$, $n^2 + 1 \equiv 0 \,(\text{mod} \, 5)$
So, $n^5 + 5n^3 + 4n \equiv 0 \,(\text{mod} \, 5)$
$\Rightarrow \ n^5 + 5n^3 + 4n$ is divisible by 5 for all $n \in \mathbb{Z}^+$

REVIEW SET 11B

2 a only
$$(n+1)! = (n+1)(n)(n-1) \, ... \, (3)(2)(1)$$
contains at least one factor of 2
$\Rightarrow \quad (n+1)!$ is even
$\Rightarrow \quad (n+1)! + 2$ is even

$(n+1)!$ also is divisible by 3
i.e., $(n+1)! \equiv 0 \,(\text{mod} \, 3)$
$\Rightarrow \quad (n+1)! + 2 \equiv 2 \,(\text{mod} \, 3)$ i.e., $m \equiv 2 \,(\text{mod} \, 3)$
$\Rightarrow \quad m+1 \equiv 0 \,(\text{mod} \, 3)$
$\Rightarrow \quad 3 \mid m+1$

3 $21\,020\,010\,221\,102_3$

4 $x \equiv 13, \, 30, \, 47 \,(\text{mod} \, 51)$

5 An integer is divisible by 36 if it is divisible by 4 and 9.

As the number ends in 24, which is divisible by 4, the number is divisible by 4.

Also the sum of the number's digits is 78 which is not divisible by 9 (but is divisible by 3).
So, the number is divisible by 3, but not 9

Hence, the number is not divisible by 36, but is by 12.

6 $x \equiv 101 \,(\text{mod} \, 260)$

7 If $a \in \mathbb{Z}^+$, then $a \equiv 0, \, 1, \, 2 \,(\text{mod} \, 3)$
$\Rightarrow \quad a^3 \equiv 0, \, 1, \, 2 \,(\text{mod} \, 3)$ and
$$5a \equiv 0, \, 2, \, 1 \,(\text{mod} \, 3)$$
$\Rightarrow \quad a^3 + 5a \equiv 0, \, 0, \, 0 \,(\text{mod} \, 3)$
$\Rightarrow \quad a^3 + 5a \equiv 0 \,(\text{mod} \, 3)$
$\Rightarrow \quad 3 \mid a^3 + 5a$

8 a 1, 2, 3, 5, 8, 13, 21, 34, 55, 89

$$S_1 = 1 = 3 - 2$$
$$S_2 = 3 = 5 - 2$$
$$S_3 = 6 = 8 - 2$$
$$S_4 = 11 = 13 - 2$$
$$S_5 = 19 = 21 - 2$$
$$S_6 = 32 = 34 - 2$$

This suggests that
$$\sum_{k=1}^{n} L_k = L_{n+2} - 2$$
for all $n \in \mathbb{Z}^+$
then strong induction

9 a $110\,001_2$ **b** 61_8

11 Consider $n = 6$. $12 \mid 6^2$, but $12 \nmid 6$

12 $n = 2a$ or $2a + 1$ for all $n \in \mathbb{Z}$
$\Rightarrow \quad n^2 = 4a^2$ or $4a^2 + 4a + 1$
$\Rightarrow \quad n^2 \equiv 0, \, 1 \,(\text{mod} \, 4)$
$\Rightarrow \quad n^2 - 1 \equiv 3, \, 0 \,(\text{mod} \, 4)$

$\Rightarrow \quad n^2 - 1$ is divisible by 4   or
$$n^2 - 1 = 4k + 3, \quad k \in \mathbb{Z}$$

13 Show that $4^{35}(47) - 48 \equiv 2 \,(\text{mod} \, 3)$
$\Rightarrow$ the number leaves a remainder of 2 when divided by 3
$\Rightarrow$ the number is not divisible by 3

14 $4^2 \equiv 2^2 \,(\text{mod} \, 12)$ $\not\Rightarrow$ $4 \equiv 2 \,(\text{mod} \, 12)$
$\therefore \quad a^2 \equiv b^2 \,(\text{mod} \, n)$ $\not\Rightarrow$ $a \equiv b \,(\text{mod} \, n)$
The converse is true
i.e., $a \equiv b \,(\text{mod} \, n)$ $\Rightarrow$ $a^2 \equiv b^2 \,(\text{mod} \, n)$
$3^2 \equiv 2^2 \,(\text{mod} \, 5)$ $\not\Rightarrow$ $3 \equiv 2 \,(\text{mod} \, 5)$
So, the statement is not true for n a prime.
$a^2 \equiv b^2 \,(\text{mod} \, n)$ $\Rightarrow$ $a \equiv \pm b \,(\text{mod} \, n)$

15 n is prime

REVIEW SET 11C

1 a $m = 2$ **b** $m = 2$ **c** never

2 a m vertices $\dfrac{m(m-1)}{2}$ edges

b m vertices m edges

c $m + 1$ vertices $2m$ edges

d $m + n$ vertices mn edges

3 If the graph has e edges, then the sum of the degrees of its vertices is $2e$.
$\therefore$ if the minimum degree is m and the maximum is M,
$$mv \leqslant 2e \leqslant Mv$$
$$m \leqslant \frac{2e}{v} \leqslant M$$

4 $\dfrac{v(v-1)}{2} - e$

5 Suppose the graph has v vertices. The sum of the edges of G and $\overline{G}$ is the number of edges of K_v.

i.e., $17 + 11 = \dfrac{v(v-1)}{2}$
$$\therefore \quad v(v-1) = 56$$
$$\therefore \quad v^2 - v - 56 = 0$$
$$\therefore \quad (v-8)(v+7) = 0$$
$$\therefore \quad v = 8 \quad \{\text{as } v > 0\}$$
$\therefore$ G has 8 vertices

6 Since G is bipartite, it has two disjoint sets of vertices. Suppose there are m vertices in one set and $v - m$ vertices in the other.
If G is simple, the total number of edges possible is
$m(v - m) = -m^2 + mv$, which is a quadratic in m whose maximum occurs when $m = \dfrac{-v}{2(-1)} = \dfrac{v}{2}$
$\therefore$ the max. possible number of edges is $\dfrac{v}{2} \times \dfrac{v}{2} = \dfrac{v^2}{4}$
i.e., $e \leqslant \dfrac{v^2}{4}$

7 a $\begin{bmatrix} 0 & 1 & 1 & 1 \\ 1 & 0 & 1 & 1 \\ 1 & 1 & 0 & 1 \\ 1 & 1 & 1 & 0 \end{bmatrix}$ **b** $\begin{bmatrix} 0 & 1 & 1 & 1 & 1 \\ 1 & 0 & 0 & 0 & 0 \\ 1 & 0 & 0 & 0 & 0 \\ 1 & 0 & 0 & 0 & 0 \\ 1 & 0 & 0 & 0 & 0 \end{bmatrix}$

c $\begin{bmatrix} 0 & 0 & 1 & 1 & 1 \\ 0 & 0 & 1 & 1 & 1 \\ 1 & 1 & 0 & 0 & 0 \\ 1 & 1 & 0 & 0 & 0 \\ 1 & 1 & 0 & 0 & 0 \end{bmatrix}$

8 These are examples only.

a

b

9 **a** 6 paths   **b** $4! = 24$ paths   **c** $4! = 24$ paths

10 **a** 0 paths   **b** 0 paths   **c** 36 paths

11 m and n must both be even.

12 If the shortest cycle has length 5, then each region has at least 5 edges.

Hence, $2e \geqslant 5r$, i.e., $r \leqslant \frac{2}{5}e$

Using $e + 2 = v + r$,

$\Rightarrow \quad e + 2 \leqslant v + \frac{2}{5}e$

$\therefore \quad \frac{3}{5}e \leqslant v - 2$

$\therefore \quad 3e \leqslant 5v - 10$ and so $e \leqslant \dfrac{5v - 10}{3}$

13 Since the graph is planar, $e + 2 = v + r$

Now if there are 8 vertices of degree 3, there are 24 ends of edges. $\therefore \quad e = 12$

$\therefore \quad 12 + 2 = 8 + r$

$\therefore \quad r = 6$

i.e., there are 6 regions

14 8 regions   {using the same argument as in **13**}.

REVIEW SET 11D

1 A, B, D

2 Suppose there are n vertices, each of different degree.
For the graph to be simple, the highest degree that any vertex can be is $n - 1$.
Hence the degrees must be $0, 1, 2, \ldots, n - 1$.

However, this is a contradiction because if a simple graph has a vertex with degree $n - 1$ then it must be connected, yet we also have a vertex with degree 0.

$\therefore$ there are at most $n - 1$ different degrees, and so at least two vertices have the same degree. (Pigeonhole Principle)

3 **a i** Eulerian   **ii** Hamiltonian
   b i traversable **ii** neither
   c i neither   **ii** Hamiltonian
   d i Eulerian   **ii** Hamiltonian

4 A graph is bipartite $\Leftrightarrow$ each of its circuits is of even length.
$\Rightarrow$ if a bipartite graph has an odd number of vertices, it cannot contain a circuit visiting *every* vertex.
$\Rightarrow$ G cannot be Hamiltonian.

5 From the definition of isomorphism:
- for every vertex in G there is a unique corresponding vertex in H, and vice versa.
  $\Rightarrow$ the order of G = the order of H.
- the adjacency of all vertices is preserved.
  $\Rightarrow$ the size of G = the size of H.

Converse example:

order 4   size 3   order 4   size 3

but the graphs are not isomorphic.

6 No. B has an extra edge. In A and C, the adjacency of vertices is not preserved.

7 **a**

b Those in **a**, plus

8 **a** If there are 28 edges, then there are 56 ends of edges.
$\Rightarrow$ the sum of the degrees of the vertices is 56.
If there are m vertices of degree 3, and $12 - m$ vertices of degree 4, then
$3m + 4(12 - m) = 56$
$\Rightarrow -m + 48 = 56$
$\Rightarrow m = -8$,   which is impossible
Hence, no.

b Using the same argument as in **a**, suppose there are m vertices of degree 5 and $12 - m$ vertices of degree 6. Show that $m = 16$ which is impossible.   Hence, no.

9 For a simple connected graph to have as many edges as possible, we consider the complete graphs K_n.

For n vertices, they have $\dfrac{n(n - 1)}{2}$ edges.

Hence, we seek the lowest n such that $\dfrac{n(n - 1)}{2} \geqslant 500$

From this inequality show that we need at least 33 vertices.

10 Suppose G has order n. Together, G and $\overline{G}$ have the same number of edges as K_n, i.e., $\dfrac{n(n - 1)}{2}$.

However, if G and $\overline{G}$ are both trees, then they both must have $n - 1$ edges.   Thus, $\dfrac{n(n - 1)}{2} = 2(n - 1)$

$\therefore \quad n(n - 1) = 4(n - 1)$

$\therefore \quad (n - 1)(n - 4) = 0$

$\therefore \quad n = 1$ or 4

But $n = 1$ is not a particularly sensible solution,
So, G has order 4.

11 G is planar and cubic. If G has order n, then the sum of the degrees of its vertices is $3n$, and so it has $\dfrac{3n}{2}$ edges.

Using Euler's formula, $e + 2 = r + v$

$\therefore \quad \dfrac{3n}{2} + 2 = r + n$

$\therefore \quad r = \dfrac{n}{2} + 2$

K_4 has 4 nodes and 4 regions.

$\dfrac{n}{2} + 2 = \dfrac{4}{2} + 2 = 4$ ✓

REVIEW SET 11E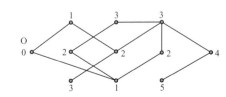

1

2

Each vertex of W_3 has degree 3, and in fact W_3 is the same as K_4.
Now a spanning tree of K_4 has only 3 edges, so the sum of the degrees of the vertices is 6.

We can have the configurations:

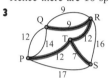

Degrees of vertices	Example	Combinations
3 1 1 1		4 (4 ways to choose vertex of degree 3)
2 2 1 1		12 (4 × 3 ways to choose vertices of degree 2, × 2 ways to choose which vertex of degree 1 is attached to which of degree 2, ÷ 2 for symmetrical solutions which are the reverse of others.)

Hence there are 16 spanning trees of W_3.

3

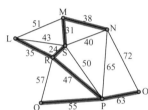

min. weight = 40

4

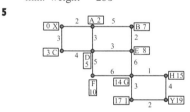

min. weight = 293

5

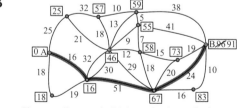

Min. connector has length 19.
Either $O \rightarrow A \rightarrow D \rightarrow E \rightarrow G \rightarrow H \rightarrow Y$
  or $O \rightarrow A \rightarrow D \rightarrow E \rightarrow G \rightarrow I \rightarrow Y$

6

Shortest distance is 91 km, via the path shown.

7 a The graph has two vertices with odd degree, B and C.
  ⇒ while it is not Eulerian, it is traversable.
  ⇒ if we start and finish at B and C (either order), we can walk around all tunnels without having to repeat any.
  b $B \rightarrow A \rightarrow E \rightarrow B \rightarrow C \rightarrow E \rightarrow D \rightarrow C$. **c** BC
  d The sum of the lengths of the tunnels is 831 m.
  The shortest path from B to C is 146 m, and this is the length that is repeated.
  ⇒ the min. distance is 831 + 146 = 977 m.

8 There are 4 vertices with odd degrees: A, B, C and D.
Repeating AB and CD has min. length 10 + 13 = 23.
Repeating AC and BD has min. length 25 + 24 = 49.
Repeating AD and BC has min. length 22 + 15 = 37.
Thus, we repeat AB and CD. The sum of the length of all roads is 113 ⇒ the min. distance = 113 + 23 = 136 units.

9 a i

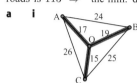

min. length = 51
⇒ upper bound 102.

  ii Shortcut $C \rightarrow O \rightarrow A \rightarrow B \rightarrow O \rightarrow C$ gives an upper bound of 90.

  iii

Vertex deleted	MST length	Shortest deleted edges	Total
A	34	17 + 24	75
B	32	19 + 24	75
C	36	15 + 25	76
O	47	15 + 27	79

  ⇒ lower bound is 79

  iv Shortest path is $O \rightarrow A \rightarrow B \rightarrow C \rightarrow O$ with length 81 units.

b i

min. length = 26
⇒ upper bound 52.

  ii Shortcut $B \rightarrow A \rightarrow C \rightarrow O \rightarrow D \rightarrow B$ gives an upper bound of 46.

  iii

Vertex deleted	MST length	Shortest deleted edges	Total
A	26	3 + 8	37
B	16	10 + 13	39
C	24	3 + 7	34
D	20	6 + 11	37
O	24	6 + 7	37

  ⇒ lower bound is 39

  iv Shortest path is $O \rightarrow C \rightarrow A \rightarrow B \rightarrow D \rightarrow O$ with length 46 units.

INDEX

INDEX